SOIL MECHANICS FOR OFF-ROAD VEHICLE ENGINEERING

Other volumes in the
Series on Rock and Soil Mechanics

W. Reisner, M. v. Eisenhart Rothe:
Bins and Bunkers for Handling Bulk Materials
– Practical Design and Techniques –
1971

W. Dreyer:
The Science of Rock Mechanics
Part I Strength Properties of Rocks
1972

T. H. Hanna:
Foundation Instrumentation
1973

C. E. Gregory:
Explosives for North American Engineers
1973

M. & A. Reimbert:
Retaining Walls Vol. I
– Anchorages and Sheet Piling –
1974

Vutukuri, Lama, Saluja:
Handbook on Mechanical Properties
of Rocks Vol. I
1974

M. & A. Reimbert:
Retaining Walls Vol. II
– Study of Passive Resistance in Foundation Structures –
1976

H. R. Hardy, Jr. & F. W. Leighton:
First Conference on Acoustic Emission/Microseismic Activity
in Geologic Structures and Materials
1977

Baguelin, Jézéquel, Shields:
The Pressuremeter and Foundation
Engineering
1978

Editor-in-Chief
Professor Dr. H. Wöhlbier

Series on Rock and Soil Mechanics
Vol. 2 (1974/77) No. 5

SOIL MECHANICS FOR OFF-ROAD VEHICLE ENGINEERING

by

Leslie L. Karafiath
Staff Scientist
Grumman Aerospace Corporation
Bethpage, New York

and

Edward A. Nowatzki
Associate Professor of
Civil Engineering
University of Arizona
Tucson, Arizona

First Edition
1978

TRANS TECH PUBLICATIONS

Distributed by
TRANS TECH S. A.
CH-4711 Aedermannsdorf, Switzerland

International Standard Book Number

ISBN 0-87849-020-5

Printed in Germany

TABLE OF CONTENTS

Part 1

FUNDAMENTALS OF SOIL MECHANICS FOR PROBLEMS IN OFF-ROAD LOCOMOTION

Part 2

PLASTICITY THEORY FOR SOILS

Part 3

APPLICATION OF SOIL MECHANICS THEORIES TO PROBLEMS OF MOBILITY

PREFACE

The primary purpose of this book is to introduce the latest developments in the field of soil mechanics to the solution of problems in off-road vehicle engineering by presenting theoretically sound approaches to the problems and comparing solutions by these approaches with available experimental data. There are several reasons why this has not been done previously, not least among which is the fact that it is only in the last two decades that our knowledge of the mechanical behavior of soils has advanced to the point where such an undertaking is possible. In those two decades old techniques of experimental investigations have improved and new ones have been developed. Reliable experimental evidence has become available on the behavior of a wide variety of soils not only under normal conditions, but also under the extremes of ultra-high vacuum, reduced gravity, impact loading, etc. Advances in other disciplines have also enhanced the development of more theoretically rigorous methods of analysis in soil mechanics problems. For example, with the widespread availability of high speed computational facilities, the most sophisticated analyses of soil behavior are now possible where full use can be made of the refinements achieved in experimental techniques. Investigations of soil behavior on the microscopic level have been made using physico-chemical analyses and the techniques of x-ray diffraction, electron microscopy, etc. As a result of such advances soil mechanics predictions have become an accepted way of improving civil engineering design.

One of mankind's earliest major achievements was the invention of the wheel, which, at its inception, was undoubtedly used without the benefit of a roadway. However, only recently has the problem of off-road locomotion been recognized as a soil-wheel interaction problem and, as such, amenable to theoretical soil mechanics analysis. Why then have advancements in soil mechanics, a recognized discipline in civil engineering, not been utilized in the field of off-road locomotion sooner? Certainly the complexity of the problem deterred many researchers from pursuing a theoretically rigorous formulation. But even more serious was the retrograde influence exerted on the science of off-road locomotion by failures of some simplistic, semi-empirical approaches to the problem that often ignored fundamental concepts of soil behavior. As a matter of fact, the level of soil mechanics applied even today by some researchers to problems in off-road locomotion is no better than that applied to civil engineering problems some 30 years ago! This lag in the use of advanced concepts of soil mechanics in off-road locomotion research is due in most part to a difficulty in communications among the various disciplines involved. The ability to move vehicles over natural terrain is of paramount importance to a wide variety of disciplines, for example, automotive, military, mechanical, aerospace, construction and agricultural engineering. Workers in these disciplines would have to evaluate an enormous quantity of soil mechanics publications to extract the information that is useful for them. Conversely, a wealth of geotechnical information that is available from the areas of geology, soil physics and chemistry, and agricultural soil science and that is particularly useful in off-road locomotion research has not, even yet, made its way into the disciplines of off-road locomotion and soil mechanics. Recognizing this difficulty, the authors will attempt to assess the value of published soil mechanics and other related literature from the viewpoint of off-road locomotion and to present a balanced discussion of the most important ideas.

The major emphasis, however, will be on showing that soil-vehicle interaction is fundamentally a soil mechanics problem; that the difference in the force system acting on off-road and on-road vehicles is essentially that between soil and rigid surface reactions. The state of the art of soil mechanics and applied mathematics today is such that theoretically sound formulations of problems in off-road locomotion are possible and mathematically acceptable numerical techniques for their solution are available.

The theories and solutions presented in this book are intended for use by advanced students as well as by engineers and researchers working in the field of vehicle design and mobility analysis.

Part 1 of the book is devoted to a presentation of basic soil mechanics principles that apply to off-road locomotion problems. Definitions of terms and concepts are explained briefly so that engineers with different backgrounds may be able to follow subsequent developments without recourse to a reference book. Those soil mechanics theories that are applicable and essential to the solution of soil-vehicle interaction problems are discussed thoroughly so that the concepts and underlying assumptions can be clearly understood. The relevant soil mechanics laboratory tests required to obtain soil properties for use in the theories are described. Less emphasis is given to those soil mechanics theories that are of only marginal interest in off-road locomotion analyses, such as theories of consolidation, creep, etc.

In Part 2 of the book, the principles of plasticity theory and an appropriate yield condition for soils are applied to derive the basic differential equations of plastic equilibrium in soils. The governing differential equations for a number of conditions of special interest in mobility analyses are also derived. Since closed form solutions to these equations do not exist, numerical methods of solution are presented in great detail. Boundary conditions are thoroughly discussed and applications of plasticity theory to a number of general soil-structure interaction problems are used to show the mechanics of the solution method.

In Part 3 of the book, soil mechanics principles and the theory of plasticity as presented in the previous two parts are applied to problems in off-road locomotion. The nature of the interaction between soil and vehicle running gears (rigid wheels, pneumatic tires, tracks) is explained and the selection of applicable theories for the formulation of a variety of interaction problems is shown in great detail. General relationships between vehicle performance and soil parameters obtained by computer techniques are shown in graphical form. It is very seldom that these complex problems can be solved by slide rule or graphs and whoever tries will be disappointed. From that viewpoint this book is for the future when large computing systems will be as economically available as slide rules and electronic hand calculators are today. Details are presented of soil mechanics laboratory investigations, sampling methods and field measurements that pertain specifically to the determination of soil properties for use in off-road mobility predictions. The soil mechanics aspects of special problems in vehicle mobility are indicated.

The authors realize that a problem area that has existed since man's earliest days cannot be resolved in all respects by one book. However, proper recognition of a problem is very often half of its solution. We hope that the concepts presented in this book provide the reader with a fuller understanding and appreciation of the problems in off-road locomotion and a new direction toward their solution.

In a book of this type where the subject matter crosses the lines of a number of disciplines and in which the results of many diversified research interests have been brought to bear on specific problems in off-road locomotion, it is difficult for the authors to acknowledge properly all the organizations and/or individuals who have contributed to it. In addition, there are, of course, a number of different ways in which these contributions have been made: some have been in the form of direct technical input and/or the availability of data resources; others have been made through financial sponsorship of relevant research projects undertaken by the authors; still others have been made in the form of support whether through the availability of laboratory, computer, or technical support facilities or through the less tangible "moral support" all authors require at some time in their writing.

Since the authors are indebted to so many individuals for their contributions (large or small) and since people are more likely to be offended by omission of recognition than are organizations, the authors chose not to risk offending anyone but to thank all personal contributors here collectively without mentioning names. On the other hand, the authors wish to single out the following organizations for their special contributions: The Research Department of the Grumman Aerospace Corporation for providing both the intellectual atmosphere in which many of the ideas expressed in this book were conceived and the laboratory and computer facilities by which these ideas could be developed and eventually applied, first to problems of lunar locomotion and subsequently to problems of terrestrial off-road locomotion. The authors are also grateful to the Surface Mobility Division of the U.S. Army Tank Automotive Command (TACOM) not only for its generous financial support of projects from which evolved many of the new approaches to mobility problems presented here, but also for its personnels' overall interest in our work and their many valuable suggestions that made the results more relevant to problems facing vehicle designers. In addition, the authors are indebted to the Waterways Experiment Station of the U. S. Army Corps of Engineers whose well documented experiments provided data with which theories could be validated or modified to conform with field and laboratory observations. Personnel at the WES were always most cooperative and whenever possible were willing to supply information beyond what was contained in the formal reports of that agency. Similarly, the authors wish to acknowledge the Stevens Institute of Technology, Hoboken, New Jersey, in whose full scale mobility bin rigid wheel experiments were performed where stress measurements taken across the wheel provided validation of some of the authors' early theories on soil-wheel interaction. In addition, personnel there offered the authors suggestions on instrumentation, testing procedures and data reduction that proved helpful in their later work. Similarly, the authors wish to thank the National Tillage Machinery Laboratory, Auburn. Alabama, for the unselfish cooperation of its members in providing the authors with the wealth of experimental data generated there with reference to soil-tire interaction. Also, we would be remiss if we did not mention the work of the U.S. Army Cold Regions Research and Engineering Laboratory, Hanover, New Hampshire in the area of the mobility of tracked vehicles especially the track grouser plate problem.

Finally, there is one institution which is responsible for most of the "moral support" we received and that is the institution of marriage. We therefore wish to acknowledge this most important contribution of our wives, Marietta and Patricia, and thank them for understanding that "nil sine magno vita labore dedit mortalibus".

Huntington, New York — L. L. Karafiath
Tucson, Arizona — E. A. Nowatzki

June 1977

PART 1

FUNDAMENTALS OF SOIL MECHANICS FOR PROBLEMS IN OFF-ROAD LOCOMOTION

CHAPTER 1.1

INTRODUCTION

Because of the complexity of the man-vehicle-soil system, problems in the area of off-road vehicle engineering are multidisciplinary by their very nature. Consequently, workers in this field can become more effective only as they understand the contributions of more and more of the other disciplines involved and still maintain a high level of expertise in their own area of interest. It is with the sense of promoting this type of interdisciplinary understanding that the authors decided to devote Part 1 of this book to the discussion of certain fundamentals of soil mechanics. It is not the authors' intent to provide here a complete course in soil mechanics nor to burden the reader with learning a massive new vocabulary of soil mechanics terms. Consequently, the treatment here may seem shallow and incomplete to soil mechanicians, however the authors purposely present only those principles that pertain to off-road locomotion problems in the hope that vehicle designers will master them and thereby appreciate the role of the soil in what is basically a soil-structure interaction problem.

For presenting the fundamentals of soil mechanics for problems in off-road locomotion, the authors decided first to identify soil and its constituents in the soil mechanics sense, then to discuss some of the permanent and transient characteristics of soil, and finally to show how soil is classified according to the needs of the classifier. Following this comes a detailed consideration of soil strength properties, the factors that influence them, and the methods for their determination in the laboratory. Special emphasis is given to the principle of effective stresses and the nature of shearing resistance between solids and soils. The concepts of consolidation and shear strength are presented and their relevance to mobility problems is indicated. Then the more widely accepted theories for the determination of stress states in soil under applied load are described and the advantages and disadvantages of their use in mobility problems are discussed. Finally the question of what constitutes failure in soil is addressed and the failure theories in conventional soil mechanics evaluated with respect to their applicability to the soil-vehicle running gear interaction problem.

Throughout all of these discussions ample references are given to the current literature as well as to the accepted "standards" for the specific topic being considered. However, the reader who is unfamiliar with soil mechanics concepts and terminology is advised to consult the general soil mechanics references such as TAYLOR (1948), LAMBE and WHITMAN (1969), SCOTT (1963), WU (1966) or YONG and WARKENTIN (1966) given in the bibliography at the end of Part 1.

CHAPTER 1.2

CHARACTERIZATION OF SOILS

1.2.1 Identification of Soils for Trafficability Purposes

The word "soil" is defined in Webster's New World Dictionary as "the surface layer of earth, supporting plant life". This definition, although perfectly acceptable to the agronomist, is, at best, incomplete to researchers and practitioners in a host of other geotechnically related disciplines. For example, such a narrow definition excludes the "soil" that is the concern of the soils and foundation engineer when he designs a building foundation, be it a spread footing or a pile group. And what is the "soil" of the terrain vehicle engineer who must design an off-road vehicle that is capable of negotiating the sand dunes of the Sahara or the desolate wastes of the moon? The point is that the word "soil" means many different things to many different people and a general, all inclusive definition acceptable to all geo-disciplines does not exist. Consequently, before the reader can begin to understand the soil mechanics of off-road vehicle engineering he must appreciate the authors' definition of soil, master the terminology used to describe the characteristics of soil, and understand the interrelationships between these characteristics and their effect on the physical properties important to trafficability.

Soil is a natural or artificial assemblage of a specified range of solid particles and fluids in a three-phase system consisting of combinations of the following: primary rock minerals, clay minerals, intergranular cement, organic matter, water, dissolved salts, air, water vapor and other gases. An identificition of the infinite variety of soils that exists in nature can be made through specification of certain permanent characteristics of soils such as particle size and shape, mineral composition, specific gravity, Atterberg limits, etc. The use of these characteristics alone results in a generic identification such as "sand", "silt", "loam", or "clay". It is impossible, however, to associate a general set of physical properties to any one of these generic identifications because of the effect of certain transient factors such as moisture content, void ratio, and soil structure. Therefore, in any application of soil mechanics to the prediction of soil behavior it is absolutely necessary to supplement generic identifications with information on the in situ conditions. This is especially true in the soil mechanics of off-road locomotion where the properties of surface and near surface soils are concerned. The in situ condition of soils at the surface is particularly subject to environmental changes which overwhelmingly influence the behavior of soils under wheels and tracks.

Since soil properties may vary even within a specific group or type of soil and since concern with the way variation of these properties affects soil behavior may differ from discipline to discipline, numerous classification systems have been developed that group soils according to user-oriented criteria. Unfortunately, no universally accepted, all inclusive classification system exists. In fact, it may be a practical impossibility to devise such a system since classification grouping depends on the user's need! However, in the following sections of this chapter the bases of existing classification systems will be discussed and their adaptation to the needs of mobility examined.

1.2.2 Permanent Characteristics of Soil

In the soil mechanics for off-road vehicle engineering, the permanent characteristics of soils are considered to be those which do not change significantly under all conditions usually encountered in off-road locomotion. Since the interaction of soil and wheel for a given situation is a transient phenomenon, the effect on the interaction of long term changes in soil composition or structure due to environmental factors such as weathering, leaching, etc. is discounted. Therefore, in this text characteristics such as particle size and shape, mineral composition, specific gravity, and the various "limit" moisture contents associated with fine-grained soil are considered permanent since they are not significantly altered by externally imposed stress fields or by short term environmental effects. Permanent characteristics are the basis of identification systems.

Particle Size

Particle size in all branches of geotechnical and soil science is defined by the "effective diameter" of the soil particle. Obviously it is not possible to define an arbitrarily shaped particle by a single dimension. For particles seized by sieving, the effective diameter is the minimum sieve opening through which the particle passes. Table 1.1 is a partial list of sieve sizes and designations in current use. For very small particles, electrostatic effects prevent sizing by sieving and hydrometer analyses based on the principles of sedimentation and STOKES' Law are used to determine particle size. In this case the effective diameter is the diameter of an equivalent sphere that would settle in a fluid of known viscosity with the same velocity as the arbitrarily shaped particle.

TABLE 1.1
Standard Sieve Sizes

No.	Tyler Standard Diameter (mm)	No.	U.S. Standard Diameter (mm)	No.	British Standard Diameter (mm)	No.	Metric Standard Diameter (mm)
4	4.699	4	4,76	5	3.36	5000	5.00
6	3.327	6	3.36	8	2.06	3000	3.00
10	1.651	10	2.00	12	1.41	2000	2.00
20	0.833	20	0.84	18	0.85	1500	1.50
48	0.295	40	0.42	25	0.60	1000	1.00
60	0.246	60	0.25	36	0.42	500	0.50
100	0.147	100	0.149	60	0.25	300	0.30
200	0.074	200	0.074	100	0.15	150	0.15
				200	0.076	75	0.075

In geotechnical engineering, structures such as earth- and rock-fill dams are treated analytically as "soil" structures, even though the constituent particles may be several feet in thickness. On the other hand, consolidation analyses often involve soil deposits having particles as small as 1×10^{-6} mm (10Å) which can be observed only through an electron microscope. This enormous range of 1 to 10^9 is better appreciated by analogy, noting that it is about the same as the size range between a child's marble and our earth (LAMBE and WHITMAN, 1969)! It is no wonder then that many different schemes exist whereby particle sizes are identified with the generic name of the soil in which they predominantly occur. These classifications exist for any number of nonscientific reasons such as the convenience of equating the limits to certain standard sieve sizes or the convenience of identifying the limits with length units customary in and peculiar to the country of origin.

Attempts to reconcile these differences and adopt an international standard for the limit of particle size ranges have been fruitless, essentially because there is no overwhelming argument in favor of any of the limits under dispute. In off-road locomotion engineering workers of various backgrounds must be aware that such differences exist and avoid further confusion by indicating the particle size range both by its name and by the limiting diameters.

Figure 1.1 shows the sizes of various particles and the ranges of some methods of detecting particle size. The generic soil names according to a widely used soil particle size classification scheme (the MIT System) are shown at the top. Other sizes and size limits are given for the purpose of lending perspective to the entire subject of particle size.

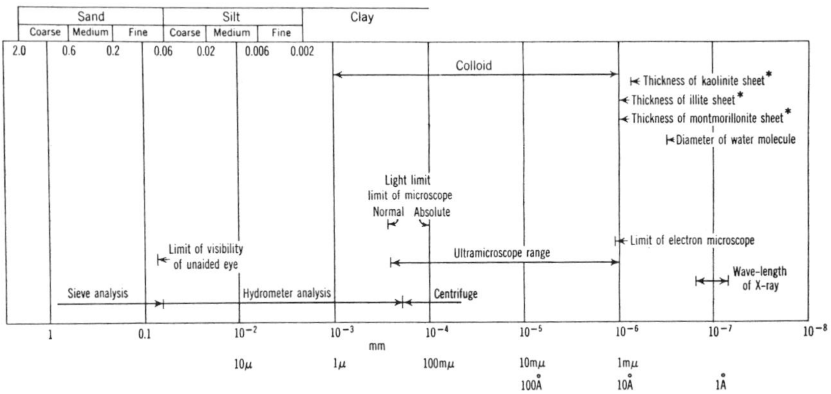

Fig. 1.1
Soil Particle Sizes Relative to Other Sizes
(From LAMBE and WHITMAN, 1969)

There are a number of systems for identifying particle size. The difference among the various systems lie in the limits each sets to the various fractional divisions each considers significant. The most well known and widely used of the gradational classification systems are:

a) United States Department of Agriculture (USDA) Bureau of Soils Classification

b) American Society for Testing Materials (ASTM) Classification

c) Massachusetts Institute of Technology (MIT) Classification

d) International Society of Soil Science Classification (ISSS)

e) German Industrial Norms Classification (DIN)

f) British Classification

Table 1.2 shows the ranges for particle size and their related generic soil name according to a few of the above mentioned systems.

The names for particle size ranges also denote the natural soil types which frequently contain particles in more than one particle size range. Where there is a possibility of misunderstanding it is advisable to add the word "size" to the designation in Table 1.1 to indicate particle size range. For example, rock flour is not a clay although its particle size is in the < 0.002 mm range.

Identification of soils according to grain size is generally accomplished by one of three methods:

a) Sieve analysis. This method consists of shaking a representative soil sample (usually about 500 gms) through a nest of wire screens of known size opening sequentially arranged in a stack with the coarsest screen on top and the finest just above a pan at the bottom. The number of sieves and their opening sizes are chosen as a matter of convenience to suit the requirements for the specific problem being studied. Table 1.1 lists the designations and sizes of the most commonly used types of sieves.

TABLE 1.2
Particle Size (mm) Ranges For Soils According to Various Organizations

	Lower Limit				Upper Limit			
	MIT	USDA	ASTM	ISSS	MIT	USDA	ASTM	ISSS
Gravel	2.0	1.0	2.0	2.0	185			
Sand	0.06	0.05	0.074	0.02	2.0	1.0	2.0	2.0
Silt	0.002	0.002	0.005	0.002	0.06	0.05	0.074	0.02
Clay					0.002	0.002	0.005	0.002

A sieve combination often suitable for conventional soil mechanics identification purposes is U.S. Standard Sieve Numbers 4, 8, 20, 40, 100 and 200. After the sample has been shaken sufficiently the weights retained on each sieve are expressed as a percentage of the total sample weight and the results plotted semilogarithmically, usually as "percent finer by weight" on the arithmetic ordinate versus "grain size diameter in mm" on the logarithmic abscissa. "Diameter" in this context obviously refers to the side dimension of a square hole and should not be taken to imply sphericity or any other shape characteristic. The results plotted in this way constitute or contribute to the so-called grain size distribution curve for the soil sample. Examples of grain size distribution curves for various types of soil are given in Figure 1.2.

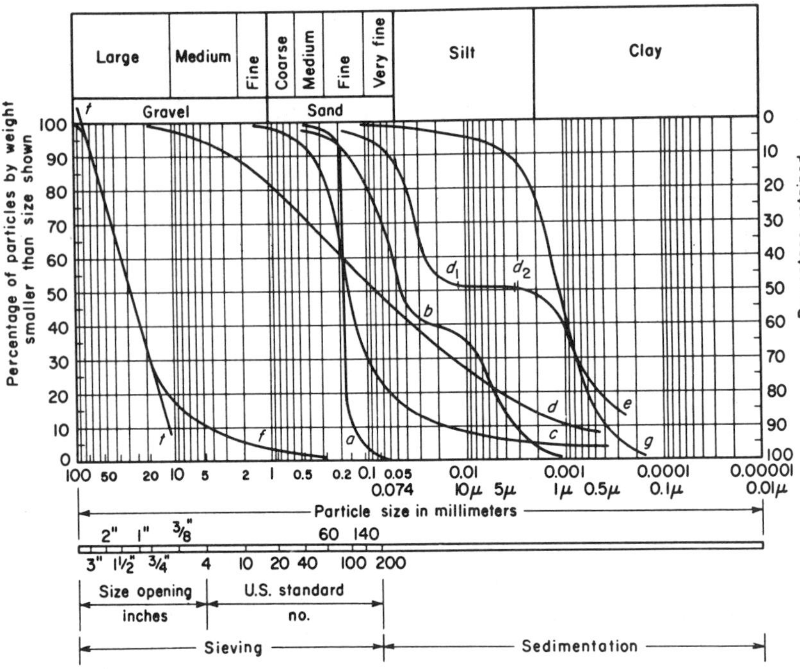

Fig. 1.2
Gradation Curves for Various Types of Soils
a. Uniform fine sand
b. Fine sand and silt
c. Weathered silty sand
d. Well graded soil
e. Gap (between $d_1 — d_2$) — graded sandy clay
f. Coarse gravel
g. Silty clay
(From Jumikis, 1966)

b) Hydrometer analysis. This method is based on Stokes' equation for the settling velocity of spheres falling freely through a viscous fluid. This velocity is a direct function of the diameter of the settling spheres.

The relationship between Stokes' equation and particle diameter is made through the time rate of change of density of the fluid as the soil particles settle out of suspension. Obviously, not all soil particles are spheres, therefore for the hydrometer analysis, particle diameter means the diameter of an "equivalent sphere" having the same density and settling velocity as the soil particle. The hydrometer analysis is used for soil particle sizes that are too small to be separated by sieving. There is a practical lower limit of sieve opening below which electrostatic forces on the particles exceed gravity forces and the particles cling to the sieve screen and clog the openings. Results of the hydrometer analysis are usually presented in the same way as those of the sieve analysis.

c) Combined analysis. This method employs both of the above methods and is used in practice to cover the full range of particle sizes generally found in natural soils.

In addition to identifying soils, the "gradation curves" obtained by sieving and/or hydrometer analysis are used for estimating some soil properties such as permeability and relative density (refer to Section 1.2.3).

A knowledge of the gradation characteristics of surface and near surface soils is of interest in trafficability studies since it may provide the first indication of potential mobility problems due to poor drainage, fine-grained soils, etc.

Particle Shape

A more complete description of the size of a particle is obtained if, in addition to the effective diameter of the particle, the shape of the particle is also noted. The shape of the particle refers not only to the relative proportions of its length, breadth and thickness but also to the surface geometry. Generally most of the particles in the silt range and coarser are virtually equidimensional and the surface geometry designations shown in Figure 1.3 are usually used as particle size modifiers.

Various methods have been proposed to define the shape of particles by a "shape factor" or "sphericity factor". However, the accurate determination of these factors is difficult and time consuming, and it is usually simpler to determine the property of the soil which is affected by these factors directly than to determine the shape factor and try to evaluate its effect on the strength, permeability or other properties.

On the other hand, most particles in the clay size range are irregularly shaped, generally being either elongated, flat, flaky, rod like or lath-shaped as shown in Figure 1.4. Although the shape of these fine particles plays an important role in the mechanical behavior of the soils containing them, the effect can be evaluated by other indicators more easily than by the direct determination of the shape. While this determination is too complex for identification purposes it is an important means in studying the effect of reworking on the mechanical properties of soils. Further reference to the shape of very fine particles will be made in that context.

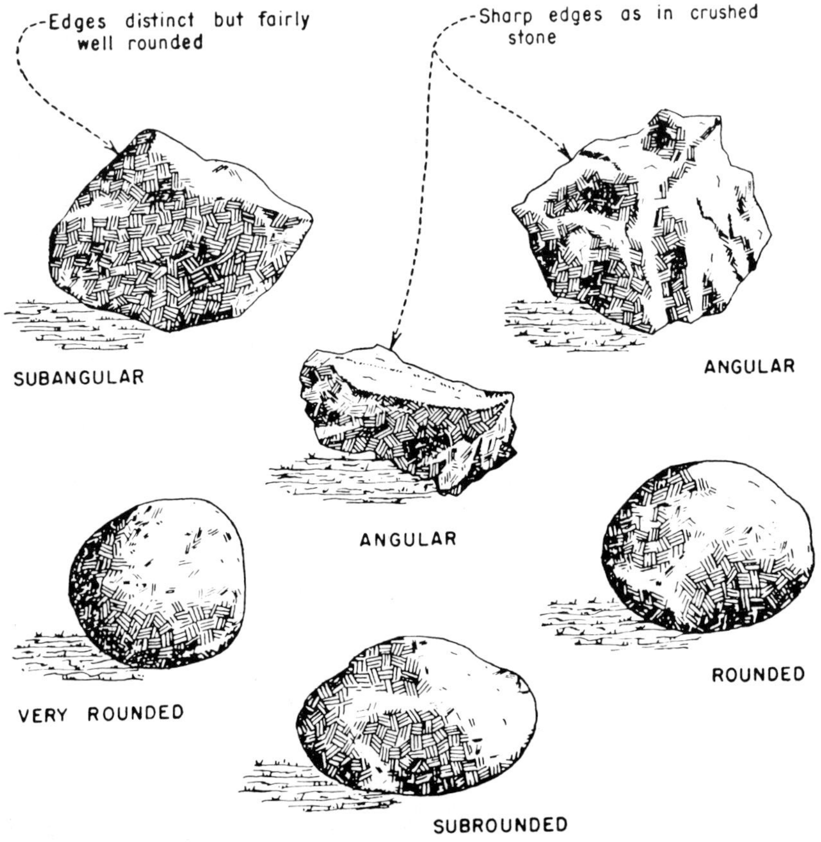

Fig. 1.3
Particle Shape of Soils in the Silt Range or Coarser
(From ABDUN-NUR, 1950)

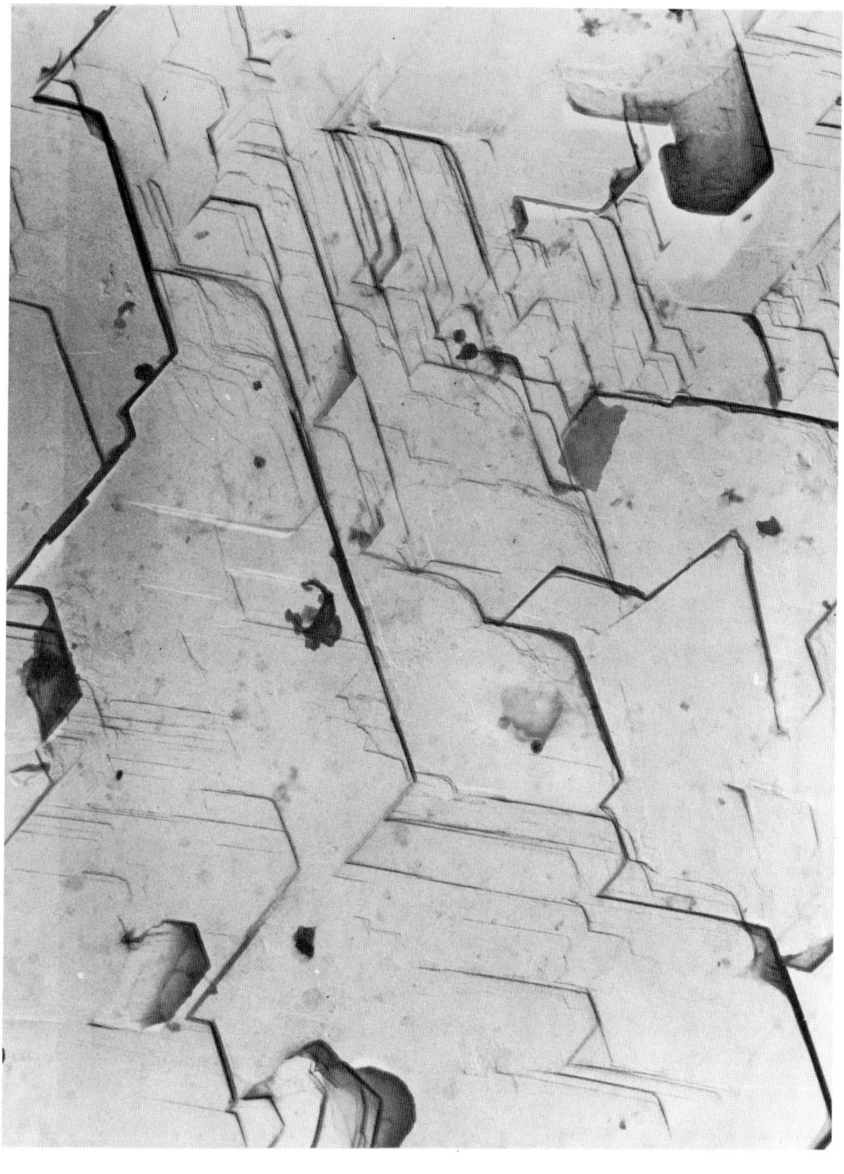

Fig. 1.4
Micrographs of Clay Minerals
a) Kaolinite 31 000X (bulk material)

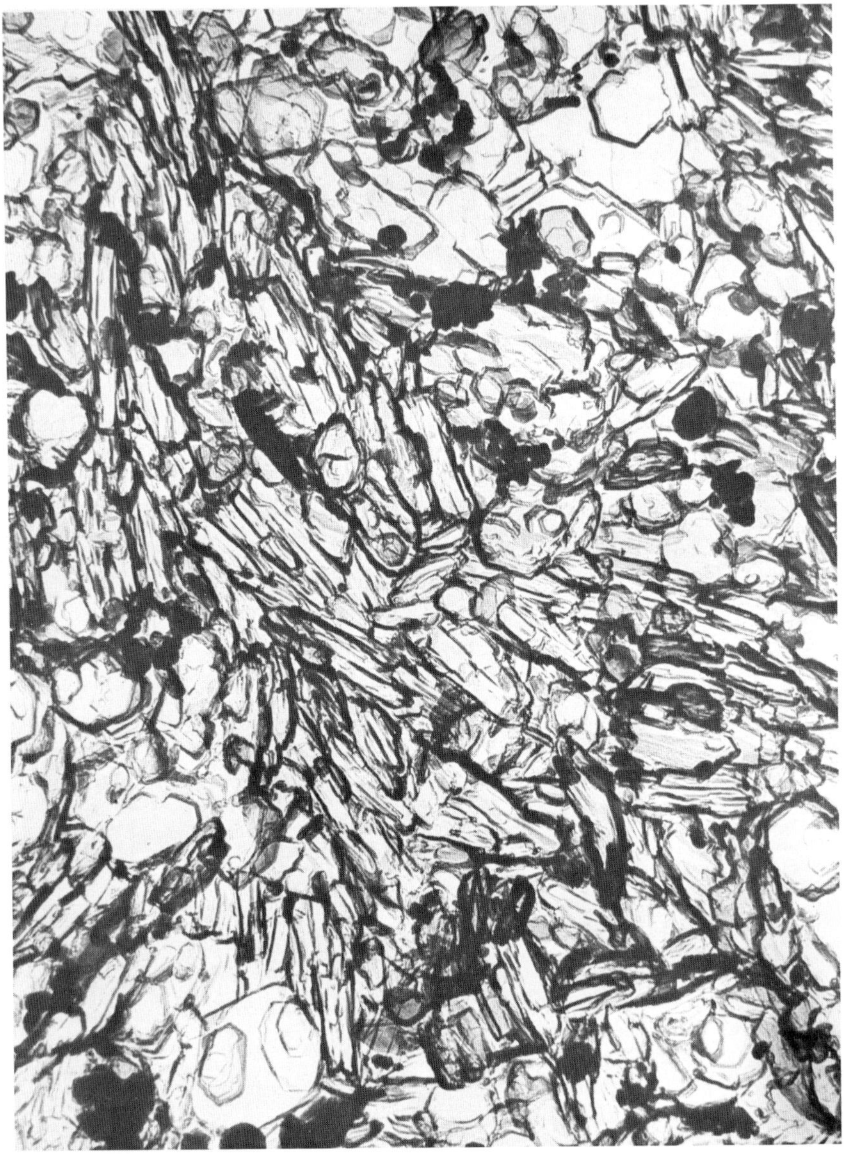

Fig. 1.4
Micrographs of Clay Minerals
b) Compacted Kaolin 38000X

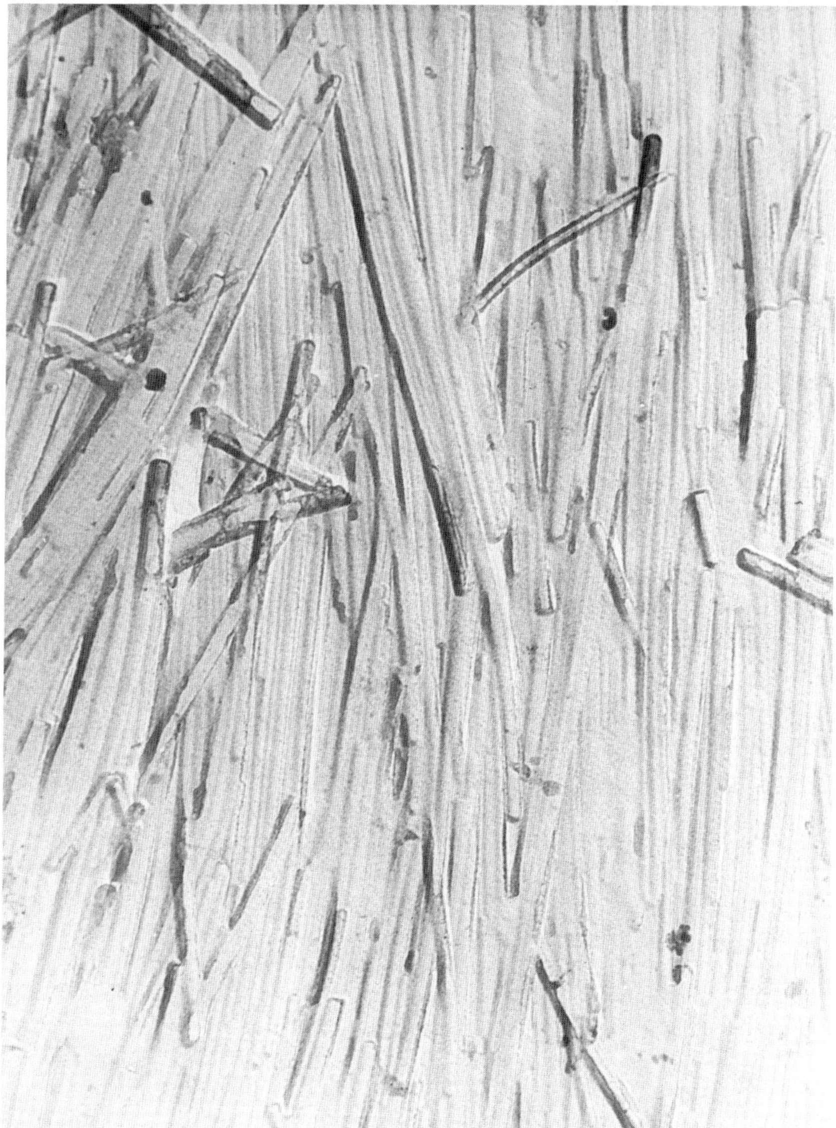

Fig. 1.4
Micrographs of Clay Minerals
c) Attapulgite 150000X (bulk material)

Mineral Composition

A mineral is a naturally occurring chemical element or compound formed by a geologic process. Consequently its chemical composition can be expressed by a formula as, for example, quartz (SiO_2) or pyrophyllite ($Al_2Si_4O_{10}(OH)_2$).

Mineralogical composition of the particles in the sand and gravel size range has little effect per se on those properties of soils which are of interest from the viewpoint of off-road locomotion. The strength of the individual particles is closely related to their mineralogical composition and is generally not critical for the behavior of soils in the range of stresses encountered in off-road locomotion or compaction. However, the shape and surface geometry of particles into which rocks disintegrate upon weathering or mechanical comminution is predominantly controlled by the mineralogical composition of the parent rock. Thus mineralogical composition affects the mechanical properties of coarse-grained soils in an indirect way, through its effect on the particle shape and surface geometry. However, mineralogical composition of the particles in the sand and gravel size range is rarely determined for the purpose of soil mechanics analyses.

On the other hand, the mineralogical composition of the fine particles profoundly affects the behavior of soils even if the fine particles constitute only a small percentage of the total sample. The primary reason for this is that the gravitational forces acting on particles having a smallest dimension of about 1 μ, are approximately equal to their bond forces, and the magnitude of bond forces is directly related to the mineralogical composition of the particle. Mineralogy, as a subdivision of the earth sciences, addresses this topic and all its ramifications directly. Therefore, it is obviously impossible to go into this matter in great detail here. However, mineralogy relates directly to problems in off-road locomotion because most of these problems arise in fine-grained soils. Consequently, an appreciation of some of the principles involved will help the reader to better understand why the physical properties of some fine-grained soils are very susceptible to changes in environmental conditions and those of others are not.

Most minerals present in a soil are crystalline in nature. A crystal, in terms of morphology, is a homogeneous solid, bounded by smooth regular surfaces which are a reflection of an orderly internal atomic arrangement (Hurlbut, 1959). Crystals have the following properties: a definite structure that is a function of the arrangement of its atoms or ions; cleavage (usually) on specific crystallographic planes; a characteristic morphology; constant interfacial angles; diffraction characteristics; and symmetry which is a function of some long range spatial atomic order in at least two dimensions, often three. Table 1.3 defines crystal systems in terms of geometry and in order of decreasing symmetry. Clay minerals are usually either monoclinic or triclinic crystalline systems. By translating the fixed vector distances of a given crystal system over and over again in each direction, a lattice is produced.

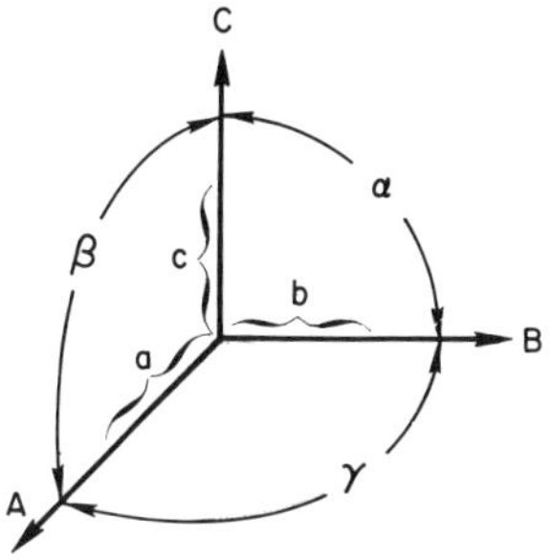

TABLE 1.3
Crystal Systems
(In order of Decreasing Symmetry)

System Name	Axes	Interfacial Angle	Bravais Lattice Types (refer to Figure 1.5)
Isometric	$a = b = c$	$\alpha = \beta = \gamma = 90°$	P, I, F
Hexagonal	$a = b \neq c$	$\alpha = \beta = 90°, \gamma = 120°$	P
Tetragonal	$a = b \neq c$	$\alpha = \beta = \gamma = 90°$	P, I
Orthorhombic	$a \neq b \neq c$	$\alpha = \beta = \gamma = 90°$	P, I, C, F
Monoclinic	$a \neq b \neq c$	$\alpha = \gamma = 90°, \beta \neq 90°$	P, C
Triclinic	$a \neq b \neq c$	$\alpha \neq \beta \neq \gamma \neq 90°$	P
Rhombohedral	$a = b = c$	$\alpha = \beta = \gamma \neq 90°$	R

The crystal structure and/or lattice is held together internally by bonding forces. These bonds may be primary (valence) bonds or secondary (proximity) bonds. The primary bonds are usually quite strong and may be covalent (ion sharing), ionic, (ion trading), heteropolar (mixed ionic-covalent), or metallic. The secondary bonds are usually weak and may be due to internal strain energy, mass attraction or electrostatic effects.

There are certain characteristics of the atomic structure of a crystal that can be used to determine the relative stability of a mineral to chemical or mechanical stimuli. These characteristics are:

a) Isomorphous substitution which denotes the process by which one ion may be substituted for another within the crystal lattice with change in chemical composition, but without change in the crystal structure.

b) Coordination number *(N)* which defines the number of like ions that surround an unlike ion as nearest neighbors in a crystalline structure.

c) Relative bond strength which in ionic or mixed bond structures refers to the ratio of v (valence of coordinated ion) to N (coordination number).

d) Radius ratio which is the ratio of ionic radii of coordinated to coordinating ions in the crystal structure (usually cation radius/anion radius).

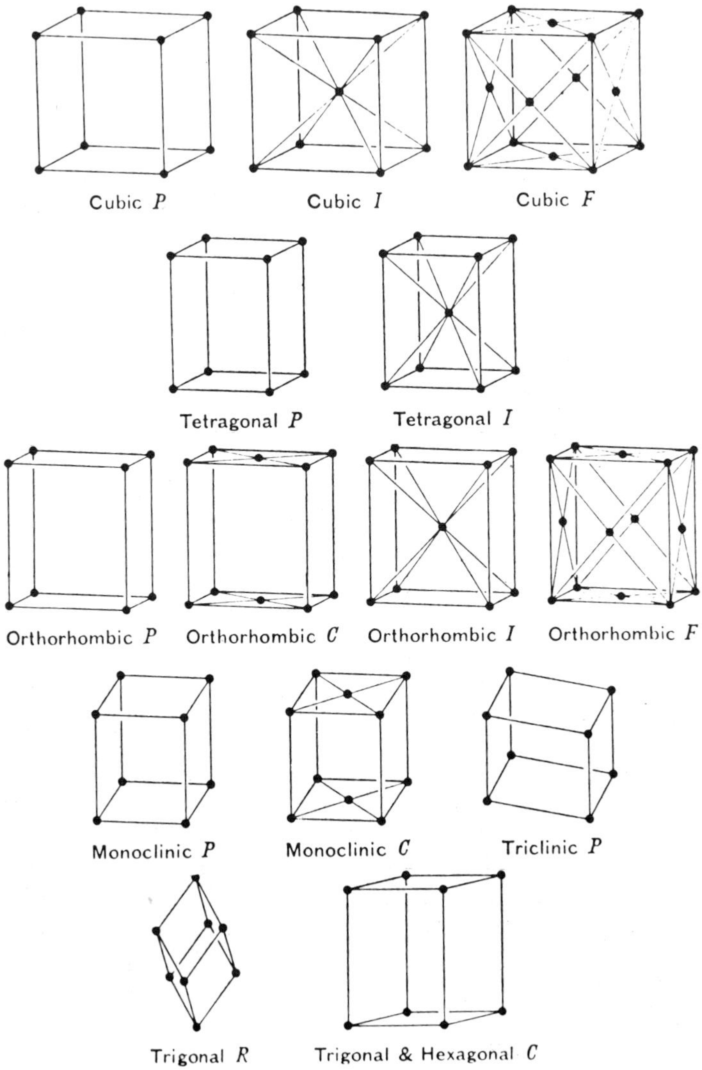

Fig. 1.5
The Fourteen Bravais Lattice Types (From PHILLIPS, 1971)

In general, isomorphous substitution, the coordination number and the radius ratio can be used to indicate the type of crystal structure existing in a mineral whereas the relative bond strength is usually used to define the type of bonding that is active. In crystals having ionic and heteropolar bonding, the geometry and electronic neutrality govern the crystal structure. This is the type of bonding that exists in most clay minerals. Table 1.4 shows how some of the characteristics dicussed above relate to crystal geometry and stability for representative compounds. In general, the various types of clay minerals are formed from combinations of tetrahedral and octrahedral units, specifically silica and alumina, accompanied by cationic isomorphous substitution in one or both of the units. The two-dimensional combination of silica tetrahedrons forms the silica sheet; the two-dimensional combination of alumina octahedrons forms the gibbsite sheet. If the trivalent (Al^{+3}) cations in the alumina sheet are replaced by divalent (Mg^{+2}) cations the brucite sheet is formed. Unit cells made up of combinations of the gibbsite or brucite sheets and the silica sheet(s) are bonded together to form the various types of clay minerals. Although the bonding within the unit cells that make up a sheet is usually quite strong, the bonding between sheets varies depending upon the types of units being linked and the magnitude of their charge imbalance which is a function of the type and amount of isomorphous substitution. Table 1.5 shows the structural arrangements and physico-chemical characteristics of some sheet silicate minerals or commonly known clays.

TABLE 1.4
Relationships Between Atomic Characteristics and Geometry for Crystals Having Ionic or Heteropolar Bonding

Radius Ratio	N	Geometry	Schematic	Example	Stability (energy needed to break bond)
0.155	2	Linear	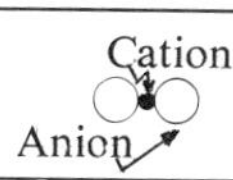	CO_2 Carbon Dioxide	Very High
0.155–0.220	3	Planar	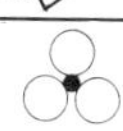	$(CO_3)^{-1}$ Carbonate	Very High
0.220–0.410	4	Tetrahedral	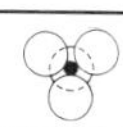	$(SiO_4)^{-4}$ Silica	Moderately High
0.410–0.730	6	Octahedral	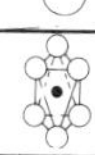	$(Al(OH)_6)^{-3}$ Alumina	High
0.730–1.00	8	Cubic	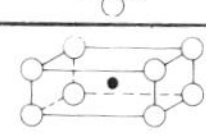	Fe Metals	Low to High
1.00	12	Sheet	Mostly Proximity Bonds	$(K — O_{12})^{-1}$	Very Low

TABLE 1.5
Structural Arrangements and Physico Chemical Characteristics of some of the Common Clay Minerals
(Adapted from LAMBE and WHITMAN, 1969)

Mineral	Structure Symbol	Isomorphous Substitution (nature and amount)	Linkage between Sheets (type and strength)	Specific Surface (m^2/g)	$\frac{1}{\text{Charge Density}}$ ($Å^2$/ion)	Potential Exchange Capacity (me/100 g)	Actual Exchange Capacity (me/100 g)	Particle Shape	Particle Size
Serpentine	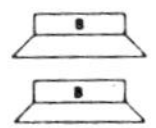	none	H-bonding + secondary valence			1	1	Platy or fibrous	
Kaolinite	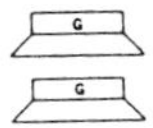	Al for Si 1 in 400	H-bonding + secondary valence	10–20	83	3	3	Platy	$d = 0.3$ to $3\ \mu$ thickness $= {}^1/_3$ to ${}^1/_{10}\ d$
Halloysite (4 H_2O)	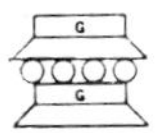	Al for Si 1 in 100	Secondary valence	40	55	12	12	Hollow rod	OD $= 0.07\ \mu$ ID $= 0.04\ \mu$ $L = 0.5\ \mu$
Halloysite ($2H_2O$)	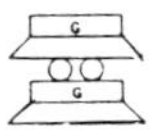	Al for Si 1 in 100	Secondary valence	40	55	12	12	Hollow rod	OD $= 0.07\ \mu$ ID $= 0.04\ \mu$ $L = 0.5\ \mu$
Talc	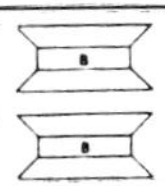	none	Secondary valence			1	1	Platy	
Pyrophyllite	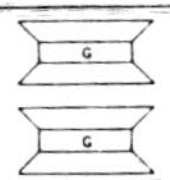	none	Secondary valence			1	1	Platy	

Muscovite	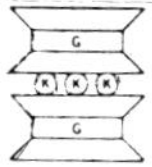	Al for Si 1 in 4	Secondary valence + K linkage			250	5–20	Platy	
Vermiculite	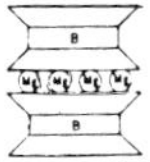	Al, Fe, for Mg Al for Si	Secondary valence + Mg linkage	5–400	45	150	150	Platy	$t = {}^1/_{10}\, d$ to ${}^1/_3\, d$
Illite	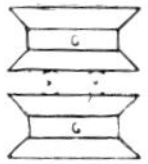	Al for Si, 1 in 7 Mg, Fe for Al Fe, Al for Mg	Secondary valence + K linkage	80–100	67	150	25	Platy	d = 0.1 to 2 μ $t = {}^1/_{10}\, d$
Mont-morillonite	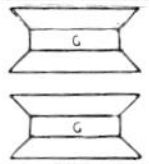	Mg for Al, 1 in 6	Secondary valence + exchangeable ion linkage	800	133	100	100	Platy	d = 0.1 to 1 μ $t = 1/100\, d$
Nontronite	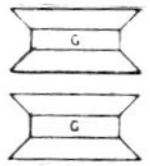	Al for Si, 1 in 6	Secondary valence + exchangeable ion linkage	800	133	100	100	Lath	$l = 0.4$ to 2 μ $t = {}^1/_{100}\, l$
Chlorite	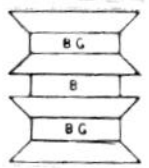	Al for Si, Fe, Al for Mg	Secondary valence + brucite linkage	5–50	700	20	20	Platy	

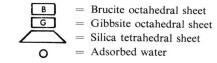

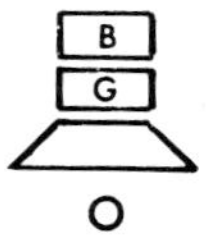

= Brucite octahedral sheet
= Gibbsite octahedral sheet
= Silica tetrahedral sheet
= Adsorbed water

Definitions for some of these characteristics follow:

a) Specific surface is the ratio per unit weight of the surface area to the volume of a substance. Chemically and electrostatically, the greater the specific surface the more "active" is the mass. The units of specific surface in clay mineralogy are usually given in m^2/gm. To appreciate the meaning of the term, about 10 gms of montmorillonite would cover a football field if the particles could be spread out one layer thick!

b) Cation Exchange Capacity is the property of a colloid that enables it to absorb at its surface certain cations (or anions) and retain them in an exchangeable state, i.e. the absorbed ion of one element may be replaced by ions of another element. The exchange capacity is usually expressed in terms of milliequivalents/100 gms. Since bonding energies differ among the different clay minerals, a single replaceability characteristic or series does not exist for all clay minerals. However, the activity of some clay minerals is affected significantly by the type of ion absorbed at its surface.

c) Charge Density is merely the number of charges or ions per unit area. Frequently the inverse of the charge density is given in terms of $Å^2$/ion. The surface charge density of an individual clay mineral and the nature of its bounded exchangeable cation determines the number of cations that will be available for the formation of the diffuse electrical double layer, a phenomenon that affects the behavior of clay soils.

The micro-mechanical and physico-chemical properties of soils as outlined above relate to the macro-mechanical behavior of soils that is of interest in mobility studies mainly through their effect on the physical properties customarily used to describe soil behavior. For example, the Gouy Chapman theory of the diffuse double layer has been applied to clay-water systems (Bolt, 1955) to explain why soils composed of montmorillonite are more susceptible to swelling and reduced strength upon wetting than soils composed of kaolinite. Soil structure, which for fine-grained soils is a direct function of the physico-chemical properties of the soil particles and their depositional environment, has been shown to influence the shear strength (Lambe, 1960; Seed and Chan, 1959; Olson, 1962), compaction characteristics (Lambe, 1958 a and b), and other engineering properties of clay soils (Lambe and Martin, 1953–57). Indeed, the concept of effective stress, which will be shown in Chapter 1.3 to be fundamental to the understanding of soil behavior for *all* soil-structure interaction problems, has been modified (Bolt and Miller, 1958) to account for physico-chemical effects.

Since mineral composition is such an important factor in predicting the behavior of fine-grained soils, it is often determined either instrumentally or chemically. Among the instrumental methods of clay mineral identification are: x-ray diffraction, differential thermal analysis, infrared adsorption spectroscopy and electron microscopy. The most common chemical methods of identification are cation exchange capacity and potassium oxide (K_2O) analysis. Generally none of the above methods is uniquely diagnostic and a combination of two or more methods is required. A detailed explanation of these and other methods of soil analysis is found in Monograph 9 of the American Society of Agronomy (1965).

Specific Gravity

Specific gravity is defined, in general, as the ratio between the unit weight of a substance and the unit weight of some reference substance; in most cases the reference substance is distilled water at 4 °C. Although this definition is applied sometimes to the mass of soil, it is strictly applicable only to the constituent minerals. The authors prefer the term "unit weight" for the concept of mass specific gravity and discuss it in Section 1.2.3. The specific gravity of the soil constituents is a permanent characteristic that is needed in many volumetric and gravimetric calculations. The specific gravity of solids is

$$G_s = \gamma_s/\gamma_w$$

where:

γ_s = unit weight of the solid portion of the soil mass

γ_w = unit weight of water at 4 °C

Table 1.6 gives specific gravities (G_s) for most of the mineral constituents of soil. Table 1.7 gives average specific gravities of the mineral constituents for some of the broad categories of soils encountered in practice. In natural soils, the size of the particles as well as their mineralogical composition varies, therefore the specific gravity of a natural soil is really an average specific gravity representative of the assemblage of different types of minerals. This is apparent from Table 1.6 and 1.7. For example, most beach sands are composed almost entirely of quartz, therefore their specific gravities are very close to or exactly equal to that of the mineral quartz. Soils of organic origin (humus, peat, organic silts) have specific gravities significantly lower than the soils derived entirely from rocks. The specific gravity of clays is difficult to measure not only because clay particles are so small but also because specific gravity is usually measured on an oven-dry (110 °C) basis, a temperature at which much of the interlayer water of clays (especially expansive clays) is removed. Therefore, the method of the determination of specific gravity is different for coarse (larger than No. 4 sieve size, + 4 fraction) particles and for fine (smaller than No. 4 sieve size, – 4 fraction) particles. In the case of soils containing a wide range of particle sizes it should be ascertained whether specific gravities determined in the laboratory refer to the + 4 or – 4 fraction. The weighted average of the two specific gravities should be used in the computations. The details of specific gravity determinations are given in LAMBE (1967) and will not be discussed here. However, it will become apparent to the reader in subsequent chapters that for soil mechanics analyses it is essential that the average specific gravity of a soil be properly and accurately determined.

TABLE 1.6
Specific Gravities of Common Soil Minerals

Mineral	G_S
Anhydrite	2.90–2.98
Attapulgite	2.30
Augite	3.20–3.60
Biotite Mica	2.70–3.20
Calcite	2.71–3.72
Chlorite	2.60–3.00
Dolomite	2.80–3.00
Feldspar (Potassium)	2.54–2.57
Feldspar (Sodium or Calcium)	2.62–2.76
Glauconite	2.20–2.80
Gypsum	2.20–2.40
Halloysite ($2H_2O$)	2.55
Hematite	4.30–5.30
Hornblende	2.90–3.50
Illite	2.60
Iron oxide hydrates	3.73
Kaolinite	2.50–2.66
Limonite	3.50–4.00
Magnesite	3.00–5.17
Magnetite	5.16–5.18
Montmorillonite	2.00–2.40
Muscovite Mica	2.76–3.10
Oligoclase	2.63–2.69
Orthoclase	2.50–2.60
Plagioclase	2.67–2.74
Pyrite	4.95–5.10
Pyrophyllite	2.84
Quartz	2.65
Serpentine	2.20–2.70
Talcum	2.60–2.70

Consistency Limits and Indices Based on Moisture Content

The concept that the moisture content of a finegrained soil profoundly influences the state in which that soil exists is expressed through the ATTERBERG limits and related indices. These limits, originally taken from agronomy and named after the Swedish soil scientist who first proposed them, have widespread use in soil mechanics. Basically, the ATTERBERG limits are moisture contents at which remolded cohesive soils pass from one state to another. To visualize ATTERBERG limits conceptually, consider a pat of perfectly dry soil such as is shown schematically in Figure 1.6. Water is added until all the voids of the dry pat of soil are filled so that if moisture were then reduced, there would be no accompanying reduction in the volume of the pat. The moisture content of the soil in this state is called the shrinkage limit (w_s). More water is added. The soil becomes semisolid. The moisture content at which the soil begins to act as a plastic solid is termed the plastic limit (w_p). More water is added until the soil acts more like a liquid than a plastic solid. This moisture content defines the liquid limit (w_l). Since the dividing line

TABLE 1.7
Average Specific Gravities of the Mineral Constituents in Various Soil Types

Soil		Specific Gravity
Beach Sands:		
	Atlantic City, N.J.	2.65
	Daytona Beach, Fla.	2.62–2.64
	Jones Beach, N.Y.	2.65
	Lake Champlain, N.Y.	2.64
	Platte River, Nebraska	2.65
Clays:		
	Alluvial montmorillonitic clay	2.65
	Bentonite clay	2.34
	Clayey organic silt	2.53–2.56
	Silty clays	2.64–2.77
	Varved clays	2.73–2.80
Chalk		2.63–2.81
Humus		1.37
Kaolin		2.47–2.61
Loess		2.65–2.75
Limestone		2.70
Oxisol (Latosol), Hawaii		3.00
Peat		1.26–1.80
Peat (Sphagnum)		0.50–0.80
Silts:		
	Clayey organic silt	2.53–2.56
	Sandy silt	2.63–2.70
Volcanic Ash		2.32

between these states is often imperfectly defined, specific procedures have been developed and tests standardized for their determination. LAMBE (1967) describes these procedures in detail. A brief description of the limits and the tests is given below.

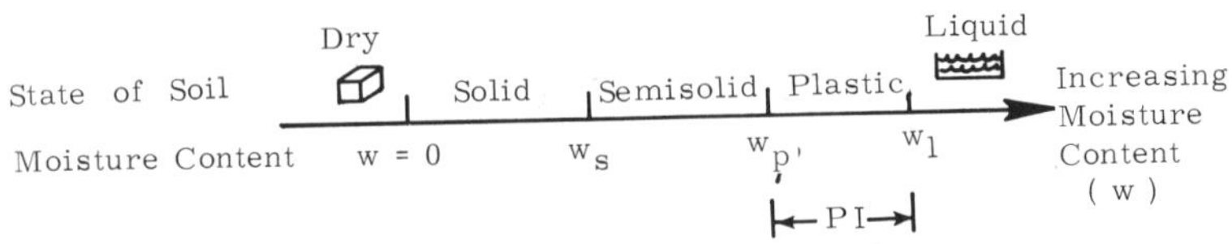

Fig. 1.6
Atterberg Limits and Related Indices

Liquid Limit (w_l). The liquid limit is the water content, expressed in percentages of dry weight, at which a suspension of soil particles acquires a small, but measureable shear strength when its water content is reduced. Soils with water content higher than the liquid limit behave like heavy or viscous fluids; thus liquid limit marks the transition from the liquid to the plastic state. The liquid limit is determined experimentally by letting a small groove, made in the soil paste by a special cutting tool, flow together under the repeated impact of dropping the cup containing the soil paste from a specified height. The original method proposed by ATTERBERG was later modified by CASAGRANDE and is now standardized (ASTM-423-66 or AASHO-T-89-68) so that the subjective elements in the determination are largely eliminated.

TABLE 1.8
Consistency Limits for Some Typical Soil Types

Type of Soil	Degree of Plasticity	Liquid Limit w_l	Consistency Limits Plastic Limit w_p	Plasticity Index *PI*	Limits of Plasticity Indexes
1	2	3	4	5	6
Sand	Non-plastic	20	20	0	0
Silt	Low-plastic	25	20	5	<7
Silty Clay Clayey silt	Medium-plastic	40	25	15	7–17
Clay	High-plastic	70	40	30	> 17

Typical values of liquid limit for various soil types are shown in Column 3 of Table 1.8.

The liquid limit of soils is determined in the remolded state; therefore, it is independent of the in situ condition of the soil. For the purposes of off-road locomotion engineering it is considered as an important permanent characteristic which is useful in identifying soils.

The remolded shear strength of soils at the liquid limit is in the range of 0.02—0.04 kg/cm²; in the in situ condition the shear strength may be higher. Liquid limit is also a characteristic water content of "normally consolidated" sediments, i.e. sedimentary soils which have not been subjected to pressures (due either to overburden load or stresses due to desiccation) higher than existed at the time of their formation. Recent sediments at lake or sea bottoms are likely to have a water content close to the liquid limit.

Plastic Limit (w_p). The plastic limit is the water content, expressed as a percentage of the ovendried weight of the soil, at which the soil gradually changes from the plastic to the semisolid state and becomes friable. The plastic limit is defined, rather arbitrarily, as the lowest water content at which the soil can be rolled into threads 3 mm in diameter whithout the threads breaking into pieces. This definition is based on the method of determination of the plastic limit, as proposed originally by ATTERBERG and adopted, with slight modifications, as a standard method in the U.S. (ASTM-D424-59 or AASHO-T-90-70) and in many other countries.

The plastic limit is also related to the clay content of soils and to the mineralogical composition of the clay fraction, although the correlation is not immediately apparent. Explanation of the physical significance of the plastic limit and its correlation with the properties of the clay fraction is discussed in detail by SEED et al (1964).

The plastic limit varies within a much smaller range than the liquid limit. Typical values of plastic limit for various soil types are shown in Column 4 of Table 1.8.

The determination of plastic limit is to some extent subjective and influenced by human factors. Attempts have been made to determine the plastic limit by more objective methods (RUSSELL and MICKLE, 1970) but the almost universal acceptance of the ATTERBERG method prevents the introduction of new methods. Standardization of the method reduces, but does not eliminate the human factor in the determination. Variations in the determination of the plastic limit due to human factors are not likely to exceed ±2 % in the water content. Plastic limits determined by standard procedures are, within this range of accuracy, good indicators of soil behavior.

The plastic limit, besides being a simple means for identification of soils, is also meaningful for estimating trafficability. Plastic limit signifies the transition from the plastic to the semisolid state; therefore, soils exhibiting water contents at or below the plastic limit are likely to be trafficable by most off-road vehicles. Water contents of cultivated soils in the temperate climates are likely to be at or near plastic limit.

Shrinkage Limit (w_s). The shrinkage limit is the water content at which the soil ceases to decrease its volume upon reduction of its water content. The shrinkage limit is determined by measuring the volume of an oven-dried soil pat and calculating the water content necessary to fill the voids completely (ASTM-D427-61 or AASHO-T-92-68). This test can be performed on either a remolded or an undisturbed sample. Other methods of determination of the shrinkage limit include volume measurements of samples at various water contents and determining the volume-change water content relationship experimentally. This relationship is closely linear over a range of moisture contents above the w_s. The intersection of this straight line with constant volume line at $w = 0$ is the shrinkage limit (see Figure 1.7).

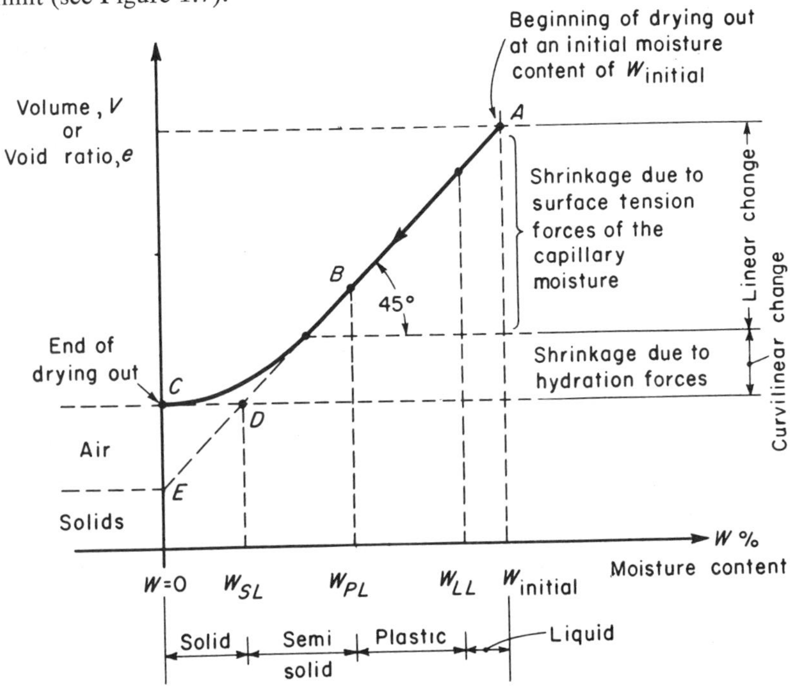

Fig. 1.7
Relationship Between Moisture Content and Volume for Soils
(From JUMIKIS, 1966)

The shrinkage limit is not as widely used in soil mechanics as are the liquid and plastic limits. Its value for off-road locomotion engineering is that it provides a water content limit typical of desiccated soils.

The ATTERBERG limits are useful for soil identification and classification. However, since they have been rather arbitrarily set up, the specific limits themselves are not indicative of a fundamental soil property. By using them to define indices, however, or by defining limits for a specific soil-structure phenomenon, they can be adopted for such use. The more common of these indices or specialized moisture limits are discussed in the following paragraphs.

Plasticity Index (*PI*). The plasticity index is the difference between the liquid limit and the plastic limit. The *PI* is actually a measure of the cohesive properties of the soil and indicates the degree of surface chemical activity and bond strength of the finegrained ($< 2\mu$) portion of the material. This index has practical application to vehicle mobility since materials that have a high *PI* tend to soften in wet weather and become slippery (for example in Figure 1.8 soils above the "*A*" line and to the right of the "*B*" line become slippery when wet). GRIER and PERRY (1972) in their study on the trafficability of roadways report that the develop-

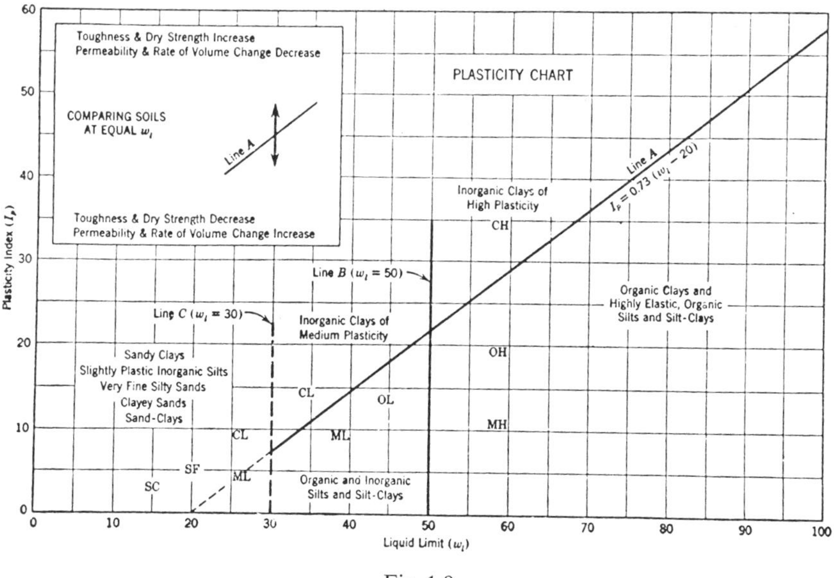

Fig. 1.8
Plasticity Chart
(A. CASAGRANDE, 1947)

ment of ruts and washboard surfaces is common in such materials under repeated traffic loads. On the other hand, materials having low PIs (< 6) become friable in dry weather, crack, ravel at the edges, and abrade under traffic. The resulting dust is easily blown about and efficient operation of vehicles becomes difficult.

Column 5 of Table 1.8 gives typical values of plasticity index for various soil types.

Table 1.9 gives the PIs of most of the common clay minerals. The reason for the relatively high w_l and PI for montmorillonite is understandable in terms of its crystalline structure and the implications of charge imbalance in swelling clays as mentioned briefly at the beginning of this section and as discussed in detail by Bolt (1955).

Sticky Limit (w_t). The sticky limit is the lowest water content at which soil adheres to metal tools. The importance of the sticky limit in determining acceptable operating conditions for farm machinery or steel treaded

TABLE 1.9
ATTERBERG Limits For Some Common Clay Minerals
(Data from Cornell, 1951)

Mineral	Exchange-able Ion	Liquid Limit (%)	Plastic Limit (%)	Plasticity Index (%)	Shrinkage Limit (%)
Montmorillonite	Na	710	54	656	9.9
	K	660	98	562	9.3
	Ca	510	81	429	10.5
	Mg	410	60	350	14.7
	Fe	290	75	215	10.3
	F*	140	73	67	—
Illite	Na	120	53	67	15.4
	K	120	60	60	17.5
	Ca	100	45	55	16.8
	Mg	95	46	49	14.7
	Fe	110	49	61	15.3
	Fe*	79	46	33	—
Kaolinite	Na	53	32	21	26.8
	K	49	29	20	—
	Ca	38	27	11	24.5
	Mg	54	31	23	28.7
	Fe	59	37	22	29.2
	Fe*	56	35	21	—
Attapulgite	H	270	150	120	7.6

* After five cycles of wetting and drying.

military vehicles is obvious. The sticky limit is determined by gradually reducing the moisture content of a soil pat until a nickel-plated spatula can be drawn over the surface of the pat without any of the soil sticking to it.

Liquidity Index (*LI*). The liquidity index is the ratio of the difference between the moisture content of an in situ saturated soil and its plastic limit to the plasticity index.

$$LI = \frac{w - w_l}{PI} \qquad \text{Eq. 1.2.1}$$

This index is used to assess the relative softness of a natural clay deposit since its moisture content in situ may lie anywhere within the plastic range. If the natural soil is at w_p, $LI = 1$; if it is at w_l, $LI = 0$. The use of *LI* in mobility studies is limited by the fact that it refers only to saturated cohesive soils. Generally cohesive soils at the surface are not saturated and in such cases the use of *LI* is meaningless and could be misleading.

Activity Index (*A*). Activity index is defined as the plasticity index divided by the $<$ 0.002 mm clay fraction

$$A = \frac{PI}{\%\text{ by weight} < 2\text{ micron clay}} \qquad \text{Eq. 1.2.2}$$

The activity index was first proposed by Skempton (1953) to account for the fact that because of the great increase in surface area per mass with decreasing particle size (increase in specific surface) the amount of attracted water is largely influenced by the amount of $<$ 2 micron clay particles present in the soil. This is shown in Figure 1.9(a). Here the plasticity index for various clay soils is plotted versus respective clay fraction ($<$ 2 micron). The slope of the curve is the "Activity Index". Figure 1.9(b) and Table 1.10 give values of *A* for some common clay minerals. Table 1.10 also shows the effect of cation exchange an *A*. The figures suggest that soils having a high activity index are potentially troublesome for vehicle mobility. The table indicates that the high activity of some clay minerals might be modified by the use of chemical additives as is often done for the stabilization of earth structures and foundation soils in civil engineering practice.

Saturation Limit w_{sat}. The saturation limit is defined as the water content at which a drop of water at the soil surface ceases to infiltrate into the soil. This limit is related to the liquid limit; its value is roughly half of the liquid limit for inorganic clays of medum plasticity. Although not generally used for engineering purposes, this limit is relevant to off-road locomotion, earthmoving and agricultural problems.

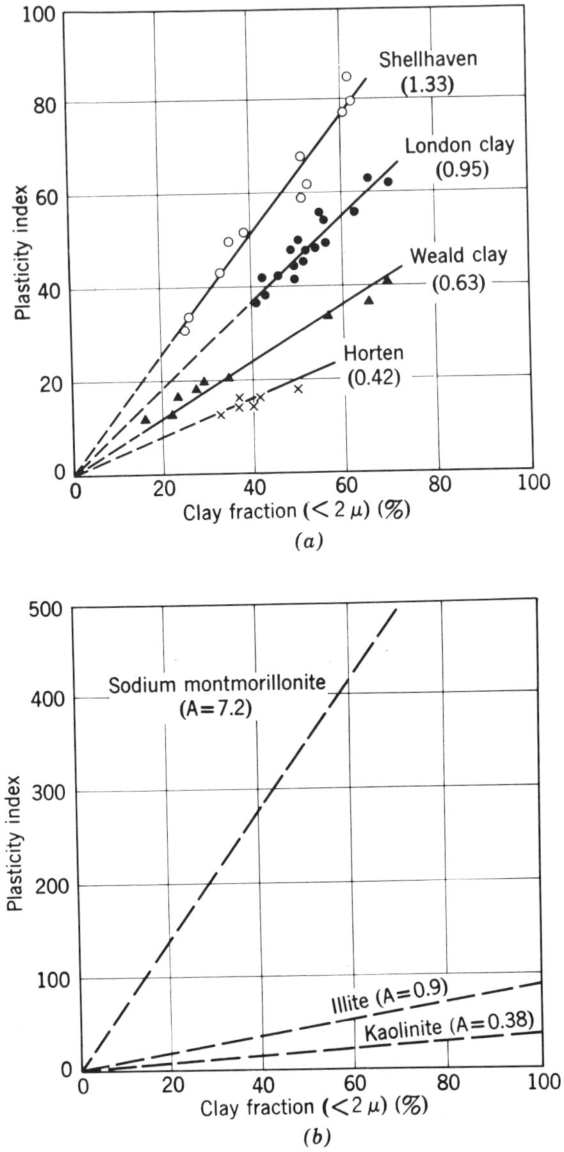

Fig. 1.9
Relation Between Plasticity Index and Clay Fraction for
a) Some natural soils
b) Some pure clay minerals
Figures in Parentheses are the "Activities" of the Clays.
(From Skempton, 1953)

TABLE 1.10
Activity Indices of Selected Clay Minerals
(Data from GRIM, 1962)

Na^{+}-montmorillonite	3–7
Ca^{+2}-montmorillonite	1.2–1.3
Illite	0.3–0.6
Kaolinite (poorly crystallized)	0.3–0.4
Kaolinite (well crystallized)	0.1

1.2.3 Transient Characteristics of Soil

The permanent soil characteristics discussed in the previous section describe the soil material without regard to the in situ condition of the soil. It does not make any difference whether at the time of sampling the soil is wet or dry, compact or loose; the same permanent characteristics would result. While this feature of the permanent characteristics is very convenient from the viewpoint of identification, it inherently limits the use of these characteristics to that of estimating potential soil behavior. Actual soil behavior, or, in other words, the response of soils to some action, always depends on the state of soil prior to that action. To estimate the actual soil behavior it is necessary to know the condition of the soil; characteristics which describe the state of soils are called in this book transient characteristics to indicate changeability, especially at the surface, with environment and loading conditions. Moisture content, porosity, void ratio and unit weight are examples of some of the characteristics important in off-road locomotion studies. Such characteristics do not per se describe the behavior of the soil; the various soil properties do that. They do, however, affect the manner in which a soil mass reacts to external loads and, from correlations that exist among them, estimates of actual soil behavior can be made.

The transient soil characteristics, however, are not directly responsive to external actions since they describe the state of soil prior to such an action; in laboratory experiments where the change of these characteristics under external actions is investigated, the word initial is appended to denote that the characteristics refer to the initial state. The constants, or coefficients of relationships which describe the soil behavior under external actions will be referred to as soil property constants, or briefly soil properties. Those soil properties which are most important from the viewpoint of off-road locomotion are discussed in Chapter 1.3. In the following section of this chapter the transient characteristics of soil will be discussed in detail and their importance in off-road locomotion studies delineated.

General Concepts

Unlike most engineering materials, soil is a multiphase medium that contains to varying degrees and in various states three distinct phases: solid (inorganic and/or organic particles), liquid (water and/or ice, other fluids), and gas (air, or other gases). In natural soils the three phases are so intimately mixed that those unfamiliar with the soil sciences often tend to forget this multiphased nature of soil. To emphasize the distinction between the phases and to facilitate the derivation of the numerous phase relationships of interest in off-road locomotion studies, it is expedient to depict this three-phase system schematically, as shown in Figure 1.10.

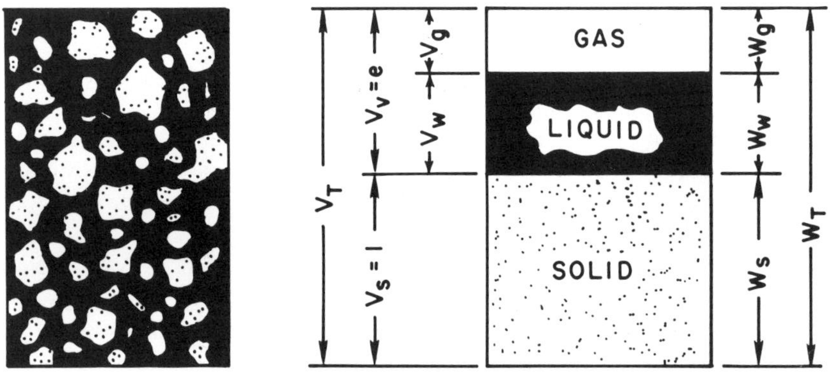

Fig. 1.10
a) Element of natural soil.
b) Element separated into phases.

Void Ratio and Porosity (*e* and *n*). The relationships among the three soil phases as shown in Figure 1.10 can be developed mathematically from the expression for void ratio (or its related parameter, porosity). By definition, void ratio is the ratio between the volume of the voids and the volume of the solids. The voids may be completely filled with water, completely filled with air, or partially filled with each; the relationship is still valid, namely:

$$\text{Void ratio} = \frac{V_V}{V_S} \qquad \text{Eq. 1.2.3}$$

Since the weight of solids in a given soil sample usually remains the same throughout a given process (excluding chemical processes which tend to dissolve solids), for convenience the volume of solids is considered constant and equal to unity with reference to the other constituents, i.e. $V_s = 1$ in Figure 1.10. The conventional symbol for void ratio is "e". Therefore, from Equation 1.2.3 the volume of voids is also designated "e" as shown in Figure 1.10 so that void ratio $= V_v/V_s = e/1 = e$. Porosity, on the other hand, is defined as the ratio between the volume of the voids and the total volume, i.e.

$$\text{Porosity} = n = \frac{V_v}{V_t} = \frac{e}{1+e} \qquad \text{Eq. 1.2.4}$$

It is apparent that both porosity and void ratio are transient soil properties that change with applied stress level. In general, void ratio is the easier parameter to deal with since the volume of the solids remains essentially constant for a given initial total volume of soil even after the soil mass has been subject to external or internal forces that alter the void volume (i.e. collapse the soil structure). This is not true when considering porosity since both the numerator and denominator in Equation 1.2.4 vary independently.

Moisture Content on Dry Weight Basis (w). A more easily measureable parameter that influences many of the transient soil characteristics is moisture content, i.e. the ratio, expressed as a percentage, between the weight of water in a given soil sample and the corresponding weight of dry solids. In equation form

$$w = (W_w/W_s) \times 100 \qquad \text{Eq. 1.2.5}$$

Depending on the composition and structural arrangement of the solid particles in the soil mass, water content can range from zero percent (dry) to many hundreds of percent as, for example, in the case of some montmorillonites. Experience has shown that moisture content, although only a transient soil characteristic, exerts more influence on soil behavior than any other single property. Equation 1.2.5 represents the only purely gravimetric relationship between the soil phases and provides the basis for most of the volumetric-gravimetric relationships used in practice.

In nature, the moisture content of soils generally varies with depth such as is shown in Figure 1.11 for a Norwegian marine clay. Figure 1.12

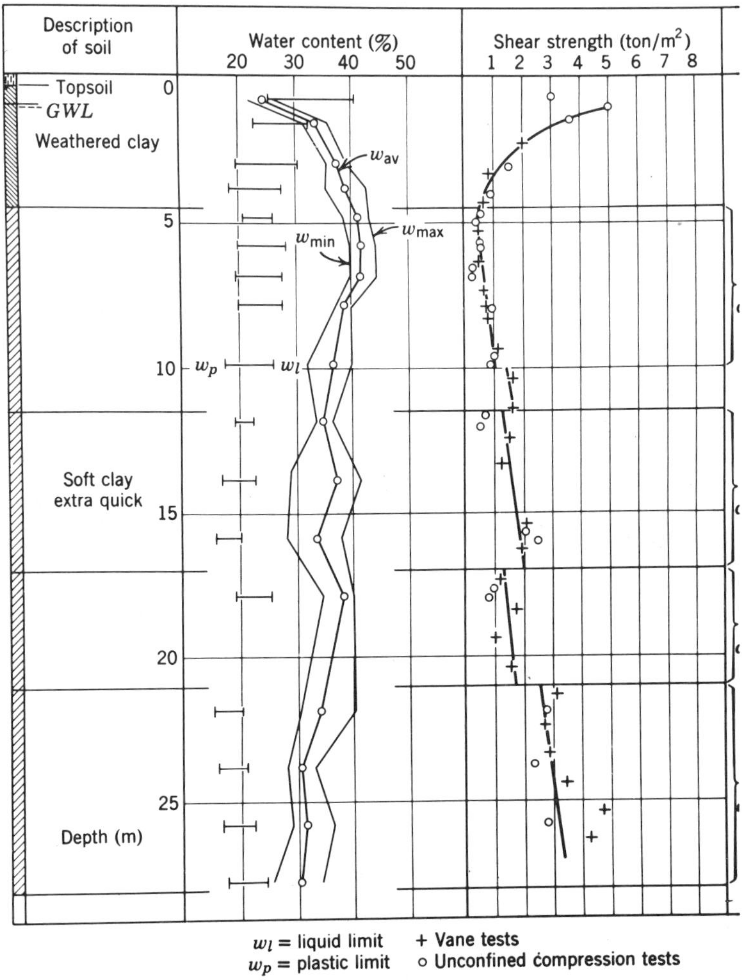

Fig. 1.11
Norwegian Marine Clay-Variation of Moisture Content, Atterberg Limits and Strength with Depth
(From BJERRUM, 1954)

w_p = Plastic Limit
w_l = Liquid Limit
+ = Vane tests
o = Unconfined compression tests
w_{av} = Average moisture content

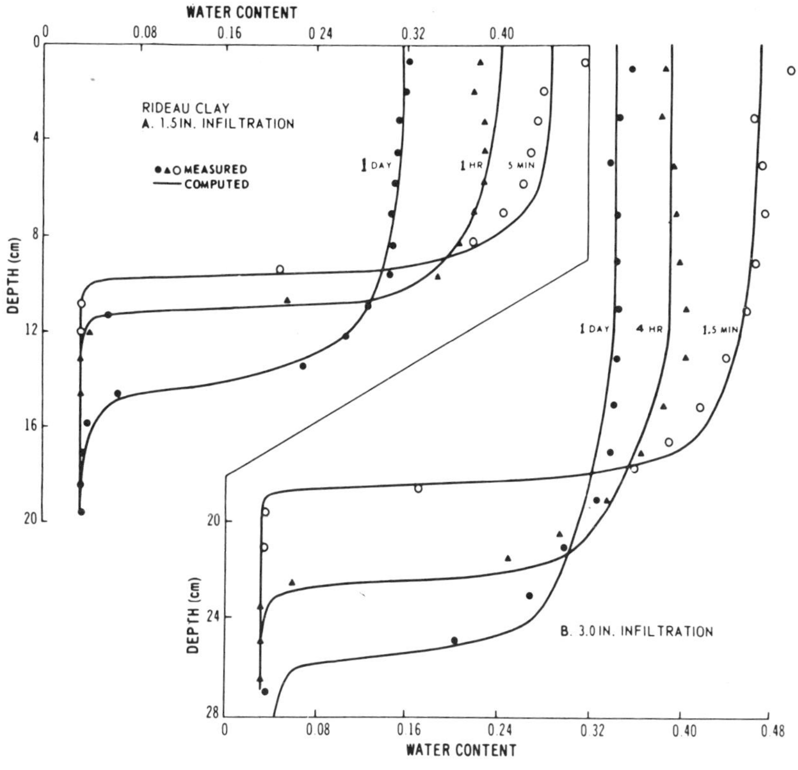

Fig. 1.12
Soil Moisture Redistribution Profiles for Clay Soil Receiving
a) 3.81 cm of water initially
b) 7.62 cm of water initially
(From STAPLE, 1969)

on the other hand indicates that the greatest variations usually take place at the surface since it is closest to daily and seasonal fluctuation of the weather and, therefore, most subject to wetting by infiltration and drying by evaporation. This is significant from the viewpoint of vehicle mobility, for a soil that is one day completely dry and capable of supporting vehicle operations, may overnight have its top few inches saturated with rain water and become essentially impassable. As mentioned above and as will be shown subsequently, soil shear strength is greatly influenced by moisture content.

Degree of Saturation (S). By definition, degree of saturation (S), is the ratio, expressed as a percentage, of the volume of water to the total void volume of a soil mass determined at its dry unit weight, i.e.

$$S = (V_W/V_V) \times 100 \qquad \text{Eq. 1.2.6}$$

Although due to some misconceptions, and more often because of miscalculations, a degree of saturation greater than 100 % is sometimes reported in the literature, it is understood in the context of the definition given here that both the volume of the water and the total volume refer to the state of the soil at a particular time. Thus the degree of saturation cannot exceed 100 % since any increase of water volume beyond 100 % saturation automatically increases the total volume.

A more convenient form of Equation 1.2.6 is developed from previously defined parameters as follows:

$$S = \frac{V_W}{V_V} = \frac{V_W}{eV_S} = \frac{W_W/\gamma_W}{eW_S/\gamma_S}$$

that is

$$Se = \frac{W_W G_S}{W_S}$$

or

$$Se = wG_S \qquad \text{Eq. 1.2.7}$$

Actually, the calculation of the degree of saturation is usually performed with Equation 1.2.7 so that if the value exceeds 100 % it is usually due to an error in the determination of e or w. The importance of degree of saturation is often overlooked as, for example, in the application of soil mechanics theories derived under the assumption of complete saturation to situations involving only partially saturated soils. In fact, natural soils rarely exist in the state of 100 % saturation, therefore careful engineering judgment must be exercised before any theory based on complete saturation is applied.

Unit Weight and Phase Relationships

The most obvious and perhaps the most widely used of the volumetric-gravimetric relationships is unit weight. The fundamental definition is given as the ratio between the weight and unit volume of a material. The parameters γ_s (unit weight of solids) and γ_w (unit weight of water) have been used in some developments thus far. However, it is important to realize that in dealing with a three-phased system such as soil, a term more specific than just "unit weight" must be employed. It is obvious that, even considered outside of the context of their being constituents of soil, the water and the solid particles of soil each have their own unit weights.

$$\gamma_s = \frac{\text{Weight of solids}}{\text{Volume of solids}} \qquad \text{Eq. 1.2.8}$$

$$\gamma_w = \frac{\text{Weight of water}}{\text{Volume of water}} \qquad \text{Eq. 1.2.9}$$

The difficulty arises in defining the total unit weight of soil that consists of solid particles and intersticial voids some or all of which may be filled with water or air. If the same basic definition is applied, the following general and specific expressions for the total unit weight of soil can be developed (refer to Figure 1.10 and all of the equations given previously).

Total Unit Weight (γ_t). Total unit weight is defined as the ratio of the total weight of the soil to the total volume of the soil. Therefore, in equation form:

$$\gamma_t = \frac{W_t}{V_t} = \frac{W_s + W_w}{V_s + V_v} = \frac{\gamma_s V_s + \dfrac{Se\, W_s}{G_s}}{V_s + eV_s}$$

$$\gamma_t = \frac{V_s\left(\gamma_s + \dfrac{Se\,\gamma_s}{G_s}\right)}{V_s\,(1 + e)} = \frac{G_s\,\gamma_w + \dfrac{Se\,\gamma_w\,G_s}{G_s}}{(1 + e)}$$

$$\gamma_t = \left(\frac{G_s + Se}{1 + e}\right)\gamma_w \qquad \text{Eq. 1.2.10}$$

This is a perfectly general expression for the total unit weight of soil having any degree of saturation (S) and any kind (G_s) and arrangement (e) of solid particles. A more convenient expression can be given in terms of more readily measureable variables as:

$$\gamma_t = \left(\frac{G_s + wG_s}{1 + e}\right)\gamma_w = \left(\frac{1 + w}{1 + e}\right)\gamma_s \qquad \text{Eq. 1.2.11}$$

Dry Unit Weight (γ_d). Dry unit weight is defined as the ratio of the weight of the solid phase only to the total volume of soil. Therefore, in equation form,

$$\gamma_d = \frac{W_s}{V_t} = \frac{V_s\gamma_s}{V_s + V_v} = \frac{V_s\gamma_s}{V_s(1 + e)} = \frac{\gamma_s}{(1 + e)} \qquad \text{Eq. 1.2.12}$$

This Equation could be obtained directly from the general expression given by Equation 1.2.10 if one recognizes that when a soil is "dry" its degree of saturation equals zero ($S = 0$) and its total weight (W_t) equals the weight of the solid phase (W_s).

Since simple laboratory and field procedures exist for determining γ_d and w, it would be advantageous to have a direct relationship between γ_d and γ_t. This can be obtained by substitution into Equation 1.2.12 of the expression for γ_s given in Equation 1.2.11. The resulting relationship is

$$\gamma_d = \frac{\gamma_t}{1 + w} \qquad \text{Eq. 1.2.13}$$

Saturated Unit Weight (γ_{sat}). The saturated unit weight is defined as the ratio between the total weight of the soil and the total volume of the soil when all voids are filled with water i.e. at $S = 100\,\%$.

The expression for saturated unit weight can be obtained directly from Equation 1.2.10 by setting the degree of saturation equal to 100 % ($S = 1.0$) This results in the equation

$$\gamma_{sat} = \left(\frac{G_s + e}{1 + e}\right)\gamma_w \qquad \text{Eq. 1.2.14}$$

Submerged (Buoyant) Unit Weight in General (γ_b). The submerged unit weight is always equal to the total unit weight (saturated or not) minus the unit weight of water. Therefore, in equation form

$$\gamma_b = \gamma_t - \gamma_w = \left(\frac{G_s + Se}{1 + e}\right)\gamma_w - \gamma_w$$

$$\gamma_b = \left(\frac{G_s + Se - 1 - e}{1 + e}\right)\gamma_w \qquad \text{Eq. 1.2.15}$$

$$\gamma_b = \left(\frac{(G_s - 1) + e(S - 1)}{1 + e}\right)\gamma_w$$

This is a perfectly general expression for the submerged unit weight of a soil having any degree of saturation (S), and any kind (G_s) and arrangement (e) of solid particles. It should be noted here that even when submerged, some soil are not fully saturated.

Submerged (Buoyant) Unit Weight for Saturated Soil ($\gamma_{b\,sat}$). An expression for the submerged unit weight for saturated soil can be obtained directly from Equation 1.2.15 by setting degree of saturation equal to 100 % (S = 1.0). The result is

$$\gamma_{b\,sat} = \frac{G_s - 1}{1 + e}\gamma_w \qquad \text{Eq. 1.2.16}$$

Table 1.11 summarizes much of what was discussed above and presents a number of useful functional relationships between various "given" soil properties and "sought" quantities. A caveat accompanies this table that warns against its indiscriminate use without complete understanding of the meaning of the terms and how or if they apply to the situation being studied.

Moisture-Density Relationships

Although it is dangerous to deal in generalities, it can be said that, in general, the more dense a soil becomes, the greater is its shear strength. A mass of soil that has a very loose arrangement of non-cemented particles contains a large number of voids and is obviously less stable under load than a very dense soil in which the particles are as tightly packed together as possible. The one extreme is mud, the other rock. Very often the only practical solution to a bad soils problem is to improve the quality of the soil by stabilizing it in some way. This improvement could be sought for a number of reasons: increased strength (as for a roadway pavement subgrade), reduced compressibility (as for obtaining less settlement under a

TABLE 1.11

Functional Relationships Among Various Transient Properties of Soil

Given G_s and	$e=$	$n=$	$w=$	$S=$	$\gamma_d=$	$\gamma_t=$	$\gamma_{sat}=$
e, S	e	$\frac{e}{1+e}$	$\frac{eS}{G_s}$	S	$\frac{G_s}{1+e}\gamma_w$	$\frac{G_s+Se}{1+e}\gamma_w$	$\frac{G_s+e}{1+e}\gamma_w$
n, S	$\frac{n}{1-n}$	n	$\frac{nS}{(1-n)G_s}$	S	$(1-n)G_s\gamma_w$	$[(1-n)G_s+nS]\gamma_w$	$[(1-n)G_s+n]\gamma_w$
w, S	$\frac{wG_s}{S}$	$\frac{wG_s}{S+wG_s}$	w	S	$\frac{SG_s}{S+wG_s}\gamma_w$	$\frac{SG_s(1+w)}{S+wG_s}\gamma_w$	$\frac{G_s(S^*+w)}{S^*+wG_s}\gamma_w$
γ_d, S	$\frac{G_s\gamma_w}{\gamma_d}-1$	$1-\frac{\gamma_d}{G_s\gamma_w}$	$S\left(\frac{\gamma_w}{\gamma_d}-\frac{1}{G_s}\right)$	S	γ_d	$\gamma_d+S\left(\gamma_w-\frac{\gamma_d}{G_s}\right)$	$\gamma_d\left(1-\frac{1}{G_s}\right)+\gamma_w$
γ_d, w	$\frac{G_s\gamma_w}{\gamma_d}-1$	$1-\frac{\gamma_d}{G_s\gamma_w}$	w	$\frac{\gamma_d wG_s}{\gamma_w G_s-\gamma_d}$	γ_d	$\gamma_d(1+w)$	$\gamma_d\left(1-\frac{1}{G_s}\right)+\gamma_w$
e, w	e	$\frac{e}{1+e}$	w	$\frac{wG_s}{e}$	$\frac{G_s}{1+e}\gamma_w$	$\frac{1+w}{1+e}G_s\gamma_w$	$\frac{G_s+e}{1+e}\gamma_w$
n, w	$\frac{n}{1-n}$	n	w	$\frac{1-n}{n}wG_s$	$(1-n)G_s\gamma_w$	$(1-n)(1+w)G_s\gamma_w$	$[(1-n)G_s+n]\gamma_w$
γ_t, w	$(1+w)\frac{G_s\gamma_w}{\gamma_t}-1$	$1-\frac{1}{G_s(1+w)}\frac{\gamma_t}{\gamma_w}$	w	$\frac{wG_s\gamma_t}{G_s(1+w)\gamma_w-\gamma_t}$	$\frac{\gamma_t}{1+w}$	γ_t	$\frac{\gamma_t}{1+w}\left(1-\frac{1}{G_s}\right)+\gamma_w$

S^* = degree of saturation at w

building foundation), and reduced permeability (as for earthfill dams). The most common and often the most economical way to obtain these types of soil improvement is by mechanically densifying the soil. In the field of soil mechanics a large body of knowledge exists concerning the methods and mechanics of soil compaction. As understood in that discipline, compaction is "any process by which the soil particles are artificially rearranged and packed together into a closer state of contact by mechanical means . . . The compaction process is accompanied by the expulsion of air only," (Jumikis, 1966) i.e. compaction is not the same as consolidation.

Although the fundamental mechanisms which control compaction are not fully understood, it has been demonstrated that the moisture content of the soil at the time of compaction is most critical, especially for fine-grained soils. The simplest and perhaps most widely accepted hypothesis (Lambe, 1951) for the relationship between moisture and density at a given compactive effort (or energy) holds that as water is added to the soil air is expelled. The soil particles meantime absorb the water until a surface film is formed that permits the soil particles to slide over each other more easily when some form of external load is applied. Since the thickness of this water film is negligible compared to the diameter of coarse-grained soils such as sands, the effect is not as pronounced for sands as for fine-grained soils.

However, even for fine-grained soils the "lubricating" effect of the water on the soil exists only up to a certain point. When additional water no longer replaces air from the soil voids and the amount of entrapped air remains essentially constant, the water has the opposite effect, i.e. it occupies pore space which could be filled with soil particles upon the application of load.

Consequently, there is an "optimum" moisture content for a given soil under a given compaction energy which will allow the wetted soil particles to come as close together as possible. Since subsequent drying of the soil does not affect this spacing, the compaction of the soil at this optimum moisture content results in a "maximum dry density". The variation of dry density over a range of mixing (or molding) moisture contents constitutes the moisture-density relationship for a given soil compacted under a given type (static, kneading, vibratory) and amount of energy. Lambe (1958a & b) has explained the phenomenon in a more sophisticated manner by using the concept of fabric and other physico-chemical characteristics of soil discussed at the beginning of this section.

In either case the moisture-density relationship is determined in the laboratory. The purpose of the laboratory tests is to predict the moisture conditions under which the same soil must be compacted in the field given a specified dry density and specific types of equipment. Until the relatively recent introduction of vibratory compactors for coarser grained soils, field compaction of *all* soils was done almost exclusively by sheepsfoot rollers or rubber tired rollers. These rubber tired rollers must perform on loose soils at least on their first pass and in that sense they can be considered as "off-road" vehicles. Consequently, the wealth of information that is available in the civil engineering literature that pertains to compaction and the performance of compaction machinery (see for example, JOHNSON and SALLBERG, 1960) should be useful to designers of other off-road vehicles. For this reason, the rest of this section will be devoted to a more detailed investigation of compaction testing and its relationship to field conditions.

As indicated previously, the "degree of compaction" of a soil is characterized by its dry density or dry unit weight (γ_d). At the risk of offending scientific purists the terms "density" and "unit weight" will be used interchangeably here. The degree of compaction is primarily a function of two variables, moisture content (w) and compactive effort or energy of compaction. Intuitively, a given mass of soil will compact less under a 5.5 lb (2.5 kg) weight dropped 25 times from a distance of 12 inches (30.5 cm) than under a 10 lb (4.54 kg) weight dropped 25 times from a distance of 18 inches (45.7 cm). The former conditions apply to what is known as the Standard AASHO compaction test; the latter to what is known as the Modified AASHO compaction test. What is not intuitively obvious is the fact that for a specific amount of compactive energy there is one moisture content, the "optimum moisture content", at which a given soil attains its maximum dry density. LAMBE (1958a, 1958b) performed an in-depth study of the mechanisms of compaction and correlated his results with the engineering behavior of compacted fine-grained soils. Practically, however, the development of a γ_d versus w curve in the laboratory is still needed since it yields the "optimum moisture content" for a particular soil and provides a method of obtaining field control of soil improvement by compaction.

Figures 1.13 and 1.14 summarize the effect of compactive effort and moisture content on the densification of fine-grained soils in the field and in the lab. Table 1.12 presents a comparison between the effects of dry-of-optimum and wet-of-optimum compaction on some soil properties. The table applies directly to the effects of off-road vehicles.

Whereas the terms "maximum dry density" and "optimum moisture content" apply to the compaction of fine-grained cohesive soils such as silts and clays, they do not apply to cohesionless soils. Cohesionless soils do

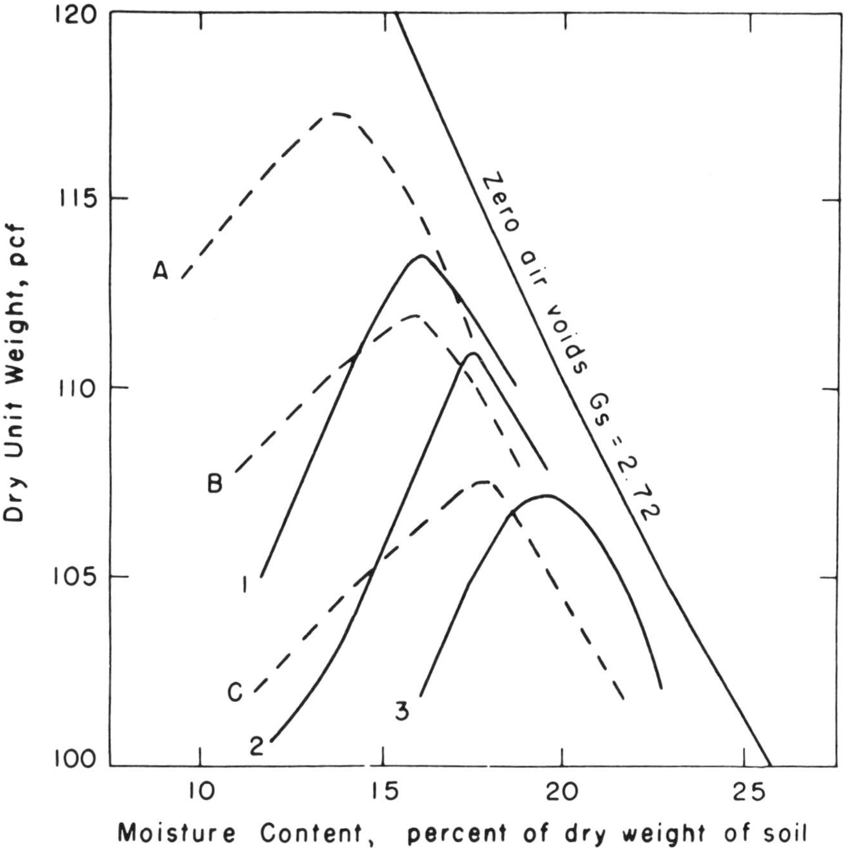

Fig. 1.13
Comparison of Laboratory Compaction Curves (Dashed Lines)
and Pneumatic — Tired Roller Compaction Curves (Solid Lines)
for a Lean Clay Soil ($w_l = 36$, $PI = 15$)
(From WES, 1956)

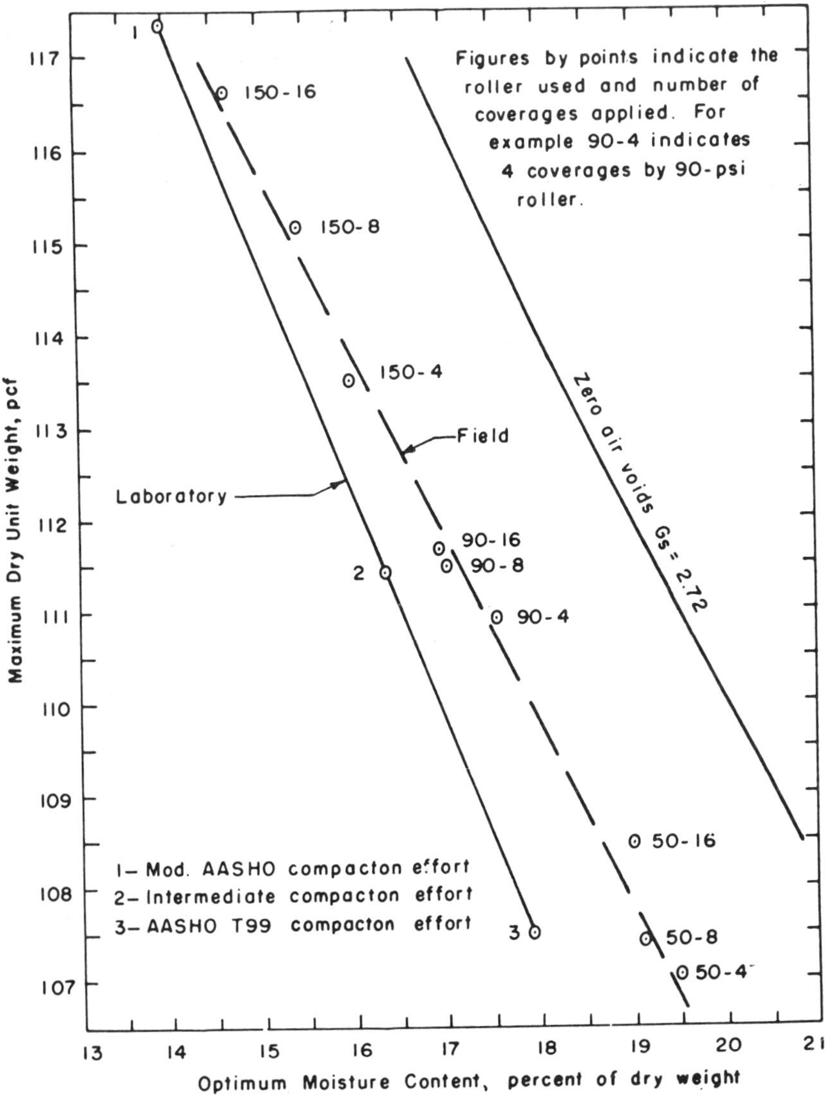

Fig. 1.14

Influence of field and laboratory compaction effort on optimum moisture content for a lean clay soil (LL = 36, *PI* = 15). Field compaction effort by pneumatic-tired rollers having 50-, 90-, and 150-psi inflation pressures each applying 4, 8, 16 coverages in constructing fills in lifts of 6-in. compacted thickness. Laboratory compaction effort from 12, 26, and 55 blows of 10-lb rammer, 18-in. drop, 5 layers in mold 4.5-in. high × 6-in. diameter, yielding efforts of 12,223, 26,483 and 56,022 ft. lb per cu ft, respectively.

(Note: Two passes required for one coverage.)

(From WES, 1956)

not respond noticeably to variations in compacting moisture content and compactive effort. Figure 1.15 shows a typical compaction curve for cohesionless sands and sandy gravels. It is immediately evident that the shape of this curve in no way resembles that of any of the curves shown in Figure 1.13. Lambe (1958a, 1958b) offers a very plausible explanation for this phenomenon known as "bulking" in terms of capillary forces at low moisture contents resisting rearrangements of the sand grains. Consequently, cohesionless soils have an entirely different measure of compaction known as "relative density".

TABLE 1.12
Comparison Dry-of-Optimum with Wet-of-Optimum Compaction
(From Lambe and Whitman, 1969)

Property		Comparison
Structure		
	Particle arrangement	Dry side more random
	Water deficiency	Dry side more deficiency, therefore more water imbibed, more swell, lower pore pressure
	Permanence	Dry-side structure more sensitive to change
Permeability		
	Magnitude	Dry side more permeable
	Permanence	Dry side permeability reduced much more by permeation
Compressibility		
	Magnitude	Wet side more compressible in low-stress range, dry side in high-stress range
	Rate	Dry side consolidates more rapidly
Strength		
	As molded	
	Undrained	Dry side much higher
	Drained	Dry side somewhat higher
	After saturation	
	Undrained	Dry side somewhat higher if swelling prevented; wet side can be higher if swelling permitted
	Drained	Dry side about the same or slightly greater
Pore-water pressure at failure		Wet side higher
Stress-strain modulus		Dry side much greater
Sensitivity		Dry side more apt to be sensitive

Relative Density

An assemblage of solid particles having various sizes and shapes such as typically exists in a mass of soil can be arranged in almost an infinite number of ways. For an idealized soil consisting of uniform spheres, Fig. 1.16(a) shows the loosest possible stable packing or "simple cubic packing". Figure 1.16(b) on the other hand represents the densest configuration for the same system of equal-size spheres. The void ratios for these two extremes can be computed readily from the geometry of the respective arrangements. The concept of relative density is based on the two extreme void ratios and is expressed as

$$D_r = \frac{e_{max} - e}{e_{max} - e_{min}} \qquad \text{Eq. 1.2.17}$$

where:

e_{max} = the "loosest" void ratio
e_{min} = the "densest" void ratio.
e = natural void ratio.

Relative density can also be expressed in terms of a more easily measureable parameter, dry unit weight, as

$$D_r = \frac{\gamma_{d\,max}}{\gamma_d} \left(\frac{\gamma_d - \gamma_{d\,min}}{\gamma_{d\,max} - \gamma_{d\,min}} \right) \qquad \text{Eq. 1.2.18}$$

where:

$\gamma_{d\,max}$ = the "densest" dry unit weight
$\gamma_{d\,min}$ = the "loosest" dry unit weight
γ_d = the natural dry unit weight

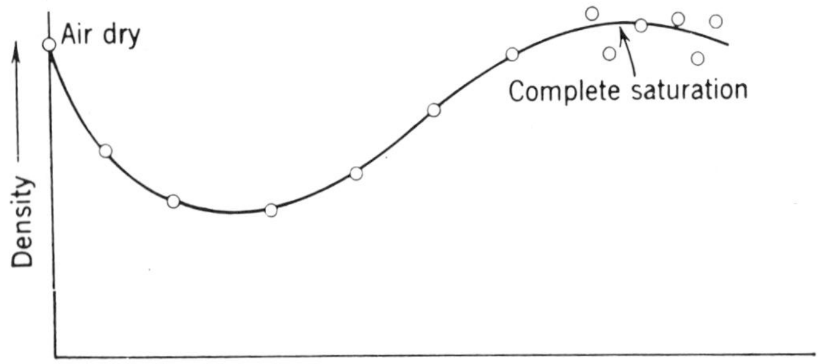

Fig. 1.15
Typical Compaction Curve for Cohesionless Sands and Sandy Gravels
(From FOSTER, 1962)

Unfortunately natural soils are not composed of spherical particles and only occasionally are they close to being uniformly sized (certain beach sands). As a result, well graded natural soils (i.e. those having a wide range of particle sizes) are generally more dense than uniformly graded soils having a predominant grain size in the same range. The reason for this is that the voids among the large particles can be filled more readily with smaller particles in the well graded soil than they can in the uniformly graded soil. Another factor influencing the relative density of natural soils is shape. An assemblage of angular particles having rough sur-

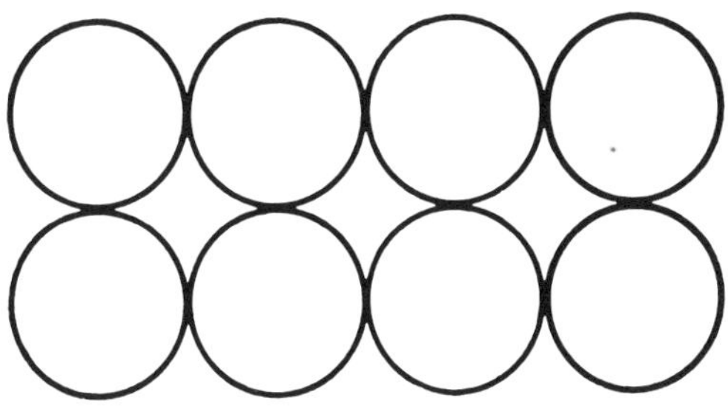

(a)

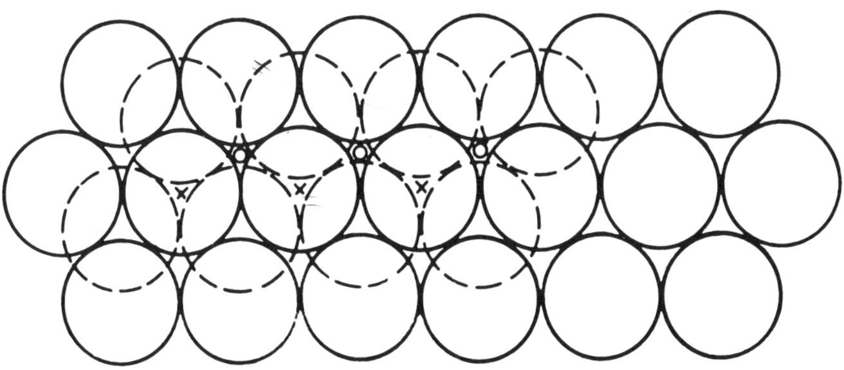

(b)

Fig. 1.16
Arrangements of Uniform Spheres
a) Plan and elevation view: simple cubic packing
b) Plan view: dense packing. Solid circles, first layer; dahed circles, second layer; o, location of sphere centers in third layer: face-centered cubic array; x, location of sphere centers in third layer: close-packed hexagonal array
(From DERESIEWICZ, 1958)

TABLE 1.13
Typical Values of Soil Index Properties
(from Hough, 1969)

	Part. Size & Gradation				Voids[1]					Unit Weight[2]) (lb./cu.ft)						
	Approx. Size Range (mm.)		Approx. D_{10} (mm.)	Approx. Range Unif. Coef., C_u	Void Ratio			Porosity (%)		Dry Wt., γ_d			Wet Wt., γ_t		Sub. Wt., γ_d	
	D_{max}	D_{min}			e_{max} (loose)	e_{cr}	e_{min} (dense)	n_{max} (loose)	n_{min} (dense)	Min. (loose)	100% Mod. AASHO	Max. (dense)	Min. (loose)	Max. (dense)	Min. (loose)	Max. (dense)
Granular Materials																
1. Uniform Materials																
a. Equal spheres (theoretical values)	—	—	—	1.0	0.92	—	0.35	47.6	26.0	—	—	—	—	—	—	—
b. Standard Ottawa SAND	0.84	0.59	0.67	1.1	0.80	0.75	0.50	44	33	92	—	110	93	131	57	69
c. Clean, uniform SAND (fine or medium)	—	—	—	1.2 to 2.0	1.0	0.80	0.40	50	29	83	115	118	84	136	52	73
d. Uniform, inorganic SILT	0.05	0.005	0.012	1.2 to 2.0	1.1	—	0.40	52	29	80	—	118	81	136	51	73
2. Well-graded Materials																
a. Silty SAND	2.0	0.005	0.02	5 to 10	0.90	—	0.30	47	23	87	122	127	88	142	54	79
b. Clean, fine to coarse SAND	2.0	0.05	0.09	4 to 6	0.95	0.70	0.20	49	17	85	132	138	86	148	53	86
c. Micaceous SAND	—	—	—	—	1.2	—	0.40	55	29	76	—	120	77	138	48	76
d. Silty SAND & GRAVEL	100	0.005	0.02	15 to 300	0.85	—	0.14	46	12	89	—	146[3])	90	155[3])	56	92
Mixed Soils																
1. Sandy or silty CLAY	2.0	0.001	0.003	10 to 30	1.8	—	0.25	64	20	60	130	135	100	147	38	85
2. Skip-graded silty CLAY with stones or rk. frag.	250	0.001	—	—	1.0	—	0.20	50	17	84	—	140	115	151	53	89
3. Well-graded GRAVEL, SAND, SILT & CLAY mixture	250	0.001	0.002	25 to 1000	0.70	—	0.13	41	11	100	140	148[4])	125	156[4])	62	94
Clay Soils																
1. CLAY (30 to 50% clay sizes)	0.05	0.5μ	0.001	—	2.4	—	0.50	71	33	50	105	112	94	133	31	71
2. Colloidal CLAY (–0.002 mm. ≥ 50%)	0.01	10Å	—	—	12	—	0.60	92	37	13	90	106	71	128	8	66
Organic Soils																
1. Organic SILT	—	—	—	—	3.0	—	0.55	75	35	40	—	110	87	131	25	69
2. Organic CLAY (30 to 50% clay sizes)	—	—	—	—	4.4	—	0.70	81	41	30	—	100	81	125	18	62

[1]) Granular materials may reach e_{max} when dry or only slightly moist. Clays can reach e_{max} only when fully saturated.
[2]) Granular materials reach minimum unit wet weight when at e_{max} and with hygroscopie moisture only. Clays reach minimum unit wet weight when fully saturated at e_{max}. The unit submerged weight of any saturated soil is the unit wet weight minus the unit weight of water.
[3]) Applicable for very compact glacial till. Unusually high unit weight values for tills are sometimes due not only to an extremely compact condition but to unusually high specific gravity values.
[4]) Applicable for hardpan.
General Note: Tabulation is based on $G = 2.65$ for granular soil, $G = 2.7$ for clays, and $G = 2.6$ for organic soils.

faces will be much looser than an assemblage of rounded particles having smooth surfaces even though both types may be of the same size and mineralogical composition. The consequence of these factors is that e_{min} and e_{max} and therefore D_r cannot be computed for natural soils from packing geometry but must be determined directly by tests or estimated. These estimates can be made from empirically derived relationships between relative density and the results of conventional soil mechanics lab tests (see for example BURMISTER's (1951) curves relating maximum density to gradation) or from the results of field penetration tests (see for example GIBBS and HOLTZ, 1957). It is unfortunate, however, that no standard test exists for determining either e_{max} or e_{min} although several have been proposed (KOLBUSZEWSKI 1948, ASTM). Generally, the tests that purport to obtain e_{min} involve some sort of vibratory compaction or tamping of the soil in a container of known volume, while those concerned with e_{max} usually require careful pouring of oven dried soil into a container of known volume. Sedimentation or "fluffing" have also been reported (LAMBE and WHITMAN, 1969) as methods suitable for obtaining e_{max}.

Table 1.13 gives values of e_{max} and e_{min} for some typical soil types. Relative density is useful in determining how far a granular material as it exists in nature can be expected to densify under externally applied load because of particle rearrangement. Again, it is emphasized that relative density generally applies only to granular, non-cohesive materials and its use for the mixed soils, clays and organic soils listed in the table could be misleading. These types of soils have very sensitive moisture-density relationships as discussed previously and e_{max} is not definable for them.

Table 1.14 presents the qualitative descriptions generally used to indicate the relative density of granular soils. Attempts have been made to correlate these qualitative descriptions to dynamic penetration resistance (GIBBS and HOLTZ, 1957; TERZAGHI and PECK, 1948) and even to soil strength properties (MEYERHOF, 1956; HOUGH, 1957), however, such correlations should never be used in their absolute sense.

TABLE 1.14
Density Descriptions

Relative Density (%)	Descriptive Term
0–15	Very loose
15–35	Loose
35–65	Medium
65–85	Dense
85–100	Very dense

Permeability

Many of the most frustrating vehicle mobility problems occur in soils which, when dry, are ideal for either wheeled or tracked vehicle operations but which, when wetted, as after a rainfall, do not drain well and, after a short time under vehicle loads, become soft and untrafficable. The drainage characteristics of soils are directly related to their permeability which, by definition, is the transient soil property that permits the passage of fluids (gas and liquid) through the soil's intersticial voids. The determination of a numerical value for permeability is based on the validity of DARCY's Law which defines the relationship between velocity and pressure head for laminar flow of a fluid through a porous medium. The most significant assumption in the expression of DARCY's Law is that the flow be laminar. This is usually the case for soils that are predominantly finer than fine gravels. As a practical matter, the velocity of water in soils is quite variable because of the non-homogeneity of their natural structures.

Consequently, in speaking of soil permeabilities one usually means an average permeability and DARCY's Law is expressed as follows:

$$v = ki \qquad \text{Eq. 1.2.19}$$

where:

v = a hypothetical fluid velocity = Q/A_t

A_t = total cross-sectional area

i = hydraulic gradient

k = a proportionality constant or so called "coefficient of permeability".

The determination of k is most often done in the laboratory by either a "constant head" permeability test for granular, pervious soils (LAMBE, 1967), a "falling head" permeability test for cohesive, more impervious soils (LAMBE, 1967) or by the rate of horizontal capillary saturation for soils that are very dry in their natural state (TAYLOR, 1948). Since the soil sample in all of the above laboratory tests is disturbed during the set up procedure, determination of k made in the laboratory must be carefully evaluated before use. More reliable values for k that account for non-homogeneity of the soil in its natural state and the probability that k varies with depth vertically as well as horizontally can be obtained from field pump tests. These tests are usually quite expensive to perform and, for vehicle mobility purposes, have limited use since they are essentially integrating k over significant depth. In fact, for the purpose of estimating the effect of rainfall on trafficability, it may be desirable to perform infiltration tests such as those performed to determine percolation rates in agricultural and sanitary engineering. Table 1.15 summarizes qualitatively and quantitatively many of the practical implications associated with the

TABLE 1.15
Coefficient of Permeability
(From A. Casagrande and R. E. Fadum, 1939)

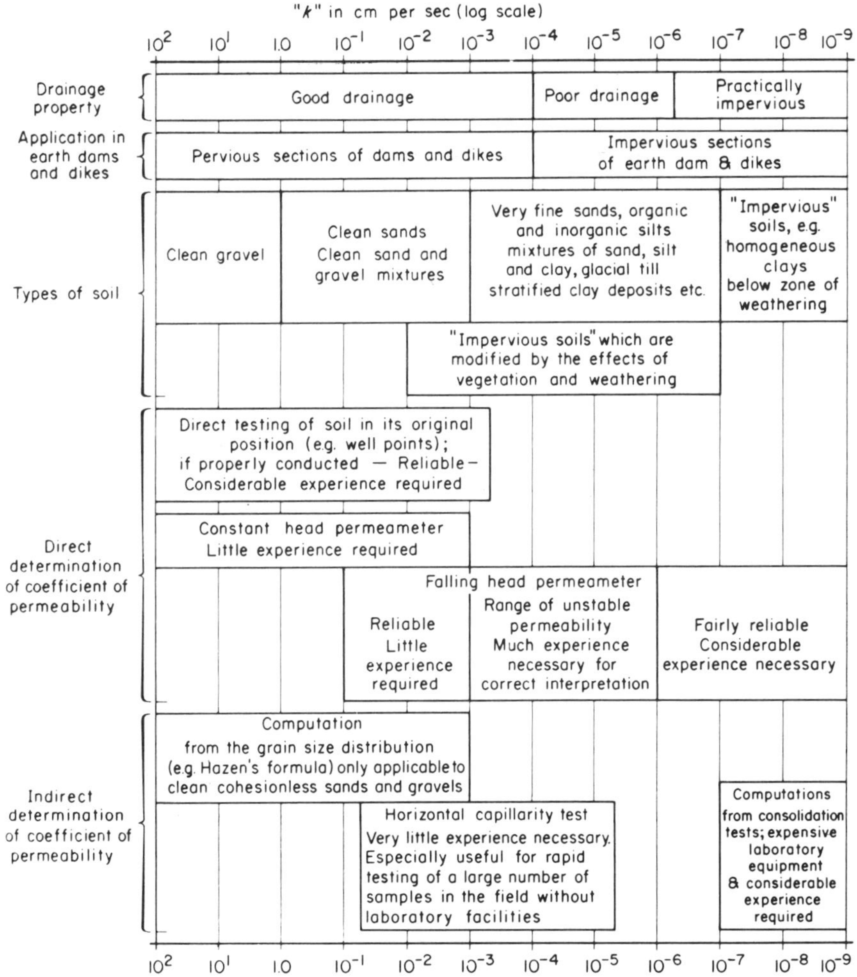
"k" in cm per sec (log scale)
10^2 10^1 1.0 10^{-1} 10^{-2} 10^{-3} 10^{-4} 10^{-5} 10^{-6} 10^{-7} 10^{-8} 10^{-9}
Drainage property
Good drainage
Poor drainage
Practically impervious
Application in earth dams and dikes
Pervious sections of dams and dikes
Impervious sections of earth dam & dikes
Types of soil
Clean gravel
Clean sands Clean sand and gravel mixtures
Very fine sands, organic and inorganic silts mixtures of sand, silt and clay, glacial till stratified clay deposits etc.
"Impervious" soils, e.g. homogeneous clays below zone of weathering
"Impervious soils" which are modified by the effects of vegetation and weathering
Direct determination of coefficient of permeability
Direct testing of soil in its original position (e.g. well points); if properly conducted — Reliable — Considerable experience required
Constant head permeameter Little experience required
Falling head permeameter
Reliable Little experience required
Range of unstable permeability Much experience necessary for correct interpretation
Fairly reliable Considerable experience necessary
Indirect determination of coefficient of permeability
Computation from the grain size distribution (e.g. Hazen's formula) only applicable to clean cohesionless sands and gravels
Horizontal capillarity test Very little experience necessary. Especially useful for rapid testing of a large number of samples in the field without laboratory facilities
Computations from consolidation tests; expensive laboratory equipment & considerable experience required
10^2 10^1 1.0 10^{-1} 10^{-2} 10^{-3} 10^{-4} 10^{-5} 10^{-6} 10^{-7} 10^{-8} 10^{-9}

concept of permeability. Implied in this summary is the fact that k itself is a function of many factors. If an analogy is drawn between flow through a soil and flow through tubes of various cross-sections, then the following mathematical expression can be developed for k that shows the influence of many of these factors

$$k = \frac{D_s^2 \gamma_w}{\mu} \frac{e^3}{(1+e)} C_s \qquad \text{Eq. 1.2.20}$$

where:

D_s = the diameter of a hypothetical spherical grain that has the same ratio of volume to surface area as holds collectively for all grains of a given soil

γ_w = unit weight of pore fluid

μ = viscosity of pore fluid

e = void ratio

C_s = a constant that defines the cross-sectional shape of the soil's void passages

From this expression it can be seen that

a) Soil particle size influences soil permeability directly as the square of some effective particle size diameter. HAZEN (1911) showed that on an average for sands $k \cong 100\ D_{10}^2$ where D_{10} is the particle diameter of the 10% finer fraction (refer to discussion of particle size at beginning of this section)

b) Fluid viscosity has an inverse effect on permeability, the more viscous the fluid, the less permeable is the soil. Practically, water is the only pore fluid of concern, however, even in this case as pore water begins to freeze, its viscosity increases with a resulting decrease in permeability and poorer drainage of surface water.

c) Void ratio has a tremendous influence on permeability. Obviously, if void ratio increases so does permeability. Not so obvious is the effective decrease in void ratio by a thin surface film of water adhering to soil particles. This effective decrease in void ratio is more evident in fine-grained soils than in sands and should be accounted for in any interpretation of lab test data.

Entrapped gases, even if in small quantities, have a similar effect on permeability. In general, however, this is not a major consideration in determination of k for trafficability purposes.

d) The influence of void shape is most apparent when a soil formation has a vertical k significantly different from k horizontal. In sedimentary soils this is often due to the environmental conditions at the time of their deposition. The effect of the soil structure, although related to void ratio, is completely different inasmuch as two soils having the same void ratio could have substantially different k because of structural effects.

1.2.4 Soil Classification Methods

In general, the primary purpose for classifying any group of elements and/or facts is to obtain an orderly system whereby the elements can be categorized according to certain predefined principles. It is obvious, therefore, that the same group of elements can be classified differently depending upon the principles used in the classification.

In the case of soils, classifications are usually made with regard to a certain limited number of qualities and potential behavior characteristics that are significant, and, in most cases, peculiar to problems in a specific area of the geotechnical sciences. This does not preclude a certain amount of similarity and commonality between systems, even though there are fundamental differences among the soil classification systems in use today.

Most soil classification systems belong to one of two broad types of classification categories: systems which attempt to define the properties of the soil constituents or raw materials (in our terminology the permanent characteristics) and systems which attempt to define the properties of the soil in its natural, undisturbed condition (A. CASAGRANDE, 1947).

Among the specific classification systems found under the former category are:

1) Classification Systems based on Gradation
2) The Public Roads *(BPR)* Classification System.
3) Airfield Classification Systems:
   a) The Civil Aeronautics Administration *(CAA)* Classification System.
   b) The Airfield (or Unified) Classification System.

Among the systems which attempt to define the properties of soil in its natural, undisturbed condition are:

1) Descriptive soil classifications.
2) Geological classifications.
3) Agricultural classifications.
4) Miscellaneous special purpose soil mechanics classification systems.

Gradation Classification Systems

Gradation classification systems are based on grain size classifications and distributions. Generally they use descriptors to classify the gradation of the soil sample. For example a "poorly graded sand" would classify the sample first as a sand and then a sand whose particle sizes all fall within a very narrow range. The classification "uniform sand" would connote the same material.

There are a number of reasons why such classifications often have only limited use or in some cases are even misleading for engineering purposes. For example, grain size data, although useful for correlating the behavior of cohesionless granular materials (refer to Section 1.2.3.), are generally not useful for categorizing either the grain size or behavioral characteristics of cohesive, fine-grained soils. The properties of the latter type of soil are dependent on their formation and past stress histories neither of which can be identified by any of the methods of gradational classification.

In fact, any evidence of these histories in the structure of the natural soils is destroyed in the process of performing either a grain size or hydrometer analysis since the soil mass must be disturbed from its natural condition. Finally, for certain types of soils, the significance of grain size data is extremely doubtful, as for example, in the case of residual soils where no clear cut particle size exists in the field. In such soils the degree of disaggregation that is imparted mechanically prior to testing often dictates the range of particle sizes that will be encountered in the analysis.

The Bureau of Public Roads (BPR) Classification System

This classification system was developed by the United States Bureau of Public Roads in the late 1920's for use in secondary road construction. The original definition of the classification groups was based on the stability characteristics of soils when directly acted upon by wheel loads. No information was given on the mechanical properties of the soils nor were such factors as frost-thaw susceptibility, dynamic response etc. considered. The original classification was based mainly on grain size distribution, plasticity and shrinkage characteristics (Hogentogler and Terzaghi, 1929). Highway engineers who attempted to use the original *BPR* System for classifying subgrades found it to contain many shortcomings in areas critical to the proper design of highway roadways. Consequently a number of revisions were advanced that overcame many of these shortcomings (Morton, 1936; Allen, 1942). The revisions contained not only the classification characteristics of the original system but also items relating to specific soil properties. A modified version of the *BPR* System is given in Table 1.16. Although it is a summary, Table 1.16 contains a good deal of detail and many categories in which classification is by numerical value obtained from standard soil mechanics testing.

Another modification of the *BPR* system was presented by STEELE (1946) and subsequently adopted by the American Association of State Highway Officials (AASHO) as one of its standards for subgrade soil classification (AASHO, 1950). In this system the *A*-1, *A*-2 and *A*-7 groups shown in Table 1.16 were divided into subgroups to allow for distinctions which were not made previously. The reader is referred to STEELE for details of the modification. The point here is that the *BPR* classification system is and was a viable system constantly evolving to meet new requirements. In fact, the comment may be made that the "general stability properties" shown in Table 1.16 are also indicative of trafficability.

Airfield Classification Systems

These systems originated during the early 1940s because of the difficulties of using existing systems to categorize soils according to their value as airfield pavement subgrades. Systems up until that time were concerned with highway pavement subgrades and the criteria for providing support under highway vehicle loadings. These criteria were not applicable to the design and construction of the many military airfields that were being built at that time all over the world in diverse and often extreme climatic conditions and in many cases unfamiliar soil types. The two best known airfield classification systems are the Civil Aeronautics Administration *(CAA)* soil classification system and the Airfield Classification *(AC)* system. Of these two the *AC* system has, over the years, been expanded and revised by various U.S. government agencies and is now applicable not only to airfield subgrades, but also to embankments, foundations and most other civil engineering structures. The most widely used of the modified versions of the *AC* system is called the Unified Soil Classification System. A brief discussion of its features follows.

The Unified Soil Classification System. As indicated above, this widely used system evolved from the Airfield Classification System as originally developed for the U.S. Engineers Department by ARTHUR CASAGRANDE. It was presented in Army courses on "Control of Soils in Military Construction" at Harvard University from 1942 to 1944. Its first formal presentation was by MIDDLEBROOKS (1946). Subsequently, CASAGRANDE himself (1947) and the U.S. Army Corp. of Engineers (1953) reported on it and its latest modifications in detail. Table 1.17 presents a summary of the Unified Classification System as it appears in one of its later revisions by the Corps of Engineers (1957). Table 1.18 shows an evaluation of the response of the various groups to conditions that affect the performance of these materials as airfield and/or roadway subgrades. Also shown are the comparable group designations in the more qualitative Public Roads

TABLE 1.16
Summary of Modified Bureau of Public Roads Classification System

Group	A–1	A–2 Friable	A–2 Plastic	A–3	A–4	A–5	A–6	A–7	A–8
1	2	3	4	5	6	7	8	9	10
General stability properties	Highly stable at all times	Stable when dry; may ravel	Good stable material	Ideal support when confined	Satisfactory when dry; loss of stability when wet or by frost action	Difficult to compact; stability doubtful	Good stability when properly compacted	Good stability when properly compacted	Incapable of support
Physical constants:									
Internal friction	High	High	High	High	Variable	Variable	Low	Low	Low
Cohesion	do.	Low	do.	None	do.	Low	High	High	do.
Shrinkage	Not detrimental	Not significant	Detrimental when poorly graded	Not significant	do.	Variable	Detrimental	Detrimental	Detrimental
Expansion	None	None	Some	Slight	do.	High	High	do.	do.
Capillarity	do.	do.	do.	do.	Detrimental	do.	do.	High	do.
Elasticity	do.	do.	do.	None	Variable	Detrimental	None	do.	do.
Gradational classification:									
General grading	Uniformly graded; corse-fine excellent binder	Poor grading; poor binder	Poor grading; inferior binder	Coarse material only; no binder	Fine sand cohesionless silt and friable clays	Micaccous and diatomaceous	Deflocculated cohesive clays	Drainable flocculated clays	Peat muck

Approximate limits:									
Sand percent	70–85	55–80	55–80	75–100	55 (max)	55 (max)	55 (max)	55 (max)	55 (max)
Silt do.	10–20	0–45	0–45	*	High	Medium	Medium	Medium	Not significant
Clay do.	5–10	0–45	0–45	*	Low	Low	30 (min)	30 (min)	do.
Physical characteristics:									
Liquid limit	14–35†	35 (max)	35 (max)	NP ‡	20–40	35 (min)	35 (min)	35 (min)	35–400
Plasticity index	4–9 †	NP–3 ‡	3–15	NP ‡	0–15	0–60	18 (min)	12 (min)	0–60
Shrinkage limit	14–20	15–25	25 (max)	Not essential	20–30	30–120	6–14	10–30	30–120
Compaction characteristics:									
Max. dry weight, pounds per cubic foot	130 (min)	120–130	120–130	120–130	110–120	80–100	80–110	80–110	90 (max)
Optimum moisture, percentage of dry weight (approximate)	9	9–12	9–12	9–12	12–17	22–30	17–28	17–28	
Max. field compaction required, percentage of maximum dry weight, pounds per cubic foot	90	90	90	90	95	100	100	100	Waste.
Required total thickness for subbase, base and surfacing, inches	0–6	0–6	2–8	0–6	9–19	9–24	12–24	12–24	

* Percentage passing No. 200 sieve, 0 to 10.

† When used as a base course for thin flexible surfaces the plasticity index and liquid limit should not exceed 6 and 25, respectively.

‡ NP-nonplastic.

TABLE 1.17
Airfield Classification System — Physical Characteristics of Soil Groups (Casagrande, **1947)**

Major divisions		Soil groups and typical names	Group symbol	General Identification (On Disturbed Samples): Dry strength	General Identification (On Disturbed Samples): Other pertinent examinations	Observations and tests relating to material in place	Principal classification tests (on disturbed samples)
	Gravel and gravelly soils	Well-graded gravel and gravel-sand mixtures, little or no fines	GW	None	Gradation Grain shape Examination of binder wet and dry Durability of grains	Dry unit weight or void ratio Degree of compaction Cementation Stratification and drainage characteristics Ground water conditions Traffic tests Large-scale load tests California bearing ratio tests	Mechanical analysis
		Well-graded gravel-sand mixtures with excellent clay binder	GC	Medium			Mechanical analysis, liquid and plastic limits on binder
		Poorly graded gravel and gravel-sand mixtures, little or no fines	GP	None			Mechanical analysis
		Gravel with fines, silty gravel, clayey gravel, poorly graded gravel-sand-clay mixtures	GF	Very slight to high			Mechanical analysis, liquid and plastic limits on binder if applicable
	Sands and sandy soils	Well-graded sands and gravelly sands, little or no fines	SW	None			Mechanical analysis
		Well-graded sand with excellent clay binder	SC	Medium to high			Mechanical analysis, liquid and plastic limits on binder
		Poorly graded sands, little or no fines	SP	None			Mechanical analysis
		Sand with fines, silty sands, clayey sands, poorly graded sand-clay mixtures	SF	Very slight to high			Mechanical analysis, liquid and plastic limits on binder if applicable
grained material	Fine-grained soils having low to medium compressibility; liquid limit < 50	Silts (inorganic) and very fine sands, *mo*, rock flour, silty or clayey fine sands with slight plasticity	ML	Very slight to medium	Shaking test and plasticity	Dry unit weight, water content and void ratio Consistency, undisturbed and remolded Stratification, root holes and fissures Drainage and groundwater conditions Traffic tests Large-scale load tests California bearing ratio tests Compression tests	Mechanical analysis, liquid and plastic limits if applicable
		Clays (inorganic) of low to medium plasticity sandy clays, silty clays, lean clays	CL	Medium to high	Examination in plastic range		Liquid and plastic limits
		Organic silts and organic silt-clays of low plasticity	OL	Slight to medium	Examination in plastic range, odor, color		Liquid and plastic limits from natural condition and after oven drying
	Fine-grained soils having high compressibility; liquid limit > 50	Micaceous or diatomaceous fine sandy and silty soils, elastic silts	MH	Very slight to medium	Shaking test and plasticity		Mechanical analysis, liquid and plastic limits if applicable
		Clays (inorganic) of high plasticity, fat clays	CH	High to very high	Examination in plastic range		Liquid and plastic limits
		Organic clays of medium to high plasticity	OH	Medium to high	Examination in plastic range, odor, color		Liquid and plastic limits from natural condition and after oven drying
ibrous organic soils with very high compressibility		Peat and other highly organic swamp soils	Pt	Readily identified		Consistency, texture and natural water content	

Administration system. The Unified Soil Classification System must be used in conjunction with the "Plasticity Chart" shown in Figure 1.8 for the proper classification of fine-grained soils. It can be seen from these tables that the *USC* system classifies soils according to the three general groups, coarse-grained, fine-grained, and highly organic. Further classification results in 15 different categories depending on gradation characteristics for the coarse-particled soils and plasticity for the fine-grained soils. The most significant features of the *USC* system are:

a) Applicability to both roadway and airfield subgrades.

b) Applicability to conditions pertaining in most foundation considerations.

c) Correlation between visual and manual designations and laboratory test data.

d) Ease of use due to simple notation and criteria for classification.

e) The classifications for "value as wearing surfaces" and "field compaction characteristics" are meaningful for trafficability. Since *CBR* values may be related to cone index, it is possible for the system to be expanded to include cone index values for mobility purposes. Therefore, the authors believe that workers in the field of mobility should acquaint themselves with and use the Unified Classification System.

Descriptive Soil Classification Systems

Contained in this category of classification systems are the myriad of systems that have been adopted by individuals and/or organizations for classifying soils according to those characteristics of interest to that particular person or group. The major disadvantage of such systems is the complete lack of uniformity in terminology and the over reliance on very subjective criteria. The major advantage of such systems is that for the specific purpose for which they are intended they give a more complete classification than systems that adhere to a rigid set of rules. In addition, they often allow for descriptions of the soil in its undisturbed state as well as for descriptions based on the results of laboratory tests, in preparation for which the soil sample has been severely disturbed. Since these systems usually contain more information in their classification descriptors than the rigidly defined systems, group equivalence between them is generally quite simple. For example, the description "Brown, fine, uniform, clean sand in very dense condition; relative density 80 per cent" could be classified equivalently as *A*-3 in the *BPR* system, or as *SP* in the Unified Classification system. Because of their broad scope, descriptive soil classification systems often contain elements of both of the broad categories of classification systems discussed at the beginning of this section.

TABLE 1.18
Unified Classification System — Engineering Properties Related to Roadway Subgrade Performance

Group symbols	Value as foundation when not subject to frost action	Value as wearing surface for stage or emergency construction: With dust palliative	Value as wearing surface for stage or emergency construction: With bituminous surface treatment	Potential frost action	Compressibility and expansion	Drainage characteristics	Field compaction characteristics and equipment	Solids at optimum compaction (lb per cu ft) and void ratio, e	California bearing ratio for compacted and soaked specimen	Comparable groups in PR classification
GW	Excellent	Fair to poor	Excellent	None to very slight	Almost none	Excellent	Excellent; crawler tractor, rubber tired equipment	>125 e <0.35	>50	A–3
GC	Excellent	Excellent	Excellent	Medium	Very slight	Practically impervious	Excellent; tamping roller, rubber tired equipment	>130 e <0.30	>40	A–1
GP	Excellent	Poor	Poor to fair	None to very slight	Almost none	Excellent	Good to excellent; crawler tractor, rubber tired equipment	>115 e <0.45	25–60	A–3
GF	Good to excellent	Poor to good	Fair to good	Slight to medium	Almost none to slight	Fair to practically impervious	Good to excellent; crawler tractor, rubber tired equipment, tamping roller	>120 e <0.40	>20	A–2
SW	Excellent	Poor	Good	None to very slight	Amost none	Excellent	Excellent- crawler tractor, rubber tired equipment	>120 e <0.40	20–60	A–3
SC	Excellent	Excellent	Excellent	Medium	Very slight	Practically impervious	Excellent; tamping roller, rubber tired equipment	>125 e <0.35	20–60	A–1
SP	Good	Poor	Poor	None to very slight	Almost none	Excellent	Good to excellent; crawler tractor, rubber tired equipment	>100 e <0.70	10–30	A–3

SF	Fair to good	Poor to good	Poor to good	Slight to high	Almost none to medium	Fair to practically impervious	Good to excellent; crawler tractor, rubber tired equipment, tamping roller	>105 $e<0.60$	8–30	A–2
ML	Fair to poor	Poor		Medium to very high	Slight to medium	Fair to poor	Good to poor; close control essential; rubber tired roller	>100 $e<0.70$	6–25	A–4
CL	Fair to poor	Poor		Medium to high	Medium	Practically impervious	Fair to good; tamping roller	>100 $e<0.70$	4–15	A–4 A–6 A–7
OL	Poor	Very poor		Medium to high	Medium to high	Poor	Fair to poor; tamping roller	>90 $e<0.90$	3–8	A–4 A–7
MH	Poor to very poor	Very poor		Medium to very high	High	Fair to poor	Poor to very poor	>100 $e<0.70$	<7	A–5
CH	Poor to very poor	Very poor		Medium	High	Practically impervious	Fair to poor; tamping roller	>90 $e<0.90$	<6	A–6 A–7
OH	Very poor	Useless		Medium	High	Practically impervious	Poor to very poor	<100 $e>0.70$	<4	A–7 A–8
Pt	Extremely poor	Useless		Slight	Very high	Fair to poor	Compaction not practical			A–8

TABLE 1.19
Classification of Principal Soil Deposits According to Origin
(From DM-7, 1971)

Geological origin	Process involved in formation	Nature of deposits	Typical gradation
Residual.	Soil weathered in place from parent rocks with little or no alteration by transport.	Almost invariably becomes more compact, rockier and less weathered with increasing depth. May reflect alternation of hard and soft layers or stratification of parent rock if weathering is incomplete.	Product of complete weathering is clay of a type depending on the weathering process and parent rock, plus varying amounts of resistant silica particles. Soil at intermediate stage reflects composition of parent rock.
Alluvial.	Materials transported and redeposited by action of water.	Usually with pronounced stratification. Typical river deposit consists of fine grained material of recent origin overlying coarser strata dating from earlier stage of river development.	Ranges from finest grained lacustrine or marine clays to very coarse gravel, cobble or boulders in alluvial fan or stream terrace deposits.
Glacial. .	Materials transported and redeposited by glacial ice or by melt waters flowing from glaciers.	Stratification varies greatly according to deposit, from heterogeneous moraines and till to finely stratified (varved) silt and clay in glacial lakes, or irregularly layered ice contact deposits and outwash plains.	Till and moraines are typically of broad gradation ranging from clay to boulders. Grain size in outwash generally decreases with distance from source of melt water.
Loessial.	Soil transported by wind without subsequent redeposition.	In loess, horizontal stratification is indistinct or nonexistent except for weathered horizons. Frequently has secondary structure of vertical cracks, joints, root holes.	Most uniform in gradation of all principal soil types. Loess range from clayey silt to silty fine sand. Dune sands generally fine to medium size lacking silt or clay.
Secondary geological origins.	Organic soils formed in place by growth and decay of plants.	Most U.S. peats formed as filled-basin deposits in irregular glacial topography or in areas of subsidence on southern and eastern coasts.	Dark colored, finely divided peats are product of advanced decomposition in the presence of air. Fibrous peat has been continuously submerged.
Do.	Ash and pumice deposited by volcanic action.	Frequently associated with lava flows and mud flows, or may be mixed with non-volcanic sediments.	Typically shard-like particles of silt size with larger volcanic debris. Weathering and redeposition produces highly plastic clay.
Do.	Materials precipitated or evaporated from solutions of high salt content.	Includes such varieties as oolites precipitated from calcium in sea water or evaporites formed in playa lakes under arid conditions.	May form cemented soils or soft sedimentary rocks including gypsum or anhydrite.

Geological Classification Systems

Geological classification systems are usually based on any one or number of factors such as age, morphology, origin etc. From a practical viewpoint the most useful geological classification system for vehicle mobility purposes is that based upon origin. Table 1.19 (DM-7, 1971) shows one such system. Characteristically, all soils fall within two broad classes: residual and transported or sedimentary. The former group contains not only those soils commonly called "residual" soils, i.e. those formed in place from parent rocks, but also most organic soils. Subgroupings under transported soils are usually made according to methods of transportation: Alluvial (rivers or streams), glacial (glaciers), marine (ocean), lacustrine (lake), aeolian (wind), volcanic (volcanos), colluvial (gravity). The value of such a classification for vehicle mobility purposes is that the categories usually pertain to soils covering a significant area of interest. These soil types often have "characteristic" properties that affect vehicle performance. Depending on the soil type, these properties may or may not be applicable over the entire area. For example, if soils in an area are classified as alluvial, the same mobility conditions can usually be expected throughout that area. Once the details pertaining to specific performance characteristics (good or bad) are determined for any portion of the area, those characteristics could be applied with moderate confidence to the rest of the area. On the other hand, if an area consists of soils that have been classified as "residual", variations in specific performance characteristics could be expected from section to section within that area if weathering has been non-uniform.

Agricultural Classification Systems

In keeping with the basic definition of "classification", most agricultural classification systems categorize soils according to those elements of importance for the growth of crop plants.

Such classifications are usually limited to surface soils and use as a point of departure the pedological soil profile (refer to Figure 1.17). In this profile the term "soil" is used with reference to the upper horizons only. The horizons themselves are categorized according to the effect of the following factors on their development:

a) vegetation (biological activity both vegetation and animal)

b) climate (particularly temperature and the amount and kind of precipitation as these affect weathering)

c) topography (as it affects internal and external drainage)

d) parent material (including texture, structure, and mineralogic and chemical composition)

e) age (the length of time the pedological processes have been acting)

Table 1.20 presents the basic shorthand lettering system that is often used to describe the various horizons and their distinguishing features. The subscripts in Table 1.21, when appended to the basic shorthand letters, allow for a broadening of the system to designate special properties of a layer. A grasslands, alkaline soil, for example, could be described as having an A_p, B_2, B_{3ca}, C_{ca}, C profile (HUNT, 1972).

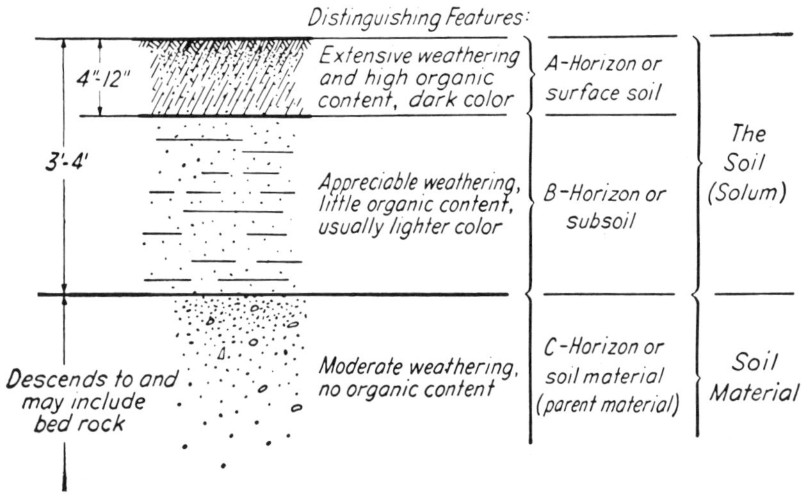

Fig. 1.17
Pedological Soil Profile
(From HOUGH, 1969)

On the basis of this type of pedological classification THORP and SMITH (1949) further categorized soils into the so-called "higher categories" according to order, suborder and "Great Soil Group". Their classification is quite complex and contains terminology that has been specifically defined for the purpose of the classification. It is not an easily used classification scheme.

From an engineering viewpoint the so-called "lower categories" as

TABLE 1.20
Basic Lettering Shorthand — Pedological Classification

O	organic layer
A_1	organic rich A layer
A_2	layer of maximum leaching
A_3	A layer gradational with the B
B_1	B layer gradational with the A
B_2	layer of maximum deposition
B_3	B layer gradational with the C
C	weathered parent material

TABLE 1.21
Descriptive Subscripts Used With Basic Lettering Shorthand in Pedological Classification System

b	Indicates a soil layer buried by a surface deposit. A leached layer buried under a sand dune would be indicated A_b.
ca	An accumulation of calcium carbonate (see above).
cn	An accumulation of concretions, usually of iron, manganese and iron, or phosphate and iron.
cs	An accumulation of calcium sulfate (gypsum).
f	Frozen ground; applicable in areas of permafrost in Tundra soils.
g	A waterlogged (gleyed) layer.
h	An unusual accumulation of organic matter.
ir	An accumulation of iron.
m	An indurated-layer, or hardpan, due to silication or calcification.
p	Layer disturbed by plowing; a plowed leached layer would be indicated A_p.
sa	An accumulation of soluble salts.
t	An accumulation of clay.

described by RIECKEN and SMITH (1949) are more relevant to mobility problems. These categories include simple units of classification according to soil family, series, type and phase. It is these units that often appear on soil maps prepared by the USDA and/or state agencies mainly for agricultural use. Many examples of such soil maps and their related descriptions of soil characteristics are contained in MINARD (1953). This information contained on such "soil maps" could be used in conjunction with other evidence, such as that obtained from airphotos, to estimate the foundation and trafficability characteristics of the surface soils without a field visit ever being made. It is noteworthy that similar classification systems have been developed in other countries so that "soil maps" are available from all over the world.

Miscellaneous Special Purpose Soil Mechanics Classification Systems

There are two general types of special purpose soil mechanics classification systems. The first classifies soils according to some pertinent engineering property such as undrained shear strength, consolidation characteristics or relative density. These classifications are usually devised for local conditions or individual projects and are generally based on field or laboratory test data.

The second type of special purpose classification system categorizes soils for identification purposes. The scheme developed by BURMISTER (1951) is an example of this type of system where soils are classified in the field according to major and minor particle size constituents. This system requires familiarity with an extensive shorthand and puts a great deal of reliance on the location of commas and other punctuation marks. More important, however, is the fact that it gives very little attention to the silt clay fractions which usually govern the engineering performance of soil. For these reasons it has only limited use and has never become widely accepted.

Soil Classifications for Soil-Vehicle and Tillage Mechanics

The previous discussion suggests that there are as many different soil classification systems as there are interests in soil related disciplines. Unfortunately, there is at present (1977) no classification system universally adopted and used by workers in the field of soil-vehicle and tillage mechanics. CLARK (1973) has proposed such a system that combines the USDA Textural Classification System with the Unified Soil Classification System and specifies values or relationships for the following: shear strength parameters, ATTERBERG limits, dry density profile, cone index vs depth, moisture content, liquidity index and clay activity, particle size distribution, and void ratio. The proposed system has the following objectives:

1) To provide a complete and accurate method of soil description.

2) To provide a means for meaningful test result comparisons between tillage and soil-vehicle mechanics researchers.

3) To provide additional information regarding the significant engineering properties of the soil (static and dynamic).

4) To provide a simple program of field and laboratory testing that can be correlated with a comprehensive but simple classification format.

This concept has much merit and, as suggested in the proposed system, some of the systems discussed in the preceding sections already fulfill at least a portion of the stated objectives.

CHAPTER 1.3

CHARACTERISTICS OF SOIL BEHAVIOR

1.3.1 The Principle of Effective Stress

Because soil is a three phase medium the conventional concept of stress must be modified to account for the interaction among the three soil phases. This interaction was described on a macro-mechanical scale by TERZAGHI (1925) in terms of effective stress. The principles underlying the concept of effective stress are analogous to those governing the reaction of a spring-piston system in a water filled cylinder shown in Figure 1.18. In this system the spring represents the compressible skeleton of soil particles. The cylinder's being completely filled with water represents a situation analogous to that of a completely saturated soil.

Figure 1.18(a) shows the system at equilibrium i.e. no external load and the spring force just balancing the weight of the piston head with no excess pressure in the water.

In Figure 1.18(b) a 100 lb force is added to the piston head. Since the water drain is closed and since water is virtually incompressible this load cannot be balanced by an increase in the spring reaction because such a reaction requires displacement. Therefore the 100 lb load is carried by the confined column of water which results in an excess pressure in the water above that due solely to hydrostatic head.

Figures 1.18c through f show that when the drain valve is opened, the excess water pressure is relieved gradually. As the water escapes, the load is transferred from the water to the spring until there is no excess water pressure and the entire load is carried by the spring. This load transfer is accompanied by a downward displacement of the piston head. When the entire load is carried by the spring the system is again in equilibrium under the external load.

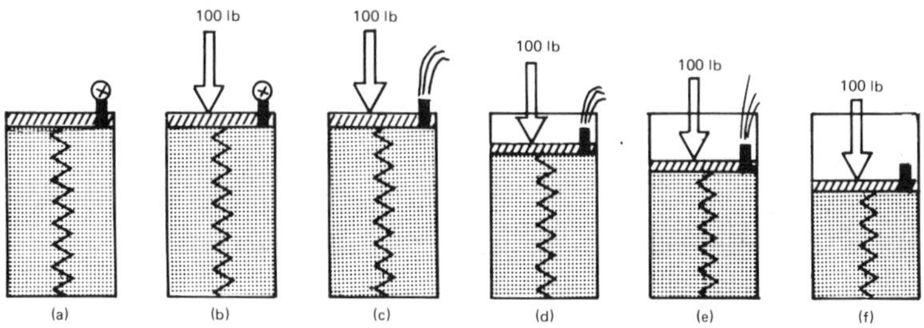

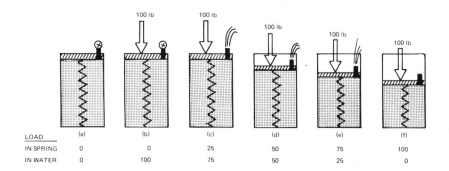

LOAD	(a)	(b)	(c)	(d)	(e)	(f)
IN SPRING	0	0	25	50	75	100
IN WATER	0	100	75	50	25	0

Fig. 1.18
Spring-Piston Analogy of Soil Consolidation and Principle of Effective Stress

In a fully saturated soil, an externally applied load (P) results in a stress increment ($\Delta\sigma$) at any point in a soil mass so that the total stress at that point after application of the load is $\sigma_t = \sigma_i + \Delta\sigma$, where σ_i is the initial stress at the point. The initial total stress may or may not be entirely carried by the soil skeleton at the time of application of the stress increment. If it is not all being carried by the soil skeleton, then part of it is carried by the pore water and causes an initial excess pore water pressure, u_i. In any case, the stress increment, $\Delta\sigma$, is first carried by the pore water (i.e. $\Delta\sigma = \Delta u$) although this is true only for saturated soils where all the voids are water voids. The case where part of the voids are air and part water will be discussed later. This excess pore water pressure ($u = u_i + \Delta u$) is relieved by drainage, the rate depending, among other things, upon the permeability of the soil. As the water drains, the soil mass consolidates and the excess pore water pressure is transferred to the soil skeleton. The stress induced in the soil skeleton during the consolidation process is called the effective stress which can now be defined in general terms as

$$\bar{\sigma} = \sigma_t - u \qquad \text{Eq. 1.3.1}$$

where

$\bar{\sigma}$ = effective stress at a point in the soil skeleton.

σ_t = total stress at a point in the soil skeleton $= \sigma_i + \Delta\sigma$

u = excess pressure in the pore fluid $= u_i + \Delta u$

For the case where equilibrium exists at the instant of load application (i.e. where $u_i = 0$ and $\sigma_t = \sigma_i = \bar{\sigma}$) the above expression yields for conditions immediately following loading:

$$\sigma_i = \sigma_i + \Delta\sigma - u$$

or

$$u = \Delta\sigma \qquad \text{Eq. 1.3.2}$$

This says that the pore water carries the entire stress increment at the instant of loading.

At the completion of drainage, the entire load increment is carried by the soil skeleton (i.e. $u = 0$) and Equation 1.3.1 becomes

$$\bar{\sigma} = \sigma_t \qquad \text{Eq. 1.3.3}$$

The applied load is then "effectively" carried by the soil structure. Therefore, in conventional terms, the effective stress can be thought of as the normal component of the applied load acting on the solids over a cross-sectional area (A_t) of the soil. In soil mechanics literature the term "intergranular stress" is often used interchangeably with "effective stress", however when the nature of a soil cross-section is considered more closely, it is obvious that such an identity is incorrect. A cross-section at any point through a soil mass contains both solid areas and void areas. The excess pore water pressure in saturated soils acts only in the void area. Therefore Equation 1.3.1 is properly expressed in terms of force as

$$\bar{\sigma} A_t = \sigma A_t - u\,(1 - a)\,A_t \qquad \text{Eq. 1.3.4}$$

where

a = the percentage of the total area (A_t) occupied by solids.

Because stress conditions at particle contact points rather than within particles are critical, the cross-section of interest is really a "wavy" surface (Lambe and Whitman, 1969) that passes through the points of contact in the soil section as close to the horizontal as the particle sizes and particle arrangements allow (refer to Figure 1.19[a]). The intergranular contact area within this "wavy" section is a small fraction of the total surface area, therefore "a" in Equation 1.3.4 is ordinarily considered equal to zero in conventional soils engineering problems.

In the case of partially saturated soils (Bishop, 1961), the voids are filled part with water, part with air. Under such conditions the water in the voids is not continuous but either contains air bubbles or is surrounded by air at atmospheric pressure which causes capillary menisci to form. In the latter case of continuous air voids, the porewater pressure is negative because of the surface tension. Consequently effective stress is not uniform throughout the soil mass under equilibrium conditions and the general expression for the total load carried by the soil over a cross-section A_t is:

$$P = \sigma_t A_t = \bar{\sigma} A_t + u_w b A_t + u_a\,(1 - a - b)\,A_t \qquad \text{Eq. 1.3.5}$$

where with reference to Figure 1.19(b):
bA_t = the fraction of the "wavy" section that passes through water.
u_w = pressure in the water.
$(1 - a - b)\ A_t$ = the fraction of the "wavy" section that passes through air.
u_a = pressure in the air.
If, as indicated previously, "a" is very small, then Equation 1.3.5 may be rewritten without loss in accuracy as

$$\sigma_t A_t = \bar{\sigma} A_t + u_a A_t - b\,(u_a - u_w)\,A_t \qquad \text{Eq. 1.3.6}$$

or in terms of stress as

$$\sigma_t = \bar{\sigma} + u_a - b\,(u_a - u_w) \qquad \text{Eq. 1.3.7}$$

By analogy to Equation 1.3.1, u now represents the pressure in the total voids, air and water, and is given as:

$$u = u_a - b\,(u_a - u_w) \qquad \text{Eq. 1.3.8}$$

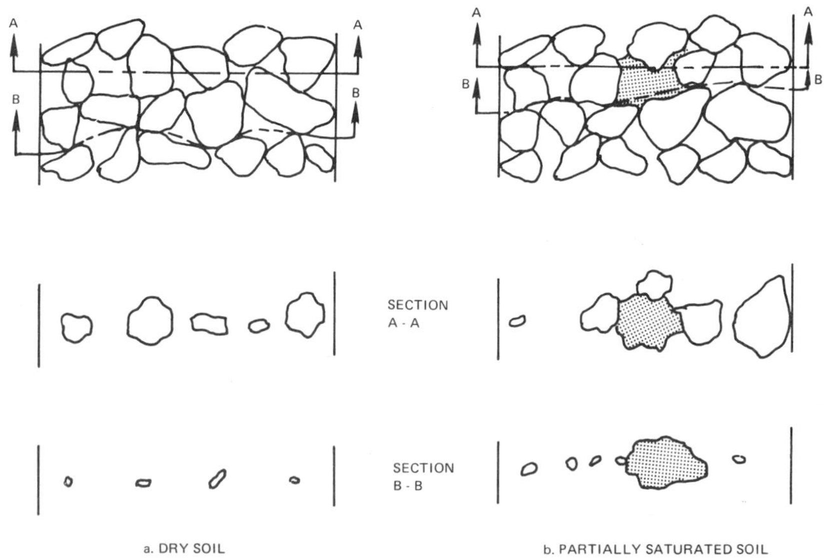

Fig. 1.19
Stress Surfaces in Soil

For dry soils, $b = 0$ and the above expression implies that the air carries all the load. Transfer to the soil skeleton, however is virtually instantaneous since air, in addition to being compressible, has very low viscosity so that it makes even the densest material act very permeable to it in accordance with the definition of "k" given by Equation 1.2.20. Consequently the air within the soil mass "drains" very rapidly and consolidation of the mass takes place quickly. For saturated soils $b = 1$ and the relationship in Equation 1.3.8 reverts to that in Equation 1.3.2. In either case, as the excess pressure in the pore fluid (be it air or water) dissipates, the applied stress increment is transferred to the soil skeleton and consolidation of the mass takes place. The concept of consolidation of fully saturated soils will be discussed subsequently in Section 1.3.2. Let it suffice here to say that the permeability of most soils to water is such that drainage and associated load transfer from pore fluid to soil skeleton does not take place instantaneously, especially within the relatively short period of time soils are subjected to loads imposed by travelling vehicles. This has implications regarding the strength properties of the soil and, therefore, the trafficability of those soils.

Natural soils are usually neither completely dry nor completely saturated. The interaction between the three soil phases under partially saturated conditions as expressed by Equation 1.3.6 was studied extensively by Skempton (1961, 1954) and is best understood with reference to a soil element subjected to hydrostatic and/or deviatoric stress increases. Figure 1.20(a) shows such an element in equilibrium under the orthogonal stress system σ_1, σ_2, σ_3 and with an initial pore pressure u_i.

The first case to be considered is shown in Figure 1.20(b) where a hydrostatic compressive stress increase is applied in all three directions so that $\Delta\sigma_1 = \Delta\sigma_3 = \Delta\sigma_2$ and $u = u_i + \Delta u_h$ where Δu_h is the excess pore pressure increment due to *hydrostatic* stress increment. Assuming that drainage of the pore fluids (water and/or air) is *not* allowed at the instant of load application, the rise in the pore pressure produces a compression of the pore volume determined by

$$\Delta V_{tv} = m_{tv}\,(\Delta u_h) \qquad \text{Eq. 1.3.9}$$

where m_{tv} is the compressibility of the pore space as an expression of the aggregate compressibility of pore fluids. For a saturated soil m_{tv} is the compressibility of water which is so small that it is usually taken equal to zero. In that case there is no change in void volume due to compression of the void fluids.

Under the same loading conditions and even though drainage is not allowed, a change in effective stress will take place ($\Delta\bar{\sigma} = \Delta\sigma_3 - \Delta u_h$) as the pore fluids compress. This change produces a compression of the soil structure equal to

$$\Delta V_s = 3m_{vl}\,(\Delta\bar{\sigma}) = 3m_{vl}\,(\Delta\sigma_3 - \Delta u_h) \qquad \text{Eq. 1.3.10}$$

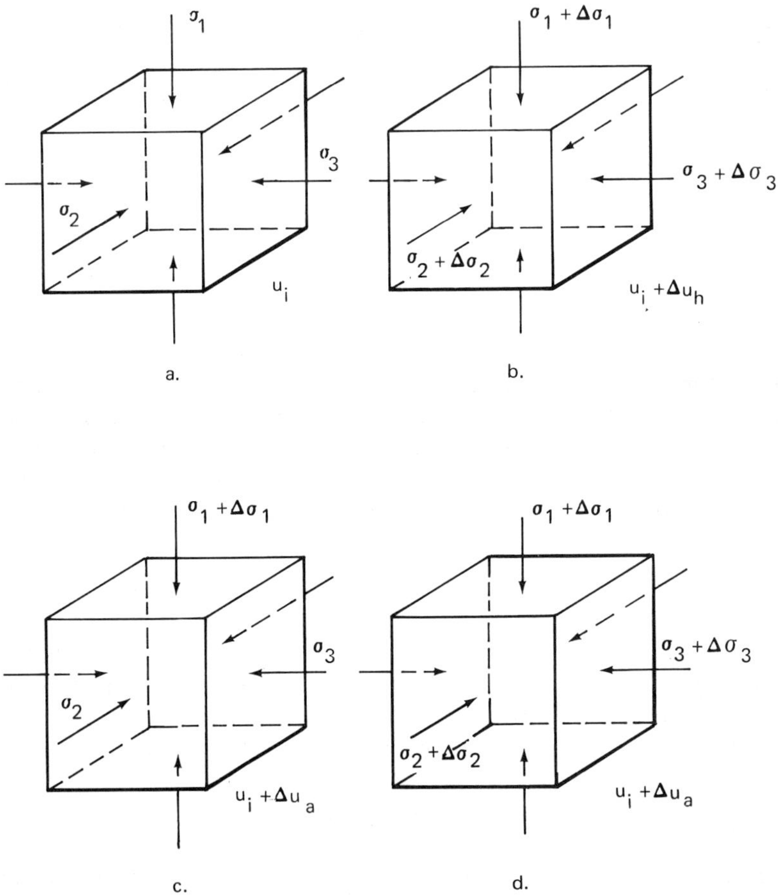

Fig. 1.20
Stress Conditions on Soil Element

a) Equilibrium Under Orthogonal Stress System and Pore Pressure
b) Element Subjected to Hydrostatic Stress Increment
c) Element Subjected to Axial Stress Increment in One Direction Only
d) Element Subjected to Axial Stress Increment in Three Directions where $\Delta\sigma_2 = \Delta\sigma_3 < \Delta\sigma_1$

where ΔV_s is the change in structural volume and m_{vl} is the compressibility of the soil *structure* along a single axis due to the $\Delta\bar{\sigma}$ along that axis. Note that m_{vl} is *not* the compressibility of the soil *particles* which, for conventional engineering loads, is about zero. Since ΔV_s is a direct expression of ΔV_{tv}, the two expressions can be equated to yield:

$$\Delta u_h = \Delta\sigma_3 \left[\frac{1}{1 + \dfrac{m_{tv}}{3m_{vl}}}\right] = \Delta\sigma_3 B \qquad \text{Eq. 1.3.11}$$

As stated previously, m_{tv} for water is approximately zero. Therefore, examination of Equation 1.3.11 reveals that for saturated soils $B = 1$. For partially saturated soils where m_{tv} is generally quite large, B is usually less than 1.

The second case to be considered is shown in Figure 1.20(c) and corresponds to the situation where only one axial stress, the σ_1 stress, is incremented by an amount $\Delta\sigma_1$, i.e. $\Delta\sigma_2 = \Delta\sigma_3 = 0$. In this case $u = u_i + \Delta u_a$ where Δu_a is the excess pore water pressure increment due to a *uniaxial* stress increment. Under these conditions, again assuming that drainage is not allowed, the pore pressure in the soil increases an amount Δu_a. In this case however, provided that the soil is saturated, there is no net volume change since compression in direction 1 is accompanied by expansion in directions 2 and 3, that is,

$$\Delta V_{s1} = \Delta V_{s2} + \Delta V_{s3} \qquad \text{Eq. 1.3.12}$$

where ΔV_{s1}, ΔV_{s2} and ΔV_{s3} are the changes in structural volume in direction 1, 2, 3 respectively. The change in volume (ΔV_{s1}) in direction 1, due to an increase in effective stress in that direction ($\Delta\bar{\sigma}_1 = \Delta\sigma_1 — \Delta u_a$) is given by an expression that has the same form as Equation 1.3.10

$$\Delta V_{s1} = m_{vl1}\,\Delta\bar{\sigma}_1 = m_{vl1}\,(\Delta\sigma_1 — \Delta u_a) \qquad \text{Eq. 1.3.13}$$

where m_{vl1} is the compressibility of the soil structure in direction 1. Since $\Delta\sigma_2$ and $\Delta\sigma_3$ are zero, there is a decrease in effective stress in those directions, i.e., $\Delta\bar{\sigma}_2 = \Delta\bar{\sigma}_3 = 0 — \Delta u_a$. The associated increase in volume is given by:

$$\Delta V_{s2} = \Delta V_{s3} = m_{vlo}\,\Delta u_a \qquad \text{Eq. 1.3.14}$$

where m_{vlo} is the "negative compressibility" or expansion of a structure due to effective stress release. Substitution of Equations 1.3.12 and 1.3.14 into Equation 1.3.12 yields

$$m_{vl1}\,(\Delta\sigma_1 — \Delta u_a) = 2m_{vlo}\,\Delta u_a \qquad \text{Eq. 1.3.15}$$

From which

$$\Delta u_a = \frac{1}{1 + (2m_{vlo}/m_{vl1})} \Delta\sigma_1 = A\Delta\sigma_1 \qquad \text{Eq. 1.3.16}$$

For highly compressible soils such as soft clays, peat, organic silts, etc., m_{vlo} is generally quite small, i.e. the compressibility in direction 1 far exceeds the expansion in directions 2 and 3 and the value of A approaches 1. Conversely, for soils of low compressibility such as stiff clays, dense sands, desiccated clays, etc. m_{vlo} is large in comparison to m_{vl1} and the coefficient A becomes small. In the case where the soil is laterally restrained from moving in directions 2 and 3 (as will be shown subsequently is the case in a consolidation test), then A is exactly equal to 1.

For partially saturated soils subjected to the loading conditions of the second case, the volume change due to compression of the void space is accounted for by modifying Equation 1.3.15 by the amount of void volume change given by Equation 1.3.9, that is

$$m_{vl1}(\Delta\sigma_1 - \Delta u_a) = 2m_{vlo}\,\Delta u_a + m_{tv}\,\Delta u_a \qquad \text{Eq. 1.3.17}$$

from which

$$\Delta u_a = \left[\frac{1}{1 + (m_{tv}/m_{vl1}) + (2m_{vlo}/m_{vl1})}\right] \Delta\sigma_1 \cong AB\Delta\sigma_1 \qquad \text{Eq. 1.3.18}$$

The third case to be considered is shown in Figure 1.20(d) and corresponds to the loading conditions usually encountered in the field, i.e. stresses are increased in all three directions by amounts $\Delta\sigma_1$ in direction 1 (the net change above isotropic stress being $\Delta\bar{\sigma}_1$, equal to $\Delta\sigma_1 - \Delta\sigma_3$), $\Delta\sigma_2 = \Delta\sigma_3$ in directions 2 and 3, and $u = u_i + \Delta u_t$ where $\Delta u_t = \Delta u_a + \Delta u_h$. The solution for this case is obtained by a superposition of the results of the preceding cases as found in Equations 1.3.18 and 1.3.11. The result for fully saturated soils is expressed in the form proposed by SKEMPTON (1954) as

$$\Delta u_t = \Delta u_h + \Delta u_a = B[\Delta\sigma_3 + A\Delta\bar{\sigma}_1] = B[\Delta\sigma_3 + A(\Delta\sigma_1 - \Delta\sigma_3)] \qquad \text{Eq. 1.3.19}$$

As indicated by SKEMPTON, the coefficients A and B are not constants as implied in the development here, but vary as a function of stress level. Consequently, their values under failure stress conditions are quite different from those under stress conditions prior to failure. In plasticity analyses, failure conditions only are considered and a knowledge of effective, total and excess pore water stresses under those conditions is desired. Therefore, usually only the "failure" values of the SKEMPTON pore pressure coefficients A_f and B_f are determined.

Values for these parameters have been obtained in the lab for certain types of soils by BJERRUM (1954a) and others. Recent experience indicates close agreement between lab and field measurements (GIBSON and MARSLAND, 1960; LAMBE, 1962). Typical "failure values" for a variety of materials are found in Table 1.22.

Table 1.22
Typical Values For SKEMPTON Coefficients A_f and B_f
(Abridged from Table 26.1, LAMBE and WHITMAN, 1969)

Values of Parameter A_f

Material ($S = 100\%$)	A_f	Reference
Very loose fine sand	2 to 3	Typical values given by BJERRUM (1954a)
Sensitive clay	1.5 to 2.5	
Normally consolidated clay	0.7 to 1.3	
Lightly overconsolidated clay	0.3 to 0.7	
Heavily overconsolidated clay	—0.5 to 0	

Values of Parameter B_f

Material	S (%)	B_f	Reference
Sandstone	100	0.286	Computed from compressibilities given by SKEMPTON (1961)
Granite	100	0.342	
Marble	100	0.550	
Concrete	100	0.582	
Dense sand	100	0.9921	
Loose sand	100	0.9984	
London clay (OC)	100	0.9981	
Gosport clay (NC)	100	0.9998	
Vicksburg buckshot clay	100	0.9990	M. I. T.
Kawasaki clay	100	0.9988 to 0.9996	M. I. T.
Boulder clay	93	0.69	Measured by SKEMPTON (1954)
	87	0.33	
	76	0.10	

The control that the principle of effective stress has over soil strength and compressibility, which are the most important factors in soil behavior, is probably the single most important feature of soils that distinguishes their behavior from that of all other engineering materials. In Section 1.3.3 it will be shown that shearing resistance or shearing strength is a frictional phenomenon and that it is a function of contact stress. Consequently, an increase in effective stress results in an increase in shearing resistance regardless of the way the increase in effective stress is brought about. For example, desiccation of surface and near surface soils is often accompanied by capillary tension in the pore water which results in a "tightening" of the soil structure and an increase in the effective stress. From a trafficability viewpoint, a soil that at one time was wet and impassable may upon drying out appear to gain strength and become trafficable. Indeed, the gain in strength is not apparent in this case; it is real and can be explained by the concept of effective stress. Similarly, any mechanism that loads the soil, be it desiccation, a static load or even the sustained passage of vehicles will increase the effective stress and therefore shear strength, provided drainage of the pore fluid (water and/or air) can take place. If drainage cannot take place upon loading of the soil, there is little or no increase in effective stress and therefore no strength gain. In fact, there is a possibility of strength loss due to remolding or rearrangement of the soil structure with its consequent decrease of effective stress. Unfortunately, this is often what happens when a vehicle passes over a wet clay surface so that the roadway becomes "softer" to following vehicles and rutting occurs.

In the following sections the concepts of consolidation and shear strength will be examined with special emphasis given to the effect these characteristics have on off-road locomotion.

1.3.2 The Concept of Consolidation

The concept of consolidation is best understood in the light of the concept of effective stress discussed in the previous section. In Section 1.3.1, the mechanism of load transfer from pore fluid to soil structure was described in detail (refer to Figure 1.18 for spring-piston analogy). There, special emphasis was given to the changes in particle to particle stress and pore water pressure that occur during the transfer, i.e. the concern was with states of stress. The concept of consolidation, on the other hand, relates to the volumetric change that takes place during the same load transfer. Figure 1.18 shows that the transfer to the soil structure of an externally applied load, which, at first, is carried solely by the pore fluid and causes in it an excess positive (compressive) pressure, occurs only if drainage of the pore fluid is allowed to release the excess pore fluid pressure. The process whereby the total volume of the soil decreases due to drainage of the pore fluids under positive pressure is called consolidation. If, as with the case of stress release in "overconsolidated" soils (i.e. soils whose stress history indicates that they have drained under stresses higher than those presently existing), the opposite occurs and the pore fluids are put into "tension", then a volume increase may occur provided free water is available to be taken on to relieve the pore fluid tension. This process is called "swelling". In either case mathematical theories have been developed to describe the complex relationships between pore pressure dissipation, stress in the soil skeleton, volumetric change and time. These theories are called "consolidation theories". Although two- and three-dimensional consolidation theories have been developed (see, for example, BIOT, 1941; SCHIFFMAN, et al, 1969), perhaps the most widely used consolidation theory in soil mechanics has been and continues to be the one-dimensional theory for saturated soils with linear stress-strain relationships developed by TERZAGHI (1925). The fundamental equation of this theory is

$$\frac{\partial u}{\partial t} = c_v \frac{\partial^2 u}{\partial z^2} \qquad \text{Eq. 1.3.20}$$

where

$\frac{\partial u}{\partial t}$ = the term expressing the dissipation of excess pore water pressure with time.

$\frac{\partial^2 u}{\partial z}$ = the term expressing the functional variation of excess pore water pressure with depth

$c_v = \frac{k_z(1+e)}{a_v \gamma_w}$ = the so-called coefficient of consolidation

where

k_z = coefficient of permeability in direction of drainage

e = void ratio

γ_w = unit weight of water

a_v = ratio of void volume change to stress change in the soil

It is outside the scope of this book to present even a cursory treatment of the one-dimensional consolidation theory much less any of the other, more sophisticated, consolidation theories. The reason is that in almost all mobility problems, loads applied by vehicles to a given soil element are so short termed that drainage of the pore fluid does not have time to occur and consolidation does not take place. This is especially true of fine-grained soils such as clays on which most mobility problems occur. Why this is so can be appreciated by considering the c_v term of equation 1.3.20. The coefficient of consolidation is a direct function of soil permeability, therefore the smaller k_z is the smaller will be the time rate of change of excess pore water pressure and the slower will be the drainage of water from the soil. Coarser-grained soils such as sands and gravels, on the other hand, have permeabilities orders of magnitude greater than those of silts and clays. Consequently they drain more easily when loaded and "consolidate" in significantly shorter periods of time. However, even in some sands, especially the finer grained ones, the time for any appreciable consolidation to take place is often greater than the time of load application so that consolidation cannot take place and trafficability problems are encountered.

The concept of consolidation can theoretically be applied to partially saturated and dry soils also, although volume change due to load increment under these conditions is not usually considered consolidation. As indicated in Section 1.2.3, the coefficient of permeability is a function of many variables including the unit weight of the flowing fluid. Most soils, including both fine-grained and coarse-grained soils are so permeable to air that excess pore air pressures are dissipated virtually instantaneously with concomitant "consolidation" or increase in effective stress and subsequent increase in shear strength. It is small wonder, then, that some soils when dry provide excellent roadways for vehicle mobility but when wet become mobility nightmares.

The concepts of effective stress and consolidation underlie soil behavior and can be used to explain some of the mechanisms that exert a strong influence on vehicle mobility. The salient points of the discussion of these concepts here and in the previous section are summarized below. These points are:

a) Effective stress controls two of the most important factors that enter into vehicle mobility analysis, compression and strength.

b) Effective stress equals total stress minus pore fluid pressure.

c) Increase in effective stress is a rate process for soils, therefore the rate of load application and the drainage conditions of the soil are important factors that influence soil behavior. More will be said concerning this in Section 1.3.5.

d) One dimensional consolidation theory can be used to predict approximately the rate of increase of effective stress. For most soils subjected to the transient type loads imposed by moving vehicles, there is not adequate time for drainage, therefore consolidation does not occur. This is particularly true for impermeable soils such as clays.

1.3.3. The Concept of Shear Strength of Soil

Failure in soil, as in most solid materials, occurs when a stress state is imposed that equals or exceeds "available strength" based on some failure criterion. The failure may be either in tension, compression or shear. In problems involving the interaction of soil with the running gear of off-road vehicles, only soil failure in shear need be considered. The ultimate resistance that a soil is capable of developing against shear failure is defined as the shear strength of the soil. The difficulty with such a definition is that, unlike most other solids, soil does not posses a unique value of shear strength. The shear strength of soil is affected by conditions of loading (triaxial, uniaxial, etc.), drainage (drained or undrained), moisture (saturated, partially saturated, dry), loading rate (rapid. slow) stress history, and displacement tolerance. Despite all these factors, many of which are often uncertain, the principle, "duplicate field conditions" should always be used in the determination of the shear strength of soil.

Failure in soil, as in most solid materials, is also always accompanied by some degree of yielding. Three different yield criteria, MOHR-COULOMB, TRESCA and VON MISES, have been traditionally used to define yield at failure mathematically in isotropic soils. Since the MOHR-COULOMB criterion is perhaps the best overall descriptor of soil failure that can be evaluated practically by the results of laboratory and field tests, only it will be used with plasticity theory to develop a formulation in Part 2 of this book for the stress states in soil under applied loads. Consequently, a detailed treatment of the MOHR-COULOMB yield criterion is given in Section 2.2.1. However, because some workers in the field of plasticity analysis of soils have used the other criteria, the equations describing the interrelationship between principal stresses are presented here for all three criteria.

MOHR-COULOMB

$$\begin{aligned}&\{(\bar{\sigma}_1 - \bar{\sigma}_2)^2 - [2\bar{c} \cdot \cos\bar{\varphi} + (\bar{\sigma}_1 + \bar{\sigma}_2)\sin\bar{\varphi}]^2\} \times \\ &\{(\bar{\sigma}_2 - \bar{\sigma}_3)^2 - [2\bar{c} \cdot \cos\bar{\varphi} + (\bar{\sigma}_2 + \bar{\sigma}_3)\sin\bar{\varphi}]^2\} \times \\ &\{(\bar{\sigma}_3 - \bar{\sigma}_1)^2 - [2\bar{c} \cdot \cos\bar{\varphi} + (\bar{\sigma}_2 + \bar{\sigma}_3)\sin\bar{\varphi}]^2\} = 0 \qquad \text{Eq. 1.3.21}\end{aligned}$$

Extended TRESCA

$$\begin{aligned}&\{(\bar{\sigma}_1 - \bar{\sigma}_2)^2 - [\bar{c} + k'\bar{p}]^2\} \times \\ &\{(\bar{\sigma}_2 - \bar{\sigma}_3)^2 - [\bar{c} + k'\bar{p}]^2\} \times \\ &\{(\bar{\sigma}_3 - \bar{\sigma}_1)^2 - [\bar{c} + k'\bar{p}]^2\} = 0 \qquad \text{Eq. 1.3.22}\end{aligned}$$

Extended VON MISES

$$(\bar{\sigma}_1 - \bar{\sigma}_2)^2 + (\bar{\sigma}_2 - \bar{\sigma}_3)^2 + (\bar{\sigma}_3 - \bar{\sigma}_1)^2 - (\bar{c} + k''\bar{p})^2 = 0 \qquad \text{Eq. 1.3.23}$$

where

$\bar{\sigma}_1, \bar{\sigma}_2, \bar{\sigma}_3 =$ the major, intermediate and minor principal effective stresses respectively.

$k' =$ a constant related to sin φ and equal to 4 in Equation 1.3.22
$k'' =$ a constant related to sin φ and equal to 8 in Equation 1.3.23

$\bar{p} = (\bar{\sigma}_1 + \bar{\sigma}_2 + \bar{\sigma}_3)/3$

Figure 1.21 shows a graphical representation of the intersection of failure surfaces for each of the criteria with the plane $p = (\bar{\sigma}_1 + \bar{\sigma}_2 + \bar{\sigma}_3)/3 = $ constant. From this figure it is evident that while the Mohr-Coulomb criterion is independent of the intermediate principal stress ($\bar{\sigma}_2 = \bar{\sigma}_1 < \bar{\sigma}_3$ in extension, $\bar{\sigma}_2 = \bar{\sigma}_3 < \bar{\sigma}_1$ in compression) the other two criteria involve all three principal stresses. The geometric shapes indicated in Figure 1.21 for the various yield criteria represent the boundaries within which states of stress correspond to conditions of static equilibrium for the material.

In considering the concept of shear strength, the first step is to see the relationship between the stress states at a point in a mass of soil and the yield criteria as defined by Equations 1.3.21, 1.3.22, or 1.3.23. Specifically with reference to the Mohr-Coulomb yield criterion, the stress states at a point in a mass of soil are defined by the magnitude and orientation of the principal stresses. Shear stresses at a point vary from 0 to $^1/_2$ (σ_1—σ_3), depending on the orientation of the plane of the shear stress relative to the principal stress axes. The plane of failure is the one

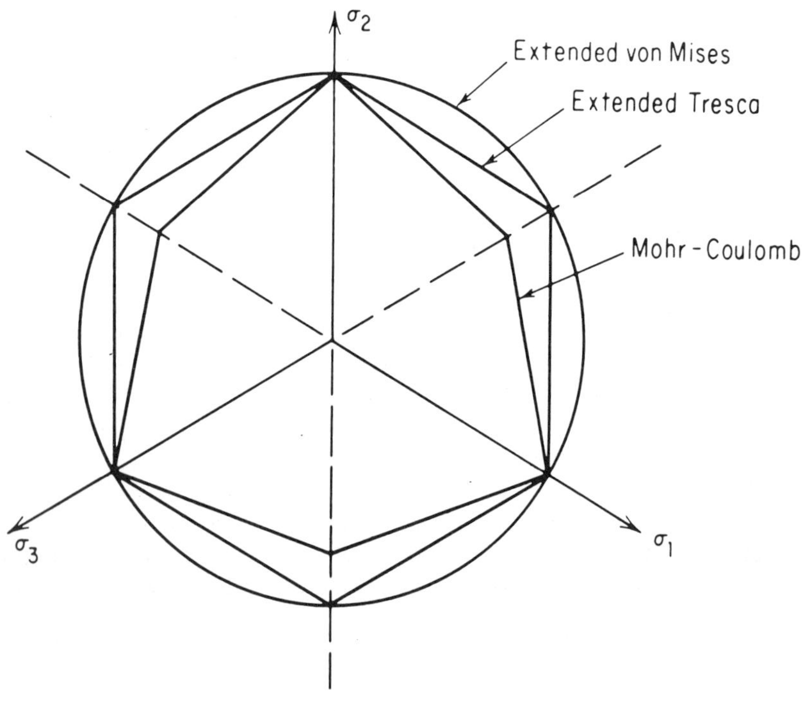

Fig. 1.21
Intersections of Various Failure Surfaces
with a Plane of Constant Mean Principal Stress $(\sigma_1 + \sigma_2 + \sigma_3)/3 = $ Constant

on which the shear stress developed by a gradually increasing applied stress system first attains the magnitude of the ultimate shear resistance or shear strength of soil.

In Section 1.3.1 the principle of effective stresses was introduced as the most useful means to analyze stress conditions at failure. An important feature of the effective stress concept is that the shear stresses are independent of the magnitude of pore water pressures. Thus, the magnitude of shear stresses may be determined without the knowledge of the magnitude of pore water pressures.

The shearing resistance of soil is in general some function of the normal stress acting on the failure plane and can be expressed as follows

$$s = c + \sigma_{\mathrm{n}} \tan \varphi \qquad \text{Eq. 1.3.24}$$

where

c = cohesion

φ = friction angle

A failure state exists at a point in the soil mass if at any plane through that point the shear stress equals the shear strength expressed by Equation 1.3.24. If the principal stresses σ_1 and σ_3 correspond to a failure state in the soil then the orientation of the failure plane may be determined either from a graphical construction (Figure 1.22) or analytically. The angle α that the failure plane encloses with the plane of the major principal stress is

$$\alpha = 45° + \frac{1}{2}\varphi \qquad \text{Eq. 1.3.25}$$

Equations 1.3.24 and 1.3.25 are valid only if tan φ has the same value for any orientation of the failure plane. If some portion of the voids of a soil is occupied by air so that the volume of the soil may change freely upon the application of a stress system and therefore, pore air and water pressures are negligible then this condition is satisfied. On the other hand, if the major portion of the voids is filled with water, then the application of a stress system generally results in the development of pore water pressures. The normal stress acting on the failure plane is then composed of an intergranular (or effective) normal stress and pore water pressure.

$$\sigma_{\mathrm{n}} = \bar{\sigma}_{\mathrm{n}} + u \qquad \text{Eq. 1.3.26}$$

The frictional part of soil resistance is generated by $\bar{\sigma}_{\mathrm{n}}$ while that part of the total normal stress that is carried by the pore water pressure does not generate frictional resistance whatsoever. The normal stress varies with the orientation of the failure plane, as can be seen from Figure 1.22, while the pore water pressure, u, is constant and independent of this orientation. Obviously, the ratio (σ_n/u) at a particular point in a soil mass also varies with the orientation of the plane that σ_n acts on. Therefore, in Equation 1.3.24, σ_n has to be replaced by the effective normal stress, whence

$$s = c + \bar{\sigma}_n \tan \varphi = c + (\sigma_n - u) \tan \varphi \qquad \text{Eq. 1.3.27}$$

This equation was first introduced by Terzaghi (1938) and may be called the revised Coulomb equation. If the relationship between pore water pressure at failure and the normal stress acting on the failure plane is linear, then the shear strength is also a linear function of the normal stress and the Coulomb equation may be written as

$$s = c + \sigma_n \tan \varphi_u \qquad \text{Eq. 1.3.28}$$

The subscript "u" designates undrained conditions during shear, since pore water pressures are generated only if drainage of the soil during shear is non-existent or incomplete. The details of "drained" and "un-

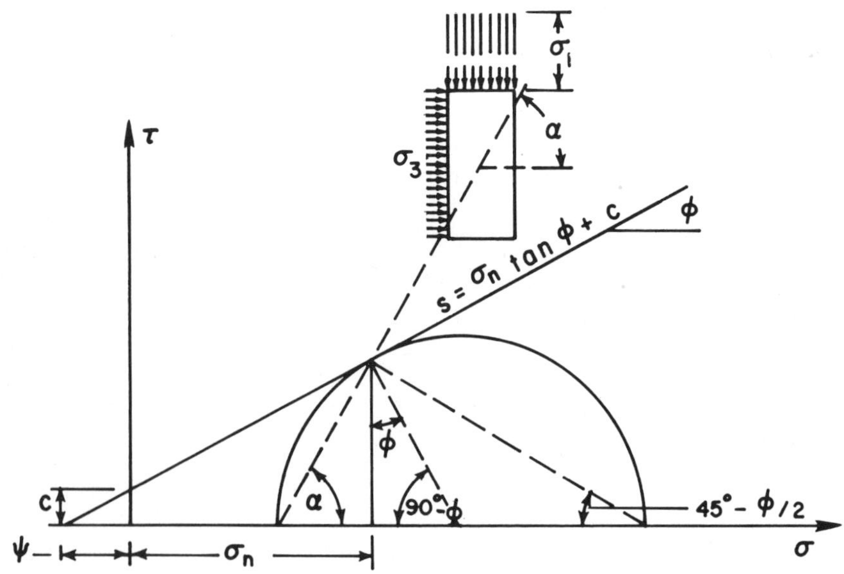

Fig. 1.22
Mohr's Circle Representation of Failure Conditions in Triaxially Loaded Sample

drained" strength tests are discussed in Section 1.3.4. In off-road soil engineering where the interaction of soil with the running gear of off-road vehicles is analyzed, drainage of the soil is generally negligible, therefore, the applicable shear strength of soil and its shear strength parameters are those expressed by Equation 1.3.28.

Equations 1.3.24, 1.3.27 and 1.3.28 express the same linear relationship between shearing resistance and normal stress. Yet there are important differences in regard to the orientation of the failure plane implied in these equations. If the shearing resistance is defined by Equation 1.3.28 then the angle α defining the orientation of the failure plane becomes

$$\alpha_u = 45° + \varphi_u/2 \qquad \text{Eq. 1.3.29}$$

Thus in an analysis of the failure state the orientation of the failure plane will be different depending on whether total or effective stresses are used in the analysis. This controversial issue has not yet been satisfactorily resolved; a detailed discussion of the problem is presented by LAMBE and WHITMAN (1969). In this discussion the authors prove that in the special case of a retaining wall with vertical back face both the effective and the total stress analysis lead to the same answer as far as the resultant earth pressure is concerned even though the orientation of the failure plane is different in the two types of analyses. However, this is not the case generally and significant differences may arise in the analysis of failure states depending on which type of analysis is used. In the application of plasticity theory to off-road mobility problems it is absolutely essential that the orientation of the failure plane be correctly assumed, since the determination of slip line field geometries and associated stresses profoundly depends on this assumption.

The paramount importance of the problem of the orientation of the failure plane for the solution of the running gear-soil interaction problem made it imperative to research this problem in depth. Since theoretical considerations are apparently inconclusive in this matter, a thorough survey of the available experimental evidence was made and some supplemental laboratory tests were performed for the clarification of some details. A brief summary of these studies follows together with the conclusions reached.

In laboratory undrained compression tests of cylindrical specimens distinct failure planes develop in most soils at strains exceeding about 20 %. If a relationship between the orientation of the failure plane and the undrained friction angle could be developed, then these compression tests would provide an excellent means to obtain cohesion and friction angle values in one single test for mobility purposes. However, not only is the orientation of the failure plane difficult to measure, but the orientation is influenced in a significant degree by the diameter/height ratio of the specimen, the degree of end restraints, the distortion of the specimen during compression and for certain soils the rate of loading. Since data on the distorted shape of the specimens were generally not available for the experiments reported in the literature, a conclusive evaluation of most of these tests was not possible. Perhaps the most reliable information on the orientation of failure planes can be obtained from the experiments reported by HVORSLEV (1960) who performed tests on cubical specimens with two types of clays and carefully measured the orientation of failure planes. He found that the angle α is approximately equal to $(45^\circ + {}^1/_2\,\varphi_e)$, where φ_e is the Hvorslev strength parameter. For the two clays tested φ_e is very close to the undrained friction angle φ_u.

A simple analytical study on the development of the failure plane in distorted cylindrical specimens gave new insight into the puzzling question why the reported experimental data were contradictory and inconclusive. In this analytical study it was assumed that the distorted specimen was barrel shaped. The conventional procedure to account for the change of the cross-sectional area by the application of an area correction factor (LAMBE, 1967) actually obliterates the effect of distortion because in this procedure it is tacitly assumed that the specimen retains its cylindrical shape during straining and its diameter changes uniformly over the height of the specimen.

The assumption that the deformed specimen is barrel shaped leads to the following method of analysis of the normal and shear stresses acting on the variously oriented planes. It is assumed that the cross-sectional area of the specimen, bisected by a plane that is inclined at an angle α to the horizontal, equals that of an ellipse with axes R and L, as shown in Figure 1.23. The minor axis $R = {}^1/_2\,D$ may be computed from the volume of the distorted, barrel shaped specimen. This volume equals

$$V = \frac{1}{15}\pi \cdot h' \,(2\,D^2 + Dd + 3/4\,d^2) \qquad \text{Eq. 1.3.30}$$

$$h' = h_o\,(1 - \varepsilon)$$

where ε = vertical strain.

For a compression test with no volume change the volume of the specimen at any strain equals the initial volume V_o:

$$V_o = \frac{1}{4}\,h_o \pi\, d^2 \qquad \text{Eq. 1.3.31}$$

From Equation 1.3.30 D may be expressed as follows

$$D = c_1 d$$

$$c_1 = \left(-1 + \sqrt{30/(1-\varepsilon) - 5}\right)/4 \qquad \text{Eq. 1.3.32}$$

The magnitude of the major axis, L, depends on the orientation of the plane and may be computed as follows.

$$L = x \cos \alpha$$

$$x = \frac{1}{2} D - x' = \frac{1}{2} D - \frac{1}{2} (D - d)\, x^2 \tan^2 \alpha \Big/ \left(\frac{1}{2} \mathrm{h}\right)^2 \qquad \text{Eq. 1.3.33}$$

Since $D = c_1 d$

$$x = \frac{-1 + \sqrt{1 + (c_1 - 1)\, c_1 d^2 \tan^2 \alpha \Big/ \left(\frac{1}{2} h\right)^2}}{(c_1 - 1)\, d \tan^2 \alpha \Big/ \left(\frac{1}{2} h\right)^2} \qquad \text{Eq. 1.3.34}$$

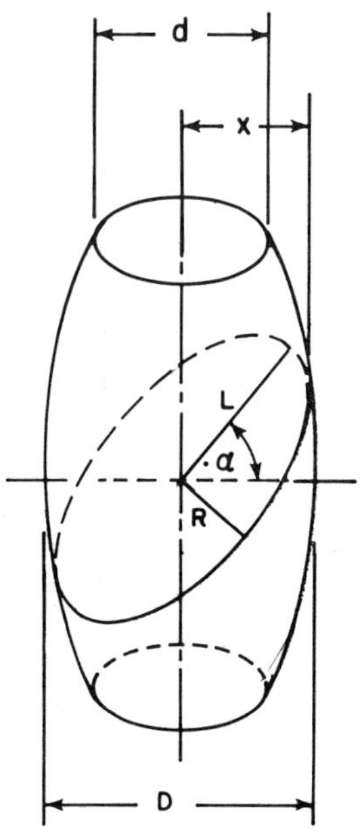

Fig. 1.23
"Barrel" Shaped Geometry of Deformed Soil Sample

The area of the ellipse is

$$A = \pi LR$$

The stresses applied to the specimen are the ambient pressure, σ_3, and the deviator stress, $\sigma_1 - \sigma_3$. On a plane oriented at an angle α to the horizontal the normal stress from such a stress system is

$$\sigma_n = \sigma_3 + \frac{(\sigma_1 - \sigma_3)\,\pi\, d^2}{\pi\, LR} \cos \alpha \qquad \text{Eq. 1.3.35}$$

and the shear stress is

$$\tau = \frac{(\sigma_1 - \sigma_3)\,\pi\, d^2}{\pi\, LR} \sin \alpha \qquad \text{Eq. 1.3.36}$$

If the shear strength of the soil is expressed by Equation 1.3.24 then

$$s = c + \sigma_n \tan \varphi$$

In a stress system, where the deviator stress increases gradually, the plane of failure will be the one where the shear stress (τ) first equals the shear strength (s) of the soil. Although the above computation of the cross-sectional areas for variously oriented planes and the normal and shear stresses acting on these planes is simple, there is no closed form solution for the orientation of the failure plane and, therefore, it was necessary to write a short computer program for the computation of cross-sectional areas, the stresses acting thereon and for their comparison with the shear strength. Figure 1.24 shows an example of the results of the computations obtained in this computer program.

This figure shows the effect of sample distortion on the determination of the friction angle if the angle of the inclination of the failure plane is measured and an "apparent" friction angle computed from the equation

$$\varphi = 2\alpha - 90° \qquad \text{Eq. 1.3.37}$$

This equation is but a different form of Equation 1.3.25. In the figure the apparent friction angles, computed from Equation 1.3.37 are shown for various values of the actual friction angle and vertical strain. The computations were performed for a sample height: diameter ratio of 2.5 and on the assumption that there was no volume change during straining.

The interesting and important information in this figure is in that portion where the relation between the friction angle and apparent friction angle is shown for strains higher than 20 %. For example, this figure shows that a soil with an undrained friction angle of 20° would exhibit an inclination of the failure plane at a strain of 20 % corresponding to a friction angle of about 29°. The value of 29° is likely to be close to the effective friction angle and, without the consideration of sample

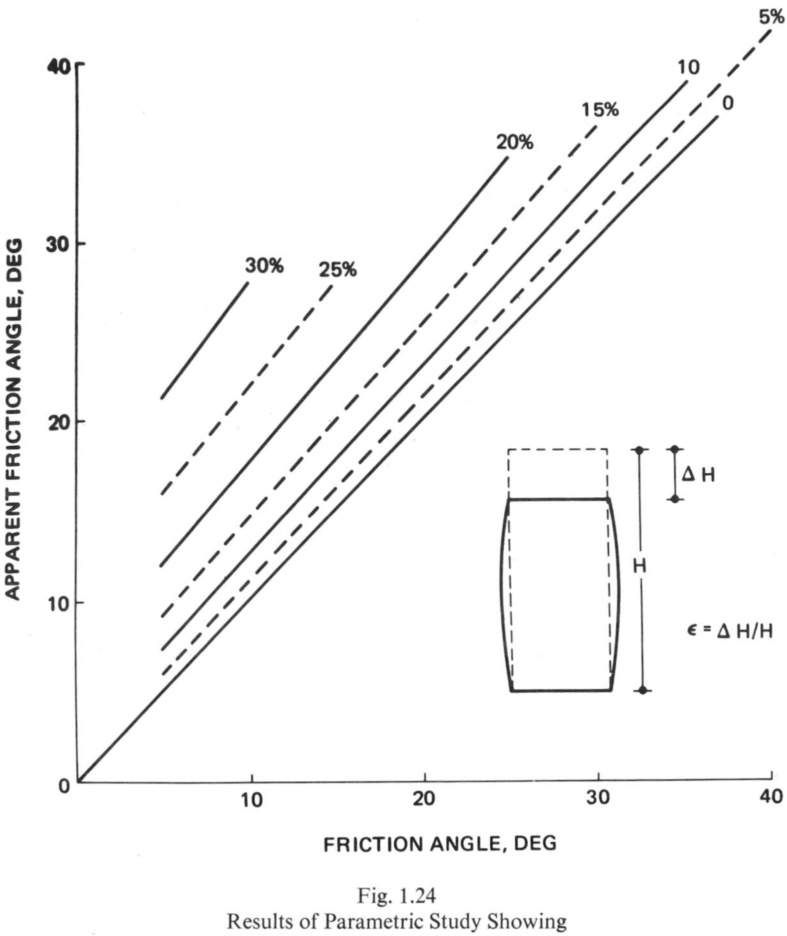

Fig. 1.24
Results of Parametric Study Showing
the Effect of Sample Distortion on Friction Angle

distortion, the conclusion would be drawn from a test that the failure plane is governed by the effective friction angle. This would be even more so if the failure plane developed at strains higher than 20 %. Apparent friction angle values are not shown in the figure for this case, because the failure plane at such inclinations would intersect the end platens in a test. Thus, this method of analysis of normal and shear stresses reveals another problem in the determination of friction angles from the orientation of failure planes. That is the problem due to the insufficiency of customarily used height: diameter ratios. The problem, of course, also exists for any other evaluation procedure, since the uninhibited development of the plane of failure is essential to meaningful testing of the strength properties of soils. In soil mechanics research the use of lubricated, practically frictionless end platens alleviates this problem but in practice the inconveniences associated with this method have prevented its widespread use.

Another interesting aspect of the effect of sample distortion on the development of normal and shear stresses is that these no longer plot as circles in the Mohr presentation of stresses predicated upon the variation of stresses without consideration of geometry changes. A Mohr circle type plot of normal and shear stresses computed with the consideration of sample distortion is shown in Figure 1.25. In this plot the difference between the conventionally computed angle of orientation of the failure plane ($\alpha = 45 + \varphi/2$) and the α_f computed for sample distortion is also shown. The plot is not continued for α angles greater than α_f since planes for such angles would intersect the end platens and the computation of normal and shear stresses would become meaningless.

The computations for a theoretically barrel-shaped specimen show that failure planes develop at angles appreciably higher than the friction angle that controls the development of the failure plane assuming a cylindrical sample. The analyses of stress conditions in distorted specimens also show that the evaluation of the orientation of failure planes is not possible unless the measurement of the inclination of the failure plane is accompanied by measurement of the vertical strain and volume change and some information on the distorted shape of the specimen. With present testing techniques this information is not generally available.

The influence of sample distortion on the angle of inclination of the failure plane explains the discrepancies among the various observations of this inclination reported in the literature. It also explains why no conclusive resolution of the question whether the effective or the undrained friction angle controls the orientation of the failure plane was possible. In light of this analytical study the available experimental information was reexamined. Since all previous evaluations were based on a computation method that was biased toward the effective friction angle being in control, this new analysis of the stresses leads to the conclusion that the undrained friction angle controls the orientation of the failure plane and the controversy arose only because of the misinterpretation of the observed angles of orientation.

1.3.4. Tests to Determine the Consolidation and Strength Characteristics of Soil

Consolidation Tests

For the reasons discussed in Section 1.3.2 consolidation in the civil engineering sense is generally not important in off-road vehicle mobility problems. Consequently the details of consolidation testing and the analysis and evaluation of the test results will not be treated here. The reader is referred instead to any of the general soil mechanics texts listed at the end of Part 1. However, it is instructive for workers in the field

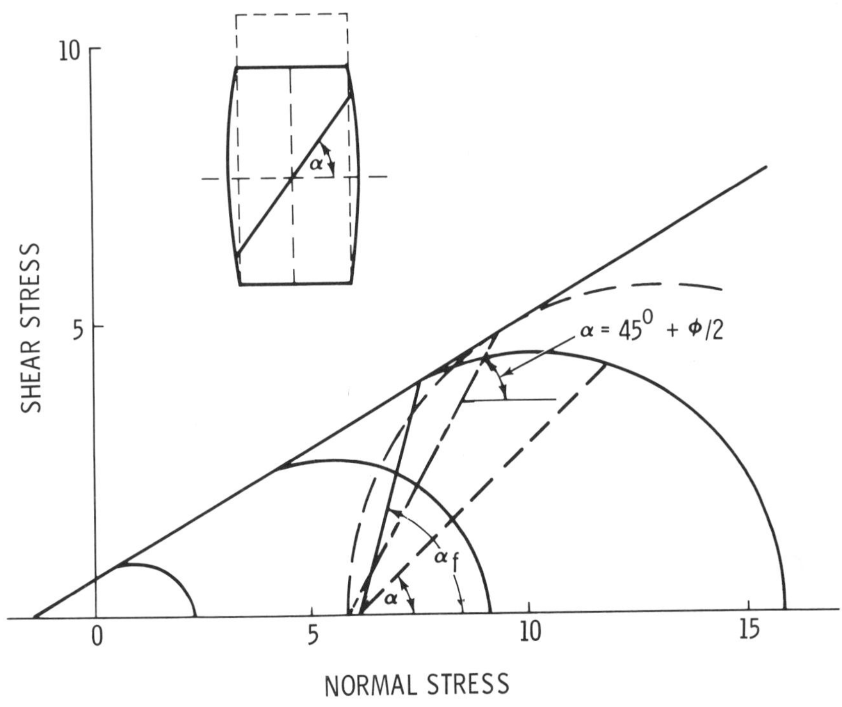

Fig. 1.25
Modified MOHR "Circle" That Accounts for Sample Distortion

of vehicle engineering to know that consolidation test results may yield more than just the compression index and coefficient of consolidation, parameters required by soils engineers to perform settlement analyses of structures.

Consolidation testing is also used to obtain information on the stress history of the sampled stratum. This is important for many civil engineering problems because soil behavior is influenced by its long term natural-(geological) and/or man made stress history. Such stress history does not generally influence the consolidation characteristics for surface and near surface soils of interest in mobility problems because these soils are usually highly disturbed by human activity and/or environmental factors so that the stress history has been obliterated. However, stress history does influence soil strength and, therefore, affects the stability of soil masses, as will be shown in Section 1.4.3. Therefore, in this sense stress history indirectly affects the mobility of off-road vehicles when they must traverse slopes and embankments.

Permeability is another soil property, important in both civil engineering and off-road mobility problems, that can be obtained indirectly from a consolidation test. Permeability is important because this parameter controls all phenomena involving flow of water through soils including shear strength due to effective stress increase associated with drainage.

Consequently, even though consolidation testing may not be directly applicable to off-road mobility problems, it would be advantageous for off-road vehicle engineers and especially vehicle users to know what they can obtain from the results of such tests if they are available.

Strength Tests

Three types of laboratory tests are commonly available to determine a soil's shear characteristics. These tests are: the direct shear test, the triaxial compression test, and the vane shear test. The material characteristics that can be determined from these tests are the strength parameters (angle of internal friction, φ or φ and cohesion, c or c) and in some triaxial tests, properties related to volume change such as load and reload modulus of elasticity, and Poisson's ratio. These parameters are used for analysis and design in conventional civil engineering problems relating to slope stability, bearing capacity and any other situations where shear strength controls.

However, laboratory strength tests are meaningful only if the laboratory conditions of loading, drainage etc. adequately represent the actual field conditions and only if the sample of soil being tested in the lab is representative of the in situ soil (type and condition). Unfortunately, samples

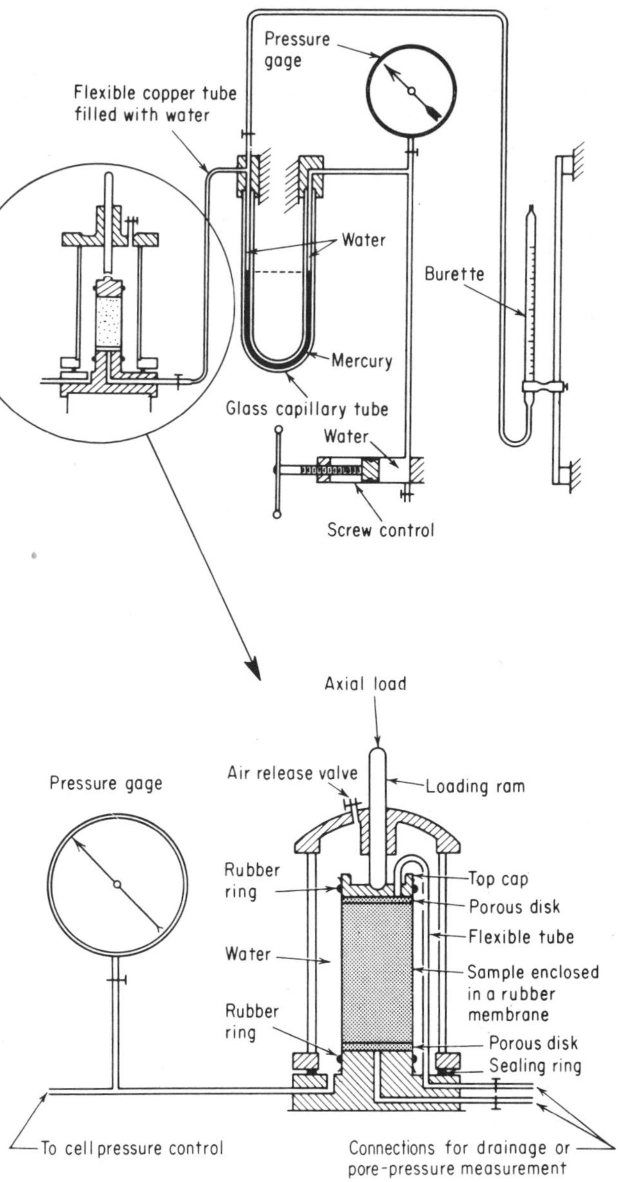

Fig. 1.26
Schematic Representation of Triaxial Test Apparatus
(After BISHOP, 1961)

obtained from the field for laboratory testing are often not representative of the condition of the soil in the field because of sampling and/or handling disturbance. This is especially true in the case of off-road locomotion studies where surface or near surface soils must be sampled. There is currently (1977) no universally accepted procedure or instrument for undisturbed sampling of surface soils. Consequently, the value of laboratory testing for off-road locomotion purposes derives from its supplying soil properties that can be used either for physical validation programs in the laboratory or as input parameters to mathematical models on the computer. In the latter sense, laboratory test data have played an integral part in the analysis of soil-vehicle interaction as presented by the authors in Part 3.

From the discussions of effective stress and the concept of shear strength presented previously, the reader is led to the conclusion that soil strength is not an absolute quantity, but depends on a number of variables.

Among the test factors that affect soil strength are:

a) level of confining stress

b) drainage conditions before and during loading

c) rate of loading (static)

d) frequency of loading (dynamic)

The effects of these factors on soil strength can be evaluated by performing one or more of the available types of laboratory tests noted above under moisture and stress conditions that simulate those that exist, or are expected to exist, in the field. Of the three tests mentioned, the triaxial test is the most versatile and, although more complex and time consuming than the others, it is more widely used, especially in research work.

The Triaxial Test. The physical set up for a triaxial test is shown schematically in Figure 1.26. The basic component of the system is a chamber wherein a saturated sample, encapsuled in a rubber membrane and capped top and bottom with a porous stone, is seated on a pedestal and submerged in a fluid (air, water, glycerin, etc.). Load is applied triaxially by pressurizing the chamber fluid and uniaxially through a load head whose shaft extends through the chamber via a hermatically tight coupling. Provision is made for measuring vertical deformation of the sample and, on some installations, devices are attached about the center perimeter of the sample to measure lateral deformations or bulge. Another important component of the apparatus is the sample drainage and pore pressure measuring system.

The components of the triaxial test apparatus may be manipulated in a number of ways so that in a triaxial test a sample may be failed in shear by either extension or compression, under stress or strain controlled conditions, before or after consolidation under an applied triaxial pressure, with or without drainage during application of axial load, at a high or low rate of axial load application, under static or pulsed loads, and with or without pore pressure measurements.

As a practical matter, there are only a few conditions of triaxial testing that are of interest in determining soil strength parameters for soil-vehicle interaction problems. In these problems the interaction usually causes only compressive stresses in the soil and usually at a relatively high loading rate. It seems, then, that the major factors to be considered in evaluating soil strength for vehicle mobility purposes are consolidation before loading and drainage during loading since the frequency of load application is relatively low. Therefore the following types of triaxial tests are appropriate depending upon the existing or anticipated field conditions:

a) "Consolidated Undrained" *(CU)* wherein complete consolidation (as evidenced by no further escape of pore water from the specimen following application of chamber pressure) is allowed prior to uniaxial vertical loading with sample drainage prevented. During loading the confining pressure is held constant. Under these conditions there is some increase in effective stress beyond that which has accompanied the consolidation of the sample under the chamber pressure. If the purpose of the test is solely to measure strength during undrained shear, then there is no need to measure pore water pressure during the test. If, however, an understanding of the relationship between drained and undrained strength is desired, then measurement of pore water pressures is required in order to evaluate the effective stress during loading. The test is then called a "consolidated undrained triaxial test with pore water pressures measured" $(\overline{CU})$.

The conditions associated with the consolidated undrained test are often met in the field when vehicles traverse wet clays. As such, a measure of the strength properties of soils under these conditions is important in terrain vehicle engineering.

Such a test is also called a "consolidated quick" test or simply an "R" triaxial test. The sequence of loading and the associated total, effective and pore water stresses are shown schematically in Figure 1.27. In the figure u_r is a residual negative pore water pressure associated with capillary tensions that are usually induced in a sample due to its removal from its in situ stress field. In step 3 where the axial stress is increased without permitting drainage, "D" is the pore pressure coefficient that expresses the fraction of the total stress increment carried by the pore pressure for one-dimensional loading. It is given in Equation 1.3.18 as a function of the directional compressibility and expansivity of the soil skeleton and the compressibility of the pore fluids.

b) "Consolidated Drained" *(CD)* wherein the procedure prior to application of the axial load is identical to that of the *CU* or $\overline{CU}$ test. The difference is that, following consolidation under the confining pressure, the axial load is applied slowly enough so that no pore water pressure increase occurs in the sample. Neutralization of potential excess pore water pressure is accomplished by allowing drainage to occur during axial loading and by applying axial load slowly enough so that such drainage has time to occur. In the *CD* (or *"S"*, meaning "slow", test as

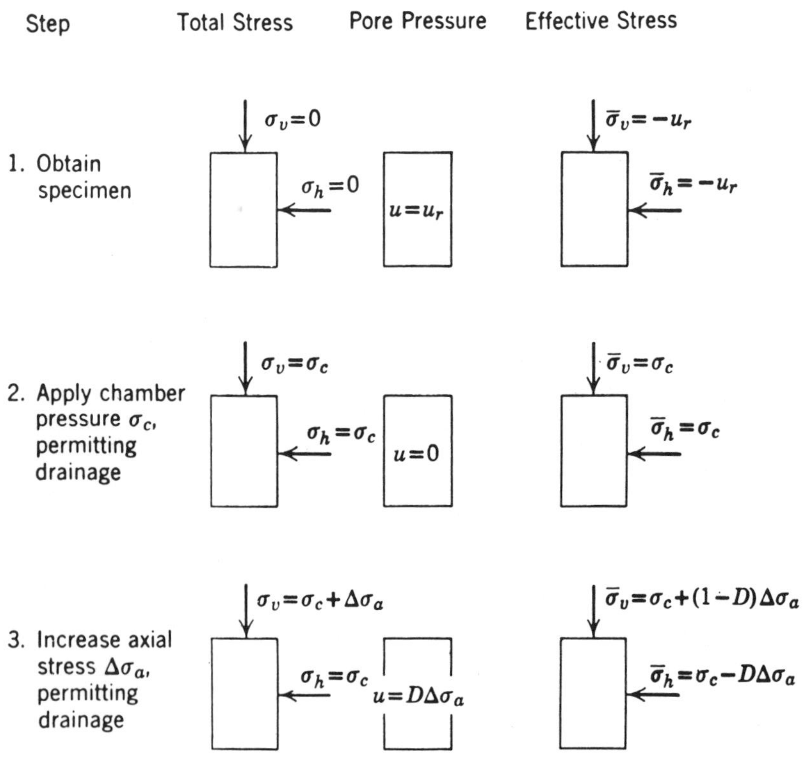

Fig. 1.27
Schematic Representation of Stress States
in a Consolidated-Undrained Triaxial Test
(From LAMBE and WHITMAN, 1969)

it is often called) there is a direct increase in effective stress as axial load is applied. This very often occurs in the case of coarse sands even under the relatively rapid load applications imposed by off-road vehicles in the field.

Figure 1.28 is a schematic representing the stress states that occur in a sample during the *CD* test. Since externally applied loads directly increase effective stress, there is no analogous test to the $\overline{CU}$ test under drained conditions, i.e. there is no such thing as a $\overline{CD}$ test.

c) "Unconsolidated Undrained" *(UU)* wherein the sample is subjected to a confining pressure and subsequently loaded uniaxially to failure without allowing any drainage to occur during either phase of load application. This test is often called a "*Q*" or "quick" test because, relative to the

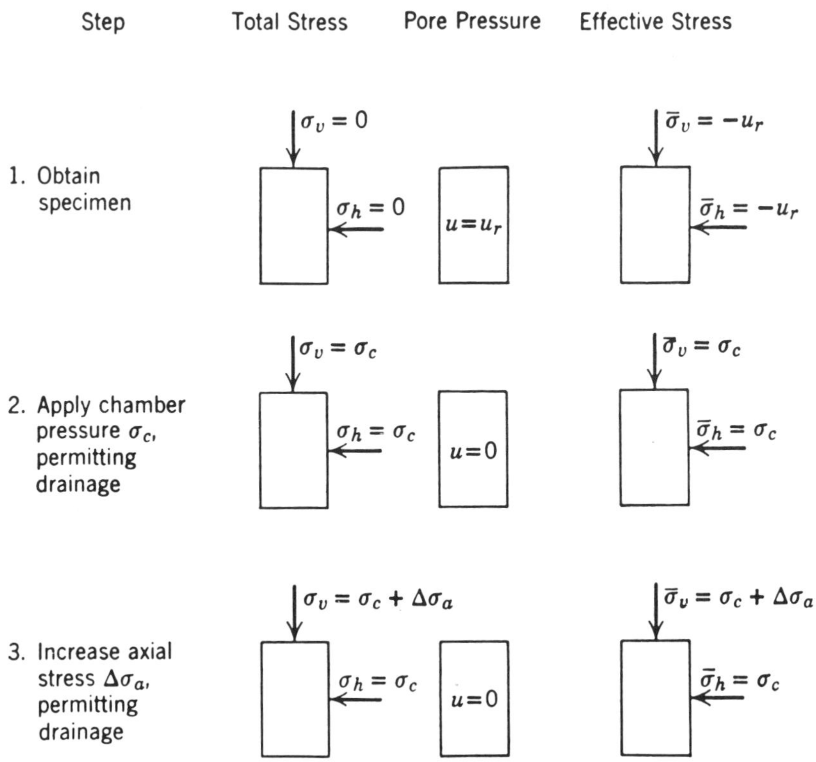

Fig. 1.28
Schematic Representation of Stress States
in a Consolidated-Drained Test
(From Lambe and Whitman, 1969)

other types of triaxial tests, the loads are applied quickly. Figure 1.29 presents a schematic of the stress states in the soil during the *UU* test. In step 2 when the chamber pressure is applied without permitting drainage, "B" is the pore pressure coefficient for triaxial loading given in Equation 1.3.11. It accounts for compressibility of the pore fluids and the soil skeleton. In step 3 where axial stress is increased without allowing drainage "*D*" is the pore pressure parameter described above for the *CU* test with reference to Figure 1.27. Although rate of axial loading is not a concern for a *UU* test since drainage is not allowed during either phase of the loading and all applied stresses are carried by the pore water anyway, the rate of loading does effect the

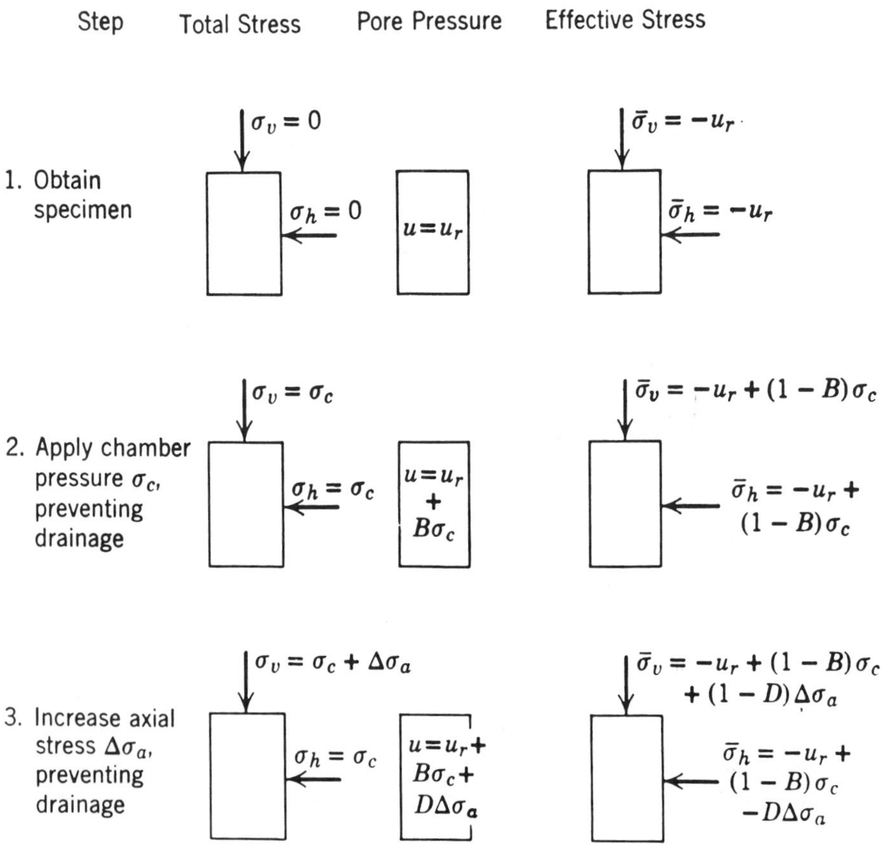

Fig. 1.29
Schematic Representation of Stress States
in an Unconsolidated-Undrained Triaxial Test
(From Lambe and Whitman, 1969)

magnitude of the compressive strength (WES, 1940—1944). Consequently, in performing the *UU* test, the rate of load application should be determined from that anticipated in the field. For application to vehicle-mobility problems that rate will obviously be quite high.

d) "Unconfined Compression Test" which is a special case of the *UU* test wherein the confining pressure during axial loading equals atmospheric only, i.e. there is no applied chamber pressure or $\sigma_c = 0$ in Figure 1.29.

It is interesting to note with reference to Figure 1.30 that regardless of the magnitude of the confining pressure, the shear strength of a fully saturated soil tested under unconsolidated undrained conditions is the same, assuming the rate of load application in all cases is constant. This phenomenon is known as the "$\varphi = 0$" concept. In the Figure, circles *B* and *C* correspond to *UU* tests where the chamber pressure in test *C* was held at a greater value than that in test *B*. The intercept, s_u, on the shear stress axis is called the "undrained strength" of the material and equals $(\sigma_1—\sigma_3)/2$ regardless of the chamber pressure. Assume now that another set of samples of the same soil are available for testing and are consolidated under a higher triaxial pressure than the set shown in Figure 1.30 prior to their being tested in the unconsolidated — undrained mode. The Mohr's circles for these samples would plot in such a way that the undrained strength would be greater for them than it was for the samples whose test results are shown schematically in Figure 1.30. This explains why undrained strength is usually found to increase with depth and leads to the conclusion that undrained strength is independent of *changes* in total stress for a sample that has already been consolidated under a given load. Therefore for every soil there exists a family of horizontal "strength

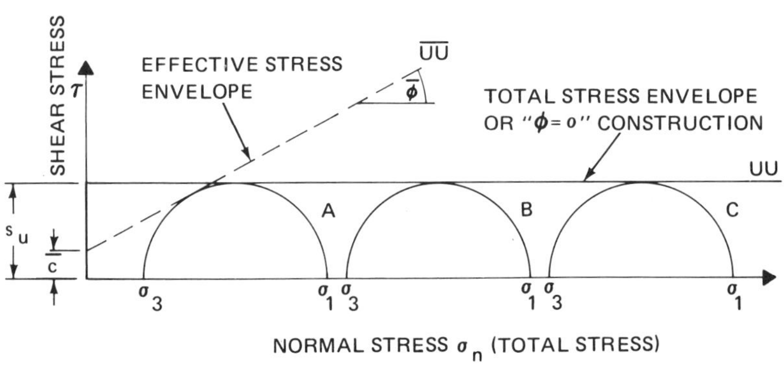

Fig. 1.30
Presentation of Unconsolidated-Undrained (*UU* and $\overline{UU}$)
Triaxial Test Results and the "$\varphi = 0$" Concept

envelopes" that shows that undrained strength is a constant regardless of total stress level but that the magnitude of undrained strength increases with increasing pre-*UU* test consolidation loads.

It is difficult to give simple, generally applicable rules for comparing the relative magnitude of drained and undrained strength. Since strength is a function of effective stress and effective stress is a function of type of loading and degree of consolidation, about all that can be said is that, all other things being equal, drained strength is usually greater than undrained strength. This is true for normally consolidated soils; it is not true for heavily overconsolidated clays. However, as noted previously, long term geologic stress history usually does not directly influence soil-vehicle interactions. Short term stress history and its effect on soil strength does, however, affect soil-vehicle interactions as witnessed by the difference in single pass and multipass performance of vehicles. More attention is devoted to this topic in Chapter 3.7.

The Direct Shear Test. The basic difference between a direct shear test and a triaxial compression test is that in the former the failure load is applied directly as a shear load along a predetermined plane whereas in the latter shear failure occurs on an arbitrary plane that is a function of the confining pressure and axially applied compressive load. Although there are a number of different types of direct shear devices the one most widely used in soil mechanics testing is the circular or square shear box shown schematically in Figure 1.31(a). However, regardless of the type of direct shear device being used, the principle underlying each is the same: the magnitude of shear load required to fail a soil sample is determined for a range of normal loads. The shear force can be applied either by increasing the force at a predetermined rate and measuring the resulting displacements (stress controlled) or by setting the rate of strain and measuring the force as a function of time (strain controlled).

Because the direct shear test does not allow for control of pore water drainage, it does not have the versatility of the triaxial test. For example, it is questionable whether a truly unconsolidated test can be run in the direct shear device because of the difficulty in preventing drainage of the sample under the normal load. On the other hand *CU* and/or *CD* tests are usually performed more efficiently on direct shear devices because test specimens are smaller than those of the triaxial test and therefore consolidate more quickly. However, because of the lack of a porewater pressure measuring capability, direct shear devices are unsuitable for $\overline{CU}$ tests. Additional difficulties are inherent in direct shear devices, especially the circular box type shown in Figure 1.31(c). It is difficult and probably impossible to maintain a constant normal stress with any degree of

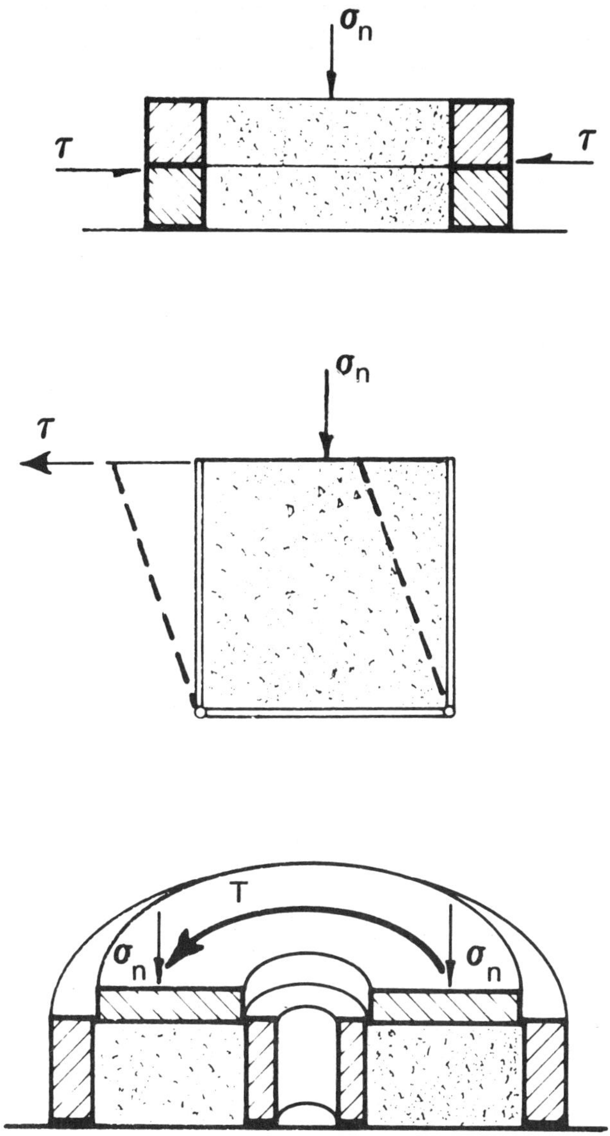

Fig. 1.31
Schematic Representation of the Different Types of Direct Shear Devices
(σ_n = Normal Stress; τ = Shear Stress; T = Applied Torque)

a) Shear Box (Circular or Square)
b) Plane Strain (Square)
c) Torsional (Circular)

certainty because of the very nature of the test, i.e. the cross-sectional area under load changes as shear strains increase. Another shortcoming of the test arises from the fact that the normal and shear stress distributions are not uniform throughout the sample because of sample geometry. These factors severely limit the accuracy of the test and weaken the usefulness of an otherwise simple testing procedure. Because of these deficiencies in the traditional direct shear type of test, more and more use is being made of the plane strain and torsional types of direct shear devices shown schematically in Figures 1.31(b) and (c). In fact, for situations where failure would be clearly in a plane strain or torsional mode, those tests are preferable even to the triaxial test wherein such conditions cannot be duplicated.

Vane Shear Tests. The vane shear test is a particularly useful method of determining shear strength of soft clays and silts. The test may be performed in the laboratory or on in situ soils. The only difference between the two tests is in the size of the vane. Field vanes are typically 2, 2.5 or 3 inches in diameter (*d*) and from 3 to 5 diameters in height (*h*). Laboratory vanes are typically square with height and diameter ranging from $^1/_4$ to $^1/_2$ inches. In either case the vane is forced into the soil and a torque applied to the shaft holding the vane. The shear strength is determined from the torque required to rotate the vane and the geometry of the vane. The shear strength equals the shear induced in the soil along the vertical and horizontal edges of the vane. Figure 1.32 shows schematically the principle behind the test and the stresses induced in the soil as a result of the applied torque T. The expression relating torque and shear strength is then:

$$T = c\,(\pi\,dh)\left(\frac{d}{2}\right) + 2c\left[\frac{\pi\,d^2}{4}\left(\frac{2d}{6}\right)\right] \qquad \text{Eq. 1.3.38}$$

Because there is no way to control either vertical or lateral stress conditions during the test and because no provision can be made for measurement of pore water pressures in the soil near the zone of shear, vane shear tests, when properly conducted, generally yield values of strength comparable to those obtained from unconfined compression tests. However, because of its simplicity and ease of execution it is often used in the field to determine the in situ undrained strength of soils.

Presentation of Results of Shear Tests

Shear tests, whether triaxial compression, direct shear, or vane shear, provide the same information, values for the frictional and cohesive shear strength parameters of the soil.

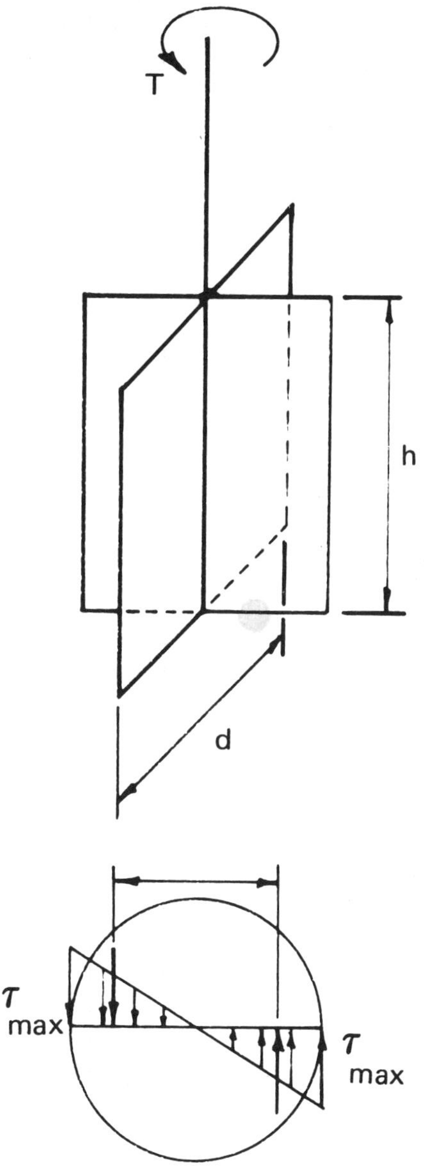

Fig. 1.32
Schematic of Vane Shear Device and Assumed
Shear Stress Distribution on Top and Bottom Shear Surfaces

For the triaxial test the confining pressure (σ_3) and the normal stress corresponding to the axial load at failure (σ_1) are plotted on the normal stress axis. The stress difference constitutes the diameter of a MOHR circle whose center is on the normal stress axis at a value equal to the average stress $(\sigma_1 + \sigma_3)/2$. When the results of a number of triaxial tests run on the same soil but at different confining pressures are plotted on the same set of axes, a series of circles is obtained. The curve tangent to all the circles is the "strength envelope", the slope angle (φ) of which at any normal stress is the frictional strength parameter. The intercept of the "strength envelope" on the ordinate (or shear stress axes) is the cohesion component of shear strength (c).

Depending on the type of triaxial test run, these parameters are either effective stress parameters ($\bar{\varphi}$ and $\bar{c}$) or total stress parameters (φ and c). The $\overline{CU}$ and CD triaxial tests as well as consolidated-drained direct shear tests yield effective stress parameters. All other tests yield total stress parameters except for the UU test which, as we have seen previously, yields $\varphi = 0$ and a shear stress intercept equal to the "undrained strength" of the soil. The differences among the "strength curves" for the various types of triaxial tests are shown schematically in Figures 1.33 thru 1.35.

Typical curves relating shear stress to total normal stress for saturated cohesionless soils are shown in Figures 1.33 and 1.34 for the consolidated-undrained (CU and $\overline{CU}$) and consolidated-drained (CD) conditions, respectively. The figures indicate that the relative density of cohesionless materials significantly affects the relative magnitude of the apparent and effective strength parameters in the case of undrained tests. In dense materials shearing causes particles to move over each other so that the soil structure expands and the pore water must go into tension since volume change is not allowed. As discussed in Section 1.3.1 for a given total stress, this situation leads to an increase in effective stress; consequently the total envelope lies above the effective envelope at a given value of shear. In loose materials, the soil structure tends to collapse when sheared and the normal stresses are carried by the pore water since volume change is not allowed. The position of the stress envelopes is therefore reversed.

In the consolidated-drained case of Figure 1.34, there is no difference in the envelopes regardless of the relative density of the soil. In this case drainage takes place and the system can adjust itself to volume changes induced by shearing.

In the case of fine-grained cohesive soils, relative density has no meaning; however, stress history is a factor that affects the relationship between shear stress and normal stress. Schematic representations of Mohr circle

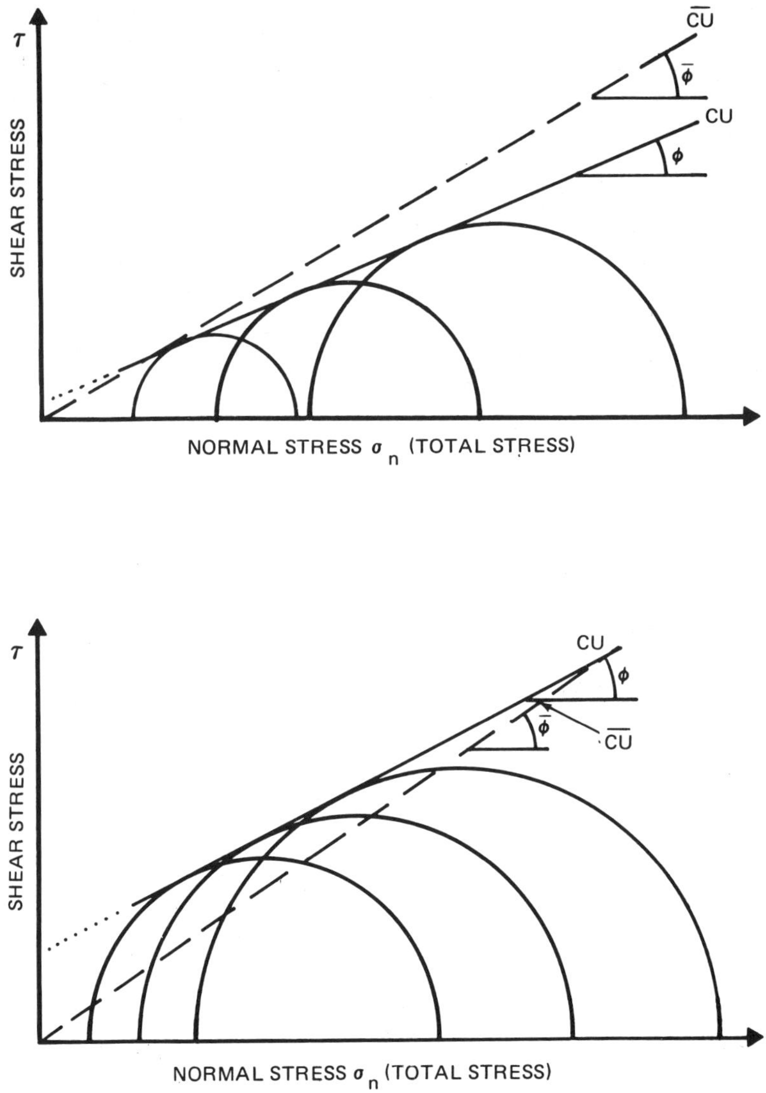

Fig. 1.33
Presentation of Consolidated-Undrained (*CU* and $\overline{CU}$)
Triaxial Test Results for Cohesionless Soils
a) Loose material
b) Dense material
(The origin is not a data point for the *CU* test; the uncertainty of the $\tau - \sigma_n$ relationship in this case is indicated by the dotted extension of the *CU* curve near the origin)

constructions for saturated cohesive soils are shown in Figures 1.35 and 1.36 for the consolidated-undrained (*CU* and $\overline{CU}$) and consolidated-drained (*CD*) condition respectively. In Figure 1.35 a significant difference can be noted between the relative position of the total and effective strength envelopes for normally and overconsolidated soils. A "normally consolidated" soil is one whose maximum past *effective* stress exactly *equals* the currently existing *total stress,* whereas an "overconsolidated" soil is one whose maximum past *effective* stress *exceeds* the currently existing *total* stress indicating that it has at one time consolidated under a larger than existing load. For example, clays in historically glaciated areas tend to be overconsolidated. In Figure 1.35 the break in the inital portion of the total stress envelope corresponds to the point where the confining pressure in the triaxial chamber about equals the in situ lateral stress. No attempt is made in the figure to express the relative magnitude of stresses between the two cases along either axis. The mechanism responsible for the difference between the normally consolidated and over-consolidated cases is analogous to that causing differences between dense and loose sands. Shearing of highly overconsolidated clays at chamber pressures less than in situ confining pressures is accompanied by expansion of the clay. Under the constant volume conditions of the consolidated-undrained test, this expansion puts the pore water into tension and causes an increase in effective stress. Consequently, the total stress envelope lies above the effective stress envelope.

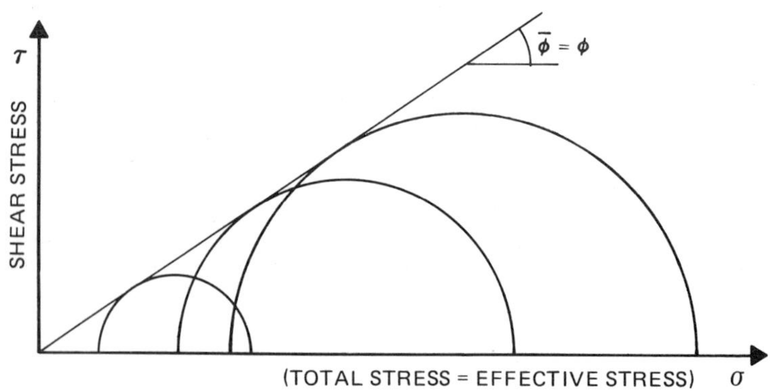

Fig. 1.34
Presentation of Consolidated-Drained (*CD*) Triaxial Test Results for Cohesionless Soils (Loose or Dense)

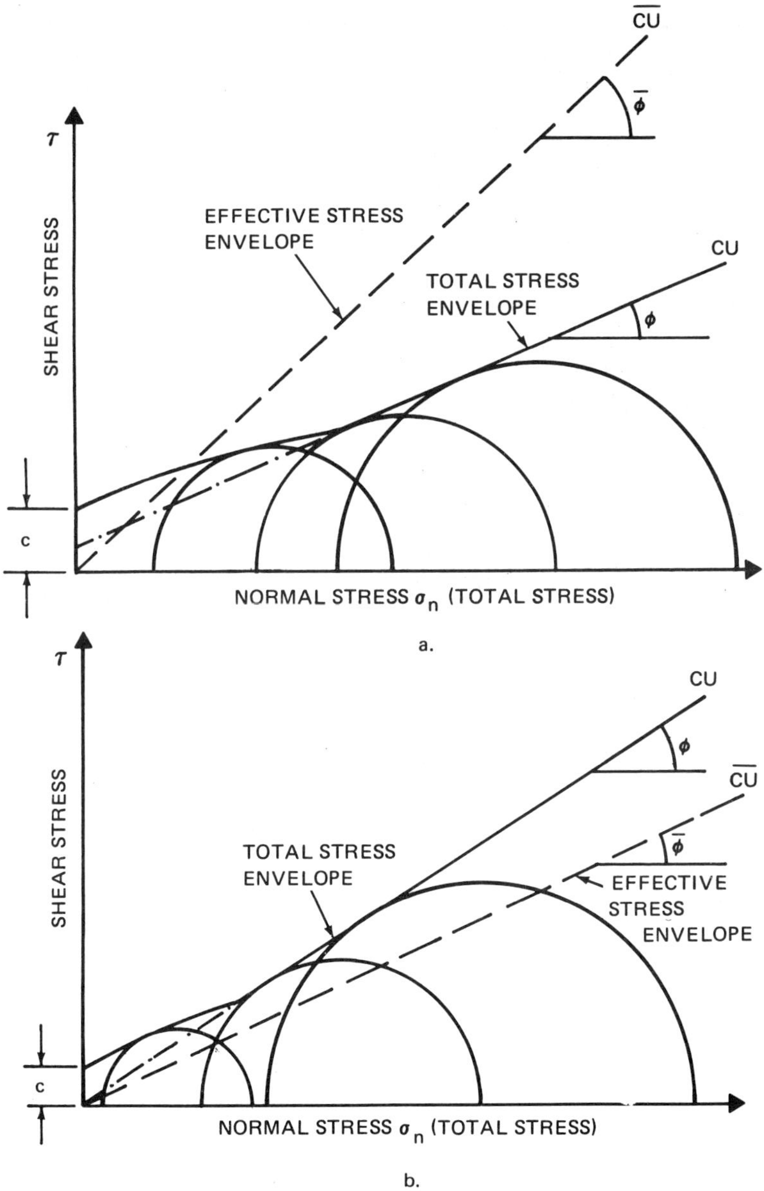

Fig. 1.35
Presentation of Consolidated-Undrained Triaxial Test Results
for Fine-Grained Cohesive Soils
a) Normally consolidated soil
b) Overconsolidated soil

In the consolidated-drained case shown in Figure 1.36, the total and effective stress envelopes coincide for both normally consolidated and overconsolidated soils. Again, the break in the curve corresponds approximately to the point where the chamber pressure equals the in situ confining pressure.

The unconsolidated-undrained or "quick" test is the final type of triaxial test to be considered here. In general, the results of this type of test plot as shown in Figure 1.30 regardless of the type of material being tested. The characteristic feature of the shear stress versus total stress plot of *UU* test results is the "$\varphi = 0$" construction and the "undrained strength" intercept s_u on the shear stress axis. The implications of this concept with respect to soil strength were discussed at the beginning of this section with reference to Figure 1.30.

The triaxial testing of soils and the interpretation of triaxial test results is much more complex than the concepts presented here. The purpose of this brief treatment of the topic is to alert the off-road vehicle engineer to the danger of accepting values of soil strength parameters obtained from triaxial tests without questioning whether the test conditions matched those existing in the field.

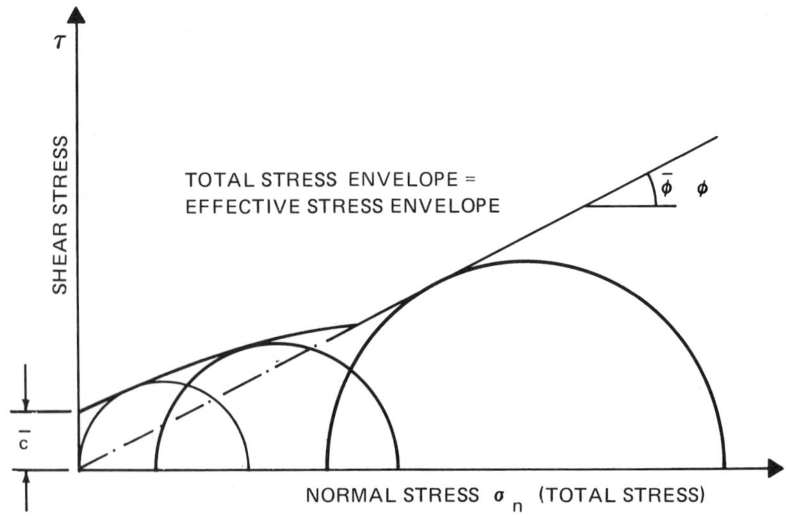

Fig. 1.36
Presentation of Consolidated-Drained Triaxial Test Results for Fine-Grained Cohesive Soils

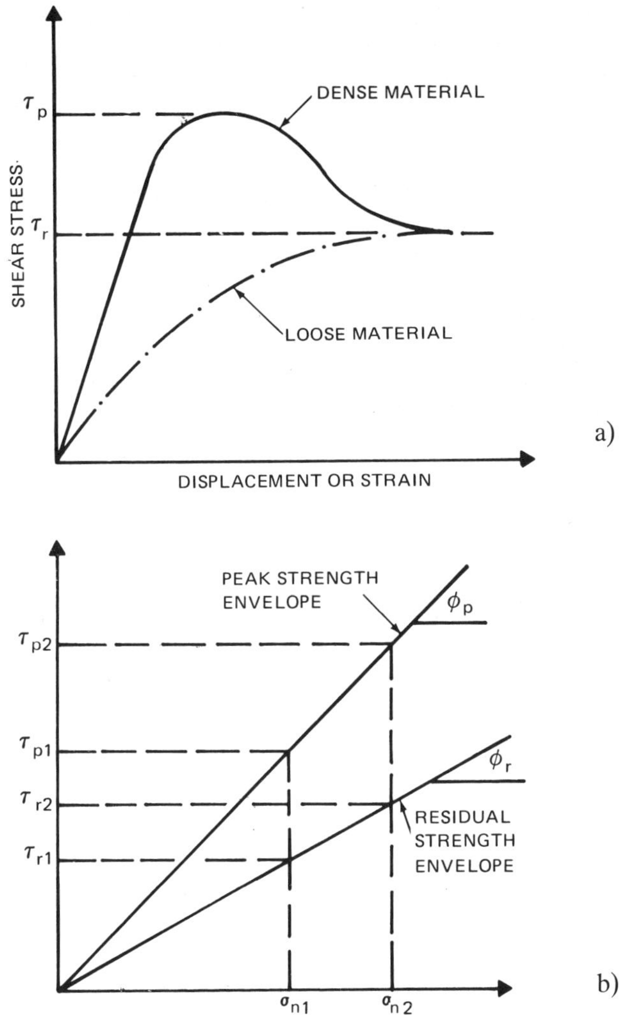

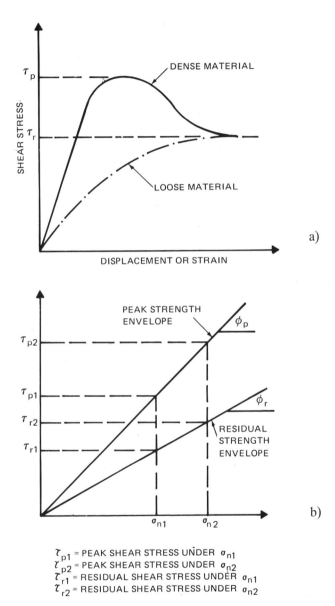

τ_{p1} = PEAK SHEAR STRESS UNDER σ_{n1}
τ_{p2} = PEAK SHEAR STRESS UNDER σ_{n2}
τ_{r1} = RESIDUAL SHEAR STRESS UNDER σ_{n1}
τ_{r2} = RESIDUAL SHEAR STRESS UNDER σ_{n2}

Fig. 1.37
Presentation of Results for Direct Shear Tests Run at Two Different Normal Stresses ($\sigma_{n1} < \sigma_{n2}$) under Given Consolidation and Drainage Conditions

a) Typical shear stress vs. displacement curves for loose and dense materials.
b) Shear stress vs. normal stress relationships for peak and residual conditions.

For the direct shear test the concepts discussed above also apply, but instead of plotting MOHR circles to obtain a strength envelope, peak (or residual) values of shear obtained in the test are plotted versus their corresponding normal loads to obtain the strength envelope directly (refer to Figure 1.37). In view of some of the caveats discussed previously with reference to the direct shear test, it is not surprising that where strain conditions affect the results, a direct shear test and triaxial compression test will not yield the same strength parameters. This occurs even if both tests are run for the same soil under the same conditions of consolidation and drainage (volume change). For vehicle mobility studies triaxial tests are more representative of field conditions where lateral strains beneath vehicle running gears are close to the minor principal stress.

1.3.5 Loading and Drainage Conditions in Off-Road Locomotion

Soil strength, as expressed by Equation 1.3.24 in terms of the Coulombic parameters c and φ, controls the interactive behavior of *all* soil-structure systems at their failure conditions. As shown in the previous section the various tests by which these parameters are determined exist because of the different conditions of drainage and loading that are possible in soil-structure interactions. For the purpose of evaluating wheel- or tire-soil interactions, as for any soils engineering problem, it is essential that actual loading and drainage conditions be duplicated in tests (whether field or lab) for the proper determination of the required strength parameters.

Field Conditions in Off-Road Locomotion

The following conditions are generally operative in actual vehicle-soil interactions:

a) Drainage conditions in the soil are generally very close to the hypothetical undrained condition during the passage of a vehicle. Exceptionally, the degree of drainage during the application of wheel load to the soil may be important in the case of submerged, relatively well draining soils, such as fine sand. For the purpose of general mobility evaluation, undrained conditions may be assumed and the above submerged condition treated as an exception (refer to Figures 1.27 and 1.29).

b) The loading rate of soil in vehicle-soil interaction is directly proportional to the translational velocity of the vehicle. Very roughly, the soil loading rate may be estimated by assuming that the stresses on a soil element rise from their initial state to peak during a time interval it takes the vehicle to pass half of the length of the contact area. For example, a vehicle traveling at the low speed of 3 ft/sec and having a 1 ft long contact area would impart full loading to the soil in 1/6th of a second. Loading rates encountered in mobility problems generally fall in the category of "quick" or rapid loading. While the strength of quickly loaded soils may be considerably different from that obtained with slow loading rates (Crawford, 1959; Leitch and Yong, 1967), it is generally not too sensitive to changes in the loading rate within the range of translational velocities of interest. Thus, in strength testing, loading rates that are approximately in the range of the rate anticipated in the field are acceptable.

c) Strain conditions in vehicle-soil interaction are generally three-dimensional since the compaction of the soil beneath the running gear is generally accompanied by lateral displacement. Consequently, the strength parameters of the soil should be determined by testing methods that allow for strains in the third dimension when such parameters are to be used for mobility evaluations.

d) The magnitude of the volumetric strain in vehicle-soil interactions is different from that encountered in many conventional civil engineering problems. With the advancement of a vehicle's running gear the soil is progressively compacted and the volumetric strain associated with the passage of the gear is generally sufficient to mobilize the full strength of the soil. In other words, a "general" rather than 'local" bearing condition exists (refer to Section 2.5.1).

In view of these rather specific conditions, the following discussion is intended to describe the manner in which laboratory tests should be conducted for the proper determination of soil strength for mobility evaluations. The implications of these conditions on the value of currently used field tests in the determination of meaningful soil properties are discussed in detail in Chapter 3.6.

Laboratory Determination of Soil Strength for Mobility Evaluation

As indicated in Section 1.3.4, the Coulombic strength parameters of soil are usually determined by using either the direct shear or the triaxial test. In conventional soil mechanics tests the Coulombic parameters refer to normal and shear stresses that act in a plane perpendicular to the failure surface and are, therefore, essentially two-dimensional in nature.

The stress and strain conditions that obtain perpendicular to that plane may affect the value of the Coulombic parameters. In experiments for the determination of the Coulombic strength parameters for mobility purposes, the transverse stress and strain conditions should duplicate those that exist in the field during running gear-soil interaction. Because of the nature of the test (plane strain) the direct shear test is not ideal for the determination of strength parameters for mobility evaluations. On the other hand, strain conditions in the triaxial test correspond to the stress condition $\sigma_2 = \sigma_3$. This condition seems to approximate that in the field more closely than the plane strain condition of the direct shear test. Karafiath et al (1973) have given strong support for this contention by reporting good agreement between measured interface stresses and those computed on the basis of triaxial shear strength parameters. Consequently, the discussion that follows pertains exclusively to triaxial testing.

The samples used in triaxial tests are either undisturbed ones obtained in the field or ones prepared in a laboratory mold. In principle, undisturbed samples should be used since the in situ strength of soil may reflect the grain structure of the soil that cannot be duplicated in laboratory preparation. This is particularly true for residual soils. However, undisturbed sampling of surface soils is difficult and undesirable where field variation in soil properties requires that a large number of samples be taken. Therefore, field testing techniques that test the in situ strength of soil are better suited for the purpose of mobility evaluation. Some of these techniques are discussed in detail in Chapter 3.6. On the other hand, the preparation of soil beds for tire performance tests can be closely duplicated in the preparation of soil samples for triaxial testing. Thus the role of triaxial testing in mobility evaluation is the determination of strength properties for model validation. Triaxial tests are also necessary for the validation of field testing techniques.

In conventional triaxial testing the chamber pressure (minor principal stress) is kept constant and the vertical load is increased until failure occurs or (in the absence of a clearly defined failure point) a certain strain is reached. (Refer to Figures 1.27 through 1.29). In the field, passage of a vehicle causes the minor principal stress to increase monotonically up to its maximum value and then decrease, also monotonically. This variation is demonstrated in Figure 1.38 where the magnitude and direction of principal stresses in the failure zones beneath a rigid wheel are shown. To account for this variation, the minor principal stress or chamber pressure in a triaxial test should increase with increasing volumetric strain. Karafiath (1974) reports the results and details of a testing program wherein modifications were made to a conventional triaxial apparatus to allow for the determination of Coulombic shear strength parameters under controlled variation of chamber pressure. A video tape replay technique was used to obtain "stop action" images of a test at specified times after the beginning of axial loading. Since the axial load frame moved at a constant rate and since load and displacement were automatically recorded, measurements of lateral deformation by circumferential gauges placed at the quarter points of the sample could be read from the "stop action" image at times corresponding to specific axial loads (major principal stresses). From a series of such data void ratio changes were computed and related to changes in chamber pressure (minor principal stress). Figure 1.39 shows the variation of chamber pressure with void ratio for a natural clay soil under consolidated-undrained triaxial test conditions. Figure 1.40 shows the corresponding MOHR's circle constructions from which the c and φ parameters were read. An advantage of this testing technique is that an undrained friction angle and value for apparent cohesion may be obtained from a single test, whereas several tests would be required with conventional triaxial testing techniques. In addition, at least ideally, any loading rate within the limitations of the testing equipment is possible so that vehicle passage conditions can be simulated quite closely.

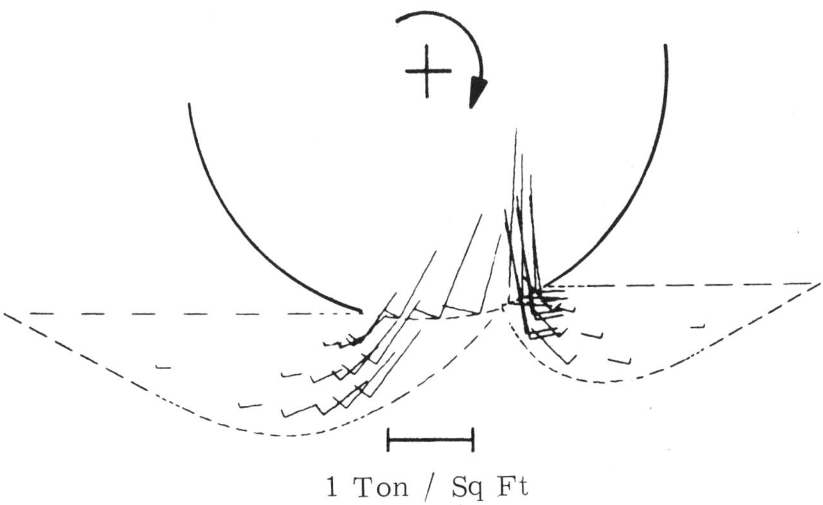

Fig. 1.38
Principal Stresses in Soil Beneath a Rigid Wheel

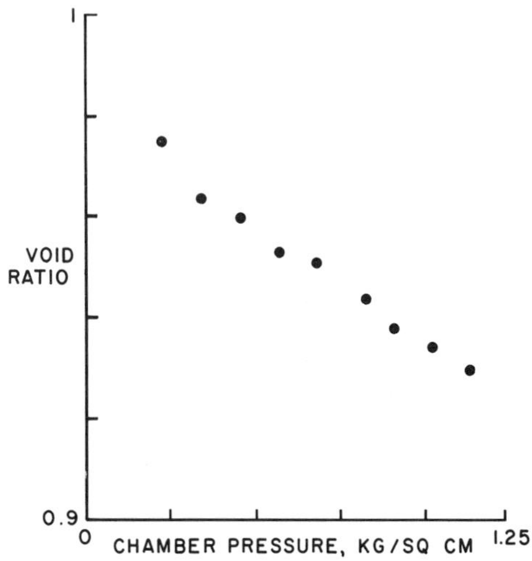

Fig. 1.39
Void Ratio Changes in Test B–1

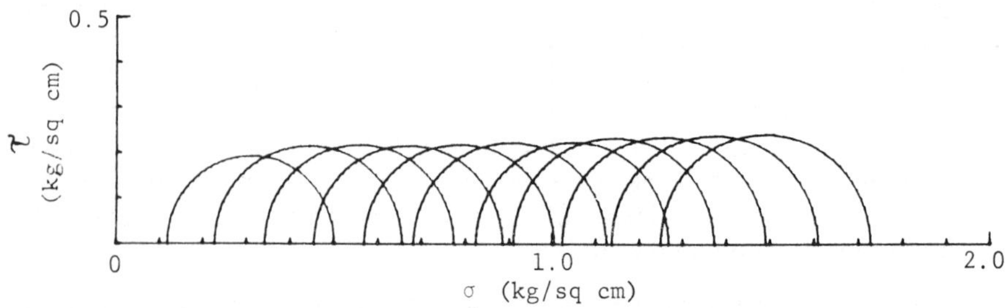

Fig. 1.40
Mohr Circles for Variable Chamber Pressure Triaxial Test B–1 – Buckshot Clay.
Moisture Content = 35%, Loading Rate: 5 cm/min

1.3.6 Shearing Resistance Between Solids and Soil

Off-road vehicles develop traction by transmitting shear stresses to the ground either directly by adhesion and friction at the solid-soil interface or by the application of various traction devices (lugs, grousers) that force at least part of the potential failure surfaces to pass through the soil. Even in the latter case the potential failure surface includes some part of the solid-soil contact area. Since the shear stresses that can be transmitted to the ground in the solid-soil contact area are limited by the shearing resistance between solid and soil, it is evidently of great interest to the off-road vehicle engineer to learn about the physical processes involved in the development of solid-soil shearing resistance, the magnitude of this resistance in various soils, and how the material of the solid surfaces influences this shearing resistance.

The shearing resistance between solids and soils may be expressed in similar fashion as the Coulombic expression of shear strength for soils as follows:

$$s = a + \sigma_n \tan \varphi_s \qquad \text{Eq. 1.3.39}$$

where

a = adhesion

φ_s = friction angle between solid and soil.

The term adhesion is used here in a sense equivalent to cohesion. In other disciplines, however, adhesion sometimes denotes the normal force required to separate a particle from the solid surface.

The sources of adhesion are manifold and include, according to ZIMON (1969) molecular, electrical, Coulomb and capillary forces. Of these the most important in off-road vehicle engineering are the capillary forces that arise if water menisci are formed in the space between a soil particle and the solid surface. The adhesion between a solid surface and soil due to capillary forces depends on the contact angle that the water makes with the solid surface, the degree of saturation and the relative humidity of the air in the voids, among others. The physical phenomena involved are very complex and the reader is referred to ZIMON's book for further information on the subject.

The role of the frictional component of the shearing resistance between solids and soils can be best explained by considering the components of the internal shearing resistance at work when a frictional soil is sheared. Figure 1.38(a) shows the shearing resistance of a frictional soil as a function of strain for two states of packing. In the loose state the shearing resistance increases gradually with strain and reaches its ultimate value assymptotically. In the dense state the frictional resistance increases more rapidly, peaks at a relatively small strain and decreases gradually afterwards until it reaches approximately the same value as the soil in the loose state. The difference between the shearing resistances in the dense and loose state is attributed to the interlocking of the particles in the dense state. For the development of a continuous failure surface in a densely packed soil it is necessary that particles override each other and thereby loosen the packing. The shear forces required to bring about the overriding of particles constitute that part of the shearing resistance that is in excess of that required to shear the soil in the loose state.

In the case of shear failure at the solid-soil interface the failure surface is preset. The degree of interlocking between the solid surface and soil depends on the size of the asperities of the solid surface relative to the size of soil particles or, in less scientific language on the roughness of the solid surface. The hardness of the solid surface may also affect this interlocking since soil particles may indent the solid surface if its hardness is less than that of the soil minerals. If the solid surface is smooth then there is practically no interlocking between the solid surface and the soil particles and, therefore, the shearing resistance between solid and soil is approximately in the range of the internal shearing resistance of loose soil.

The shearing resistance between solids and soil is usually determined in the laboratory with shear testing devices that measure the normal and shear forces applied to a predetermined failure plane. The soil in one half of the sample container is replaced by a block of the solid material. The test is carried out in essentially the same way as for the determination of the shear strength of soil. The shearing resistance between solid and soil is subject to the same variation with the drainage and loading conditions as the shear strength of soil. The shearing resistance between solid and soil determined by laboratory tests is representative of that obtained in the field only if drainage and loading conditions in the field are closely duplicated in the laboratory. The loading conditions in the field certainly belong in the "quick" category but within this category rate may vary considerably.

It is most difficult to ascertain what the drainage conditions are in the field. As far as the strength of soil is concerned we have assumed that no drainage in the soil occurs during passage of a vehicle. This assumption is reasonable as far as the total volume of the soil affected by the passage of the wheel (say the soil volume within the slip line fields) is concerned. The soil volume of interest in solid-soil shearing is a narrow band along the interface. Here water is transferred to or from adjacent layers in a short period of time since the distances are very small. In the direct or torsional shear type laboratory tests drainage conditions are equally uncertain. Thus, the present methods are less than ideal for the prediction of the solid-soil shearing resistance in the field. Nevertheless, they are valuable as research tools to study the phenomena underlying solid-soil shearing resistance. In relatively dry soils, where pore water migration is negligible, the solid-soil shearing resistance obtaining at vehicular footing-soil interfaces in the field may be predicted reasonably well by laboratory tests.

Potyondy (1961) performed laboratory experiments to determine the solid-soil shearing resistances for various construction materials and compared these with the shear strength of soil used in the experiments. The tests performed with dry and saturated rock flour showed the ratio (solid-soil friction angle/friction angle of soil) to be in the range of 0.71—1.0, varying with the roughness of the surface of the solid material. Other tests performed with moist granular soils exhibiting some cohesion showed that the ratio of adhesion/cohesion was always much lower than the ratio of the respective friction angles. This indicates that the adhesion and cohesion due to capillary forces are not governed by the same physical processes as the friction angles. Another conclusion that can be drawn from these experiments is that it is essential to perform several solid-soil shearing resistance tests at various normal pressures so that an envelope of the shearing resistance may be constructed, just as in the case of soils. In the evaluation of some experiments performed only at one normal pressure level the adhesion is neglected and a friction coefficient is computed from the ratio of the total shearing resistance to the normal pressure (Benkenstein and Lindner, 1969). The result is an apparent increase of the friction coefficient with the water content of soil that contradicts common sense.

Al-Hussaini and Gilbert (1974) performed a series of experiments in which the soil volume in a torsional shear device was maintained constant and the normal pressure was allowed to vary as was required by the constant volume condition. This is a notable effort to control the drainage conditions during solid-soil shear. The experiments were performed at shearing rates varying from 0.002 to 2 in/min in Buckshot clay. The solid materials used in the tests were polished steel and rubber. The experiments showed an appreciable increase of the solid-soil shearing resistance with the rate of shearing for both materials tested; this resistance was found to be invariably less than the shear strength of soil at the same rate of loading. Smooth rubber exhibited higher resistance than polished steel under the same conditions. In this testing program experiments were also conducted for the purpose of studying the effect of wetting of the solid surfaces on the solid-soil shearing resistance. Prewetted rubber or steel showed about 50 % less shearing resistance than the same material without prewetting. This indicates that a small amount of water is sufficient to reduce solid-soil friction substantially and cause a condition known as slipperiness. As it was mentioned earlier, soil conditions in a very narrow band adjacent to the solid-soil interface control the solid-soil shearing resistance. Thus, it is not surprising that prewetting of the solid surface is sufficient to saturate that narrow band and cause significant pore water pressures to develop upon shearing. These pore water pressures reduce the solid-soil shearing resistance.

Butterfield and Andrawes (1972) investigated the friction angle between dry sand and various solid materials. Their experiments confirmed that the friction angle between smooth solid surfaces and sand is close to the friction angle of the sand in its loosest state. Also, the experiments supported the hypothesis that the frictional mechanism between solid and sand is essentially similar to the internal frictional mechanism in sand.

Finally, results of experiments performed by the authors in ultrahigh vacuum for the purpose of lunar locomotion studies may be mentioned as shedding some light on the micromechanism of friction (Karafiath 1969, 1970; Nowatzki 1972). Under atmospheric conditions there is an absorbed layer of water at the surface of soil particles that prevents the soil minerals to come into direct contact with each other over a rather large range of applied pressure. Thus the frictional resistance measured in conventional soil mechanics tests is a measure of the shear strength of the absorbed water layer rather than of the soil minerals. Only in ultrahigh vacuum are these absorbed surface water layers removed allowing the minerals of soil particles and the material of the solid to come in contact with each other. A comparison of the friction coefficient obtained with ground basalt and various solid materials (steel, titanium, fiberglass) showed that the friction coefficient in ultrahigh vacuum was always appreciably higher than under atmospheric conditions. Thus, in this context, water indeed has a "lubricating" effect, but under atmospheric conditions the so-called lubricating effect of water is nothing else but susceptibility to generate pore water pressures that reduce friction.

CHAPTER 1.4

THEORIES FOR THE DETERMINATION OF STRESS STATES IN SOIL UNDER APPLIED LOADING

In most scientific and engineering disciplines the concept of stress is usually considered in conjunction with the concept of a continuum. As we have seen in the preceding chapters, soil has a particulate structure composed of solid, liquid and gaseous components. Thus, in the strictest sense of solid mechanics, the concept of "stress at a point" is not valid for a soil for there is no true "infinitesimal" that is representative of the soil mass. However, upon closer examination of the so-called continuum mechanics, we find that all matter is particulate at least on the submicroscopic scale. Therefore, it seems that the "infinitesimal element" upon which the derivations of many of the stress theories are based is a relative thing and on a macroscopic scale the infinitesimal element may be quite large so long as the stress variation over it is small. In the case of soil, for example, if the dimensions over which there is only a slight variation of normal or shear stresses are large compared to the size of the largest particle of the soil, then there is no reason why the concept of a continuum cannot be applied to soils. It is with this understanding that certain stress theories of continuum mechanics are applied to soil structure interaction problems.

1.4.1 Theory of Elasticity

A detailed treatment of the foundations and development of the Theory of Elasticity and its expressions for the interrelationship between stress and strain for the multitude of possible load and geometric boundary conditions is beyond the scope of this text. The reader is referred to the two classical treatments of the subject (LOVE, 1927, and TIMOSHENKO, 1951). The concern here is with the validity of the assumption that soil behaves elastically and is therefore amenable to solutions based on the Theory of Elasticity. In the application of the Theory of Elasticity the assumption is made that the stressed material is homogeneous, isotropic and linearly or nonlinearly elastic. In the purely mechanical sense, the word "elastic" strictly applies only to a material which recovers its original size and shape upon removal of an applied stress. A material having a nonlinear stress-strain relationship can in the strictest sense be elastic. However, with reference to "elastic soils", linearity of the stress-strain relationship is usually also understood because the principle of superposition, which is valid only for linearly elastic materials, is applied to the solution of many soils problems. Even then, however, the term "elastic" as applied to soils is really a misnomer because it generally implies linearity of the stress strain relationship upon loading only; unloading is usually excluded from consideration. For soils an additional constraint must be applied; elastic shear stresses must be small compared to the shear strength of soil.

Soils, because of the nature of their formation processes, are rarely homogeneous and isotropic in situ, and even under the most ideal conditions they are rarely linearly elastic except over a narrow range of stress change. In general, soils almost always exhibit some irreversibility when a stress state to which they are subjected is increased and then decreased. The most noticeable exception to this behavior occurs when the initial stress state under which the soil exists in equilibrium is high enough so that the externally applied stress increment is relatively small. Unfortunately, from the viewpoint of soil-vehicle interaction, this is rarely the case at or near the surface, so that the use of elastic theory to describe stress distributions acting on wheels or tracks is not generally warranted. Even if the soil could properly be considered "elastic", efficient application of elastic solutions to terrain-vehicle problems would be hampered by the fact that these solutions are valid only for certain distributions of boundary stresses that remain constant. This is rarely the case in mobility problems because of the interaction between applied stresses and soil reaction. In those instances where elastic solutions have been applied to rigid (AL-HUSSAINI and GILBERT, 1974) or flexible (ROBERTS, 1971) wheels, the solutions lack this interactive effect and resemble rather solutions to the well-known Hertzian "contact problem" (see, for example, MINDLIN, 1949; SMITH and LIU, 1953; HAMILTON and GOODMAN. 1966; and POPOV, 1966).

Elasticity theory is useful, however, in providing an approach to a problem peculiar to military vehicle operations, i.e. the location of pressure sensitive explosive devices. For a given type and intensity of surface load, equations of elasticity can be obtained that exactly define or at least approximate a three dimensional stress field. This stress field defines a geometric boundary for detonation of an explosive device with known pressure sensitivity. Here again, the validity of the application is based upon the notion that soils at depth tend to act more elastically than soils at the surface and that induced elastic shear stresses do not exceed the shear strength of the soil.

There are a great number of loading conditions that can be defined analytically by elasticity theory and since even a cursory treatment of each in terms of govering equations would require considerations outside the scope of this book, the authors refer to Poulos and Davis (1974) for a detailed presentation of the most important formulas and their tabular or graphical solutions where appropriate. Intrinsic to the solutions for all of the cases listed and to the many different influence charts available in Poulos and Davis are the fundamental relationships of elasticity:

$$\varepsilon_x = \frac{\sigma_x}{E} \qquad \text{Eq. 1.4.1}$$

$$\varepsilon_y = \varepsilon_z = -\frac{\mu\,\sigma_x}{E} \qquad \text{Eq. 1.4.2}$$

where

ε_x and σ_x are the strain and stress in the x-direction

ε_y and ε_z are strains in orthogonal directions

E equals Young's Modulus or Modulus of Elasticity

μ equals Poisson's Ratio

For an element that obeys Hooke's Law (Equation 1.4.1) and that is subjected to normal stresses σ_x, σ_y and σ_z, the following relationships hold:

$$\varepsilon_x = \frac{1}{E}\left[\sigma_x - \mu\,(\sigma_y + \sigma_z)\right] \qquad \text{Eq. 1.4.3}$$

$$\varepsilon_y = \frac{1}{E}\left[\sigma_y - \mu\,(\sigma_x + \sigma_z)\right] \qquad \text{Eq. 1.4.4}$$

$$\varepsilon_z = \frac{1}{E}\left[\sigma_z - \mu\,(\sigma_x + \sigma_y)\right] \qquad \text{Eq. 1.4.5}$$

Rearrangement of the above equations allows stresses to be expressed in terms of strain as follows

$$\sigma_x = \lambda\varepsilon + 2\,G\,\varepsilon_x \qquad \text{Eq. 1.4.6}$$

$$\sigma_y = \lambda\varepsilon + 2\,G\,\varepsilon_y \qquad \text{Eq. 1.4.7}$$

$$\sigma_z = \lambda\varepsilon + 2\,G\,\varepsilon_z \qquad \text{Eq. 1.4.8}$$

where

$$\varepsilon = \varepsilon_x + \varepsilon_y + \varepsilon_z = \text{Volumetric Strain} \qquad \text{Eq. 1.4.9}$$

$$\lambda = \frac{\mu E}{(1 + \mu)(1 - 2\mu)} = \text{LAMÉ's Constant} \qquad \text{Eq. 1.4.10}$$

$$G = \frac{E}{2(1 + \mu)} = \text{Shear Modulus} \qquad \text{Eq. 1.4.11}$$

If shear stresses are applied to the element there will be additional distortions due to the following shear strains

$$\gamma_{xy} = \tau_{xy}/G \qquad \text{Eq. 1.4.12}$$

$$\gamma_{yz} = \tau_{yz}/G \qquad \text{Eq. 1.4.13}$$

$$\gamma_{zx} = \tau_{zx}/G \qquad \text{Eq. 1.4.14}$$

Equations 1.4.6 through 1.4.8 and Equations 1.4.12 through 1.4.14 comprise the six equations that define the total stress state of a three-dimensional element in an elastic body.

As pointed out previously, however, the theory of elasticity applies to soil only under certain rather restrictive conditions and then only approximately since μ and E of soils are generally not constant over any significant range of loading.

In general, void ratio, mineral composition, stress history, loading rate and lateral constraint conditions are all factors that affect E. Since stress-strain curves for soils are usually non linear, a number of different moduli are often considered. These are the initial tangent modulus (i.e. the tangent to the stress-strain curve close to the origin); the secant modulus (i.e. the slope of the straight line drawn from the origin of the stress-strain curve to another point on the curve usually at a specified stress, such as the failure stress); the tangent modulus (i.e. the slope of the tangent to the stress strain curve at a specified stress). Table 1.23, taken from CHEN (1948), shows values of initial tangent modulus for some coarse-grained materials. The effect of void ratio is immediately evident. What is not evident from the table is the effect of confining stress. HARDEN and RICHART (1963), by measuring shear wave velocities, determined that for e less than 0.80 the following expressions could be used to compute shear modulus for sands and several lean clays.

For "round-grained" soils

$$G\,(\text{psi}) = 2630\,\frac{(2.17 - e)^2}{1 + e}\,(\bar{\sigma}_o\,(\text{psi}))^{\frac{1}{2}} \qquad \text{Eq. 1.4.15}$$

For "angular-grained" soils

$$G\,(\text{psi}) = 1230\,\frac{(2.97 - e)^2}{1 + e}\,(\bar{\sigma}_o\,(\text{psi}))^{\frac{1}{2}} \qquad \text{Eq. 1.4.16}$$

where in either case

$$\bar{\sigma}_o = \left[\frac{1 + 2K_o}{3}\right]\bar{\sigma}_v$$

and

K_o = Coefficient of lateral earth pressure at rest

$\bar{\sigma}_v$ = Effective vertical stress at depth of interest

TABLE 1.23
Values of Initial Tangent Modulus for Dry Cohesionless Soils (Chen, 1948)

	Modulus (ksi)	
Soil (1 atm confining pressure)	Loose	Dense
Screened crushed quartz, fine, angular	17	30
Screened crushed quartz, medium, angular	18	27
Screened Ottawa sand, fine, rounded	26	45
Standard Ottawa sand, medium, rounded	30	52
Screened sand, medium, subangular	20	35
Well-graded sand, coarse, subangular	15	28

The expression given in Equation 1.4.11 for shear modulus can be used to compute E provided Poisson's ratio, μ, is known. Here again, absolute values of Poisson's ratio are not strictly applicable to soils. At the early stages of loading μ is low (0.1—0.3) because of particle rearrangements, however, it increases as the soil begins to fail and in cases where it is determined for sand from triaxial compression tests with axial loading, it may exceed 0.5. An average value often used for dry cohesionless soils is 0.25.

The modulus of elasticity for cohesive soils is an even more complex parameter to evaluate. For cohesive soils stress history, drainage, rate of strain, disturbance, and thixotropic effects can all influence modulus significantly. Table 1.24 from Richardson and Whitman (1963), presents data derived from CU tests on normally and overconsolidated samples of remolded Vicksburg buckshot clay. These data illustrate the effect of strain rate and stress history on the value of E. In the table, $\bar{\sigma}_c$ is the isotropic consolidation stress. In general, the modulus of fine-grained cohesive soils loaded in an "undrained" manner decreases with soil disturbance and with an increase in the principal stress difference. On the other hand, the modulus generally increases with increasing consolidation stress, overconsolidation ratio, aging, and strain rate.

TABLE 1.24

Values of $E/\bar{\sigma}_c$ Ratio for Normally and Overconsolidated Vicksburg Buckshot Clay and for Various Rates of Strain

(Adapted from RICHARDSON and WHITMAN, 1963)

	$E/\bar{\sigma}_c$	
	Strain Rate = 1%/min.	Strain Rate = 0.002%/min.
Normally consolidated	160	60
Overconsolidated	200	140

In view of the many factors that can affect the modulus of elasticity of fine-grained cohesive soils, no attempt is made here to list even "representative" values for these materials. The same is true for POISSON's ratio for cohesive soils, although typically in civil engineering practice a value of 0.4 is used for clays.

In view of the above considerations it seems that in cases where displacements are small, elasticity solutions may give good approximations of soil behavior provided E and μ are representative of values in the field. However, in cases where plastic yielding occurs, which are the majority of cases of interest in vehicle mobility studies, other theories must be sought to determine stress states under applied load and to predict soil behavior as a result of those stress states.

1.4.2 Elastic-Plastic Theories

The deficiencies inherent in the application of elasticity theory to soil-structure interaction problems were of less moment up until the last decade because before that time there was no practical alternative that could describe soil behavior any more realistically. Since the advent and widespread availability of high speed digital computers, however, numerical techniques have become available for analysis in which many of the previously encountered difficulties may be overcome. The finite element methods and other numerical methods of analysis can now be used to solve problems containing previously unmanageable conditions such as layering, complex geometric and stress boundary conditions, anisotropy and three-dimensional effects. Of all such numerical methods the finite element method has gained the greatest popularity particularly for the solution of soil-structure interaction problems. The literature is replete with applications, a good summary of which can be found in DESAI and ABEL (1972).

In the finite element method (FEM) a continuum is idealized by a system of elements interconnected at nodes to form a grid. Elements can be linear, triangular, quadrilateral, tetrahedral, hexagonal or conical and the grid composed of a one-, two-, or three-dimensional coordinate system. This enables almost complete generality in geometrical description so that systems ranging from a simple beam to a complex soil structure interface can be easily represented. Figure 1.41 shows a typical grid of elements used for predicting the stress distribution and soil deformation under a tractive device (PERUMPRAL, LILJEDAHL and PERLOFF, 1971).

The real beauty of the FEM, however, lies in the fact that it also offers great flexibility in the definition of material properties. Different properties can, theoretically, be assigned to each element in the grid thereby allowing for the definition of non homogeneous and non isotropic media. Consequently, the constraint of linear elasticity no longer exists and elastic-plastic properties may easily be specified. Displacement or stress boundary conditions may also be specified at any node in the finite element system. In addition, thermal and/or mechanical loads can be specified at nodes. Distributed loads on the surface or at depth may also be represented provided a sufficient number of nodes are chosen so that the distributed loads can be approximated by a series of point loads at the nodes. Finally, individual elements or the body as a whole can be subjected to accelerations. Because of the continuity conditions imposed on the system (by definition, it is a continuum) equilibrium equations can be derived for each node in the grid under the specified boundary conditions. Obviously, for a problem requiring a fine-meshed grid to define the continuum and the loading conditions in the system adequately, a very large number of algebraic equations is generated. The simultaneous solution to this set of equations constitutes an approximate equilibrium solution to the problem. Because of its size this set of equations cannot be solved by hand. Therefore, computer codes have been developed specifically for the efficient solution of large systems of linear (or non-linear) algebraic equations by numerical methods. These codes are usually incorporated into a larger FEM program that typically generates the mesh, develops the system of simultaneous equations based on input data, and then executes the logic by which the solution is obtained.

Two of the best known and most widely used finite element computer programs are ICES-STRUDL and NASTRAN. The former was developed

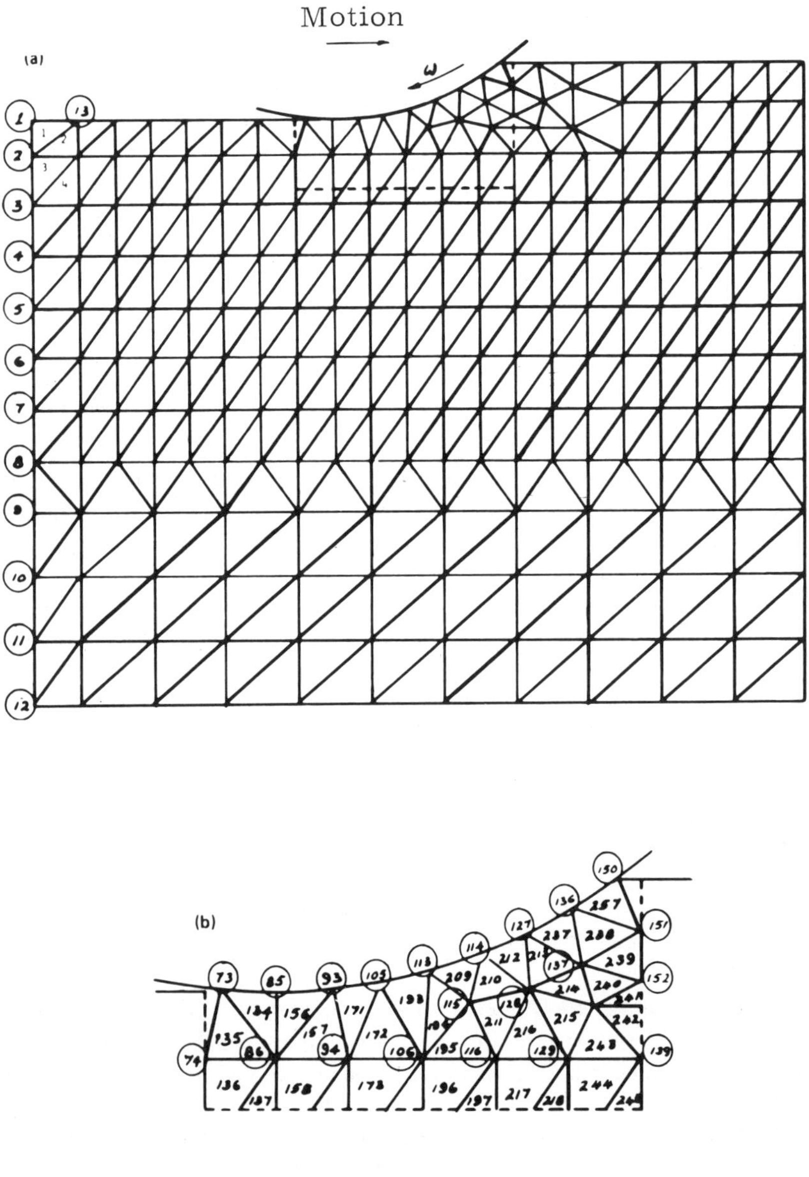

Fig. 1.41
Idealized Soil-Wheel System

a) Overall Mesh
b) Detail indicating element and node numbers at the interface
(From PERUMPRAL, et al, 1971)

by the Massachusetts Institute of Technology (1969) as part of its integrated civil engineering system (ICES) to be a general purpose structural information system containing both analysis and design capabilities. STRUDL is easily adaptable to soil-structure interaction problems. NASTRAN was developed by the National Aeronautics and Space Administration (1970) and stands for NASA structural analysis program. It also is a general purpose computer program that can be used to solve a host of problems ranging from simple linear structures made of simple beams to complex continua with many degrees of freedom.

A detailed treatment of the theoretical basis for FEM and the mechanics involved in its use is outside the scope of this book. The reader is referred to such texts as Ural (1973), Oden (1972) and Zienkiewicz and Cheung (1967). For specific two-dimensional applications in the area of soil-wheel interaction, Perumpral (1969) and Perumpral et al (1971) should be consulted.

Although FEM methods utilizing elastic-plastic theory to formulate equations whose solutions are obtained by the various approximate numerical techniques represent a major advancement in the analysis of soil-structure interaction problems, these methods are not the panacea for soil-vehicle mobility studies. For one thing, as input, they require material properties that are difficult to measure for soil. For example, the modulus of elasticity of soil varies as a function of stress level, moisture conditions, lateral restraint and other factors. Poisson's ratio is also a difficult parameter to define for a soil *a priori* since it varies as the soil is being loaded. In fact, for soils it can even become negative. In addition, some of these methods require a precise definition of the material's constitutive relationships. Anyone who has tried to determine constitutive relationships for soils in real-life situations knows that there is no unique definition of them. There is also the fact that in many practical applications of the elastic-plastic theories by FEM or finite differences, the stress distribution at the soil-structure interface must be known *a priori*. Although reasonable assumptions of this distribution can be made for some of the more common interaction problems, soil-vehicle running gear interaction results in a very complex distribution that requires improved estimates based on previous solutions. From the practical viewpoint the cost of running FEM computer programs interactively so as to obtain these improved estimates is prohibitive. For these reasons FEM and the various approximate numerical methods that utilize elastic-plastic theory are not well suited for off-road locomotion problems.

1.4.3 Failure Theories in Conventional Soil Mechanics

Failure in solids is usually described mathematically by substituting some failure criterion into a set of equilibrium equations to obtain expressions for the state of stress in the solid on the point of failure. For soils, failure has traditionally been defined by combining the Mohr-Coulomb criterion with the equations of static equilibrium. Since the Mohr-Coulomb criterion is a stress-oriented criterion, large deformations may occur before "failure" is reached. This situation may be handled by using the theory of plasticity in combination with the Mohr-Coulomb yield criterion to obtain a set of equilibrium equations. These equations, called the equations of plastic equilibrium will be discussed in great detail in Part 2. Let it suffice here to say that the equations of plastic equilibrium are quite complicated and very difficult to solve rigorously under practical boundary conditions. Therefore, soil stability problems have traditionally been solved by approximate solutions where consideration is given to the equilibrium of a large soil mass and the yield conditions investigated only along an assumed failure surface. This is in contradistinction to the rigorous solution of the equations of plastic equilibrium presented in Part 2 where the general equations of equilibrium are applied to individual elements within the soil mass and the system integrated to obtain the solution for the imposed boundary conditions. In this section, the more widely used approximate solutions for single-surfaced and zone failures will be discussed.

Single-Surface Failure

The concept of stability, particularly as expressed by the Mohr-Coulomb failure criterion is of paramount importance in conventional soil mechanics analysis. As shown in Section 1.3.3, the relationship between normal and shear stresses (and therefore stress states) can be expressed in terms of two measureable parameters, angle of internal friction φ, and cohesion c. This relationship, repeated below, is used in some form or other in almost all of the stability investigation methods of soil mechanics.

$$s = c + \sigma_n \tan \varphi \qquad \text{Eq. 1.3.24}$$

For the purpose of illustrating the manner in which the single failure surface analysis is applied, the problem of slope stability will be considered. There are a number of methods available for the analysis of slope stability all of which are based on the development of Mohr-Coulomb failure stress states along the surface of a circular arc (Bishop 1955; Fellenius, 1927). In most of these methods, stability is analyzed by evaluating the equilibrium of a finite number of "slices" taken through the section enclosed by a potential failure surface. If the moment due to forces corresponding to the shear strength developed along the potential failure arc is greater than the moment due to all actuating forces about the center of a specific trial failure arc then the slope is considered stable. The analysis is repeated for other trial circles until a minimum ratio of actuating to resisting moment is found. For the single failure surface slope stability analysis Figure 1.42 shows the complete force system acting on a representative slice and the resultant forces for each individual factor acting on the equilibrated (or non-equilibrated) mass of soil. This type of single failure surface usually occurs because of a redistribution of stresses due to pore water migration. This redistribution generally requires considerable time. It does not appear that such a mechanism would be operative in soil-vehicle mechanics because of the short interaction times involved. Consequently single-surfaced failures are not likely to occur beneath off-road vehicle running gears.

Zone Failure

Although the single-failure-surface analysis of the stability of slopes is applied in practice to all types of soils, a more realistic picture of the mode of failure for cohesionless and c—φ soils is given by the concept of zone failure. Unlike the concept of single-surface failure where only the soil along one surface is considered to fail, zone failure implies that the transition of a soil from a state of elastic equilibrium to a state of plastic equilibrium takes place when incipient shear failure occurs along two sets of surfaces of sliding within the entire earth mass. This problem was first studied by RANKINE (1885) with reference to the earth pressures acting on a rigid wall whose presence in no way disturbed the existing state of stress in the soil. The specific problem of a horizontal surface bounding a half space of soil was the first addressed by RANKINE. The solution is known in the literature (see, for example, TERZAGHI, 1943) as the First RANKINE Problem. The extension of the theory to failure conditions along a semi-infinite mass whose surface is inclined is known as the Second RANKINE Problem and has some applicability in slope stability analysis but will not be discussed here. The stress conditions associated with the First RANKINE Problem are those defined by the equilibrium solution for a soil mass at failure where the surfaces of failure are planes and the major and minor principal planes at all points lie in the same directions. The concepts of "active" and "passive" stress states so commonly applied to soil-structure interaction problems are derived from the RANKINE solutions. These states are based on the concept that a soil element at depth oriented as shown in Figure 1.43(a) has acting on it only a vertical stress σ_z and a horizontal stress σ_x. Since no

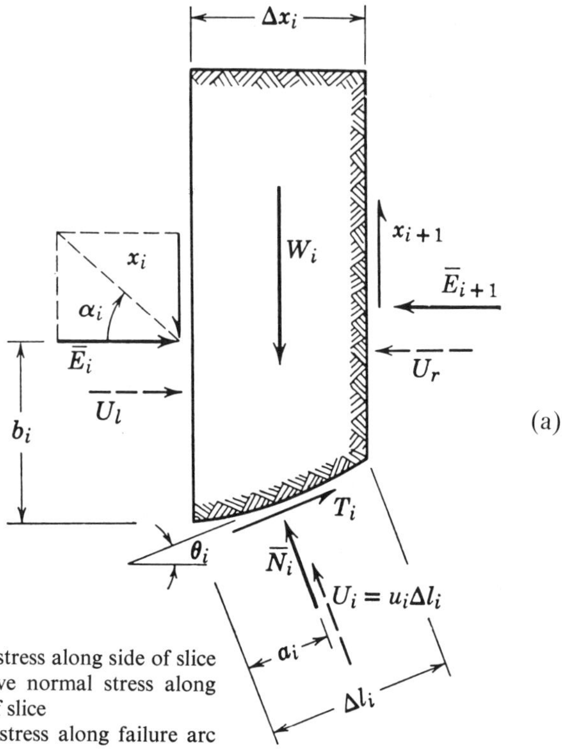

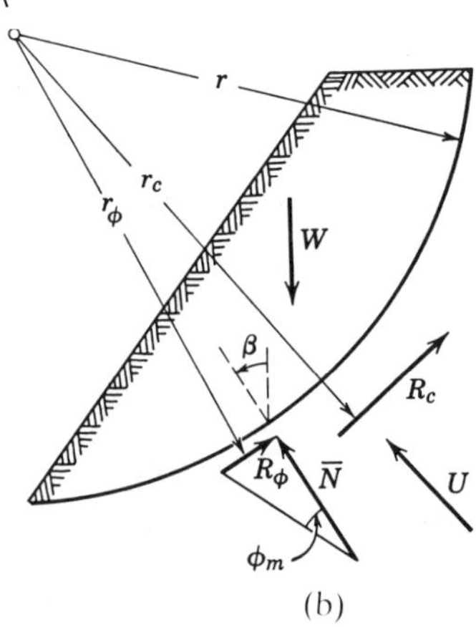

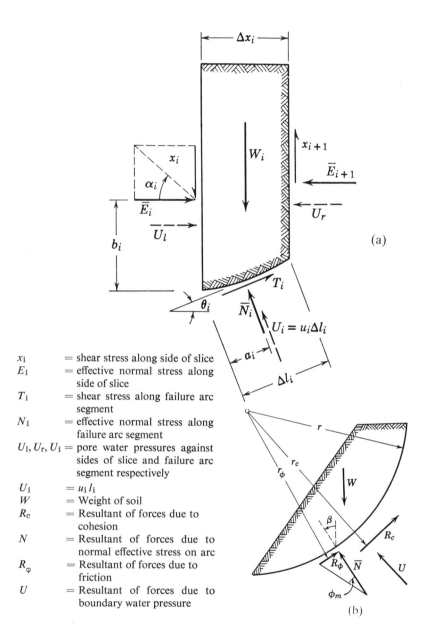

x_i	= shear stress along side of slice
E_i	= effective normal stress along side of slice
T_i	= shear stress along failure arc segment
N_i	= effective normal stress along failure arc segment
U_l, U_r, U_i	= pore water pressures against sides of slice and failure arc segment respectively
U_i	= $u_i l_i$
W	= Weight of soil
R_c	= Resultant of forces due to cohesion
N	= Resultant of forces due to normal effective stress on arc
R_φ	= Resultant of forces due to friction
U	= Resultant of forces due to boundary water pressure

Fig. 1.42
Slope Stability by Method of Slices
a) Complete system of forces acting on a slice
b) Resultant forces acting on the free body

shear stresses exist on the horizontal and vertical planes, σ_z and σ_x are principal stresses. Should lateral support be decreased, for example by removal of a rigid boundary from the vicinity of the element, deformation would occur and σ_x decrease until failure of the soil occurs. In this case $\sigma_x = \sigma_3$ and $\sigma_z = \sigma_1$ and the relationship between horizontal

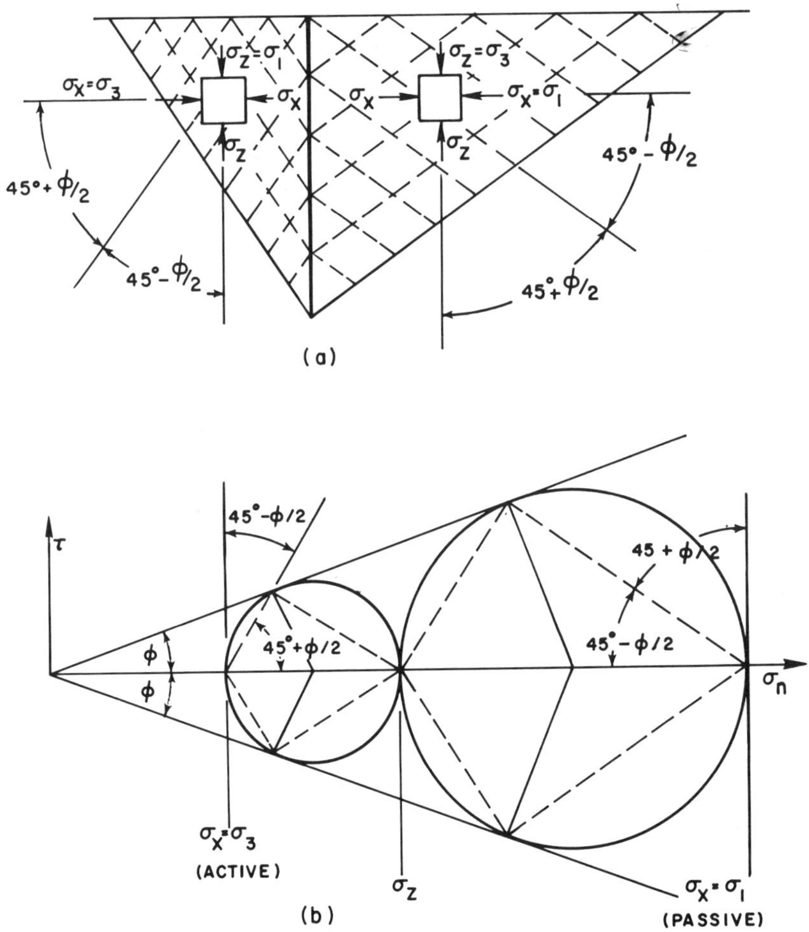

Fig. 1.43
The RANKINE Concept of Active and Passive Stress States
a) Rigid boundary movement causing active and passive stress states
b) MOHR circle representation of active and passive stress states

and vertical stress may be obtained for the "active" case from the MOHR's Circle (refer to Section 2.2.1) as

$$\sigma_x = \sigma_3 = p_a = \sigma_1 \tan^2 (45^\circ - \varphi/2) - 2c \tan (45^\circ - \varphi/2)$$
Eq. 1.4.17

On the other hand, should lateral support be increased by movement of a rigid boundary towards the element, then $\sigma_x = \sigma_1$ and $\sigma_z = \sigma_3$ and the above relationship becomes that for the "passive" case:

$$\sigma_x = \sigma_1 = p_p = \sigma_3 \tan^2 (45^\circ + \varphi/2) + 2c \tan (45 + \varphi/2)$$
Eq. 1.4.18

Figure 1.43(b) shows these stress states on a MOHR's circle where σ_z is the vertical stress and σ_x (active) and σ_x (passive) correspond to the horizontal stress σ_x for the "active" and "passive" cases, respectively. Point 1 represents the normal and shear stresses at failure in the active case where $\sigma_z = \sigma_1$ and $\sigma_x = \sigma_3$ as indicated above. These failure stresses act on planes inclined at an angle $\pm$ (45° — $\varphi/2$) from the direction of the major principal stress or $\pm$ (45° + $\varphi/2$) from the major principal stress plane. This orientation is obtained directly from the MOHR's circle in Figure 1.43(b) using the "origin of planes" concept and transferred to Figure 1.43(a) to form the slip line field shown within the soil mass. The stress conditions at "passive failure" are represented by Point 2 for the case where $\sigma_z = \sigma_3$ and $\sigma_x = \sigma_1$. In this case the failure stresses also act on planes inclined at an angle $\pm$ (45° — $\varphi/2$) from the direction of the major principal stress or $\pm$ (45° + $\varphi/2$) from the major principal stress plane. The apparent difference between the two fields is due to the fact that there is a 90° difference in the orientation of the major and minor principal stress in the active and passive cases. The term "slip line field" will be used extensively in this book and is understood to mean the two families of curves defining the bounds of regions in which stress states correspond to those of incipient plastic failure. The directions correspond to the directions of shearing stress causing the failure.

Conventional Theories of Bearing Capacity

The same concepts developed with regard to earth pressures acting on rigid vertical walls may be applied to the bearing of rigid bodies such as plates, strips, disks, etc on horizontal surfaces. The theory developed to describe the stress states beneath such bearing surfaces is called "bearing capacity theory". In soil mechanics the term "bearing capacity" is understood to mean the normal uniform pressure that is an average of the discrete ultimate bearing pressures predicted to occur at specific points on the bearing surface by a bearing capacity theory. Consequently, the terms "bearing capacity" and "ultimate bearing pressure" are not ordinarily interchangeable.

Rankine Theory. Using the concepts of active and passive states of stress at a point in a soil mass and assuming that a plane rupture surface would occur beneath a bearing surface at failure, RANKINE calculated the ultimate bearing pressure as:

$$\sigma_u = z\gamma \left[\frac{1 + \sin\varphi}{1 - \sin\varphi}\right]^2 \qquad \text{Eq. 1.4.19}$$

where

γ = unit weight of soil

z = critical depth for laying of foundation

φ = angle of internal friction

The obvious deficiency in this equation is that it predicts zero ultimate bearing pressure at $z = 0$ so that a soil would have no bearing capacity at the surface. This is a result of RANKINE's incorrect consideration of conditions below the contact surface and his assumption that the lines of rupture are straight throughout the soil mass.

Prandtl Theory. In 1903, KÖTTER succeeded in deriving the differential equations governing the stresses along a curved slip line. PRANDTL (1920, 1921) applied these solutions to his study of the penetration of hard bodies such as metal punches into other softer, homogeneous and isotropic metals. The major feature of the PRANDTL system is that the failure surface is not linear throughout the soil mass but consists of active and passive

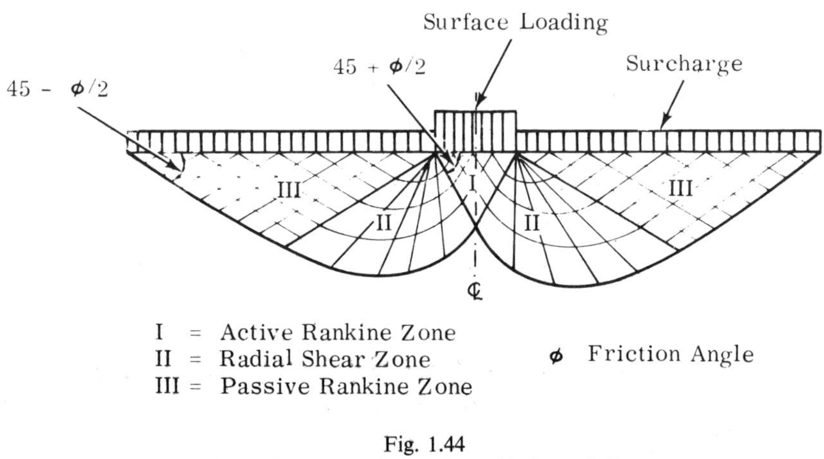

Fig. 1.44
Slip Surface Beneath Footing with Smooth Base
According to PRANDTL's Solution

RANKINE zones separated by a radial zone composed of a logarithmic spiral. The boundaries of the RANKINE zones are tangent to the spiral on its two boundaries. Figure 1.44 shows the PRANDTL system and its associated slip lines and forces for a c-φ material. PRANDTL combined MOHR's stress theory with AIRY's stress function and derived a second order differential equation which he solved to obtain an analytical expression for ultimate bearing stress at failure for a weightless, purely cohesive or c-φ soil.

TERZAGHI (1943) suggested that the original PRANDTL equation could be improved by adding a term to account for soil weight; he thereby removed the restriction inherent in the original formulation that excluded purely frictional soils. TAYLOR (1948) also modified the original PRANDTL equation to account for strength due to overburden pressure. JUMIKIS (1966) suggested that both these corrections be made and presented his form of the modified PRANDTL equation as:

$$\sigma_u = (c + c') \cot \varphi \, [K_p \exp (\pi \tan \varphi) - 1] + q \, K_p \exp (\pi \tan \varphi) \qquad \text{Eq. 1.4.20}$$

where

$c' = t\gamma \tan \varphi$
t = area $GBAEDCF$/length $GBAE$ as shown in Figure 1.44
$K_p = \tan^2 (45° + \varphi/2)$
q = actual surcharge shown in Figure 1.44 or effective surcharge ($q = \gamma D_f$) shown in Figure 1.45(a) or combination of both

The shape of the rupture surface in the original PRANDTL solution is an approximate one only. It is based on the assumption that the surface of contact between the footing and soil is frictionless so that RANKINE's active state exists in the wedge directly beneath the footing (see Figure 1.44). This implies that the angle through which the logarithmic spiral extends is always 90°. In addition, the wedge ABC in Figure 1.44 is assumed to behave as a rigid body and to move downwards with no deformation. These assumptions are not usually verified by field or laboratory observation since there is almost always friction at the soil-footing interface. Consequently, neither the original nor the modified PRANDTL solution is generally applicable to problems encountered in the field.

Terzaghi Theory. In 1943 TERZAGHI presented a solution to the bearing capacity problem that was based on the PRANDTL system but was modified to account for the deficiencies inherent in the PRANDTL assumptions as applied to soils. The TERZAGHI concept is shown in Figure 1.45(a). Failure

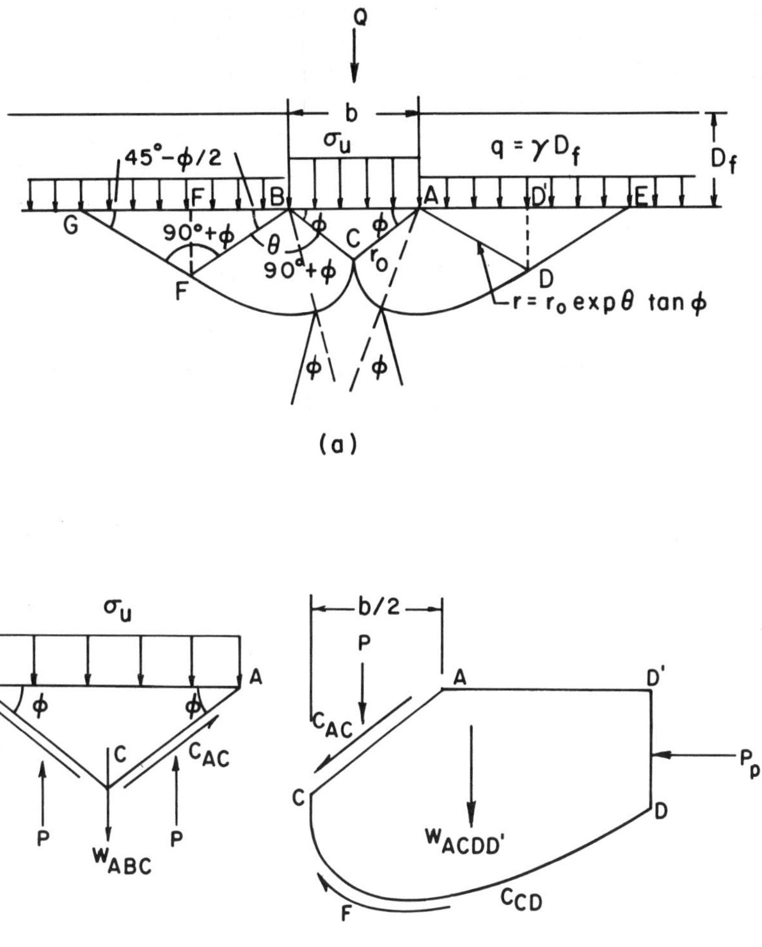

Fig. 1.45
TERZAGHI Bearing Capacity Theory
a) Slip surface beneath strip footing with rough base
b) Forces acting on soil mass *ABCDD'*

in this context occurs when the equilibrium of the wedge beneath the footing cannot be maintained under the external load Q. This failure load can be calculated from a simple summation of forces on the soil wedge at the moment of failure. The most notable difference between the geometry of the Terzaghi system in Figure 1.45(a) and that of the Prandtl system in Figure 1.44 is the shape of the wedge immediately beneath the footing. Terzaghi assumed friction to act along the interface between the soil and footing so that the base angles of the wedge are φ and not $45° + \varphi/2$ as in the Prandtl theory. This implies that the Rankine active state does not exist in the wedge.

Furthermore, Terzaghi assumed the faces of the wedge (AC and BC in Figures 1.44 and 1.45(a) to be failure surfaces also. Consequently, the surface of the logarithmic spiral has to be vertical at the point C since failure surfaces must intersect each other at $90° + \varphi$. The shape of the spiral is given by

$$r = r_0 \exp(\theta \tan \varphi) \qquad \text{Eq. 1.4.20}$$

where
r is the distance from either A or B to any point on the respective spirals.
r_0 is the spiral radius at the wedge face, i.e. either BC or AC.
θ is the angle between the wedge ABC and the Passive Rankine zone. In the Terzaghi theory θ equals $(135° - \varphi/2)$.

At any point along the spiral defined by Equation 1.4.20, the radius from the origin makes an angle φ with the normal to the spiral at that point.

The stability of a footing of width b is determined in the Terzaghi theory by simply evaluating the static equilibrium of the soil masses ABC and $ACDD'$ whose free bodies are shown in Figure 1.45(b).

The resulting expression is

$$\sigma_u 2b = 2bc\left[\frac{K_{pc}}{\cos^2\varphi} + \tan\varphi\right] + 2bq\frac{K_{pq}}{\cos^2\varphi} + b^2\gamma\tan\varphi\left[\frac{K_{p\gamma}}{\cos^2\varphi} - 1\right] \qquad \text{Eq. 1.4.21}$$

where K_{pc}, K_{pq} and $K_{p\gamma}$ are dimensionless parameters that account for the different ways that cohesion, surcharge and soil weight affect passive earth pressure. Terzaghi was able to evaluate these parameters using a trial wedge method and simplify Equation 1.4.21 to the better known expression:

$$\sigma_u = cN_c + qN_q + \frac{b\gamma}{2}N_\gamma \qquad \text{Eq. 1.4.22}$$

where

N_c, N_q and N_γ = the so-called bearing capacity factors which are a function of φ alone

q = surcharge or "effective" surcharge (γD_f) or the combination of both

c = unit cohesion

b = footing width

γ = unit weight of material on which footing rests.

TERZAGHI calculated the value of the bearing capacity factors as

$$N_c = \cot \varphi \left[\frac{l^2}{2 \cos^2 (45^\circ + \varphi/2)} - 1\right] \qquad \text{Eq. 1.4.23}$$

$$N_q = \frac{l^2}{2 \cos^2 (45^\circ + \varphi/2)} \qquad \text{Eq. 1.4.24}$$

$$N_\gamma = \frac{1}{2} \tan \varphi \, (K_{p\gamma}/\cos^2 \varphi - 1) \qquad \text{Eq. 1.4.25}$$

where

$K_{p\gamma}$ = coefficient of Passive Earth Pressure for $q = 0$, $c = 0$, and angle of wall friction $\delta = \varphi$.

l = $\exp(3\pi/4 - \varphi/2) \tan \varphi$

Charts such as that shown in Figure 1.46 present a graphical relationship between the bearing capacity factors and φ for the case of "general shear" (Figure 1.46(a)) and "local shear" (Figure 1.46(b)). The concepts of general and local shear are discussed in Section 2.5.1.

In his solution TERZAGHI assumed that the resistance offered by the weight of the soil was independent of the resistance offered by surcharge. In fact, the true failure surface is an expression of the interaction between resisting factors and is different for different combinations of φ, γ and q. However, in spite of this deficiency, the TERZAGHI solution gives reasonable agreement with experimental results especially for φ less than 35 degrees. It is today one of the most widely used "failure" theories for the evaluation of the stability of footings.

The basic TERZAGHI equation has been modified through the years to account for the geometric shape of the footing, inclined loads and embedment depth so that now the complete equation is:

$$\sigma_u = cN_c s_c i_c d_c + \gamma \frac{b}{2} N_\gamma s_\gamma i_\gamma d_\gamma + qN_q s_q i_q d_q \qquad \text{Eq. 1.4.26}$$

where

s_c, s_γ, s_q = shape factors

i_c, i_γ, i_q = inclination factors

d_c, d_γ, d_q = depth factors

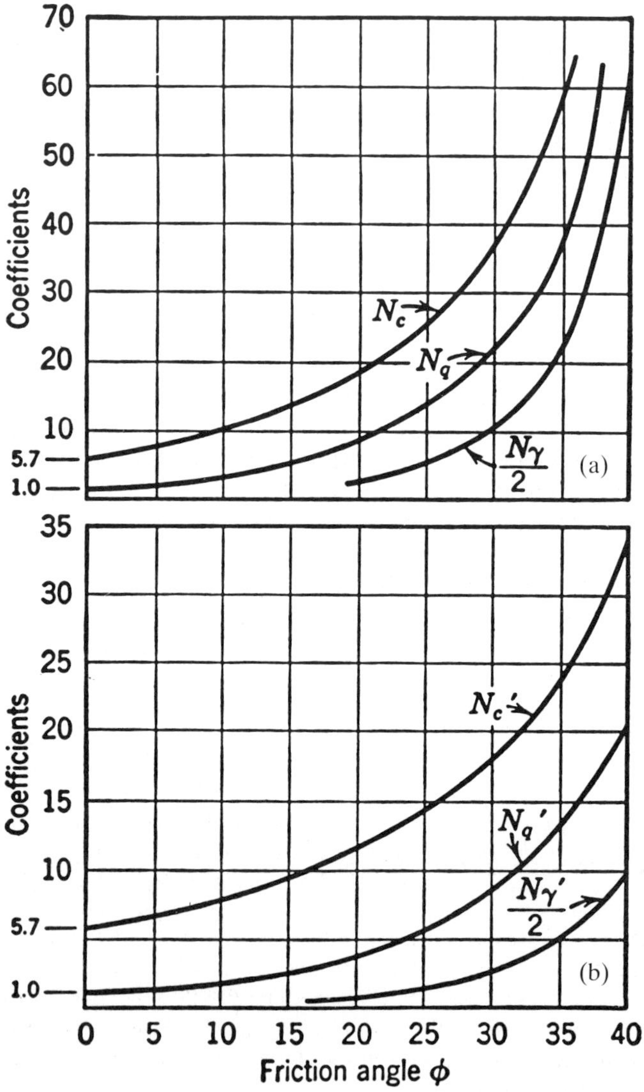

Fig. 1.46
TERZAGHI Bearing Capacity Coefficients
a) General shear
b) Local shear

TERZAGHI was the first to recognize the limitations of his basic bearing capacity equation and suggested that it be modified by empirically determined shape factors. According to TERZAGHI (1943), the values of s_c and s_q equal 1.3 and 1.0, respectively, for any square or circular shape. The value of s_γ equals 0.6 for circular bearing areas and 0.8 for square areas. To account for rectangular bearing surfaces B. HANSEN (1961) proposed the following general expressions for the shape factors in terms of internal friction angle of soil, minimum footing contact dimension *(b)*, and maximum footing contact dimension *(l)*:

$$s_c = 1 + (0.2 + \tan^6 \varphi)\, b/1 \qquad \text{Eq. 1.4.27}$$
$$s_q = s_c - (s_c - 1)/N_q \qquad \text{Eq. 1.4.28}$$
$$s_\gamma = 1 - (0.2 + \tan^6 \varphi)\, b/21 \qquad \text{Eq. 1.4.29}$$

MEYERHOF (1963) noted that for values of $\varphi > 30°$ experimental results indicated that the N_γ for square and circular footings is smaller than that for strip footings. MEYERHOF attributed this difference from what theory predicts to the influence of intermediate principal stress in the plane strain case of the strip footing. He suggested that the plane strain case requires a larger value of φ than that obtained from a triaxial test where $\sigma_2 = \sigma_3$. Therefore he proposed the following shape factors:

$$s_c = 1 + 0.2\,(b/l) \tan^2 (45° + \varphi'/2) \qquad \text{Eq. 1.4.30}$$
$$s_q = s_\gamma = 1.0 \text{ for } \varphi' = 0 \qquad \text{Eq. 1.4.31}$$
$$s_q = s_\gamma = 1 + 0.1\,(b/l) \tan^2 \left(45° + \varphi' \frac{1}{2}\right) \qquad \text{Eq. 1.4.32}$$

where

$\varphi' = (1.1 - 0.1\, b/l)\, \varphi_t$

φ_t = angle of internal friction obtained from triaxial compression test.

MEYERHOF (1963) introduced not only the above expressions for s_c, s_q and s_γ, but also factors to account for the effect of the shear strength of the material above the base of an embedded footing. The following are MEYERHOF equations for depth factors in terms of internal friction angle, the width or minimum dimension along the horizontal contact surface *(b)*, and the depth of embedment *(z)*:

$$d_c = 1 + 0.2\,(z/b) \tan (45° + \varphi/2) \qquad \text{Eq. 1.4.33}$$
$$d_q = d_\gamma = 1.0 \text{ for } \varphi = 0 \qquad \text{Eq. 1.4.34}$$
$$d_q = d_\gamma = 1 + 0.1\,(z/b) \tan (45° + \varphi/2) \qquad \text{Eq. 1.4.35}$$
$$\text{for } \varphi \geq 10° \text{ and } (z/b) < 1.0$$

MEYERHOF (1963) also presented the following expressions for approximate inclination factors:

$$i_c = i_q = (1 - \alpha/90°)^2 \quad \text{Eq. 1.4.36}$$
$$i_\gamma = (1 - \alpha/\varphi)^2 \quad \text{Eq. 1.4.37}$$

where α = angle of load inclination from the vertical.

Others have expressed the inclination factors as functions of the ratio between the horizontal component of load and shear strength to obtain approximations to theoretical values. However, values obtained by rigor-

TABLE 1.25
Bearing Capacity Coefficients Including Effect of Load Inclination (Footing Width ≥ Depth of Burial)
(From HARR, 1966)

		φ								
α		0	5	10	15	20	25	30	35	40
0	$\bar{N}_\gamma$	0.00	0.17	0.46	1.40	3.16	6.92	15.32	35.19	86.46
	$\bar{N}_q$	1.00	1.57	2.47	3.94	6.40	10.70	18.40	33.30	64.20
	$\bar{N}_c$	5.14	6.49	8.34	11.00	14.80	20.70	30.10	46.10	75.30
5	$\bar{N}_\gamma$		0.09	0.38	0.99	2.31	5.02	11.10	24.38	61.38
	$\bar{N}_q$		1.24	2.16	3.44	5.56	9.17	15.60	27.90	52.70
	$\bar{N}_c$		2.72	6.56	9.12	12.50	17.50	25.40	38.40	61.60
10	$\bar{N}_\gamma$			0.17	0.62	1.51	3.42	7.64	17.40	41.78
	$\bar{N}_q$			1.50	2.84	4.65	7.65	12.90	22.80	42.40
	$\bar{N}_c$			2.84	6.88	10.00	14.30	20.60	31.10	49.30
15	$\bar{N}_\gamma$				0.25	0.89	2.15	4.93	11.34	27.61
	$\bar{N}_q$				1.79	3.64	6.13	10.40	18.10	33.30
	$\bar{N}_c$				2.94	7.27	11.00	16.20	24.50	38.50
20	$\bar{N}_\gamma$					0.32	1.19	2.92	6.91	16.41
	$\bar{N}_q$					2.09	4.58	7.97	13.90	25.40
	$\bar{N}_c$					3.00	7.68	12.10	18.50	29.10
25	$\bar{N}_\gamma$						0.38	1.50	3.85	9.58
	$\bar{N}_q$						2.41	5.67	10.20	18.70
	$\bar{N}_c$						3.03	8.09	13.20	21.10
30	$\bar{N}_\gamma$							0.43	1.84	4.96
	$\bar{N}_q$							2.75	6.94	13.10
	$\bar{N}_c$							3.02	8.49	14.40
35	$\bar{N}_\gamma$								0.47	2.21
	$\bar{N}_q$								3.08	8.43
	$\bar{N}_c$								2.97	8.86
40	$\bar{N}_\gamma$									0.49
	$\bar{N}_q$									3.42
	$\bar{N}_c$									2.88

ous analyses (SCHULTZE, 1952; MEYERHOF, 1953; SOKOLOVSKII, 1960) are available and are presented in Table 1.25. These values were obtained by SOKOLOVSKII and put into the tabular form shown by HARR (1966). It should be noted that the values in the table are not values of inclination factors alone but have been combined with the TERZAGHI bearing capacity factors $\bar{N}_c$, $\bar{N}_q$, $\bar{N}_\gamma$ for a smooth footing. The factors $\bar{N}_c$, $\bar{N}_q$ and $\bar{N}_\gamma$ differ Equations 1.4.23 through 1.4.25. The expressions for $\bar{N}_c$, $\bar{N}_q$ and $\bar{N}_\gamma$ are:

$$\bar{N}_c = \cot\varphi\,(\bar{l}^2 \tan^2(45^\circ + \varphi/2) - 1) \qquad \text{Eq. 1.4.38}$$
$$\bar{N}_q = \bar{l}^2 \tan^2(45^\circ + \varphi/2) \qquad \text{Eq. 1.4.39}$$
$$\bar{N}_\gamma = N_\gamma \qquad \text{Eq. 1.4.40}$$

where

$$\bar{l} = \exp\left(\frac{\pi}{2}\tan\varphi\right)$$

Therefore to obtain i_c, i_q and i_γ for use in Equation 1.4.26 the values of $i_c\bar{N}_c$, $i_q\bar{N}_q$, $i_\gamma\bar{N}_\gamma$ given in Table 1.25 need only to be divided by the appropriate value of bearing capacity factor given by the equations above.

An excellent summary of the effect of secondary factors on the basic bearing capacity equation is given by HVORSLEV (1963).

As a final item under "Failure Theories", the readers' attention is called to the book by J. BRINCH HANSEN (1953) in which he devotes an entire chapter to known methods of earth pressure calculation. In this chapter he reviews extreme methods, theories of plasticity including those we have just discussed above, theories of elasticity and empirical methods. He does not go into detail regarding the failure criteria for each method. However, in his presentation of his "new method" for earth pressure calculation he does consider at length "States of Failure" and "Figures of Rupture", wherein he discusses the RANKINE and PRANDTL surfaces as well as a host of other composite zone ruptures. Although BRINCH HANSEN's work is directed toward the analysis of earth retaining structures such as rigid walls and flexible bulkheads, it has relevance to the problem of soil-wheel interaction if only because it contains an excellent summary of traditional failure theories.

PART 1
BIBLIOGRAPHY

AASHO (1950), "Standard Recommended Practice for the Classification of Soils and Soil-Aggregate Mixtures for Highway Construction Purposes," *Standard Specifications for Highway Materials and Methods of Sampling and Testing,* Part 1, Washington, D. C.

ABDUN-NUR, E. A. (1950), "A Standard Classification of Soils as Proposed by the Bureau of Reclamation," *Symposium on the Identification and Classification of Soils,* ASTM STP No. 113, Philadelphia, Pa.

ALLEN, H. (1942). "Classification of Soils and Control Procedures Used in Construction of Embankments," *Public Roads,* February.

AL-HUSSAINI, M. M. and P. A. GILBERT (1974), *Stresses and Shearing Resistance in Soil Beneath a Rigid Wheel,* WES Technical Report No. S–74–7.

ASA (1965) American Society of Agronomy, *Methods of Soil Analysis,* C. A. Black, editor-in-chief, Parts 1 and 2, American Society of Agronomy, Inc., Madison, Wisconsin.

ASTM (1967) American Society for Testing Materials, *Bituminous Materials; Soils, Skid Resistance,* Part 11 of Standards, Philadelphia, Pa.

BENKENSTEIN, H. and H. LINDNER (1969), "Scherfestigkeit, innere Reibung und Reibung Boden–Metall verschiedener Bodenarten in Abhängigkeit vom Wassergehalt," *Albrecht Thaer Archive,* Vol. 13.

BIOT, M. A. (1941), "General Theory of Three-Dimensional Consolidation," *Journal of Applied Physics,* Vol. 12.

BISHOP, A. W. (1955), "The Use of Slip Circle in the Stability Analysis of Earth Slopes," *Geotechnique*, Vol. V, No. 1.

BISHOP, A. W. (1961), "The Measurement of Pore Pressure in the Triaxial Test," *Pore Pressure and Suction in Soils,* Butterworths, London.

BJERRUM, L. (1954), "Geotechnical Properties of Norwegian Marine Clays," *Geotechnique,* Vol. IV.

BJERRUM, L. (1954a), "Theoretical and Experimental Investigations on the Shear Strength of Soils," *Norwegian Geotechnical Publication No. 5,* Oslo.

BOLT, G. H. (1955), "Analysis of the Validity of the Gouy-Chapman Theory of the Electric Double Layer," *Journal of Colloid Science,* Vol. 10.

BOLT, G. H. and R. D. MILLER (1958), "Calculation of Total and Component Potentials of Water in Soil," *Transactions,* American Geophysical Union, Vol. 39.

BURMISTER, D. M. (1951), "Identification and Classification of Soils – an Appraisal and Statement of Principles," *Special Technical Publication No. 113,* American Society for Testing Materials, Philadelphia, Pa.

BUTTERFIELD, R. and K. Z. ANDRAWES (1972), "On the Angles of Friction Between Sand and Plane Surfaces," *Journal of Terramechanics,* Vol. 8, No. 4.

CASAGRANDE, A. and R. E. FADUM (1939), "Notes on Soil Testing for Engineering Purposes," *Publication No. 268,* Harvard University, Cambridge, Mass.

CASAGRANDE, A. (1947), "Classification and Identification of Soils," *Proceedings* ASCE, Vol. 73, No. 6, Part 1.

CHEN, L-S. (1948), "An Investigation of Stress-Strain and Strength Characteristics of Cohesionless Soils by Triaxial Compression Tests," *Proceedings,* 2nd ICSMFE, Vol. 5.

CLARK, S. J. (1973), "A Proposed Soil Classification System For Soil-Vehicle and Tillage Mechanics," *Journal of Terramechanics,* Vol. 10, No. 3.

Cornell University (1951), *Final Report on Soil Solidification Research,* Ithaca, N. Y.

CRAWFORD, C. B. (1959), "The Influence of Rate of Strain on Effective Stresses in Sensitive Clays," *ASTM Special Technical Paper STP 252,* Philadelphia, Pa.

DERESCIEWICZ, H. (1958), *Mechanics of Granular Matter; Advances in Applied Mechanics,* Vol. 5, Academic Press, New York, N. Y.

DESAI, C. S. and J. F. ABEL (1972), *Introduction to the Finite Element Method,* Van Nostrand Reinhold Co., New York, N. Y.

DM–7, NAVFAC (1971), *Design Manual – Soil Mechanics, Foundations, and Earth Structures,* Department of the Navy, Naval Facilities Engineering Command, Washington, D. C.

FELLENIUS, W. (1927), *Erdstatische Berechnungen mit Reibung und Kohäsion und unter Annahme Kreiszylindrischer Gleitflächen,* Ernst, Berlin.

FOSTER, C. R. (1962), "Field Problems: Compaction," *Foundation Engineering,* G. A. Leonards (ed.), McGraw Hill, New York, N. Y.

GIBBS, H. J. and W. G. HOLTZ (1957), "Research on Determining the Density of Sands by Spoon Penetration Testing," *Proceedings,* 4th ICSMFE (London) Vol. 1.

GIBSON, R. E. and A. MARSLAND (1960), "Porewater Pressure Observations in a Saturated Alluvial Deposit Beneath a Loaded Oil Tank," *Pore Pressure and Suction in Soils,* Butterworth & Co. Ltd, London.

GRIER, J. H. and C. H. PERRY (1972), "Road Capability Study on Improved Earth Roads," *Highway Research Record Number 405,* Highway Research Board, Washington, D. C.

GRIM, R. E. (1962), *Applied Clay Mineralogy,* McGraw-Hill Book Co., Inc , New York, N. Y.

HAMILTON, G. M. and L. E. GOODMAN (1966), "The Stress Field Created by a Circular Sliding Contact," *Transactions ASME Journal of Applied Mechanics.*

HANSEN, BENT (1961), "The Bearing Capacity of Sand Tested by Loading Circular Plates," *Proceedings,* 5th ICSMFE, Paris, Vol. 1.

HANSEN, J. BRINCH (1953), *Earth Pressure Calculation,* The Danish Technical Press, The Institution of Danish Civil Engineers, Copenhagen.

HARDIN, B. O. and F. E. RICHART (1963), "Elastic Wave Velocities in Granular Soils," *Journal,* SMFD, ASCE, Vol. 89, No. SM1.

HARR, M. E. (1966), *Foundations of Theoretical Soil Mechanics,* McGraw-Hill, New York, N. Y.

HAZEN, A. (1911), "Discussion of 'Dams on Sand Foundations' by A. C. Koenig," *Transactions,* ASCE, Vol. 73.

HOGENTOGLER, C. A. and C. TERZAGHI (1929), "Interrelationship of Load, Road and Subgrade," *Public Roads,* May.

HOUGH, B. K. (1969), *Basic Soils Engineering,* Second Edition Copyright 1969, The Ronald Press Company, New York, N.Y.

HUNT, C. B. (1972), *The Geology of Soils, Their Evolution, Classification, and Uses,* W. H. Freeman and Company, San Francisco, Ca.

HURLBUT, C. S. (1959), *Dana's Manual of Mineralogy,* 17th Ed., John Wiley and Sons, New York, N. Y.

HVORSLEV, M. J. (1960), "Physical Components of the Shear Strength of Saturated Clays," *Proceedings,* Research Conference on Shear Strength of Cohesive Soils, SMFD, ASCE, Boulder, Co.

HVORSLEV, M. J. (1963), "The Basic Sinkage Equations and Bearing Capacity Theories," a paper presented to the *Mobility Consultants Conference* at U. S. Army Waterways Experiment Station, Vicksburg, Miss.

JOHNSON, A. W. and J. R. SALLBERG (1960), "Factors that Influence Field Compaction of Soils," National Research Council, Highway Research Board, *Bulletin 272,* Washington, D. C.

JUMIKIS, A. R. (1966), *Soil Mechanics,* D. Van Nostrand Company, Inc., Princeton, N. J.

KARAFIATH, L. L. and G. MOHR (1969), "Effect of Ultrahigh Vacuum on the Friction Between Metals and Granular Soils," *Journal of Vacuum Science and Technology,* Vol. 6, No. 1.

KARAFIATH, L. L. (1970), "Friction Between Solids and Simulated Lunar Soils in Ultrahigh Vacuum and its Significance for the Design of Lunar Roving Vehicles," *Proceedings,* Space Simulation Conference, National Bureau of Standards Publication No. 336, Gaithersburg, Md.

KARAFIATH. L. L., NOWATZKI, E. A., EHRLICH, I. R., and J. CAPIN (1973), *An Application of Plasticity Theory to the Solution of the Rigid Wheel-Soil Interaction Problem, Technical Report No. 11758 (LL 141),* U. S. Army Tank Automotive Command, Warren, Mich.

KARAFIATH, L. L. (1974), *Development of Mathematical Model for Pneumatic Tire-Soil Interaction, Technical Report No. 11900 (LL 147),* U. S. Army Tank Automotive Command, Warren, Mich.

KOLBUSZEWSKI, J. J. (1948), "An Experimental Study of the Maximum and Minimum Porosities of Sands," *Proceedings,* 2nd International Conference on Soil Mechanics and Foundation Engineering (Rotterdam), Vol. 1.

LAMBE, T. W. and R. T. MARTIN (1953–57), "The Composition and Engineering Properties of Soil," (a series of 5 papers), *Proceedings,* Highway Research Board, Vols. 32–36, Washington. D. C.

LAMBE, T. W. (1958a). "The Engineering Behavior of Compacted Clay " *Journal,* SMFD, ASCE, Vol. 84, No. SM 3.

LAMBE, T. W. (1958b), "The Structure of Compacted Clay," *Journal,* SMFD, ASCE, Vol. 84, No. SM 2.

LAMBE, T. W. (1960), "A Mechanistic Picture of the Shear Strength in Clays", *Proceedings,* ASCE Research Conference on Shear Strength of Cohesive Soils, Boulder, Co.

LAMBE, T. W. (1962), "Pore Pressures in a Foundation Clay," *Journal,* SMFD, ASCE, Vol. 88, SM 2.

LAMBE, T. W. (1967), *Soil Testing for Engineers,* John Wiley & Sons, Inc., New York, N. Y.

LAMBE, T. W. and R. V. WHITMAN (1969), *Soil Mechanics,* John Wiley & Sons, Inc., New York, N. Y.

LEITCH, H. C. and R. N. YONG (1967), "The Rate Dependent Mechanism of Shear Failure in Clay Soils," *Soil Mechanics Series No. 21,* McGill University, Toronto.

LOVE, A. E. (1927), *Mathematical Theory of Elasticity,* Cambridge University Press.

Massachusetts Institute of Technology (1969), *ICES – STRUDL II, Engineering User's Manual 1, 2, 3, Publication No. R 68–91, 92, 93,* Department of Civil Engineering, Cambridge, Mass.

MEYERHOF, G. G. (1953), "The Bearing Capacity of Foundations under Eccentric and Inclined Loads", *Proceedings,* 3rd ICSMFE, Paris, Vol. 1.

MEYERHOF, G. G. (1956), "Penetration Tests and Bearing Capacity of Cohesionless Soils," *Journal,* ASCE, SMFD, Vol. 82, No. SM 1.

MEYERHOF, G. G. (1963), "Some Recent Research on the Bearing Capacity of Foundations," *Canadian Geotechnical Journal,* Vol. 1, No. 1.

MIDDLEBROOKS, T. A. (1946), "Classification of Materials for Subgrades for Airfields and Granular Type Roads," *Proceedings,* 25th Annual Meeting of the Highway Research Board, Washington, D. C.

MINARD, J.P., HOLMAN, W. W., and A. R. JUMIKIS (1953), *Engineering Soil Survey of New Jersey, Report No. 9,* Rutgers University Engineering Research Bulletin Number 23, New Brunswick, N. J.

MINDLIN, R. D. (1949), "Compliance of Elastic Bodies in Contact," *Journal of Applied Mechanics,* ASME Paper No. 48-APM-24.

MORTON, J. O. (1936), "The Application of Soil Mechanics to Highway Foundation Engineering," *Proceedings,* 1st ICSMFE (Cambridge, Mass.) Vol. III.

National Aeronautics and Space Administration (1970), *SP 222 NASTRAN User's Manual,* Cosmic, University of Georgia, Athens, Ga.

NOWATZKI, E. A. (1972), "The Effect of a Thermal and Ultrahigh Vacuum Environment on the Strength of Precompressed Granular Materials," *The Moon,* Vol. 5, Nos. 1 & 2.

ODEN, J. T. (1972), *Finite Elements of Non Linear Continua,* McGraw-Hill, New York, N. Y.

OLSON, R. E. (1962), "The Shear Strength Properties of Calcium Illite," *Geotechnique,* Vol. XII.

PERUMPRAL, J. V. (1969), *The Finite Element Method for Predicting the Stress Distribution and Soil Deformation Under a Tractive Device,* PhD. Dissertation, Purdue University, Lafayette, Ind.

PERUMPRAL, J. V., LILJEDAHL, J. B. and W. H. PERLOFF (1971), "The Finite Element Method for Predicting Stress Distribution and Soil Deformation Under a Tractive Device," *Transactions,* ASAE, Vol. 14, No. 6.

PHILLIPS, F. C. (1971), *An Introduction to Crystallography,* John Wiley & Sons. Inc., New York, N. Y.

POPOV, G. I. (1966), "Plane Contact Problem of the Theory of Elasticity with Bonding or Frictional Forces," *PMM,* Vol. 30, No. 3.

POTYONDY, J. G. (1961), "Skin Friction Between Various Soil and Construction Materials," *Geotechnique,* Vol. XI, No. 4.

POULOS, H. G. and E. H. DAVIS (1974), *Elastic Solutions for Soil and Rock Mechanics,* John Wiley & Sons, Inc. New York, N. Y.

PRANDTL, L. (1920), "*Über die Härte plastischer Körper,*" Nachrichten von der Königlichen Gesellschaft der Wissenschaften zu Göttingen (Mathematisch-physikalische Klasse aus dem Jahre 1920), Berlin.

PRANDTL, L. (1921), "Über die Eindringungsfestigkeit (Härte) plastischer Baustoffe und die Festigkeit von Schneiden," *Zeitschrift für angewandte Mathematik und Mechanik,* Vol. 1, No. 1.

RANKINE, W. J. (1885), *A Manual of Applied Mechanics,* Charles Griffin and Co, London.

RICHARDSON, A. M., Jr. and R. V. WHITMAN (1964), "Effect of Strain-Rate Upon Undrained Shear Resistance of Saturated Remolded Fat Clay," *Geotechnique,* Vol. XIII, No. 4.

RIECKEN, F. F., and G. D. SMITH, (1949), "Lower Categories of Soil Classification: Family, Series, Type, Phase," *Soil Science,* Vol. 67.

ROBERTS, A. M. (1971), "Further Two-Dimensional Effects of Cylinders Rolling on an Elastic Half-Space," *Quarterly of Applied Mathematics.*

RUSSEL, E. R. and J. L. MICKLE (1970), "Liquid Limit Values by Soil Moisture Tension," *Journal,* SMFD, ASCE, Vol. 96, No. SM 3.

SCHIFFMAN, R.L., CHEN, A. and J. JORDAN (1969), "An Analysis of Consolidation Theories," *Journal,* SMFD, ASCE, Vol. 95, No. SM 1.

SCHULTZE, E. (1952), "Der Widerstand des Baugrundes gegen schräge Sohlpressungen," *Bautechnik,* Vol. 29.

SCOTT, R. F. (1963), *Principles of Soil Mechanics,* Addison-Wesley Publishing Co., Reading, Mass.

SEED, H. B. and C. K. CHAN (1959), "Structure and Strength Characteristics of Compacted Clays," *Proceedings,* ASCE, Vol. 81, No. 842.

SEED, H. B., WOODWARD, R. J., and R. LUNDGREN (1964), "Fundamental Aspects of the Atterberg Limits," *Journal,* SMFD, ASCE, Vol. 90, No. SM 6.

SKEMPTON, A. W. (1953), "The Colloidal Activity of Clays," *Proceedings,* 3rd ICSMFE (Zurich), Vol. 1.

SKEMPTON, A. W. (1954), "The Pore Pressure Coefficient A and B," *Geotechnique,* Vol. IV.

SKEMPTON, A. W. (1961), "Effective Stress in Soils, Concrete and Rocks," *Pore Pressure and Suction in Soils,* Butterworths, London.

SMITH, J. O. and C. K. LIU (1953), "Stresses Due to Tangential and Normal Loads on an Elastic Solid with Application to Some Contact Stress Problems," *Journal of Applied Mechanics,* ASME, paper No. 52–A–13.

SOKOLOVSKII, V. V. (1960), *Statics of Soil Media,* Butterworths, London.

STAPLE, W. J. (1969), "Comparison of Computed and Measured Moisture Redistribution Following Infiltration," *Proceedings,* Soil Science Society of America, Vol. 33, No. 6.

STEELE, D. J. (1946), "Classification of Highway Subgrade Materials," *Proceedings,* 25th Annual Meeting of the Highway Research Board, Washington, D. C.

TAYLOR, D. W. (1948), *Fundamentals of Soil Mechanics,* John Wiley & Sons, Inc. New York, N. Y.

TERZAGHI, K. (1925), *Erdbaumechanik,* Franz Deuticke, Vienna.

TERZAGHI, K. (1943), *Theoretical Soil Mechanics,* John Wiley and Sons, Inc., New York, N. Y.

TERZAGHI, K., and R. B. PECK (1948), *Soil Mechanics in Engineering Practice,* John Wiley and Sons, Inc., New York, N. Y.

THORP, J. and G. D. SMITH (1949), "Higher Categories of Soil Classifications: Order, Suborder, and Great Soil Groups," *Soil Science,* Vol. 67.

TIMOSHENKO, S. (1951), *Theory of Elasticity,* McGraw Hill, New York, N. Y.

URAL, O. (1973), *Finite Element Method – Basic Concepts and Applications,* Intext Educational Publishers, New York, N. Y.

U. S. Army Engineers Waterways Experiment Station (1957), *The Unified Soil Classification System, Revision # 1, Technical Memorandum No. 3–357,* Vicksburg, Miss.

U. S. Army Engineers Waterways Experiment Station (1953), *The Unified Soil Classification System, Technical Memorandum No. 3–357,* Vicksburg, Miss.

WES (1940–1944), *Shear Reports Made by M.I.T. Soil Mechanics Laboratory to U.S. Army Corps of Engineers,* Nos. 1–10, Vicksburg, Miss.

WES (1956), *Soil Compaction Investigation, Report No. 7: Effect on Soil Compaction of Tire Pressure and Number of Coverages of Rubber Tired Rollers and Foot Contact Pressure os Sheepsfoot Rollers, U.S., Army Corps of Engineers Technical Memo No. 3–271,* Vicksburg, Miss.

WU, T. H. (1966), *Soil Mechanics,* Allyn and Bacon, Inc., Boston, Mass.

YONG, R. N. and B. P. WARKENTIN (1966), *Introduction to Soil Behavior,* The Macmillan Company, New York, N. Y.

ZIENKIEWICZ, O. C. and Y. K. CHEUNG (1967), *The Finite Element Method in Structural and Continuum Mechanics,* McGraw Hill, New York, N. Y.

ZIMON, A. D. (1969), *Adhesion of Dust and Powder,* Plenum Press, New York, N. Y.

PART 2

PLASTICITY THEORY FOR SOILS

CHAPTER 2.1

INTRODUCTION

Fundamental to analyses of soil-structure interaction by plasticity theory is the assumption that the soil acts as a rigid-perfectly plastic material. This means that, under load, the soil reacts in a manner illustrated by the solid line in Figure 2.1. The material does not deform regardless of loading sequence, stress history, rate of loading etc. until it reaches a condition of stress at which failure occurs. This is in contradistinction to an elastic-plastic material illustrated by the dashed line in Figure 2.1 which undergoes recoverable deformation before reaching a stress condition at which failure occurs. In both cases, deformation at failure takes place at a constant rate without change in stress.

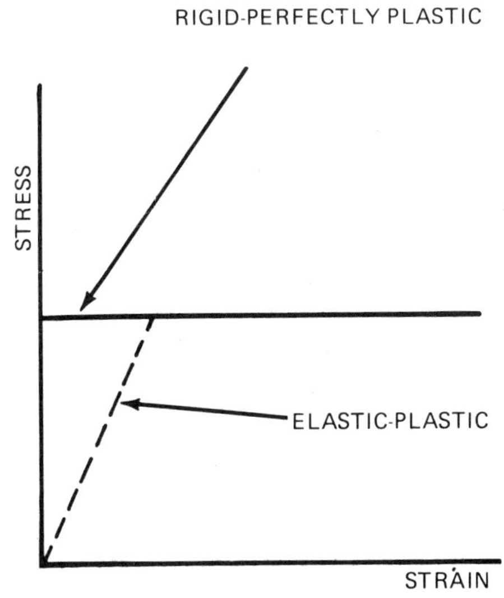

Fig. 2.1
Material Behavior

The perfectly general representation of the stresses existing at any point within the soil mass is shown in Figure 2.2(a). In a stress field, variation of these stresses with the coordinates have to be taken into account to analyze the equilibrium conditions. The stresses acting on an element (refer to Figure 2.2(b)) may be integrated over their respective differential surface areas and summed to obtain the following general equilibrium relationships:

In the *x*-direction:

$$-\tau_{yz}\,dxdz + \left(\tau_{zx} + \frac{\partial\tau_{zx}}{\partial z}dz\right)dxdy + \left(\tau_{yx} + \frac{\partial\tau_{yx}}{\partial y}dy\right)dxdz$$
$$-\tau_{zx}\,dydx - \sigma_x\,dydz + \left(\sigma_x + \frac{\partial\sigma_x}{\partial x}dx\right)dydz \pm X = 0$$

Eq. 2.1.1 a

In the *y*-direction:

$$-\tau_{xy}\,dydz + \left(\tau_{zy} + \frac{\partial\tau_{zy}}{\partial z}dz\right)dydx + \left(\tau_{xy} + \frac{\partial\tau_{xy}}{\partial x}dz\right)dydz$$
$$-\tau_{zy}\,dydx - \sigma_y\,dzdx + \left(\sigma_y + \frac{\partial\sigma_y}{\partial y}dy\right)dzdx \pm Y = 0$$

Eq. 2.1.1 b

In the *z*-direction:

$$-\tau_{xz}\,dydz + \left(\tau_{xz} + \frac{\partial\tau_{xz}}{\partial x}dx\right)dzdy + \left(\tau_{yz} + \frac{\partial\tau_{yz}}{\partial y}dy\right)dxdz$$
$$-\tau_{yz}\,dxdz - \sigma_z\,dydx + \left(\sigma_z + \frac{\partial\sigma_z}{\partial z}dz\right)dydx \pm Z = 0$$

Eq. 2.1.1 c

In these equations *X, Y, Z* are body forces due to soil weight, seepage, and/or inertia. The sign depends upon the element orientation with respect to gravity, flow, and/or acceleration. These forces are expressed in general terms as follows:

Body Forces = Weight + Inertia + Seepage

$$X = W_x + \frac{\gamma}{g}\left(\frac{\partial^2 x}{\partial t^2}\right) + \gamma_w\left(\frac{\partial h}{\partial x}\right) \qquad \text{Eq. 2.1.2a}$$

$$Y = W_y + \frac{\gamma}{g}\left(\frac{\partial^2 y}{\partial t^2}\right) + \gamma_w\left(\frac{\partial h}{\partial y}\right) \qquad \text{Eq. 2.1.2b}$$

$$Z = W_z + \frac{\gamma}{g}\left(\frac{\partial^2 z}{\partial t^2}\right) + \gamma_w\left(\frac{\partial h}{\partial z}\right) \qquad \text{Eq. 2.1.2c}$$

where W_x, W_y and W_z are the soil weight components in the *x*, *y* and *z* directions respectively and $\partial h/\partial x$, $\partial h/\partial y$, and $\partial h/\partial z$ are the gradients of the

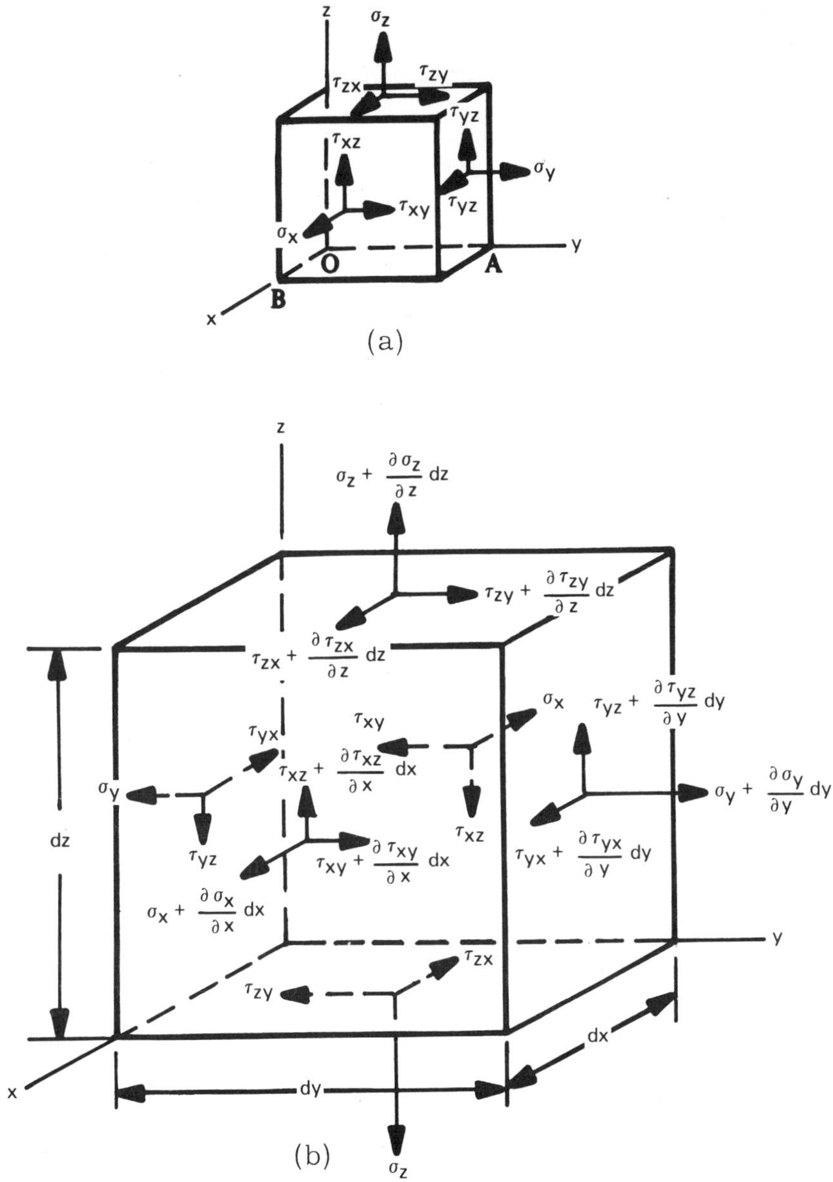

Fig. 2.2
Stress Acting Within a Soil Mass
a) At a point
b) On an element

hydraulic head, h, causing flow in the x, y and z directions respectively.

Inspection of the soil element in Figure 2.2(b) reveals that moment equilibrium requires that $\tau_{xy} = \tau_{yx}$; $\tau_{yz} = \tau_{zy}$ and $\tau_{zx} = \tau_{xz}$. Therefore Equations 2.1.1 reduce to

$$\frac{\partial \sigma_x}{\partial x} + \frac{\partial \tau_{xy}}{\partial y} + \frac{\partial \tau_{xz}}{\partial z} \mp X = 0 \qquad \text{Eq. 2.1.3a}$$

$$\frac{\partial \sigma_y}{\partial y} + \frac{\partial \tau_{yz}}{\partial z} + \frac{\partial \tau_{yx}}{\partial x} \mp Y = 0 \qquad \text{Eq. 2.1.3b}$$

$$\frac{\partial \sigma_z}{\partial z} + \frac{\partial \tau_{zx}}{\partial x} + \frac{\partial \tau_{zy}}{\partial y} \mp Z = 0 \qquad \text{Eq. 2.1.3c}$$

In the application of plasticity theory to soil mechanics problems, these equations of equilibrium are combined with a yield or failure criterion that adequately represents soil behavior to provide a mathematical model by which soil reaction to load can be predicted. As with any other mathematical representation of a natural phenomenon, the results must be interpreted in the light of how closely the model conforms to actual conditions. The following sections assume that the combination of the equations of plastic equilibrium with a representative yield criterion is valid and can be used to describe soil behavior. The next section considers the MOHR-COULOMB yield criterion which is the one most frequently used in conventional soil mechanics analyses. The necessary equations for use with the equations of plastic equilibrium are developed. Subsequent sections describe how these two concepts are combined to yield sets of equations that are applicable to vehicle mobility problems in which the effects of various factors such as symmetry, inertia, pore water pressure, etc. are considered.

CHAPTER 2.2

DIFFERENTIAL EQUATIONS OF PLASTIC EQUILIBRIUM

2.2.1 The Mohr-Coulomb Yield (Failure) Criterion

The MOHR-COULOMB failure theory is one of a number of failure theories that define failure in terms of stress conditions in contradistinction to those based on strain. Simply stated, the MOHR-COULOMB yield criterion defines failure to occur in a material when the shear stress on any plane equals or exceeds the shear strength of the material on that plane. Shear strength is itself a function of the normal stress on that plane, i.e.

$$s = f(\sigma_n) \qquad \text{Eq. 2.2.1}$$

COULOMB (1776) defined $f(\sigma_n)$ as a linear function of the normal stress, however it need not always be so. The linear function has the advantage that computations of shear strength can be made readily and for most soils it describes the relationship between strength and normal stress adequately. The linear form of the COULOMB expression was given in Section 1.3.3 as

$$s = c + \sigma_n \tan \varphi \qquad \text{Eq. 1.3.24}$$

where

c = cohesion.

σ_n = normal stress.

φ = an internal friction angle.

Stress history and conditions of loading and drainage have a significant effect on the shear strength since these factors influence the values of c and φ. The meaning of "effective strength parameters" and "total strength parameters" and their implications on the vehicle mobility problem have been discussed in Chapter 1.3. Use of the generic terms "cohesion" and "friction angle" in our discussion here allows the COULOMB yield criterion to be restated as follows: Any combination of normal and shear stresses that together result in a state of stress which plots below the material strength function as shown by points A and E in Figure 2.3 can be sustained by the material without its yielding or failing. Any combination of normal and shear stresses that plots on (point B) or above (points C and D) this function results in a Coulombic type failure. The figure shows clearly that, depending on the magnitude of the normal stress, a given shear stress (τ_1) may in one case cause failure ($\sigma_n = \sigma_D$ or $\sigma_n = \sigma_1$) and in another case not ($\sigma_n = \sigma_E$). Conversely, for a given normal stress (σ_1), one degree of shear stress ($\tau = \tau_c$ or $\tau = \tau_1$) results in failure and another ($\tau = \tau_A$) does not. Obviously, the strength function defines the "limiting stress" conditions for the material.

MOHR's contribution to the COULOMB concept of failure came later in the form of relationships between the stresses on an inclined plane and the principal stresses as determined from his well known graphical construction. Figure 2.4 shows a series of MOHR circles of stress (solid circles A, B, and C) each of which was obtained by imposing on the material different conditions of major (σ_1) and minor (σ_3) principal stress so as to obtain failure. The curve (or line) described by the common tangent to these circles is called the "failure envelope" and is identical to the COULOMB strength function described previously. The significance of the MOHR circle construction is that in many cases where the magnitude of principal stresses is known and the orientation of the failure plane is not known beforehand, it indicates whether the stress state characterized by the principal stresses is permissible or not. It should be noted that there are principal stress conditions (σ_{3Q} and σ_{1Q}) under which failure does not occur and the MOHR circle (dashed circle in Figure 2.4) is nowhere tangent to the COULOMB strength function.

The general expressions relating normal and shear stresses acting on two orthogonal planes to the normal and shear stress acting on any other plane inclined at an angle from one of the orthogonal planes can be derived with reference to Figure 2.5(a). If a unit dimension into the plane of the paper is considered and the stresses acting on each of the faces of the element ABC are integrated over their respective faces, the resulting forces can be summed perpendicular and parallel to the face AC as follows:
From summation of forces perpendicular to face AC:

$$\sigma\,\overline{AC} = \sigma_x\,\overline{AB}\sin\alpha + \sigma_z\,\overline{BC}\cos\alpha + \tau_{xz}\,(\overline{AB}\cos\alpha + \overline{BC}\sin\alpha)$$

Dividing by $\overline{AC}$ and substituting $\sin\alpha = \overline{AB}/\overline{AC}$ and $\cos\alpha = \overline{BC}/\overline{AC}$ yields:

$$\sigma = \sigma_x\sin^2\alpha + \sigma_z\cos^2\alpha + 2\,\tau_{xz}\sin\alpha\cos\alpha \qquad \text{Eq. 2.2.2}$$

From summation of forces parallel to face AC:

$$\tau\,\overline{AC} = \sigma_z\,\overline{BC}\sin\alpha - \sigma_x\,\overline{AB}\cos\alpha + \tau_{xz}\,(\overline{AB}\sin\alpha - \overline{BC}\cos\alpha)$$

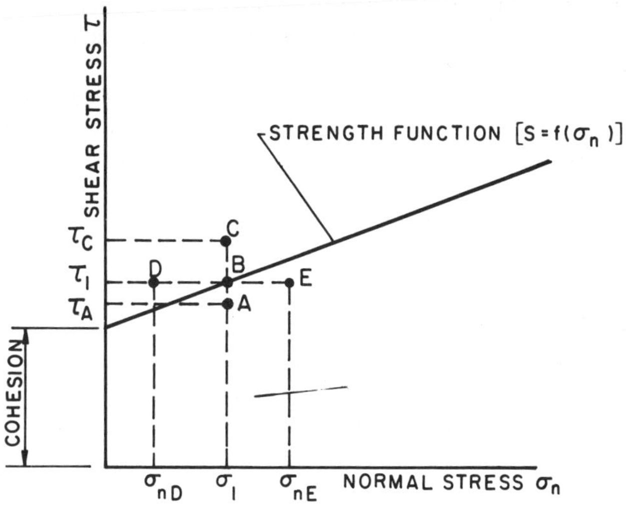

Fig. 2.3
Possible Stress States and Their
Relationship to the Coulombic Strength Function

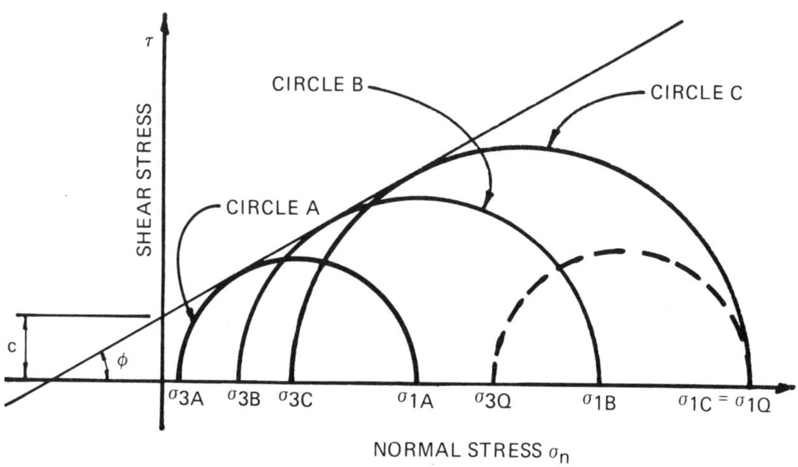

Fig. 2.4
MOHR Circle Construction and the Relationship between Major (σ_1)
and Minor (σ_3) Principal Stresses

Dividing and substituting as above yields:

$\tau = \sigma_z \cos\alpha \sin\alpha - \sigma_x \cos\alpha \sin\alpha + \tau_{xz} (\sin^2\alpha - \cos^2\alpha)$

Since $\sin\alpha \cos\alpha = \sin 2\alpha/2$ and $\sin^2\alpha - \cos^2\alpha = -\cos 2\alpha$

$$\tau = \frac{\sigma_z - \sigma_x}{2} \sin 2\alpha - \tau_{xz} \cos 2\alpha \qquad \text{Eq. 2.2.3}$$

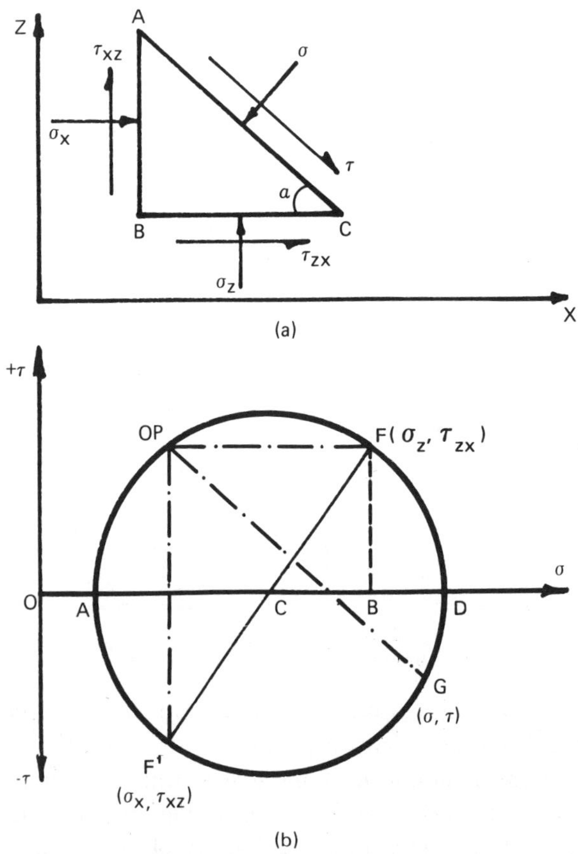

Fig. 2.5
Relationship Between Stress States on a Soil Element
and the MOHR Circle Construction
a) General stress state on soil element
b) Corresponding MOHR circle construction

Expressions relating σ_x, σ_z, τ_{zx}, τ_{xz} and α with the major and minor principal stresses can also be derived analytically, but it is much easier to obtain these expressions graphically from the MOHR circle construction.

If $\sigma_z > \sigma_x$ and if shears causing counterclockwise rotation of the element are considered positive (numerically $\tau_{zx} = \tau_{xz}$ to maintain moment equilibrium), the stress state depicted in Figure 2.5(a) can be expressed on a MOHR circle as shown in Figure 2.5(b). The distance $\overline{OD}$ corresponds to the major principal stress and the distance $\overline{OA}$ corresponds to the minor principal stress. From the figure, the following analytical expressions can be derived:

$$\sigma_1 = \overline{OD} = \overline{OC} + \overline{CD}$$

but

$$\overline{OC} = (\sigma_z + \sigma_x)/2$$

$$\overline{CD} = \sqrt{\overline{CB}^2 + \overline{FB}^2} = \sqrt{\left(\frac{\sigma_z - \sigma_x}{2}\right)^2 + \tau_{zx}^2}$$

or

$$\sigma_1 = \frac{\sigma_z + \sigma_x}{2} + \sqrt{\left(\frac{\sigma_z - \sigma_x}{2}\right)^2 + \tau_{zx}^2} \qquad \text{Eq. 2.2.4}$$

Similarly

$$\sigma_3 = \frac{\sigma_z + \sigma_x}{2} - \sqrt{\left(\frac{\sigma_z - \sigma_x}{2}\right)^2 + \tau_{zx}^2} \qquad \text{Eq. 2.2.5}$$

From inspection of the figure, the maximum and minumum values of shear stress are:

$$\tau_{\substack{max\\min}} = \pm \sqrt{\left(\frac{\sigma_z - \sigma_x}{2}\right)^2 + \tau_{zx}^2} \qquad \text{Eq. 2.2.6}$$

The values of σ and τ acting on the plane $\overline{AC}$ may also be obtained graphically by using the "origin of planes" construction. If on the MOHR circle in Figure 2.5(b) lines are drawn through the stress points F and F' parallel to $\overline{BC}$ and $\overline{BA}$, the corresponding planes in Figure 2.5(a) on which those stresses act, the point on the MOHR circle at which the lines intersect defines the origin of planes, OP. The usefulness of the origin of planes construction is that the stress conditions on any other plane in the element may be determined by drawing a line through the origin of planes parallel to the plane of interest. Where that line intersects the circle corresponds to the stress state on the plane of interest. Thus, for example, the line $\overline{OPG}$ is drawn parallel to the plane $\overline{AC}$ and its intersection at G defines the stress state on $\overline{AC}$. The simplicity of this construction also enables one to determine the orientation of the major or minor principal stress planes quite readily.

The real value of the origin of planes construction, however, arises when failure conditions occur and the orientation of the failure plane is desired with reference to other planes on which stress conditions are known. In soil mechanics, the orientations of the principal stress planes are often known as well as the magnitude of the stresses acting on those planes. Figure 2.6 shows the MOHR circle for the case where the major principal stress acts vertically and the minor principal stress acts horizontally (Note that by definition no shear stresses act on principal stress planes). In this case the origin of planes is at point A and the normal stress on any plane inclined at an angle α with respect to the major principal stress plane is:

$$\sigma_n = \overline{OB} = \overline{OC} + \overline{CB} = \left(\frac{\sigma_1 + \sigma_3}{2}\right) + \left(\frac{\sigma_1 - \sigma_3}{2}\right) \cos 2\alpha \qquad \text{Eq. 2.2.7}$$

The relationship between α and 2α as shown on the MOHR circle construction is dictated by the geometric axiom that the central angle (2α) sub-

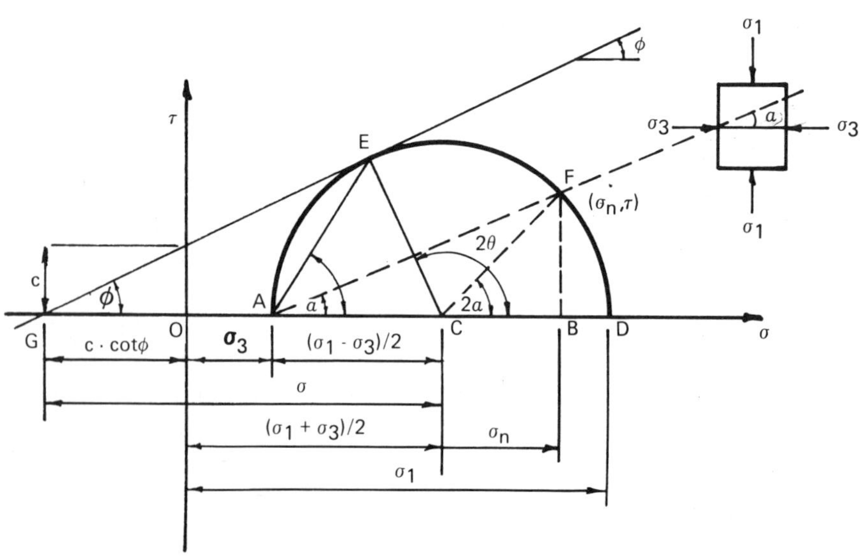

Fig. 2.6
MOHR Circle Construction for Failure Condition

tending a certain arc of a circle *(DF)* is equal to twice the inscribed angle (α) subtending the same arc at any point on the circle.

The shear stress on the same plane is:

$$\tau = \overline{BF} = \left(\frac{\sigma_1 - \sigma_3}{2}\right) \sin 2\alpha \qquad \text{Eq. 2.2.8}$$

Consequently, at failure

$$\tau = c + \sigma_n \tan \varphi \qquad \text{Eq. 1.3.24}$$

or

$$\left(\frac{\sigma_1 - \sigma_3}{2}\right) \sin 2\alpha = c + \left(\frac{\sigma_1 + \sigma_3}{2} + \left[\frac{\sigma_1 - \sigma_3}{2}\right] \cos 2\alpha\right) \tan \varphi \qquad \text{Eq. 2.2.9}$$

from which (since $\sin 2\alpha = 2 \sin \alpha \cos \alpha$; $\cos 2\alpha = 2 \cos^2 \alpha - 1$)

$$\sigma_1 = \sigma_3 + \frac{\sigma_3 \tan \varphi + c}{\dfrac{\sin 2\alpha}{2} - \cos^2 \alpha \tan \varphi} \qquad \text{Eq. 2.2.10}$$

If one assumes that the MOHR-COULOMB yield criterion in terms of principal stresses (Equation 2.2.9.) is satisfied on all the variously oriented planes, then the one for which σ_1 is the minimum will be the actual failure plane (i.e., the value of σ_1 that makes the circle just touch the failure envelope at point E for a given value of σ_3). With reference to Equation 2.2.10, σ_1 is minimum when $\alpha = \theta$ and the denominator of the second term ($f = {}^1/_2 \sin 2\theta - \cos^2 \theta \tan \varphi$) is maximum.

Therefore,

$$\frac{df}{d\theta} = \cos 2\theta + 2 \cos \theta \sin \theta \tan \varphi = 0$$

or

$$\cos 2\theta + \sin 2\theta \tan \varphi = 0$$

This equation is satisfied when

$$2\theta = 90^\circ + \varphi$$

or

$$\theta = 45^\circ + \frac{1}{2} \varphi \qquad \text{Eq. 2.2.11}$$

Substitution of Equation 2.2.11 into Equation 2.2.10 yields

$$\sigma_1 = \sigma_3 \tan^2 \left(45^\circ + \frac{1}{2} \varphi\right) + 2c \tan \left(45^\circ + \frac{1}{2} \varphi\right) \qquad \text{Eq. 2.2.12}$$

Although not shown in Figure 2.6, all stresses are symmetrical (circles) with respect to the σ_1 and σ_3 axes. Therefore, two sets of failure planes making angles $\pm\theta$ with the major principal plane exist. It is this angle, θ, that defines the orientation with respect to the major principal stress plane of the failure surfaces or "slip lines" which are identical to the *i*- and *j*- characteristic lines obtained from plasticity theory. The manner in which the differential equations of plastic equilibrium are used with the MOHR-COULOMB yield criterion to describe conditions in a mass of soil where the directions of principal stress axes change from point to point (i.e. the failure zone consists of a series of curved slip surfaces) is described in the following section. Cases where the stresses in the soil mass are such that the failure zone consists of two sets of intersecting planes only will be discussed in Chapter 2.5.

In the development of the MOHR-COULOMB failure criterion it is implied that the intermediate principal stress (σ_2) has no effect on the failure of soils. Since maximum shear stresses develop on planes perpendicular to the $\sigma_1 - \sigma_3$ plane, as the MOHR circle construction for three-dimensional stress states (Figure 2.7) indicates, the intermediate principal stress does not affect the failure conditions.

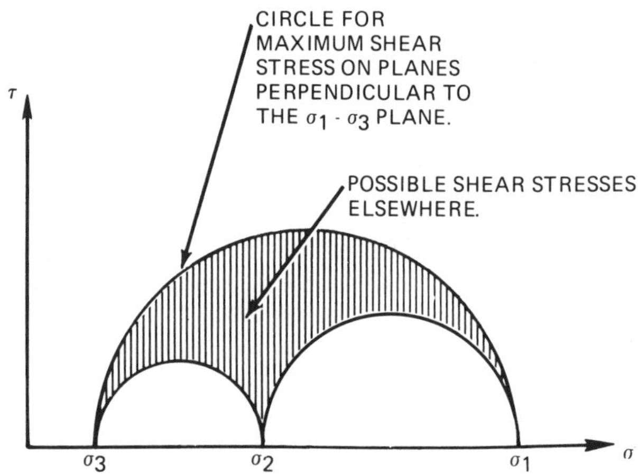

Fig. 2.7
Schematic Representation of MOHR Circle for Three-Dimensional Stress States

2.2.2 Derivation of the Basic Differential Equations of Plasticity for Soil Under Plane Strain Conditions

This section illustrates how the MOHR-COULOMB failure criterion is combined with the differential equations of plastic equilibrium to yield a set of equations that completely describes the geometry of the slip lines and their associated stresses within the failure zone for soils under plane strain conditions.

In two dimensions, the differential equations of static equilibrium (Equations 2.1.3) reduce to

$$\frac{\partial \sigma_x}{\partial x} + \frac{\partial \tau_{xz}}{\partial z} = X \qquad \text{Eq. 2.2.13a}$$

$$\frac{\partial \sigma_z}{\partial z} + \frac{\partial \tau_{zx}}{\partial x} = Z \qquad \text{Eq. 2.2.13b}$$

With reference to Figure 2.8 in which perfectly general conditions of boundary loading and geometry are shown, it can be seen that $X = \gamma \sin \varepsilon$ and $Z = \gamma \cos \varepsilon$ (assuming that seepage and inertia forces are zero).

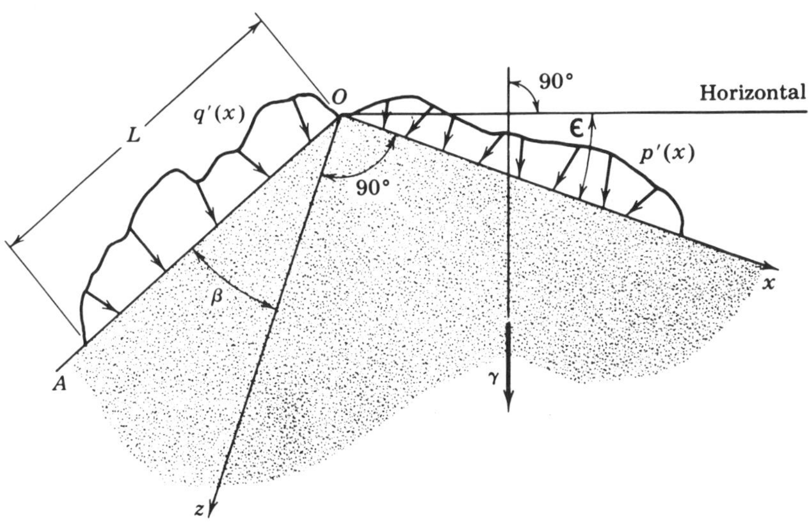

Fig. 2.8
Boundary Conditions for Plastic Equilibrium
(After HARR, 1966)

In order to combine the MOHR-COULOMB yield relationship with these equilibrium equations, Equation 1.3.24 ($s = c + \sigma_n \tan \varphi$) must be expressed in terms of σ_x, σ_z, and τ_{xz} instead of s and σ_n.

From the graphical representation of the MOHR-COULOMB relationship shown in Figure 2.6 it can be seen that $\overline{GC} = c \cdot \cot \varphi + (\sigma_1 + \sigma_3)/2$ and

$\overline{EC} = (\sigma_1 - \sigma_3)/2$. Geometric relationships apparent in the figure yield:

$$\sin \varphi = \overline{EC}/\overline{GC}$$

or

$$\frac{(\sigma_1 - \sigma_3)}{2} = \left(\frac{(\sigma_1 + \sigma_3)}{2} + c \cdot \cot \varphi\right) \sin \varphi \qquad \text{Eq. 2.2.14}$$

and

$$\overline{OC} = \overline{GC} - \overline{GO}$$

or

$$\frac{(\sigma_1 + \sigma_3)}{2} = \left(\frac{(\sigma_1 + \sigma_3)}{2} + c \cdot \cot \varphi\right) - c \cdot \cot \varphi \qquad \text{Eq. 2.2.15}$$

These equations represent failure conditions only. However, general relationships between the principal stresses and stresses on other planes can also be obtained from Figure 2.6. Let point F represent the state of stresses on any plane inclined at an angle α from the principal stress plane where the normal stress is σ_x and the shear stress is τ_{zx}. Then, bearing in mind that Figure 2.6 shows only half the stress circle (there is an orthogonal plane where the normal stress is σ_z and the shear stress is $\tau_{xz} = -\tau_{zx}$) the normal stresses are given by Equation 2.2.7 as:

$$\sigma_x = \frac{(\sigma_1 + \sigma_3)}{2} + \left(\frac{\sigma_1 - \sigma_3}{2}\right) \cos 2\alpha \qquad \text{Eq. 2.2.16a}$$

$$\sigma_z = \frac{(\sigma_1 + \sigma_3)}{2} - \left(\frac{\sigma_1 - \sigma_3}{2}\right) \cos 2\alpha \qquad \text{Eq. 2.2.16b}$$

Shear stress is given by Equation 2.2.8 as

$$\tau_{zx} = \left(\frac{\sigma_1 - \sigma_3}{2}\right) \sin 2\alpha \qquad \text{Eq. 2.2.16c}$$

$$\tau_{xz} = -\tau_{zx} \qquad \text{Eq. 2.2.16d}$$

Substitution of Equations 2.2.16 into Equations 2.2.14 and 2.2.15 yields the following basic equations:

$$\sigma_x = \sigma (1 + \sin \varphi \cos 2\alpha) - \psi \qquad \text{Eq. 2.2.17a}$$

$$\sigma_z = \sigma (1 - \sin \varphi \cos 2\alpha) - \psi \qquad \text{Eq. 2.2.17b}$$

$$\tau_{xz} = \sigma \sin \varphi \sin 2\alpha \qquad \text{Eq. 2.2.17c}$$

where

$$\sigma = \frac{(\sigma_1 + \sigma_3)}{2} + c \cdot \cot \varphi$$

$$\psi = c \cdot \cot \varphi$$

These equations represent the conditions of failure at any point in the soil mass. As shown in Figure 2.9 the directions of the associated slip lines in the x-z plane are generally referenced to the case where the x-plane is horizontal and θ is the angle between it and the direction of the major principal stress. In that case the failure surfaces or sliplines are oriented $\pm\mu$ from the direction of the major principal stress where $\mu = 45° - \varphi/2$. The same relationship between the failure planes and principal stress directions can be obtained from Figure 2.6 if one realizes that at failure, $\alpha =$ angle $DAE = 45° + \varphi/2$ as indicated by Equation 2.2.11 where α is the angle between the failure plane and the major principal stress *plane*. Since the major principal stress acts perpendicularly to that plane, the failure plane has an orientation of $\mu = (90° - \alpha)$ or $(45° - \varphi/2)$ with respect to the major principal stress direction.

Substitution of Equations 2.2.17 into Equations 2.2.13 yields the basic differential equations of plasticity for soil under plane strain conditions. These equations are:

$$(1 + \sin\varphi \cos 2\theta)\frac{\partial \sigma}{\partial x} + \sin\varphi \sin 2\theta \frac{\partial \sigma}{\partial z} - 2\sigma \sin\varphi \left(\sin 2\theta \frac{\partial \theta}{\partial x} - \cos 2\theta \frac{\partial \theta}{\partial z}\right) = \gamma \sin\varepsilon \qquad \text{Eq. 2.2.18a}$$

$$\sin\varphi \sin 2\theta \frac{\partial \sigma}{\partial x} + (1 - \sin\varphi \cos 2\theta)\frac{\partial \sigma}{\partial z} + 2\sigma \sin\varphi \left(\cos 2\theta \frac{\partial \theta}{\partial x} + \sin 2\theta \frac{\partial \theta}{\partial z}\right) = \gamma \cos\varepsilon \qquad \text{Eq. 2.2.18b}$$

where

ε = angle of inclination of x-axis from the horizontal.

θ = angle between the horizontal and the direction of the major principal stress.

Sokolovskii (1960) proposed modifying these basic equations by multiplying the first by $\sin(\theta \pm \mu)$ and the second by $-\cos(\theta \pm \mu)$. These operations transform Equations 2.2.18 into:

$$\left(\frac{\partial \sigma}{\partial x} \mp 2\sigma \tan\varphi \frac{\partial \theta}{\partial x} - \gamma \frac{\sin(\varepsilon \mp \varphi)}{\cos\varphi}\right)\cos(\theta \mp \mu) +$$

$$\left(\frac{\partial \sigma}{\partial z} \mp 2\sigma \tan\varphi \frac{\partial \theta}{\partial z} - \gamma \frac{\cos(\varepsilon \mp \varphi)}{\cos\varphi}\right)\sin(\theta \mp \mu) = 0$$

Eqs. 2.2.19a and 2.2.19b

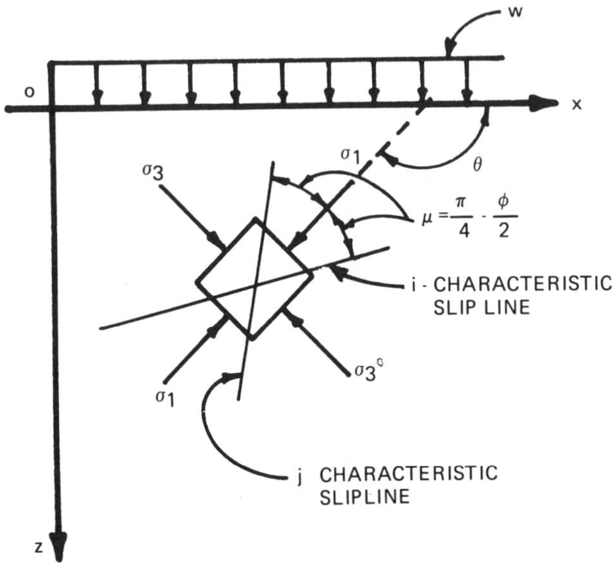

Fig. 2.9
Pertinent Orientations

At this point SOKOLOVSKII introduced a set of "dummy" variables that enabled him to modify Equations 2.2.19 into more tractable form. He chose these dummy variables in such a way that not only was the modified system mathematically simpler than the original system but there was also a direct correspondence between the variables in both systems. By mapping the simpler, modified system of equations on to a "dummy" plane, SOKOLOVSKII was able to obtain solutions rather easily and then transfer these solutions back to the "real" plane. In the mapping process the solution in the "dummy" plane has as its corresponding solution in the real plane two families of "characteristic" curves or lines of slip which intersect at an angle of 2μ everywhere in that plane. SOKOLOVSKII found that the following general system of equilibrium equations described the grid or "slip line field" composed of these characteristic curves and the stress conditions within it:

$$dz = dx \tan(\theta \pm \mu)$$ Eqs. 2.2.20a and 2.2.20b

$$d\sigma \pm 2\sigma \tan\varphi \, d\theta = \frac{\gamma}{\cos\varphi}\left[\sin(\varepsilon \pm \varphi)\,dx + \cos(\varepsilon \pm \varphi)\,dz\right]$$

Eqs. 2.2.20c and 2.2.20d

where the (+) sign applies to "*i*-characteristic" slip lines inclined at a slope of tan $(\theta + \mu)$ from the horizontal and the (—) sign refers to "*j*-characteristic" slip lines inclined at a slope of tan $(\vartheta - \mu)$ from the horizontal as shown in Figure 2.9.

The mathematical details of the mapping process involved in obtaining these equations are outside the scope of this book. An excellent treatment of this topic was presented by HARR (1966). In his book, examples are given of the advantage of using the dummy variables to put together slip line fields that provide solutions to specific problems.

In his development of Equations 2.2.20 SOKOLOVSKII also recognized that the variable θ was a function of the local stress state within the soil mass and therefore proposed the general relationship

$$\theta = (1 - k)\frac{1}{4}\pi + (k\Delta - \delta) + n\pi \qquad \text{Eq. 2.2.21}$$

where

δ = obliquity angle in the classical soil mechanics sense i.e.
$\delta = \arctan [\tau_{xz}/(\sigma_z + \psi)]$

$\Delta = \arcsin (\sin \delta/\sin \varphi)$

$k = +1$ (passive); $k = -1$ (active)

n = any integer; usually 0 or ± 1

Equations 2.2.20 and 2.2.21 are the most general form of the basic differential equations of plastic equilibrium under plane strain conditions for soil with weight whose free surface is inclined at an angle ε from the horizontal. Except for the case where $\gamma = 0$, which is the PRANDTL solution, these equations do not have a closed form solution. For practical purposes, numerical methods are customarily used to integrate these expressions. The most widely used methods are considered in detail in Chapter 2.3. The general equations given above are easily adapted to special situations by modifying the terms to meet the special conditions of interest. For example, if the effects of soil weight can be neglected then $\gamma = 0$; similarly, if the free surface is horizontal, $\varepsilon = 0$. Certain other situations are not as easily handled and require the detailed discussion given in the following sections of this chapter.

2.2.3 Nonlinear Yield Criteria

In the derivation of Equations 2.2.20 and all throughout the discussion in Section 2.2.1, the tacit assumption was made that the relationship between normal and shear stress is linear and that the internal friction angle, φ (the angle described by the "failure envelope") is constant. It is customary to make this assumption in civil engineering practice for the entire range of stresses of interest even though it is more often valid over only a very limited range of stresses, especially when the failure envelope is highly nonlinear. For soils having nonlinear envelopes soils engineers usually use either an "average" φ or a bilinear envelope consisting of two segments with different friction angles over two different ranges of stress. From a practical viewpoint, this is often adequate for the design of many civil engineering structures. However, in situations where structural performance is critical and soil strength properties are very sensitive to stress level, further refinement is necessary. One way of accomplishing this refinement is by formulating an expression for the MOHR-COULOMB envelope in terms of τ, σ_n, c, φ and certain constants derived from test data. For example, the stress envelope (linear or nonlinear) shown in Figure 2.10 is defined by an equation in which soil strength parameters c (cohesion) and φ (angle of internal friction) relate shear stress to normal stress at failure. The nonlinear envelope represents the curve that is tangent to the three MOHR stress circles shown. The straight line usually used to approximate the curvilinear failure envelope can introduce errors at the lower stress levels. The failure envelope for effective stresses may be defined in general terms by the equation

$$\left(\frac{\tau}{d}\right)^m - \frac{\bar{\sigma}_n}{k} - \bar{c} = 0 \qquad \text{Eq. 2.2.22}$$

where

τ = shear stress at failure

$\bar{\sigma}_n$ = effective normal stress at failure as defined by TERZAGHI (1943).

$\bar{c}$ = cohesion

m, d, k = constants that define the curvature of the failure envelope

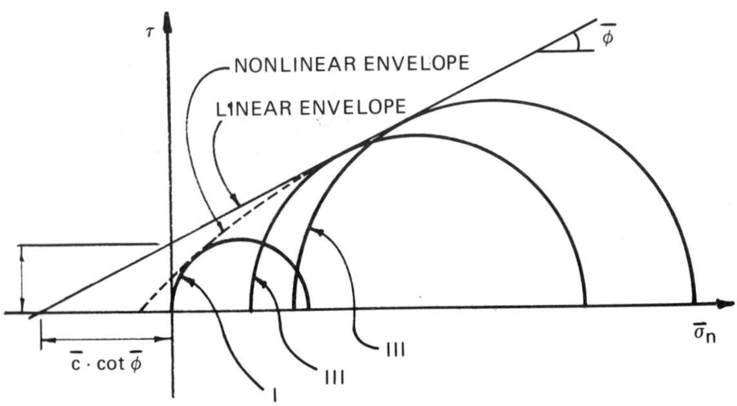

Fig. 2.10
Linear and Nonlinear MOHR Failure Envelopes

For the linear case ($d = m = 1$ and $k = \cot \bar{\varphi}$) Equation 2.2.22 reduces to the more conventional MOHR-COULOMB form widely used in soil mechanics and given by Equation 1.3.24. In terms of effective stress parameters

$$\tau = \bar{\sigma}_n \tan \bar{\varphi} + \bar{c} \qquad \text{Eq. 2.2.23}$$

In the nonlinear case, the constants d, m, and k are determined from test data, usually triaxial test data, for the specific soil and range of normal stresses under consideration. The authors (NOWATZKI and KARAFIATH, 1972a) presented such a determination for a medium dense, dry beach sand. From their evaluation of triaxial test data for this material they found that the nonlinear MOHR-COULOMB envelope could be defined by Equation 2.2.22 with $d = 1.0$, $m = 1.027$, $k = 1.1605$ and $c = 0$, that is

$$\left(\frac{\tau}{1.0}\right)^{1.027} - \frac{\sigma_n}{1.1605} - 0 = 0$$

where all stresses have units of pounds per square inch and the constants have units consistent with the units of the stress variables and the requirement that Equation 2.2.22 be dimensionally correct. The friction angle can be determined from this equation for any specific level of normal stress by evaluating $d\tau/d\sigma_n = \tan \varphi$. When this is done, the following rather simple expression results:

$$\varphi = \text{arc tan}\left(\frac{0.84}{\sigma_n{}^{0.0263}}\right)$$

By inspection of this equation it can be seen that φ varies nonlinearly. For example, $\varphi = 40°$ at a stress level of 1 psi and decreases nonlinearly to 35° at a stress level of 1000 psi. Although this is a relatively small variation for so large a range of normal stress, it demonstrates the manner whereby nonlinear yield criteria may be taken into account.

The development of the differential equations of plastic equilibrium for the case where φ is variable does not differ from that given in the preceding section for the case where φ is constant. In fact, the resulting equations for the plane strain case have the exact same form as Equations 2.2.20. Here also, no closed form solutions exist. The difference between the two cases lies in the procedures required for the numerical solution. These are discussed in detail for both cases in Chapter 2.3.

2.2.4 Differential Equations of Plasticity Including Inertia Forces

If the soil weight (γ-term) on the right side of the equal sign in Equations 2.2.20b and d is considered a "body force" term, then the terms to the left of the equal sign are unaffected by the addition of other body forces such as dynamic forces and/or seepage forces (refer to Equations 2.1.2). The solutions, of course, will be different, but the basic form of the equations will not change.

A moving vehicle imposes dynamic loads on the supporting soil, therefore it is desirable to have expressions that include inertia terms so that the effects of soil inertia forces on vehicle performance can be evaluated. Since force equals mass times acceleration, the component of force in the x-direction is $m\ddot{x}$, which for a unit volume, equals $\gamma\ddot{x}/g$; in the z-direction the magnitude of the inertia force is $\gamma\ddot{z}/g$ where $\ddot{x} = \partial^2 x/\partial t^2$ and $\ddot{z} = \partial^2 z/\partial t^2$. These terms are included in the basic differential equations of equilibrium by modifying Equations 2.2.19 as follows to account for an inclined free surface and the x and z components of inertia forces due to dynamic loads on that free surface:

$$\left[\frac{\partial \sigma}{\partial x} \mp 2\sigma \tan\varphi \frac{\partial \theta}{\partial x} - \left[\left(\gamma + \frac{\gamma\ddot{z}}{g}\right)\frac{\sin(\varepsilon \mp \varphi)}{\cos\varphi} + \right.\right.$$

$$\left.\left.\left(\frac{\gamma\ddot{x}}{g}\right)\frac{\cos(\varepsilon \mp \varphi)}{\cos\varphi}\right]\right] \cos(\theta \mp \mu) + \left[\frac{\partial \sigma}{\partial z} \mp 2\sigma \tan\varphi \frac{\partial \theta}{\partial z} - \right.$$

$$\left.\left[\left(\gamma + \frac{\gamma\ddot{z}}{g}\right)\frac{\cos(\varepsilon \mp \varphi)}{\cos\varphi} - \left(\frac{\gamma\ddot{x}}{g}\right)\frac{\sin(\varepsilon \mp \varphi)}{\cos\varphi}\right]\right] \sin(\theta \mp \mu) = 0$$

Eq. 2.2.24a and 2.2.24b

The same manipulations as described in Section 2.2.2 for the static, plane strain case yield the following basic differential equations for the dynamic loading of a ponderable soil under plane strain conditions with a free surface inclined at an angle ε from the horizontal:

$$dz = dx \tan(\theta \mp \mu)$$

Eqs. 2.2.25a and 2.2.25b

$$d\sigma \mp 2\sigma \tan\varphi\, d\theta = \frac{\gamma}{g \cos\varphi}\left[\left[(g + \ddot{z}) \sin(\varepsilon \mp \varphi) + \right.\right.$$

$$\left.\left.\ddot{x}\cos(\varepsilon \mp \varphi)\right]dx + \left[(g + \ddot{z})\cos(\varepsilon \mp \varphi) - \ddot{x}\sin(\varepsilon \mp \varphi)\right]dz\right]$$

Eqs. 2.2.25c and 2.2.25d

For the case where $\varepsilon = 0$ (horizontal free surface), the last two equations reduce to

$$d\sigma \mp 2\sigma \tan\varphi \, d\theta = \frac{\gamma}{g}\left[\left(\ddot{x} \mp (\ddot{z} + g)\tan\varphi\right)dx + \left(\ddot{z} + g \pm \ddot{x}\tan\varphi\right)dz\right]$$

Eqs. 2.2.26a
and 2.2.26b

In the preceding derivation, x and z are taken as independent variables. Since there is interdependence of acceleration and slip line field geometry, the consequences of the assumption made above must be considered not only with respect to the practicality of pursuing coupled solutions, but also with respect to the compatibility of "statically" and "kinematically" admissible uncoupled solutions. These topics are discussed in detail in Chapters 2.4 and 3.3.

2.2.5 Differential Equations of Plasticity for Soils in Terms of Effective Stresses

Soils, unlike most engineering materials, are three-phased (solid, liquid, gas) media. The influence of the fluid phases, especially the liquid phase, on the reaction of the soil mass to external and internal loading was discussed in detail in Chapter 1.3. We need recall here only that pore pressures will develop in the soil upon loading if the moisture content of the soil is higher than a certain level. Certain pore pressure and stress distributions give rise to pore water migration in the vicinity of the most stressed surface, which results in a progressive development of a single-failure surface. Criteria for this to occur have not yet been established, however, for transient wheel loads, loose surface soils are not likely to exhibit this phenomenon even if they are saturated to a high degree. Thus it is reasonable to assume that pore pressure development will not alter the character of failure zones beneath wheels. The existence of the solution of the appropriate differential equations is an assurance that this is, indeed, the case.

In deriving the differential equations governing the geometry of and the stresses in the failure zones, the following basic assumptions are made:

a) The principle of effective stresses, introduced by Terzaghi (1925) and discussed in Section 1.3.1, is valid. According to this principle

$$\bar{\sigma} = \sigma_t - u \qquad \text{Eq. 1.3.1}$$

This assumption implies that either pore air pressure is negligible or the area over which it acts is negligibly small, as is the case when the soil is highly (> 90 %) saturated.

b) The incremental pore pressure can be determined by SKEMPTON's (1954) equation as

$$\Delta u = B\,[\Delta\sigma_3 + A\,(\Delta\sigma_1 - \Delta\sigma_3)] \qquad \text{Eq. 1.3.19}$$

where the pore pressure parameters A and B are assumed to be constant. In the following derivations, this equation is used for the determination of pore pressure only when the soil is in failure condition, therefore, the assumption that A and B are constant is reasonable. As indicated in Section 1.3, the pore pressure parameters at failure are sometimes distinguished by the subscript "f", In the present case, since no other condition is considered, this is not deemed necessary and the non-subscripted variables "A" and "B" are used.

For external loads at the surface, the initial stresses in the soil near the surface from overburden pressure are negligible and Equation 1.3.19 becomes

$$u - u_0 = B\sigma_3 + A\,(\sigma_1 - \sigma_3)$$

Substituting for effective stresses according to Equation 1.3.1 and expressing pore pressure in terms of $\bar{\sigma}$ yields:

$$u = M\bar{\sigma} - \frac{B}{1-B}\,\psi + \frac{1}{1-B}\,u_0 \qquad \text{Eq. 2.2.27}$$

where

$$M = \frac{B}{1-B}\,(1 + (2A/B - 1)\sin\varphi) \qquad \text{Eq. 2.2.28}$$

As in the previous sections, the differential equations of plasticity are derived by combining the differential equations of static equilibrium and the MOHR-COULOMB yield criterion. In the case of pore pressures, however, all equations are written in terms of effective stresses and excess pore water pressures. Equation 2.2.27 provides the relationship between excess pore water pressures and effective stresses so that pore pressures can also be expressed in terms of effective stresses. The resulting differential relationships for the i and j family of slip lines are as follows

$$dz = dx\,\tan\,(\theta \mp \mu) \qquad \text{Eqs. 2.2.29a and 2.2.29b}$$

and

$$(1 + M)\, d\bar{\sigma} \mp 2\bar{\sigma} \tan\varphi\, d\theta \mp M \tan\varphi \frac{\partial\bar{\sigma}}{\partial x}\, dz$$

$$\mp M \tan\varphi \frac{\partial\bar{\sigma}}{\partial z}\, dx = \frac{\gamma}{\cos\varphi}\left[\sin(\varepsilon \mp \varphi)\, dx + \cos(\varepsilon \mp \varphi)\, dz\right]$$

Eqs. 2.2.29 c
and 2.2.29 d

In these equations the upper sign refers to the first or j-family of slip lines and the lower sign refers to the second or i-family of slip lines. For $M = 0$, i.e., no pore pressures, Equations 2.2.29 revert to those developed by Sokolovskii (1960). The above equations, in slightly different form, have been derived by Siva Reddy and Mogaliah (1970).

Equations 2.2.29 establish relationships among the four unknown quantities x, z, $\bar{\sigma}$ and θ at any point within the slip line field and yield a unique solution to problems sufficiently defined by boundary conditions. A comparison of these equations for $M = 0$ with the differential equations of Sokolovskii (1960) shows that in Equations 2.2.29 the total differential of $\bar{\sigma}$ is multiplied by the factor $(1 + M)$ and, in addition, two terms containing partial differentials of $\bar{\sigma}$ occur.

Here, as with the cases discussed previously, a closed form solution of these equations does not exist and a modified form of the method of characteristics is used. The details of the numerical solution procedure are given in Section 2.3.5.

2.2.6 Differential Equations of Plasticity for Purely Cohesive Soils

In discussions concerning soil failure mechanisms and soil strength, purely cohesive soils are defined as those which do not exhibit significant frictional resistance to shear stress but which derive their strength primarily from cohesion. From Figure 2.11 and from Equation 1.3.24 for $\varphi = 0$, it can be seen that for purely cohesive soils

$$s = (\text{shear strength}) = c = \frac{(\sigma_1 - \sigma_3)}{2} \qquad \text{Eq. 2.2.30}$$

In the basic differential equations of plastic equilibrium for ponderable soils under plane strain conditions (repeated below for the sake of continuity) the cohesion term, c, does not appear explicitly.

$$dz = dx \tan(\theta \pm \mu)$$

Eqs. 2.2.20 a
and 2.2.20 b

$$d\sigma \pm 2\sigma \tan\varphi \, d\theta = \frac{\gamma}{\cos\varphi}\left[\sin(\varepsilon \pm \varphi)\,dx + \cos(\varepsilon \pm \varphi)\,dz\right]$$

Eqs. 2.2.20c and 2.2.20d

The cohesion term is, however, included in the value of σ which, as shown in Figure 2.6 and as defined for Equations 2.2.17 is:

$$\sigma = c \cdot \cot\varphi + \frac{(\sigma_1 + \sigma_3)}{2} \qquad \text{Eq. 2.2.31}$$

At $\varphi = 0$, σ becomes infinite and Equations 2.2.20 are meaningless. Consequently, another approach to the formulation of the differential equations of plasticity for purely cohesive soils is required. This formulation was developed in detail by Sokolovskii (1960) and is summarized below.

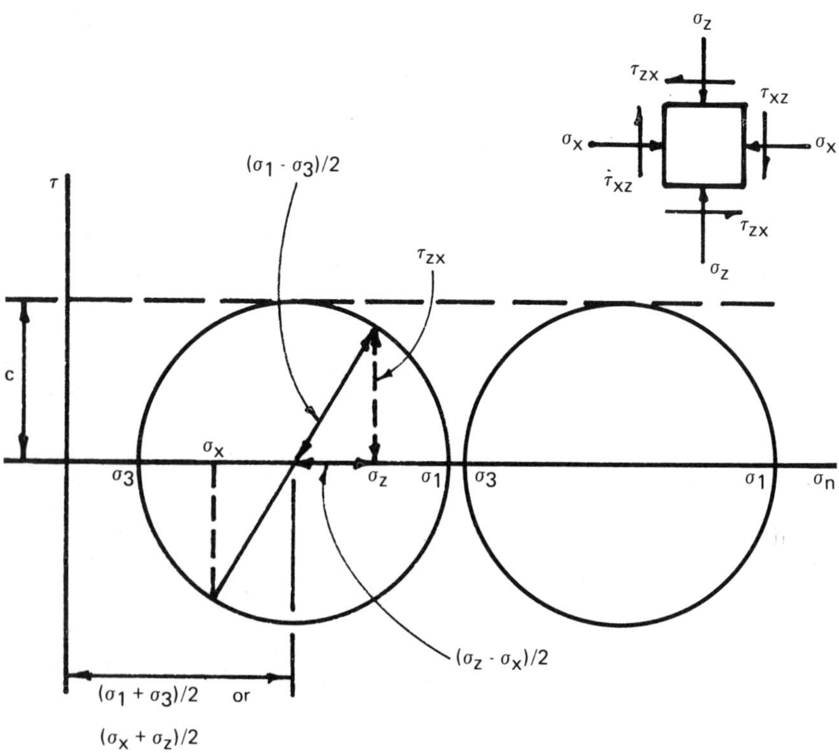

Fig. 2.11
Relationships between Principal Stresses and Normal and Shear Stresses for Purely Cohesive Soil

For the case when $\varphi = 0$ the following equations relating principal stresses to normal and shear stress components may be obtained straightforwardly from Figure 2.11.

$$\sigma_1 = \frac{\sigma_z + \sigma_x}{2} + \left[\frac{(\sigma_z - \sigma_x)^2}{4} + \tau_{zx}^2\right]^{\frac{1}{2}} \qquad \text{Eq. 2.2.32a}$$

$$\sigma_3 = \frac{\sigma_z - \sigma_x}{2} - \left[\frac{(\sigma_z - \sigma_x)^2}{4} + \tau_{zx}^2\right]^{\frac{1}{2}} \qquad \text{Eq. 2.2.32b}$$

$$\frac{(\sigma_z - \sigma_x)^2}{4} + \tau_{zx}^2 = \frac{(\sigma_1 - \sigma_3)^2}{4} = c^2 \qquad \text{Eq. 2.2.32c}$$

A new variable, σ_s, analogous to the variable σ which was used in the development of the general formulation for c-φ soils, is introduced to account for the fact that cohesive soils are capable of taking a small amount of tension and will stand unsupported laterally to a critical height $z = 2c/\gamma$. The expression relating this new variable to the major and minor principal stresses is:

$$2c\sigma_s = \frac{(\sigma_1 + \sigma_3)}{2} - \gamma z \qquad \text{Eq. 2.2.33}$$

Equations 2.2.30, 2.2.33 and the transformation functions given by Equations 2.2.16 and 2.2.8, all of which are still valid for the case of a $\varphi = 0$ material, are used to obtain the following expressions relating σ_x, σ_z and τ_{zx} to σ_s and θ:

$$\sigma_z = c\,(2\sigma_s + \cos 2\theta) + \gamma z \qquad \text{Eq. 2.2.34a}$$

$$\sigma_x = c\,(2\sigma_s - \cos 2\theta) + \gamma z \qquad \text{Eq. 2.2.34b}$$

$$\tau_{zx} = c \sin 2\theta \qquad \text{Eq. 2.2.34c}$$

Substitution of the appropriate derivatives of these equations into the differential equations of plastic equilibrium given by Equations 2.2.13 yields the following system of equations

$$\frac{\partial \sigma_s}{\partial z} - \sin 2\theta \frac{\partial \theta}{\partial z} + \cos 2\theta \frac{\partial \theta}{\partial x} = 0 \qquad \text{Eq. 2.2.35a}$$

$$\frac{\partial \sigma_s}{\partial x} + \cos 2\theta \frac{\partial \theta}{\partial z} + \sin 2\theta \frac{\partial \theta}{\partial x} = 0 \qquad \text{Eq. 2.2.35b}$$

The procedure presented by Sokolovskii (1960) for the solution of the equations follows the format he used in solving the general equations presented in Section 2.2.2. Again, new variables are introduced and mapping is done between "real" and "dummy" planes to obtain the following system of differential equations that represent the conditions of plastic equilibrium under plane strain for a purely cohesive, ponderable soil with a horizontal free surface:

$$dz = dx \tan(\theta \mp \mu) \qquad \text{Eqs. 2.2.36a and 2.2.36b}$$

and

$$ds \mp 2s\, d\theta = \gamma dz \qquad \text{Eqs. 2.2.36c and 2.2.36d}$$

where s is now defined as $(2c\sigma_s - \gamma z)$ or $(\sigma_1 + \sigma_3)/2$.

As with the general case of c-φ soils, the governing equations for the purely cohesive case have no closed form solution but must be integrated numerically by the methods discussed in Chapter 2.3. Since $\mu = \pi/4$ for $\varphi = 0$ (refer to Equations 2.2.19) the equations for the j-characteristics in the x-z plane reduce to:

$$dz = dx \tan\left(\theta - \frac{\pi}{4}\right) \qquad \text{Eq. 2.2.37a}$$

and

$$ds - 2s\, d\theta = \gamma dz \qquad \text{Eq. 2.2.37b}$$

Along the i-characteristics the equations are:

$$dz = dx \tan\left(\theta + \frac{\pi}{4}\right) \qquad \text{Eq. 2.2.37c}$$

and

$$ds + 2s\, d\theta = \gamma dz \qquad \text{Eq. 2.2.37d}$$

The above equations indicate that in isotropic cohesive soils the i- and j-family of slip lines intersect perpendicularly and form a field that is characteristic of cohesive soils.

These concepts have been applied to anisotropic cohesive materials by LIVNEH and GREENSTEIN (1974). Although a full development of their work is beyond the scope of this book, one important conclusion from their analyses merits attention. They have shown that for a soil possessing a considerable amount of anisotropy, a misleading evaluation of soil-structure interaction may be reached if the anisotropic phenomenon is disregarded.

2.2.7 Differential Equations of Plasticity for Soil Under Axially Symmetric Conditions of Geometry and Loading

Berezancev (1952) was among the first to consider the problem of axially symmetric plastic deformations in soils. He presented complete solutions for the problem of incipient plastic flow in a semi-infinite region of soil due to load applied through a flat-ended, smooth, rigid, circular cylinder. Berezancev's assumption of weightless soil, however, severely limits the application of his equations to real problem situations.

More recently, Cox, Eason and Hopkins (1961), Cox (1962), Larkin (1968), and Graham (1968), among others, have devised systems of differential equations in which this limitation is overcome. The differences in these approaches lie mainly in the numerical procedures each of the authors used. In all of these treatments of the axially symmetric case, however, the plane strain condition is modified by the assumption that the circumferential stress is the intermediate principal stress (σ_2) and that it is equal to the minor principal stress (σ_3). Because of the axial symmetry, the formulation of the equilibrium equations is done more efficiently in polar coordinates as shown in Figure 2.12 where σ_r, σ_λ, σ_z, $\tau_{\lambda z}$, τ_{rz} and $\tau_{r\lambda}$ are the stress components acting on the soil mass. The principal stress directions and orientation definitions are analogous to those of the plane strain case. These are shown in Figure 2.13. Axial symmetry requires that the shear stresses $\tau_{\lambda z}$ and $\tau_{\lambda r}$ vanish so that at equilibrium the summation of the forces in the r and z directions yields

$$\frac{\partial \sigma_r}{\partial r} + \frac{\partial \tau_{zr}}{\partial z} + \left(\frac{\sigma_r - \sigma_\lambda}{r}\right) n = 0 \qquad \text{Eq. 2.2.38a}$$

$$\frac{\partial \tau_{rz}}{\partial r} + \frac{\partial \sigma_z}{\partial z} + \gamma + \frac{n \tau_{zr}}{r} = 0 \qquad \text{Eq. 2.2.38b}$$

where n is a constant that equals 0 for plane strain conditions and 1 for the axially symmetric case.

The basic equations for the transformation of stress components between stresses in polar coordinates and principal stresses when $\sigma_1 > (\sigma_2 = \sigma_3)$ is:

$$\sigma_1 = \frac{1}{2}(\sigma_r + \sigma_z) + \left\{\frac{1}{4}(\sigma_r - \sigma_z)^2 + \tau_{rz}^2\right\}^{\frac{1}{2}} \qquad \text{Eq. 2.2.39a}$$

$$\sigma_3 = \frac{1}{2}(\sigma_r + \sigma_z) - \left\{\frac{1}{4}(\sigma_r - \sigma_z)^2 + \tau_{rz}^2\right\}^{\frac{1}{2}} \qquad \text{Eq. 2.2.39b}$$

$$\sigma_2 = \sigma_\lambda = \sigma_3 \qquad \text{Eq. 2.2.39c}$$

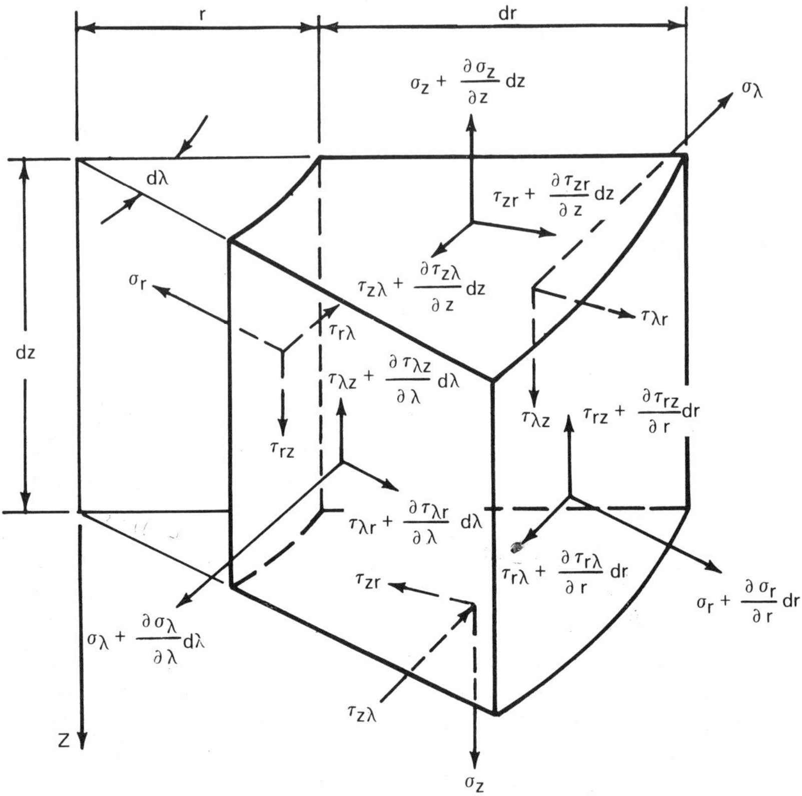

Fig. 2.12
Stresses on Element — Polar Coordinates

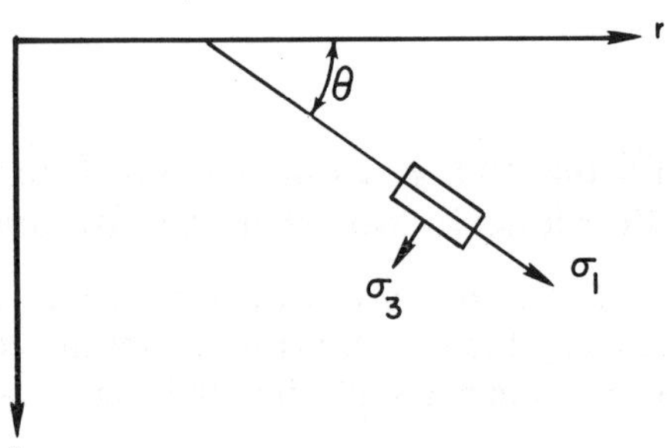

Fig. 2.13
Pertinent Orientations

from which

$$\sigma_r = \frac{1}{2}(\sigma_1 + \sigma_3) + \frac{1}{2}(\sigma_1 - \sigma_3)\cos 2\theta \qquad \text{Eq. 2.2.40a}$$

$$\sigma_z = \frac{1}{2}(\sigma_1 + \sigma_3) - \frac{1}{2}(\sigma_1 - \sigma_3)\cos 2\theta \qquad \text{Eq. 2.2.40b}$$

$$\tau_{rz} = \frac{1}{2}(\sigma_1 - \sigma_3)\sin 2\theta \qquad \text{Eq. 2.2.40c}$$

If the appropriate partial derivatives of Equations 2.2.40 are obtained and substituted into Equations 2.2.39, and if mathematical procedures analogous to those used in the development of the differential equations of plastic equilibrium for soil under plane strain conditions are applied here, the following general differential equations are obtained for the axially symmetric case ($n = 1$):

$$dz = dr \tan(\theta \mp \mu) \qquad \text{Eqs. 2.2.41a and 2.2.41b}$$

$$d\sigma \mp 2\sigma \tan\varphi \, d\theta - (dz \mp \tan\varphi \, dr)\,\gamma + \frac{n\sigma}{r}[\sin\varphi \, dr \mp \tan\varphi\,(1 - \sin\varphi)\, dz] = 0 \qquad \text{Eq. 2.2.41c and 2.2.41d}$$

In comparing these equations to Equations 2.2.20 it is immediately evident that the two sets of equations are identical for $n = 0$ and $dr = dx$, assuming, of course, that the free surface is horizontal ($\varepsilon = 0$). This condition is required for axial symmetry. In both sets of equations the upper sign corresponds to the first or j-family of characteristics and the lower sign to the second or i-family of characteristics. As with the plane strain equations, Equations 2.2.41 have no closed form solution. Details of an acceptable numerical procedure used by the authors (Nowatzki and Karafiath, 1972; Nowatzki, 1971) to obtain solutions to practical civil engineering problems is contained in Section 2.3.1.

2.2.8 Similitude in the Application of Plasticity Theory to Problems in Soil-Structure Interaction

The concept that the interface stresses are governed by the differential equations of plasticity for soils leads to interesting considerations regarding the use of the principles of similitude in soil-structure interaction studies.

Figure 2.14 shows the Mohr circle construction and failure envelope for the general case of a c-φ soil. From the figure the following expressions relating shear stress and normal stress components to the principal stresses may be written as:

$$\sigma_1 = \frac{\sigma_z + \sigma_x}{2} + \sqrt{\frac{(\sigma_z - \sigma_x)^2}{4} + \tau_{zx}^2} \qquad \text{Eq. 2.2.42a}$$

$$\sigma_3 = \frac{\sigma_z + \sigma_x}{2} - \sqrt{\frac{(\sigma_z - \sigma_x)^2}{4} + \tau_{zx}^2} \qquad \text{Eq. 2.2.42b}$$

$$\frac{(\sigma_z - \sigma_x)^2}{4} + \tau_{zx}^2 = \sin^2 \varphi \frac{(\sigma_x + \sigma_z + 2\psi)^2}{4} \qquad \text{Eq. 2.2.42c}$$

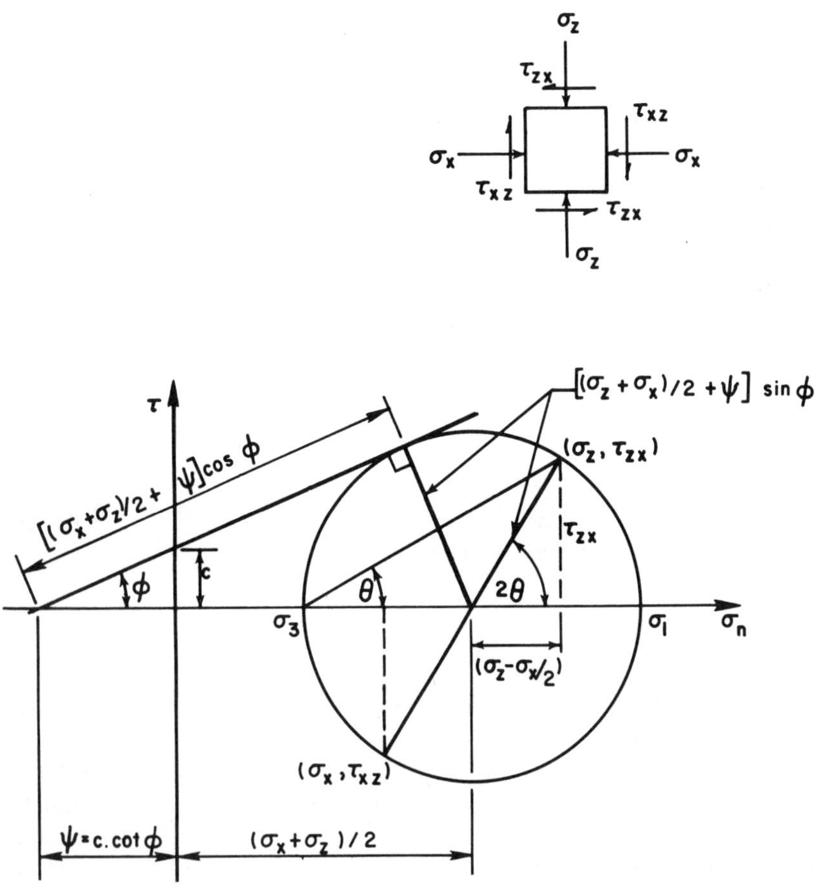

Fig. 2.14
Relationships between Principal Stresses and Normal Shear Stresses for General Case of a $c - \varphi$ Soil

Equations 2.2.42a and b are identical to Equations 2.2.32a and b and Equation 2.2.42c is actually an expression for the MOHR-COULOMB yield criterion. When it is combined with the conditions of static equilibrium given by Equations 2.2.13, three independent equations with three unknowns σ_x, σ_z, and τ_{zx} are obtained. These equations can be written in dimensionless form by introducing l, a characteristic length, and s, a reference stress (often taken equal to the cohesion, c) as follows:

$$x' = x/l \qquad \text{Eq. 2.2.43a}$$
$$z' = z/l \qquad \text{Eq. 2.2.43b}$$
$$\sigma'_x = \sigma_x/s \qquad \text{Eq. 2.2.43c}$$
$$\sigma'_z = \sigma_z/s \qquad \text{Eq. 2.2.43d}$$
$$\tau'_{zx} = \tau_{zx}/s \qquad \text{Eq. 2.2.43e}$$

The basic set of differential equations and the failure criterion then take the following form:

$$\frac{\partial \sigma'_x}{\partial x'} + \frac{\partial \tau'_{xz}}{\partial z'} = \frac{\gamma \cdot l}{s} \sin \alpha \qquad \text{Eq. 2.2.44a}$$

$$\frac{\partial \sigma'_z}{\partial z'} + \frac{\partial \tau'_{xz}}{\partial x'} = \frac{\gamma \cdot l}{s} \cos \alpha \qquad \text{Eq. 2.2.44b}$$

$$\frac{(\sigma'_z - \sigma'_x)^2}{4} + \tau'^2_{xz} = \sin^2 \varphi \frac{(\sigma'_x + \sigma'_z + 2\psi)^2}{4} \qquad \text{Eq. 2.2.44c}$$

Inspection of these equations reveals that geometric similarity of the slip line fields in soil-structure interaction problems involving materials having the same φ requires the following equality to hold:

$$\frac{\gamma_m \, l_m}{s_m} = \frac{\gamma_p \, l_p}{s_p} \qquad \text{Eq. 2.2.45}$$

where the subscripts m and p denote model and prototype, respectively.

This implies that geometrically similar boundary conditions yield geometrically similar slip line fields only if Equation 2.2.45 holds true, More importantly this requirement precludes the valid use of superposition to obtain solutions to complex problems. For example, the "correct" solution for the bearing capacity of a soil under inclined loading yields a value different from that obtained by superimposing the plasticity solution for stresses acting normal to the surface with that of shear stresses acting parallel to the surface. The reason is that the basic differential equations of plastic equilibrium are non-linear and, strictly speaking, require that each normalized coupling in Equations 2.2.43 be considered separately before superposition is attempted. This is not done in the SOKOLOVSKII solution where two cases: (1) $c \neq 0$, $\varphi \neq 0$, $\gamma = 0$ and (2) $c = 0$, $\varphi \neq 0$, $\gamma \neq 0$ are considered and the results superimposed to yield a solution for any inclination of bearing pressure. HARR (1966) discusses the implications of this superimposed plasticity solution relative to the solutions obtained by TERZAGHI (1943) for smooth and rough footings.

Equation 2.2.45 also implies that if geometrically similar slip line fields are to be obtained and if $s = \sigma = c \cdot \cot \varphi + (\sigma_1 + \sigma_3)/2$ then:

$$\frac{\sigma_m}{\sigma_p} = \frac{s_m}{s_p} \qquad \text{Eq. 2.2.46}$$

This means that for geometrically similar situations the *distribution* of σ at the soil-structure interface is the *same* for model and prototype, but the *magnitude changes* according to Equation 2.2.46.

For the case where $c = 0$, $s = \sigma = (\sigma_1 + \sigma_3)/2$ and for geometrically similar situations, the normal and shear stresses along the soil-structure interfaces of model and prototype are directly proportional to their respective σ.

The same is also true for the case where $\varphi = 0$. It was shown in Section 2.2.6 that in this case σ goes to infinity because of the $c \cdot \cot \varphi$ term. A solution is obtained by using Equations 2.2.32. Here again the σ of these equations equals $(\sigma_1 + \sigma_3)/2$ so that in similitude problems involving purely cohesive soils, the normal and shear stresses along the soil-structure interfaces of model and prototype are directly proportional to their respective σ.

The implications of these considerations in vehicle mobility studies involving either purely cohesive or purely frictional soils is that certain dimensionless parameters, such as the pull coefficient, will be the same for all geometrically similar slip line fields. This is due to the fact that for these soils a constant ratio of interface normal and shear stresses can be factored out in the integration for both load and drawbar pull. Thus, in the case of $c = 0$ or $\varphi = 0$ soils, the application of plasticity theory to soil-wheel interaction confirms the validity of results obtained in similitude studies regarding the selection of dimensionless parameters (SCHURING and EMORI, 1964) at least for wheels travelling at velocities where soil inertia effects are negligible and provided that wheel (tire) deflection is similar also.

Most real soils, however, exhibit both frictional and cohesive characteristics. For these soils, as for the $\varphi = 0$ or $c = 0$ soils, geometrically similar slip line fields also result in similar distributions of σ along soil-structure interfaces of model and prototype. However, unlike the others, normal stresses (σ_n) along the boundary of a structure and a c-φ soil are not directly proportional to σ since σ contains the $c \cdot \cot \varphi$-term and σ_n does not. On the other hand, similarity does exist between shear stress and σ for these soils.

The implication of these factors in vehicle mobility studies involving most real soils is that there is a built in distortion in the integration formulas for load, drawbar pull, and torque. The ψ-constant ($\psi = c \cdot \cot \varphi$), however, can be computed seperately and applied as a correction factor to the similitude relationships of c-φ soils to compensate for this distortion.

It is noteworthy that geometric similitude in plasticity analysis of soil is highly dependent upon the nature of the yield criterion. Although Equations 2.2.13 apply for non-linear as well as linear yield criteria, they cannot be put into the dimensionless form of Equations 2.2.44 unless the yield criterion is linear. Therefore, similitude in soil-structure interaction as expressed by Equations 2.2.45 and 2.2.46 is restricted to soils that follow a linear Mohr-Coulomb failure envelope. Unfortunately this invalidates application of the concepts discussed above to many soils of practical interest.

Also, geometric similarity of the boundaries is a prerequisite for a similarity to exist between the stress states existing in the soil. This geometric similarity exists only in the case of rigid vehicular footings or loading surfaces. In order for similarity to exist in an interaction between a flexible footing and soil, the deflections of various-sized footings would also have to be similar. That is a requirement not generally met with pneumatic tires.

CHAPTER 2.3

NUMERICAL SOLUTIONS

As indicated in Chapter 2.2, the solution of the basic differential equations of plasticity for soil under all stress and strain conditions of loading (plane strain, axially symmetric geometry and loading, etc) cannot be obtained in closed form except for the PRANDTL solution where $\gamma = 0$. Therefore numerical methods are required for cases of practical interest.

In this chapter a finite difference formulation of the basic differential equations will be presented. A computational method using the resulting recurrence relationships will be discussed with reference to boundary conditions and grid systems. Solutional difficulties such as singular points and lines will be investigated as well as the methods available for overcoming these difficulties. Finally, a number of special cases will be addressed and the basic solutional procedures applied to problems dealing with layered soils, cases wherein soil pore water pressures are significant, and situations where soil inertia is important.

2.3.1 Basic Recurrence Relationships

In an attempt to keep this discussion as general as possible, recurrence relationships will be developed for the differential equations of plasticity for soil having a nonlinear yield criterion. A surface inclination, ε, will also be included in the general development as well as an "n-term" that describes axially symmetric geometry and loading conditions. However, the reader is reminded that axial symmetry does not exist for loading on a slope so that when $\varepsilon \lesseqgtr 0$, n must $= 0$; but when $\varepsilon = 0$ then either $n = 1$ for the axial symmetric case or $n = 0$ for plane strain conditions. With this understanding, the general basic differential equations in polar coordinates may be written as a combination of Equations 2.7.41 and 2.2.20 in the following form:

$$dz = dr \tan(\theta \mp \mu) \qquad \text{Eqs. 2.3.1 a and 2.3.1 b}$$

$$d\sigma \mp 2\sigma \tan\varphi \, d\theta - \frac{\gamma}{\cos\varphi}\left[\sin(\varepsilon - \varphi)\, dr + \cos(\varepsilon - \varphi)\, dz\right] +$$

$$+ \frac{n\sigma}{r}\left[\sin\varphi \, dr \mp \tan\varphi\,(1 - \sin\varphi)\, dz\right] = 0 \qquad \text{Eqs. 2.3.1 c and 2.3.1 d}$$

The corresponding recurrence relationships for stress are:

$$\sigma_{i,j} - \sigma_{i-1,j} - 2\sigma_{i-1,j}\tan\varphi_{i-1,j}(\theta_{i,j} - \theta_{i-1,j}) - C + \frac{n\sigma_{i-1,j}A}{r_{i-1,j}} = 0$$

Eq. 2.3.2a

$$\sigma_{i,j} - \sigma_{i,j-1} + 2\sigma_{i,j-1}\tan\varphi_{i,j-1}(\theta_{i,j} - \theta_{i,j-1}) - D + \frac{n\sigma_{i,j-1}B}{r_{i,j-1}} = 0$$

Eq. 2.3.2b

where

$$A = \sin\varphi_{i-1,j}(r_{i,j} - r_{i-1,j}) - \tan\varphi_{i-1,j}(1 - \sin\varphi_{i-1,j})(z_{i,j} - z_{i-1,j})$$

$$B = \sin\varphi_{i,j-1}(r_{i,j} - r_{i,j-1}) + \tan\varphi_{i,j-1}(1 - \sin\varphi_{i,j-1})(z_{i,j} - z_{i,j-1})$$

$$C = \frac{\gamma}{\cos\varphi_{i-1,j}}\Big[\sin(\varepsilon - \varphi_{i-1,j})(r_{i,j} - r_{i-1,j}) + \cos(\varepsilon - \varphi_{i-1,j})(z_{i,j} - z_{i-1,j})\Big]$$

$$D = \frac{\gamma}{\cos\varphi_{i,j-1}}\Big[\sin(\varepsilon + \varphi_{i,j-1})(r_{i,j} - r_{i,j-1}) + \cos(\varepsilon + \varphi_{i,j-1})(z_{i,j} - z_{i,j-1})\Big]$$

If Equation 2.3.2a is multiplied by $(\sigma_{i,j-1}\tan\varphi_{i,j-1})$ and Equation 2.3.2b is multiplied by $(\sigma_{i-1,j}\tan\varphi_{i-1,j})$ the two equations can be solved simultaneously for $\sigma_{i,j}$. The $\theta_{i,j}$ — term drops out and simple algebraic operations yield:

$$\sigma_{i,j} = \Big[\sigma_{i-1,j}\sigma_{i,j-1}(\tan\varphi_{i,j-1} + \tan\varphi_{i-1,j}) - 2\sigma_{i,j-1}\sigma_{i-1,j}\tan\varphi_{i-1,j}\tan\varphi_{i,j-1}(\theta_{i-1,j} - \theta_{i,j-1}) + C\sigma_{i,j-1}\tan\varphi_{i,j-1} + D\sigma_{i-1,j}\tan\varphi_{i-1,j} - n\sigma_{i-1,j}\sigma_{i,j-1}\left\{\frac{A\tan\varphi_{i,j-1}}{r_{i-1,j}} + \frac{B\tan\varphi_{i-1,j}}{r_{i,j-1}}\right\}\Big] \Big/ \Big[\sigma_{i,j-1}\tan\varphi_{i,j-1} + \sigma_{i-1,j}\tan\varphi_{i-1,j}\Big]$$

Eq. 2.3.3a

Equation 2.3.2 can be solved directly for $\theta_{i,j}$ by eliminating the $\sigma_{i,j}$— term. The resulting expression is:

$$\theta_{i,j} = \Big[\sigma_{i,j-1} - \sigma_{i-1,j} + 2(\sigma_{i-1,j}\tan\varphi_{i-1,j}\theta_{i-1,j} + \sigma_{i,j-1}\tan\varphi_{i,j-1}\theta_{i,j-1}) - C + D + n\left\{\frac{\sigma_{i-1,j}A}{r_{i-1,j}} - \frac{\sigma_{i,j-1}B}{r_{i,j-1}}\right\}\Big] \Big/ \Big[2(\sigma_{i-1,j}\tan\varphi_{i-1,j} + \sigma_{i,j-1}\tan\varphi_{i,j-1})\Big]$$

Eq. 2.3.3b

The corresponding recurrence relationships for slip line field geometry are:

$$z_{i,j} - z_{i-1,j} = (r_{i,j} - r_{i-1,j})\tan(\theta_{i-1,j} - \mu) \qquad \text{Eq. 2.3.4a}$$

$$z_{i,j} - z_{i,j-1} = (r_{i,j} - r_{i,j-1})\tan(\theta_{i,j-1} + \mu) \qquad \text{Eq. 2.3.4b}$$

Letting
$$\alpha_1 = \tan(\theta_{i,j-1} + \mu)$$
$$\alpha_2 = \tan(\theta_{i-1,j} - \mu)$$

and solving the two finite difference equations first for $z_{i,j}$ and then for $r_{i,j}$ yields:

$$z_{i,j} = z_{i-1,j} + \alpha_2 (r_{i,j} - r_{i-1,j}) \qquad \text{Eq. 2.3.5a}$$

or

$$z_{i,j} = z_{i,j-1} + \alpha_1 (r_{i,j} - r_{i,j-1}) \qquad \text{Eq. 2.3.5b}$$

and

$$r_{i,j} = [z_{i-1,j} - z_{i,j-1} + \alpha_1 r_{i,j-1} - \alpha_2 r_{i-1,j}] / (\alpha_1 - \alpha_2) \qquad \text{Eq. 2.3.5c}$$

These equations are perfectly general and apply to the axially symmetric case ($\varepsilon = 0$, $n = 1$) as well as to the plane strain case for loading on a slope ($\varepsilon \gtrless 0$, $n = 0$). The recurrence relations for special cases relating to pore water pressures and soil inertia will be considered separately in Section 2.3.5.

Recurrence Relationships for Plane Strain Conditions and $\varphi \neq$ Constant

For plane strain conditions the "n-term" in the general recurrence relationships given by Equations 2.3.2 through 2.3.5 is zero, i.e. conditions of axial symmetry do not apply. Also, the more general three-dimensional, axially symmetric variable r now becomes the planar variable x. The recurrence relationships for z, x, σ and θ then reduce to

$$z_{i,j} = z_{i-1,j} + \alpha_2 (x_{i,j} - x_{i-1,j}) \qquad \text{Eq. 2.3.6a}$$

or

$$z_{i,j} = z_{i,j-1} + \alpha_1 (x_{i,j} - x_{i,j-1}) \qquad \text{Eq. 2.3.6b}$$

$$x_{i,j} = [z_{i-1,j} - z_{i,j-1} + \alpha_1 x_{i,j-1} - \alpha_2 x_{i-1,j}] / (\alpha_1 - \alpha_2) \qquad \text{Eq. 2.3.6c}$$

$$\sigma_{i,j} = [\sigma_{i-1,j}\,\sigma_{i,j-1} (\tan\varphi_{i,j-1} + \tan\varphi_{i-1,j}) - 2\,\sigma_{i,j-1}\,\sigma_{i-1,j} \tan\varphi_{i-1,j} \tan\varphi_{i,j-1} (\theta_{i-1,j} - \theta_{i,j-1}) + C^*\,\sigma_{i,j-1} \tan\varphi_{i,j-1} + D^*\,\sigma_{i-1,j} \tan\varphi_{i-1,j}] / [\sigma_{i,j-1} \tan\varphi_{i,j-1} + \sigma_{i-1,j} \tan\varphi_{i-1,j}] \qquad \text{Eq. 2.3.6d}$$

where

$$C^* = \frac{\gamma}{\cos\varphi_{i-1,j}} \Big[\sin(\varepsilon - \varphi_{i-1,j})(x_{i,j} - x_{i-1,j}) + \cos(\varepsilon - \varphi_{i-1,j})(z_{i,j} - z_{i-1,j})\Big]$$

$$D^* = \frac{\gamma}{\cos\varphi_{i,j-1}} \Big[\sin(\varepsilon + \varphi_{i,j-1})(x_{i,j} - x_{i,j-1}) + \cos(\varepsilon + \varphi_{i,j-1})(z_{i,j} - z_{i,j-1})\Big]$$

$$\theta_{i,j} = [\sigma_{i,j-1} - \sigma_{i-1,j} + 2(\sigma_{i-1,j} \tan\varphi_{i-1,j}\,\theta_{i-1,j} + \sigma_{i,j-1} \tan\varphi_{i,j-1}\,\theta_{i,j-1}) - C^* + D^*] / [2(\sigma_{i-1,j} \tan\varphi_{i-1,j} + \sigma_{i,j-1} \tan\varphi_{i,j-1})] \qquad \text{Eq. 2.3.6e}$$

The σ values in these equations include the $\psi = $ c.cot φ term (refer to Eqs. 2.2.17) that in the case of a variable φ is not constant but is to be computed for every nodal point with the φ value appropriate for that nodal point.

Recurrence Relationships for Plane Strain Conditions and φ = Constant

Here as for the previous case the "*n*-term" is zero and the *r* of the general expression becomes the planar *x*. Since *x* and *z* are not functions of φ, the recurrence relationships for these two variables are the same as given by Eqs. 2.3.6a through *c*. However, with φ constant, the recurrence relationships for σ and θ reduce to the following more familiar forms found in the literature (e.g. HARR, 1966; SOKOLOVSKII, 1965):

$$\sigma_{i,j} = [2\,\sigma_{i-1,j}\,\sigma_{i,j-1}\,(1 - \tan\varphi\,(\theta_{i-1,j} - \theta_{i,j-1})) + \overline{C}\sigma_{i,j-1} + \overline{D}\sigma_{i-1,j}] / [\sigma_{i,j-1} + \sigma_{i-1,j}] \qquad \text{Eq. 2.3.7a}$$

where

$$\overline{C} = \frac{\gamma}{\cos\varphi}\left[\sin(\varepsilon - \varphi)(x_{i,j} - x_{i-1,j}) + \cos(\varepsilon - \varphi)(z_{i,j} - z_{i-1,j})\right]$$

$$\overline{D} = \frac{\gamma}{\cos\varphi}\left[\sin(\varepsilon + \varphi)(x_{i,j} - x_{i,j-1}) + \cos(\varepsilon + \varphi)(z_{i,j} - z_{i,j-1})\right]$$

$$\theta_{i,j} = [\sigma_{i,j-1} - \sigma_{i-1,j} + 2\tan\varphi\,(\sigma_{i-1,j}\,\theta_{i-1,j} + \sigma_{i,j-1}\,\theta_{i,j-1})] / [2\tan\varphi\,(\sigma_{i-1,j} + \sigma_{i,j-1})] \qquad \text{Eq. 2.3.7b}$$

Recurrence Relationships for Axially Symmetric Case and $\varphi \neq$ Constant

As indicated previously, the axially symmetric case requires that slope angle, ε, equals zero. Even though loading perpendicular to the slope can overcome the otherwise asymmetrical geometry of the problem caused by the slope, the gravity component of body forces downslope destroys the axial load symmetry regardless of the direction of externally applied loads.

As an example of how the general recurrence relationships given by Equations 2.3.2. through 2.3.5 are used in the case of axially symmetric conditions once stress and geometric boundary conditions have been defined, consider the specific problem of a cylindrical soil-sampler with bevelled edges being driven into a ponderable soil having a nonlinear MOHR-COULOMB failure envelope. Figure 2.15 shows that the boundary conditions and slip lines are symmetric with respect to the *Z*-axis.

In the figure:

R_o = outside radius of the sampler
w = uniformly distributed surface load or "equivalent surcharge" or combination of both.
β = 90° minus the angle of the cutting tip bevel.
L = length along sampler that defines the vertical boundary of the passive zone.

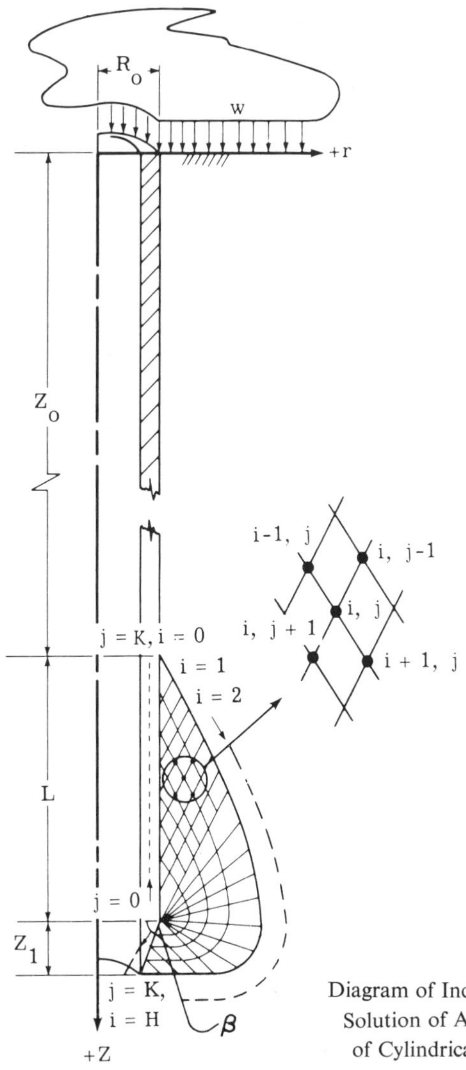

Fig. 2.15
Diagram of Indexing Scheme for Numerical Solution of Axially Symmetric Problem of Cylindrical Soil — Sampler (*SPT*)

The conditions shown in the figure closely parallel those that occur in the Standard Penetration Test *(SPT)* so widely used in conjunction with exploratory borings in civil engineering practice. For this case Equations 2.3.2. reduce to:

$$\sigma_{i,j} - \sigma_{i-1,j} - 2\sigma_{i-1,j} \tan\varphi_{i-1,j}(\theta_{i,j} - \theta_{i-1,j}) - C^{**} + \frac{\sigma_{i-1,j} A^{**}}{r_{i-1,j}} = 0$$

$$\sigma_{i,j} - \sigma_{i,j-1} + 2\sigma_{i,j-1} \tan\varphi_{i,j-1}(\theta_{i,j} - \theta_{i,j-1}) - D^{**} + \frac{\sigma_{i,j-1} B^{**}}{r_{i,j-1}} = 0$$

Eqs. 2.3.8a and 2.3.8b

where

$$A^{**} = \sin\varphi_{i-1,j}(r_{i,j} - r_{i-1,j}) - \tan\varphi_{i-1,j}(1 - \sin\varphi_{i-1,j})(z_{i,j} - z_{i-1,j})$$

$$B^{**} = \sin\varphi_{i,j-1}(r_{i,j} - r_{i,j-1}) + \tan\varphi_{i,j-1}(1 - \sin\varphi_{i,j-1})(z_{i,j} - z_{i,j-1})$$

$$C^{**} = \frac{\gamma}{\cos\varphi_{i-1,j}}\left[\cos\varphi_{i-1,j}(z_{i,j} - z_{i-1,j}) - \sin\varphi_{i-1,j}(r_{i,j} - r_{i-1,j})\right]$$

$$D^{**} = \frac{\gamma}{\cos\varphi_{i,j-1}}\left[\cos\varphi_{i,j-1}(z_{i,j} - z_{i,j-1}) + \sin\varphi_{i,j-1}(r_{i,j} - r_{i,j-1})\right]$$

The recurrence relationships for $\sigma_{i,j}$ and $\theta_{i,j}$ then become:

$$\sigma_{i,j} = \Big[\sigma_{i-1,j}\sigma_{i,j-1}(\tan\varphi_{i,j-1} + \tan\varphi_{i-1,j}) - 2\sigma_{i,j-1}\sigma_{i-1,j}\tan\varphi_{i-1,j}\tan\varphi_{i,j-1}(\theta_{i-1,j} - \theta_{i,j-1}) + C^{**}\sigma_{i,j-1}\tan\varphi_{i,j-1} + D^{**}\sigma_{i-1,j}\tan\varphi_{i-1,j} - \sigma_{i-1,j}\sigma_{i,j-1}\left\{\frac{A^{**}\tan\varphi_{i,j-1}}{r_{i-1,j}} + \frac{B^{**}\tan\varphi_{i-1,j}}{r_{i,j-1}}\right\}\Big] \Big/ [\sigma_{i,j-1}\tan\varphi_{i,j-1} + \sigma_{i-1,j}\tan\varphi_{i-1,j}]$$

Eq. 2.3.8c

and

$$\theta_{i,j} = \Big[\sigma_{i,j-1} - \sigma_{i-1,j} + 2(\sigma_{i-1,j}\tan\varphi_{i-1,j}\theta_{i-1,j} + \sigma_{i,j-1}\tan\varphi_{i,j-1}\theta_{i,j-1}) - C^{**} + D^{**} + \left\{\frac{A^{**}\sigma_{i-1,j}}{r_{i-1,j}} - \frac{B^{**}\sigma_{i,j-1}}{r_{i,j-1}}\right\}\Big] \Big/ [2(\sigma_{i-1,j}\tan\varphi_{i-1,j} + \sigma_{i,j-1}\tan\varphi_{i,j-1})]$$

Eq. 2.3.8d

The expressions for z and r in this case are given directly by Equations 2.3.5 with the condition that in the numerical solution any computed value of $r_{i,j}$ must be greater than the inside radius of the soil sampler. The ψ term for the σ values (refer to Eqs. 2.2.17) is to be computed with the φ value appropriate for the nodal point.

Recurrence Relationships for Axially Symmetric Case (n = 1) and φ = Constant

Here again ε must equal zero and $n = 1$ in the general expressions given by Equations 2.3.2 through 2.3.5. In addition, $\varphi_{i,j-1} = \varphi_{i-1,j} = \varphi$ so that the recurrence relationships for σ and θ reduce to:

$$\sigma_{i,j} = \Big[2\,\sigma_{i-1,j}\,\sigma_{i,j-1}\,(1 - \tan\varphi\,(\theta_{i-1,j} - \theta_{i,j-1})) + \overline{\overline{C}}\sigma_{i,j-1} + \overline{\overline{D}}\sigma_{i-1,j} - \sigma_{i-1,j}\,\sigma_{i,j-1}\left\{\frac{\overline{\overline{A}}}{r_{i-1,j}} + \frac{\overline{\overline{B}}}{r_{i,j-1}}\right\}\Big] \Big/ [\sigma_{i,j-1} + \sigma_{i-1,j}]$$

Eq. 2.3.9a

and

$$\theta_{i,j} = \Big[\sigma_{i,j-1} - \sigma_{i-1,j} + 2\tan\varphi\,(\sigma_{i-1,j}\,\theta_{i-1,j} + \sigma_{i,j-1}\,\theta_{i,j-1}) - \overline{\overline{C}} + \overline{\overline{D}}\left\{\frac{\sigma_{i,j-1}\,\overline{\overline{A}}}{r_{i-1,j}} - \frac{\sigma_{i,j-1}\,\overline{\overline{B}}}{r_{i,j-1}}\right\}\Big] \Big/ [2\tan\varphi\,(\sigma_{i-1,j} + \sigma_{i,j-1})]$$

Eq. 2.3.9b

where

$$\overline{\overline{A}} = \sin\varphi\,(r_{i,j} - r_{i-1,j}) - \tan\varphi\,(1 - \sin\varphi)\,(z_{i,j} - z_{i-1,j})$$

$$\overline{\overline{B}} = \sin\varphi\,(r_{i,j} - r_{i,j-1}) + \tan\varphi\,(1 - \sin\varphi)\,(z_{i,j} - z_{i,j-1})$$

$$\overline{\overline{C}} = \gamma\,[z_{i,j} - z_{i-1,j} - \tan\varphi\,(r_{i,j} - r_{i-1,j})]$$

$$\overline{\overline{D}} = \gamma\,[z_{i,j} - z_{i,j-1} + \tan\varphi\,(r_{i,j} - r_{i,j-1})]$$

The expressions for z and r in this case are obtained directly from Equations 2.3.5. An example of the application of these equations is given in Section 2.5.3. with reference to problems involving penetration resistance, in particular the cone indentation problem.

2.3.2 Boundary Conditions and Grid Systems

The formulation of the basic differential equations of plasticity in finite difference form allows the solution of these equations to be carried out in an orderly fashion from one geometrically defined boundary where x (or r), z, σ and θ are known to another boundary, usually also geometrically defined, where one or more of these variables is sought. Depending on the conditions at the boundaries, one of three types of problems may be encountered in the solution: the "Cauchy problem", the "Goursat problem" or the "mixed boundary value problem". Regardless of the type of boundary value problem being solved, the transition from one boundary to another is accomplished by proceeding from two nodal points in a grid where x, z, σ and θ are known to another point where these variables are unknown. Actually, this process of proceeding from point to point forms the grid and results in the solution, i.e. the determination of the state of stresses within the soil mass under the given boundary conditions assuming that a state of limiting equilibrium has been reached.

The previous section presented four equations or recurrence relationships for the four unknowns that define the grid. These equations allow the computation of z, x, σ and θ to be performed at any point (i, j) in the grid from values known at any two neighboring points along adjacent characteristics (i, j-1 and i-1, j).

Figure 2.15 showed the solutional set up for the axially symmetric case of a cylindrical soil-sampler. For a given set of loading conditions over the horizontal soil surface (the load "w" may be due to an "equivalent surcharge" or an actual uniformly distributed load), the values of $r_{i,j}$, $z_{i,j}$, $\sigma_{i,j}$, $\theta_{i,j}$ are computed from adjacent (i-1, j and i, j-1) nodal points by use of the set of recurrence relationships given by Equations 2.3.8. Nodal points are simply i and j characteristic intersection points. The grid system formed by these lines and their intersections is called the "slip line field".

The basic concept of a slip line field or grid system applies to a wide variety of soil mechanics problems. Applications of plasticity theory to such problems will be discussed in detail in Chapter 2.5. However, specific reference is made here to the slip line field associated with the wheel problem. Figure 2.16 presents a schematic of the slip line field for the wheel problem. Note that the complete grid system consists of two slip line fields, a forward field, and a rear field each of which is composed of the three zones (active, transitional, and passive) discussed previously in Chapter 2.2. The computations for each field are performed independently except that each solution must yield identical results for x, z, σ and θ at the internal ($j = k$, $i = h$) intersection point of the two fields.

From the above considerations it follows that the extent and the shape of the slip line field are determined by the recurrence relationships and boundary conditions specified for the problem. Figure 2.9 defines schematically the meaning of the various terms and orientations contained in the recurrence relationships. Thus, for example, in a problem for which the surcharge on the free surface equals zero ($w = 0$), the slip lines in the transitional zone at equilibrium will have a different orientation to the horizontal than those in a problem for which $w > 0$. This is so because the change in boundary stress conditions effects a change in the magnitude and direction of σ_1 in this zone. These changes are accompanied by changes in the magnitudes of σ and θ. As shown in Figure 2.9, the slopes of the i- and j-characteristics which define the shape of the slip lines are $\pi - \theta \pm \mu$. It may be inferred from the figure that in the passive zone the magnitude of σ may change with change in w, but so long as the direction of w is vertical, the direction of σ in the passive zone will not change. This means that the orientation of the *i*- and *j*-characteristics in the passive zone will not be affected by changes in the magnitude of w. The same concepts apply to the slip lines in the active zone.

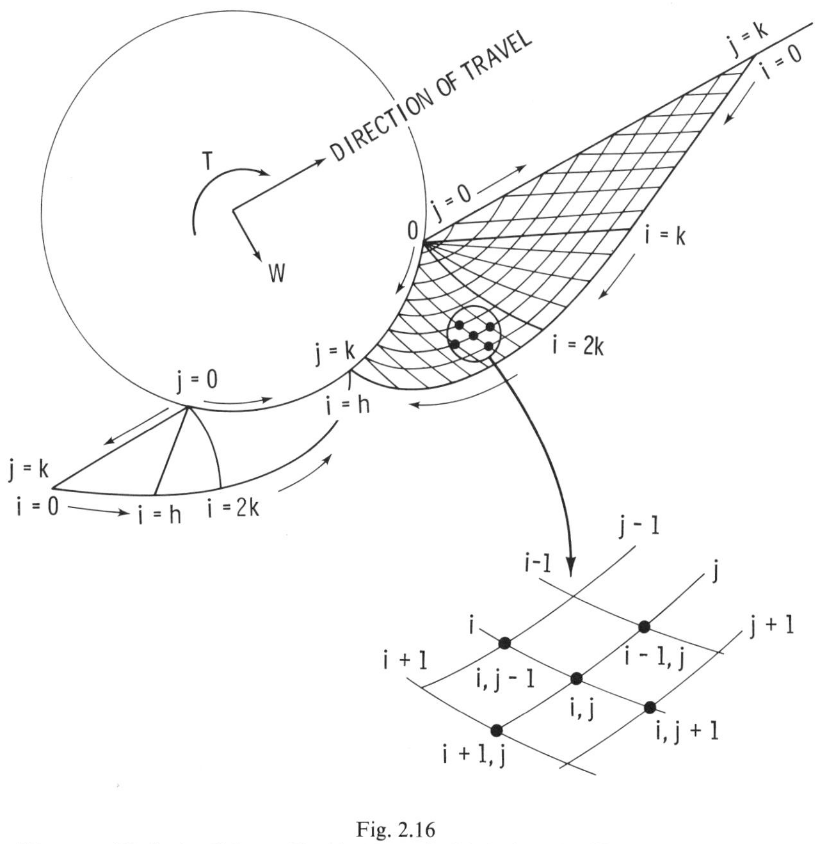

Fig. 2.16
Diagram of Indexing Scheme Used in Numerical Solution of Differential Equations (Arrows along Boundaries Indicate Direction of Increasing *i*- and *j*-Indices)

The manner in which quantities specified for x, z, σ and θ along one or more boundaries are used to determine values for these variables on other boundaries and/or within the area between boundaries through the expedient of a grid system and recurrence relationships is best described with reference to the three different types of problems mentioned previously.

In the CAUCHY problem the quantities x, z, σ and θ are known at all points on a non-characteristic line. The problem is to determine the corresponding values of these variables within and on other boundaries of the problem. This is shown schematically in Figure 2.17 where x, z, σ and θ are known along the non-characteristic line AB. The recurrence relationships given in the previous section can be used to compute x, z, σ and θ along the j-characteristics AC and/or along the i-characteristics CB by proceeding through the entire region in the directions indicated by the arrows (dashed arrows refer to subsequent operations from computed points).

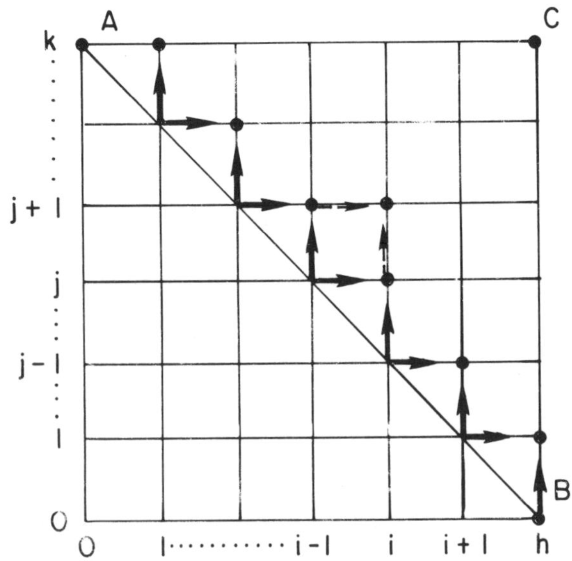

Fig. 2.17
Schematic of Boundary Conditions for the CAUCHY Problem

The computation of the slip line field for the passive zone exemplifies the CAUCHY problem where, with reference to Figure 2.16, the slip line field defined by $j = 0$ to k and $i = 0$ to k represents the passive zone. In the authors' method of computation, the solution is obtained by starting at the point where $j = 0$ and proceeding from boundary to boundary along one j-characteristic after another until the entire field has been determined. For each j-characteristic this method involves the CAUCHY problem at i-characteristic intersection (nodal) points in the passive zone, the GOURSAT problem, as will be shown below, at nodal points in the transition or radial zone, and, as will also be shown below, the "mixed boundary value" problem at nodal points in the active zone. This, however, is a characteristic of the authors' method of solution; any method that proceeds from two "known" nodal points to a third "unknown" point will work as well. This is shown by the arrows in Figure 2.17.

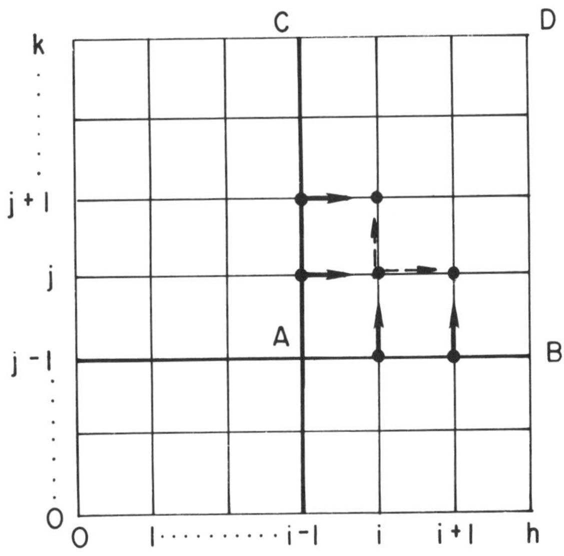

Fig. 2.18
Schematic of Boundary Conditions for the GOURSAT Problem

In the GOURSAT problem the quantities x, z, σ and θ are *assumed* to be known at all points along two intersecting characteristic lines. The problem is to determine the corresponding values of these quantities within the region defined by these characteristics. Since the boundaries of the problem are not known beforehand the solution must be checked for compatibility with known conditions along other characteristics or along non-characteristics. It is apparent from the direction of the arrows in Figure 2.18 that the recurrence relationships can again be used to go from known values along AC and AB to corresponding values along the boundaries CD and BD as well as to points on the grid within the boundaries. Dashed arrows again refer to subsequent operations from computed points.

The computation of the slip line field in the transitional or radial zone exemplifies the GOURSAT problem where, with reference to Figure 2.16, the slip line field defined by $j = 0$ to k and $i = k$ to $2k$ represents the radial zone. It should be noted that the point $j = 0$ is a "singular point" in that all i-characteristics converge at that point. Singularites and the concept of a "degenerate j-characteristic" are discussed more fully in Section 2.3.3. As with the CAUCHY problem, the GOURSAT problem is solved by proceeding from two known points to an unknown point as shown by the arrows in Figure 2.18.

In the mixed boundary value problem some of the quantities x, z, σ and θ are specified on both characteristic and non-characteristic lines. Obviously a number of variations of this case are possible. For purposes of illustration, Figure 2.19 shows one such case where x, z, σ and θ are all known along the i-characteristics AB and only z and θ are known along the non-characteristic line AC. The problem is to determine the value of all quantities on and within the boundary ABC. Examination of the figure indicates that because of the number, types and orientation of the unknowns, the recurrence relationships given by Equations 2.3.3 and 2.3.5 are not needed to obtain the solutions for x and σ along AC. Instead, the finite difference form of the differential equations as given by Equations 2.3.2 and 2.3.4 can be solved directly (assuming φ = constant, $n = 0$, and $\varepsilon = 0$) for the required unknown as follows:

$$x_{i,j} = (z_{i,j} - z_{i-1,j}) \cot(\theta_{i-1,j} - \mu) + x_{i-1,j} \qquad \text{Eq. 2.3.10}$$

$$\sigma_{i,j} = \sigma_{i-1,j} + 2\sigma_{i-1,j} \tan\varphi\,(\theta_{i,j} - \theta_{i-1,j}) + \\ + \gamma\,[(z_{i,j} - z_{i-1,j}) - (x_{i,j} - x_{i-1,j}) \tan\varphi] \qquad \text{Eq. 2.3.11}$$

For points within the boundaries, however, where neither x, z, σ nor θ are known, the recurrence relationships must be used. Again, dashed arrows indicate subsequent computations made from points where one or more of the quantities x, z, σ or θ have been computed.

The computation of the slip line field for the active zone exemplifies the "mixed boundary value" problem where, with reference to Figure 2.16, the slip line field defined by $j = 0$ to k and $i = 2k$ to h represents the active zone. This example also illustrates that one of the boundaries (the soil-wheel interface in this case) is specified by an independent relationship between two of the geometry variables x and z.

The computational techniques involved in obtaining solutions to practical soils problems are not usually as straightforward as indicated in the above discussions. Some of the complications that may be encountered are considered in the next section.

2.3.3 Singularities

In the execution of the numerical procedures required to solve any of the boundary value problems discussed in the previous section, discontinuities in either the σ or θ variable are often encountered at the inter-

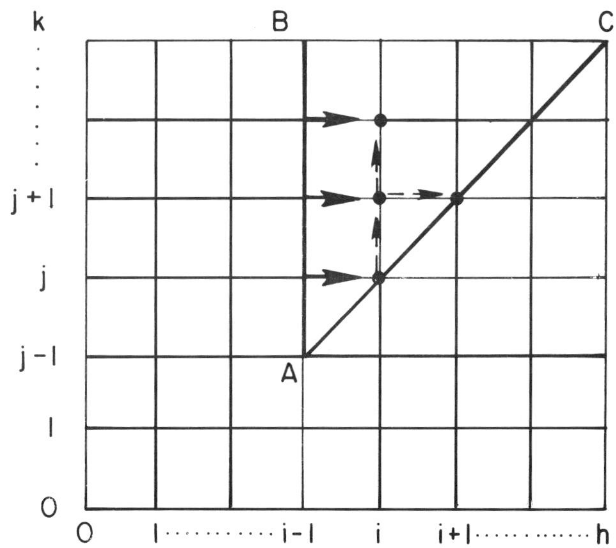

Fig. 2.19
Schematic of Boundary Conditions for the Mixed Boundary Value Problem

section of the boundaries or elsewhere within the stress field. These intersections constitute singularities that require special treatment in the solution procedure.

In the plane strain case the singularity occurs at the intersection point of the active and passive zone boundaries, as, for example, at point 0 in Figure 2.16. In this case θ at point 0 must pass from its value in the passive zone to its active zone value as given by Equation 2.2.21:

$$\theta = (1 - k)\frac{\pi}{4} + (k\Delta - \delta) + n\pi \qquad \text{Eq. 2.2.21}$$

where

δ = obliquity angle in the classical soil mechanics sense,
i.e. $\delta = \arctan[\tau_{xz}/(\sigma_z + \psi)]$

$\Delta = \arcsin(\sin\delta/\sin\varphi)$

$k = +1$ (passive); $k = -1$ (active)

n = any integer; usually 0 or $\pm$ 1.

The direct consequence of this requirement is that the first *j*-characteristic line degenerates to a point (singular point 0) and all of the *i*-characteristic lines converge at this point throughout the radial transition zone between the active and passive zones. In the numerical solution procedure, the singular point is treated by dividing the total change in θ by the number of *i*-lines converging at the point. This results in an equal $\Delta\theta$ increment between adjacent *i*-lines at the singular point. It is difficult to visualize this happening at a "point", therefore, as an aid, imagine that the singular point consists of a number of points equally spaced infinitesimally close to each other. If the assumption is made that the x and z coordinates for each of the constituent points are equal to the x and z coordinates of the singular point, and if, as indicated above, θ at each of the constituent points can be determined from known values of θ in either the active or passive zones ($\pm$ a multiple of $\Delta\theta$), then only σ remains to be evaluated at each point. Since dx and $dz = 0$ along the degenerate *j*-characteristic line at the singular point, inspection of Equation 2.2.20d suggests that under these conditions its solution is:

$$\sigma = \sigma_0 \exp[2(\theta - \theta_0)\tan\varphi] \qquad \text{Eq. 2.3.12}$$

where $\theta - \theta_0 = \Delta\theta$. With x, z, σ and θ known at each of the constituent points of the singular point, the recurrence relationships presented in the previous section may now be used to compute the coordinates and σ and θ values for all other points in the radial (or transition) zone.

A detailed mathematical analysis of the singular point as given by HARR (1966) wherein the x–z plane is mapped into an auxiliary plane is beyond the scope of this book.

In the axially symmetric case a similar situation exists not only at the intersection of the active and passsive zone boundaries, but also along the entire axis of symmetry. Consider the cone penetration problem such as that considered in detail in Section 2.5.3 and shown schematically in Figure 2.37. The former type of singularity is seen to exist at the point Q. Less obvious is the existence of a singularity at 0 also. This singularity is due to the fact that all boundary conditions and slip lines are symmetric with respect to z-axis. The situation becomes apparent if a section is taken through the axis of symmetry. It can be seen then that an abrupt change in θ is required at 0 for the orientation of the slip lines to be symmetric. A number of methods (for example, J. Auriault and R. Negre, 1967; J. Kravtchenko and R. Sibille, 1961) have been proposed to solve this singularity, however, thus far, none appears to be entirely satisfactory. The approach thus far has been to assign a value for θ at the axis of symmetry and to calculate σ as if the problem were two-dimensional.

In reality, the stress at 0 approaches infinity as "r" approaches zero in Equation 2.3.8. The method proposed and used by Nowatzki (1971) for the cylindrical soil-sampler and by Nowatzki and Karafiath (1972) for the solution of the cone indentation problem, although a trial and error method, is a compromise that is satisfactory for practical purposes.

Another more subtle type of singular point occurs in the numerical procedure currently being employed by the authors in their research on layered systems. The details of that singular point are discussed in Section 2.3.4 within the context of the layered system problem and the conditions existing at the layer interface.

2.3.4 Boundary Conditions at Layer Interfaces

The assumption of material homogeneity that was tacitly made in all considerations thus far is often not encountered in actual field operations. In many cases where off-road vehicles must operate, the soil is distinctly layered or often bedrock is close to the surface. Layered soil conditions were first treated by Burmister (1945) who applied the theory of elasticity for the computation of stresses and displacements in layered systems. In elasticity, he considered two kinds of boundary conditions at the layer interfaces: 1) Full continuity of stresses and displacements across the interface (no limitations on shear stresses on account of shear strength of soils) and 2) Continuity of normal stress and normal displacement with a frictionless interface that allows relative displacement of the adjoining layers along the interface. In his theory each layer is considered homogenenous and is characterized by its elastic modulus and Poisson's ratio. The numerical evaluation of the general equations for layered systems set forth by BURMISTER indicated that the boundary conditions at the layer interface, the ratio of the elastic moduli of the adjoining layers, and the ratio of the upper layer thickness to the dimensions of the loaded area strongly influence the distribution of stresses due to surface loading.

In tire-soil interaction problems of interest the stress levels in soil far exceed those for which the theory of elasticity applies. In the theory of plasticity there is no general treatment of layered systems. SOKOLOVSKII (1965) treated a very special case of layered systems, that of a "lamellar medium", where the layering is such that on horizontal planes the shear stresses may not exceed a value defined by a COULOMB type failure condition along the horizontal plane. In the theory of plasticity for soils, the deformations in the soil that occur prior to the plastic state are disregarded, and the stress states are calculated solely on the basis of MOHR-COULOMB yield criterion. As a consequence, in a logical expansion of the plasticity theory to layered systems the boundary conditions at layer interfaces must be defined in terms of stresses alone. This definition states that normal and shear stresses across the interface boundary must be continuous and that the shear stress at the interface may not exceed the shear strength of either adjoining layer. In mathematical terms:

$$\tau_i \leq c_l + \sigma_n \tan \varphi_l \qquad \text{Eq. 2.3.13a}$$

and

$$\tau_i \leq c_u + \sigma_n \tan \varphi_u \qquad \text{Eq. 2.3.13b}$$

where the subscripts u and l denote the upper and lower layers, respectively, in a horizontally layered system and the subscript i refers to the interface.

In numerical computations it is more convenient to express these boundary conditions in terms of the interface friction angle, δ, as follows:

$$\delta_i \leq \varphi_l \qquad \text{Eq. 2.3.14a}$$

$$\delta_i \leq \varphi_u \qquad \text{Eq. 2.3.14b}$$

In plasticity theory, elastic deformations are not considered. However, the displacements due to plastic flow are subject to certain restraints. The application of the theory of velocity fields to the boundary conditions at the interface yields the following boundary conditions:

a) Velocity vectors normal to the interface must either be equal in both layers or greater in the upper layer than in the lower layer so that separation along the boundary cannot occur.

b) Velocity vectors tangential to the interface can be (and usually are) different so that one layer can slide past the other.

In layered systems plasticity theory solutions have to satisfy the boundary conditions both at the surface and at layer interfaces. Solutions exist only for a limited range of the relative strength of the adjoining layers and only for certain loading conditions. There are no general rules for finding these solutions; for the consideration of the interface boundary conditions in the numerical computations and in the construction of slip line fields across layer interfaces the following comments apply.

In a bearing capacity type problem with a horizontal surface the shear stress on horizontal layer interfaces is either zero or minimal in the active and passive zones. Therefore, these zones may be continued in the adjoining layer with the following steps in the numerical computations:

a) Compute coordinates for nodal point *i, j*.

b) Determine intersection points of slip lines with the layer interface.

c) Determine σ and θ values for these points by interpolation.

d) Compute σ_n, τ and δ values for the intersection point.

e) Recompute σ and θ values from σ_n and τ with the strength parameters of the layer to be entered with the slip line field.

f) Continue computation of the zone with these values as boundary conditions at the layer interface.

The boundary conditions at the layer interface that limit the shear stresses there become constraints for those zones of the slip line fields where the tangent of a slip line at any point is coincident, or parallel to the interface. The radial zone in a bearing capacity problem is such a zone. At the point of tangency the interface friction angle δ becomes equal to the friction angle φ and modifications are neccessary in the construction of slip line fields to comply with the boundary conditions expressed by Equations 2.3.13. These modifications depend on the relative strength of adjacent layers.

If the strength of the upper layer is less than that of the lower layer, the zone in the upper layer is not affected by the boundary conditions at the layer interface. It is necessary, however, to choose the dimensions of the grid system so that one of the slip lines touches the layer interface. The point of contact separates the passive and active state of stresses in the upper radial zone, since the value of "k" in Equation 2.2.21 changes at this contact point from $+1$ to -1. In terms of normal stresses the passive case ($k = +1$) includes all stress states where

$$\sigma_{nf} > \sigma_n > \sigma_3$$

and the active case ($k = -1$) all stress states where

$$\sigma_{nf} < \sigma_n < \sigma_1$$

σ_{nf} = normal stress at the failure plane.

Figure 2.20 illustrates this point.

The variation of the θ angle along the layer interface is continuous, even though the value of "k" changes at the contact point abruptly from -1 to $+1$. Equation 2.2.21

$$\theta = (1 - k)\frac{\pi}{4} + (k\Delta - \delta) + n\pi \qquad \text{Eq. 2.2.21}$$

yields the same value for θ with either value of "k" if $\delta = \varphi$ (assume $n = 0$). In this case

$$\Delta = \text{arc} \sin 1 = \frac{\pi}{2}$$

$$k = +1, \ \theta = \frac{1}{2}\left(\frac{1}{2}\pi - \varphi\right) = \frac{\pi}{4} - \frac{\varphi}{2}$$

$$k = -1, \ \theta = \frac{1}{2}\pi + \frac{1}{2}\left(-\frac{1}{2}\pi - \varphi\right) = \frac{\pi}{4} - \frac{\varphi}{2}$$

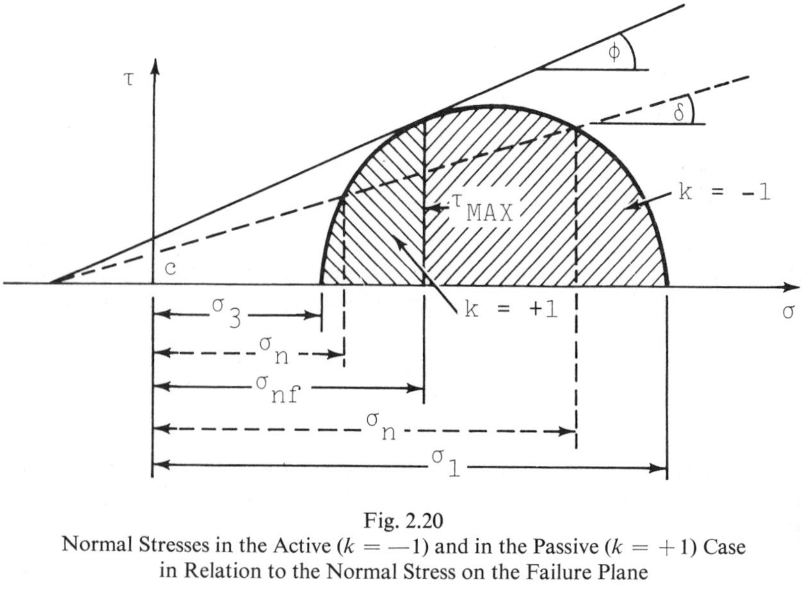

Fig. 2.20
Normal Stresses in the Active ($k = -1$) and in the Passive ($k = +1$) Case in Relation to the Normal Stress on the Failure Plane

In the case of the radial zone of the bearing capacity problem, the only conceivable solutions for the continuation of the slip line field across the layer interface are those where the character of the stress state (the "k" value) does not change across the interface. A change of the "k" value would result in a permissible, but inappropriate stress discontinuity across the interface.

In the lower layer, at an infinitesimal distance to the right of the contact point the θ value could be computed using "k" $= +1$, while at an infinitesimal distance to the left it could be computed using "k" $= -1$. While in the upper layer this change of the sign of "k" does not affect the continuity of θ, in the lower layer, where $\delta < \varphi$, there will be a discontinuity at this point. This situation is identical to that at the singular point at the edge of the loaded area in the bearing capacity case.

If the upper layer is the stronger one, then the strength of the lower layer limits the shear stresses that are generated in an upper layer slip line field along the interface. The construction of an upper layer slip line field cannot be continued if at any location along the interface the following condition holds:

$$\tau \geq \tau_{max} = (c_1 + \sigma_n) + \tan \varphi_1 \qquad \text{Eq. 2.3.15}$$

If the shear stresses generated by an upper layer radial zone exceed the shear strength of the lower layer along some length of the interface, the upper layer slip line field cannot be continued beyond the point where Equations 2.3.13 take control. Along a certain length of the interface the equality condition in Equations 2.3.13 will hold and the interface is a slip line in a field in the lower layer. This is a basic feature of composite slip line fields where the upper layer is stronger; intuitively one feels that upon loading a stronger upper layer sliding must occur somewhere along the layer interface.

In the lower layer a "square" zone accomodates that length of the interface that is a slip line. The interface friction angle δ equals φ and is constant along this slip line, and therefore, the θ angle must be also constant and equal to

$$\theta = \frac{\pi}{4} - \frac{\varphi}{2} \qquad \text{Eq. 2.3.16}$$

The differential equation of plasticity that governs the variation of σ in this case is the same as the basic differential equation given in Section 2.2.2 for a horizontal surface, i.e.

$$d\sigma + 2\sigma \tan \varphi \, d\theta = \gamma \, (dz + \tan \varphi \, dx) \qquad \text{Eq. 2.2.20d}$$

As explained previously, along this slip line θ = constant, and, since the slip line is parallel to the x-axis, z = constant. Consequently, $d\theta = 0$ and $dz = 0$ and Equation 2.2.20d reduces to

$$d\sigma = \gamma \tan \varphi \, dx \qquad \text{Eq. 2.3.17}$$

Equation 2.2.20d allows the computation of σ along the slip line that is coincident with the layer interface. With the values of all four variables defined along this slip line, a "square" zone may be computed if the four variables along a conjugate slip line are also known. This situation corresponds to the GOURSAT problem discussed in Section 2.3.2.

The above considerations are helpful for the composition of slip line fields that are compatible with the boundary conditions at both the surface and layer interface. Solutions exist, however, only for specific cases where the relative strength of the layers and the base friction angle are such that the boundary conditions can be met. There are no general rules for finding such solutions. More detailed discussion of these problems is given by KARAFIATH (1975).

2.3.5 Solution Methods for Special Cases

Effect of Pore Water Pressures

The derivation of the basic differential equations that pertain to soils wherein pore water pressures develop upon loading was given in Section 2.2.5. For convenience, the equations are repeated below for the family of slip lines corresponding to the i and j characteristic lines (where the minus (–) sign refers to the j-characteristic and the plus (+) sign refers to the i-characteristic):

$$dz = dx \tan (\theta \mp \mu) \qquad \text{Eq. 2.2.29a and 2.2.29b}$$

$$(1 + M)\, d\bar{\sigma} \mp 2\bar{\sigma} \tan \varphi \, d\theta \mp M \tan \varphi \frac{\partial \bar{\sigma}}{\partial x} dz \mp$$

$$M \tan \varphi \frac{\partial \bar{\sigma}}{\partial z} dx = \frac{\gamma}{\cos \varphi} [\sin (\varepsilon \mp \varphi)\, dx + \cos (\varepsilon \mp \varphi)\, dz \qquad \text{Eq. 2.2.29c and 2.2.29d}$$

As indicated in Section 2.2.5, for $M = 0$, Equations 2.2.29 revert to those for plane strain conditions in a soil with no pore water pressures. Therefore, it is reasonable to expect that the solution of Equations 2.2.29 consists essentially of the same type of slip line, i.e. one having a passive, radial, and active zone. In addition, a similar finite difference numerical technique applies. The major difference lies in the evaluation of M and the partial differentials $\partial\bar{\sigma}/\partial x$ and $\partial\bar{\sigma}/\partial z$ along the boundaries of the active and passive zones, at the inner points of the slip line field, and at the singular ($j = 0$) point. The following techniques are used in the numerical computation for the evaluation of the partial differentials:

a) Boundary conditions at the free surface in the passive zone.

The partial differentials $\partial\bar{\sigma}/\partial x$ and $\partial\bar{\sigma}/\partial z$ have to be specified here in addition to the normal and shear stresses, which, in the case of wheel loading, are zero at the free surface. For a horizontal free surface $\partial\bar{\sigma}/\partial x = 0$, $\theta = 0$, $d\theta = 0$, $\partial\bar{\sigma} = (\partial\bar{\sigma}/\partial z)\, dz$. After substitutions in Equations 2.2.29:

$$\frac{\partial\bar{\sigma}}{\partial z} = \frac{\gamma}{(1 - \sin\varphi)\,(1 + M + M\tan\varphi\cot\mu)} \qquad \text{Eq. 2.3.18}$$

b) Computation of $\partial\bar{\sigma}/\partial x$ and $\partial\bar{\sigma}/\partial z$ at an inner point of the slip line field.

At a nodal point of the slip line field, designated by the subscripts i, j (Figure 2.21), the values of $\partial\bar{\sigma}/\partial x$ and $\partial\bar{\sigma}/\partial z$ are approximated on the basis of values of $\bar{\sigma}$ at neighboring points. The relationship $\bar{\sigma} = f(x, z)$ represents the variation of $\bar{\sigma}$ over the various (x, z) points of the slip line field. Assuming that this variation is linear in the vicinity of the $x_{i,j}$, $z_{i,j}$ point, the $\bar{\sigma} = f(x, z)$ relationship in the neighborhood can be expressed as follows:

$$P\bar{\sigma} + Qz + Sx - V = 0 \qquad \text{Eq. 2.3.19}$$

The coefficients in Eq. 2.3.19 can be expressed by known values of $\bar{\sigma}$ at three points as follows:

$$P = \begin{bmatrix} z_1 & x_1 & 1 \\ z_2 & x_2 & 1 \\ z_3 & x_3 & 1 \end{bmatrix} \qquad \text{Eq. 2.3.20a}$$

$$Q = \begin{bmatrix} x_1 & \bar{\sigma}_1 & 1 \\ x_2 & \bar{\sigma}_2 & 1 \\ x_3 & \bar{\sigma}_3 & 1 \end{bmatrix} \qquad \text{Eq. 2.3.20b}$$

$$S = \begin{bmatrix} \bar{\sigma}_1 & z_1 & 1 \\ \bar{\sigma}_2 & z_2 & 1 \\ \bar{\sigma}_3 & z_3 & 1 \end{bmatrix} \qquad \text{Eq. 2.3.20c}$$

$$V = \begin{bmatrix} \bar{\sigma}_1 & z_1 & x_1 \\ \bar{\sigma}_2 & z_2 & x_2 \\ \bar{\sigma}_3 & z_3 & x_3 \end{bmatrix} \qquad \text{Eq. 2.3.20d}$$

At an inner point of the slip line field, the three points designated by the subscripts 1, 2, 3 may be taken as the nodal points designated by the subscripts $i, j\text{–}1$; $i\text{–}1, j\text{–}1$; and $i\text{–}1, j$ where x, z, and $\bar{\sigma}$ values are known from previous computations. The partial differentials sought are as follows:

$$\frac{\partial \bar{\sigma}}{\partial x} = -\frac{S}{P} \qquad \text{Eq. 2.3.21 a}$$

$$\frac{\partial \bar{\sigma}}{\partial z} = -\frac{Q}{P} \qquad \text{Eq. 2.3.21 b}$$

c) Computation of stress at the singular point ($j = 0$).

The singular point is a degenerate slip line of the second family of slip lines (j-lines). Near the singular point, the weight of the soil has no influence on the stress state and γ may be taken as zero in Equation 2.2.20 (Sokolovskii, 1965). If pore water pressures are zero, the differential relationships are integrable, and the following relation is obtained for the

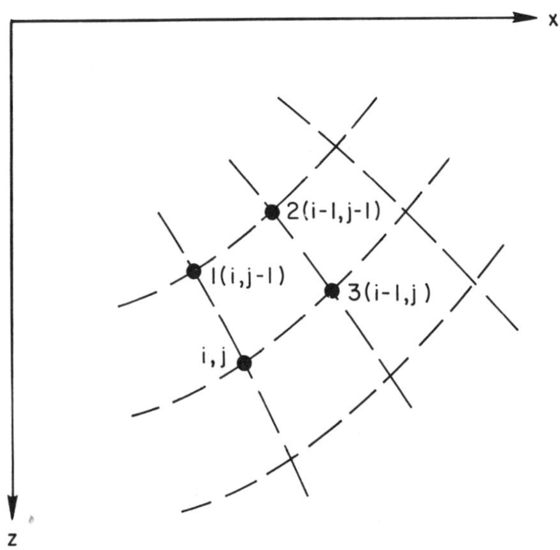

Fig. 2.21
Designations for Numerical Solution

computation of σ values at the singular point:

$$\sigma = \sigma_0 \exp\left[2 \tan \varphi \left(\theta - \theta_0\right)\right] \qquad \text{Eq. 2.3.12}$$

To derive a similar relationship when pore pressures exist it is expedient to write Equations 2.2.29 in polar coordinates. For the second family of slip lines and $\gamma = 0$ Equation 2.2.29c becomes

$$(1 + M)\, d\bar{\sigma} - M \tan \varphi \cot (\omega - \mu)\, d\bar{\sigma} - 2\bar{\sigma} \tan \varphi\, d\theta = 0 \qquad \text{Eq. 2.3.22}$$

where

ω = angle enclosed by major principal stress and radial coordinate.

If a Prandtl field consisting of logarithmic spirals and straight lines is assumed in the vicinity of the singular point, $\omega = -\mu$ and Equation 2.3.22 reduces to

$$(1 + M + M \tan^2 \varphi)\, d\bar{\sigma} - 2\bar{\sigma} \tan \varphi\, d\theta = 0 \qquad \text{Eq. 2.3.23}$$

Integration of Equation 2.3.23 yields:

$$\bar{\sigma} = \bar{\sigma}_0 \exp\left[\frac{2 \tan \varphi\, (\theta - \theta_0)}{(1 + M + M \tan^2 \varphi)}\right] \qquad \text{Eq. 2.3.24}$$

or

$$\bar{\sigma} = \bar{\sigma}_0 \exp\left[2 \tan \bar{\varphi}\, (\theta - \theta_0)\right] \qquad \text{Eq. 2.3.25}$$

where

$$\bar{\varphi} = \arctan\left[\frac{\tan \varphi}{1 + M + M \tan^2 \varphi}\right]$$

d) Computation of $\partial\bar{\sigma}/\partial x$ and $\partial\bar{\sigma}/\partial z$ at the slip line of the second family adjacent to the singular point ($j = 1$).

In the radial zone the computation of the partial differentials of $\bar{\sigma}$ for points adjacent to the singular point is not possible by Equations 2.3.21 because the points i–1, j and i–1, j–1 coincide. Along the $j = 1$ line an approximate value for the partial differentials of $\bar{\sigma}$ is obtained on the assumption that the field in the vicinity of the singular point is a Prandtl field where the $\bar{\sigma}$ values increase linearly with r along the radii, and the logarithmic spirals correspond to the angle $\bar{\varphi}$. The resulting partial differentials are

$$\frac{\partial \bar{\sigma}}{\partial x} = -2 \tan \varphi \, \bar{\sigma}_0 \frac{F^2}{E^2} \frac{z}{(x^2+z^2)} + \frac{GF^3}{E^3} \left[\frac{x}{\sqrt{x^2+z^2}} - 3 \tan \bar{\varphi} \frac{z}{\sqrt{x^2+z^2}} \right] \qquad \text{Eq. 2.3.26a}$$

$$\frac{\partial \bar{\sigma}}{\partial z} = 2 \tan \bar{\varphi} \, \sigma_0 \frac{F^2}{E^2} \frac{z}{(x^2+z^2)} + \frac{GF^3}{E^3} \left[\frac{z}{\sqrt{x^2+z^2}} + 3 \tan \bar{\varphi} \frac{z}{\sqrt{x^2+z^2}} \right] \qquad \text{Eq. 2.3.26b}$$

where

$$E = \exp \left[\left(\theta_0 + \frac{\pi}{4} - \frac{\bar{\varphi}}{2} \right) \tan \bar{\varphi} \right]$$

$$F = \exp \left[\tan \bar{\varphi} \arctan \left(\frac{z}{x} \right) \right]$$

$$G = \frac{\gamma \sin \mu}{(1 - \sin \varphi)(1 + M + M \tan \varphi / \tan \mu)}$$

e) Computation of $\partial\bar{\sigma}/\partial x$ and $\partial\bar{\sigma}/\partial z$ at the boundary of the active zone.

Equations 2.3.20 and 2.3.21 are not immediately applicable for points at the boundary because the values of $\bar{\sigma}$ at nodal point i–1, j–1 are outside of the field and not defined. Therefore an approximate value of $\bar{\sigma}$ at the i, j point at the boundary is computed first. Then the values of the partial differentials are computed by Equations 2.3.20 and 2.3.21 using $\bar{\sigma}$ values at the i, j; i–1, j; and i–1, j–1 points. The values are improved by iteration, which is rapidly convergent.

Figure 2.22 shows the general organization of the computer program for the computation of the geometry and associated stresses for a typical slip line field. For a wheel, the rear field is an image of the forward field (refer to Figure 2.16); therefore, the same computer program can be used for the computation of both provided changes in the signs of the variables are made where appropriate.

Details of the application of these procedures to the analysis of soil-wheel interaction have been presented with an example problem by KARAFIATH (1972).

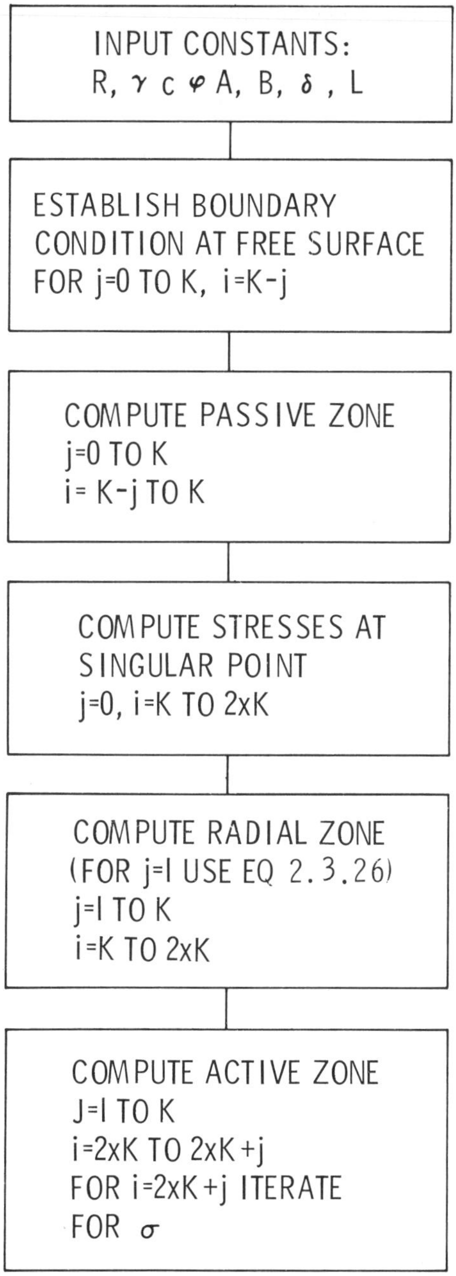

Fig. 2.22
Flow Chart to Compute Single Slip Line Field

Effect of Soil Inertia Forces

The derivation of the basic differential equations that pertain to the cases of soil-wheel interaction wherein soil inertia forces are considered was given in Section 2.2.4. For convenience, Equations 2.2.25a and b and 2.2.26a and b are repeated below where the upper signs refer to the *j*-characteristic lines while the lower signs refer to the *i*-characteristic lines.

$$dz = dx \tan(\theta \mp \mu)$$ Eqs. 2.2.25a and 2.2.25b

$$d\sigma \mp 2\sigma \tan\varphi \, d\theta = \frac{\gamma}{g}\left[\ddot{x} \mp (\ddot{z} + g)\tan\varphi \, dx + (\ddot{z} + g \pm \ddot{x}\tan\varphi)\, dz\right]$$

Eqs. 2.2.26a and 2.2.26b

where

$\ddot{x}$ = horizontal component acceleration
$\ddot{z}$ = vertical component of acceleration
g = acceleration due to gravity

All other variables are as defined in Section 2.3.1.

Attention is again called to the fact that $\ddot{x}$ and $\ddot{z}$ are independent variables so that there is an interdependence or coupling between the accelerations and the slip line field geometry. The implications of this interdependence on the solution have been discussed in Section 2.2.4 and will not be repeated here except to say that, at the present state of the art, one of two approaches can be used to establish the necessary interrelationship. In the first approach the velocity field corresponding to a computed slip line field is used to determine particle accelerations. The second approach is quasi-empirical and is based on an analytic simulation of observed particle path geometries, if such exist for the structure and loading being considered. Even if functional relationships could be established among soil properties, stress boundary conditions and particle accelerations, the direct numerical solution of Equations 2.2.25 or 2.2.26 would be formidable because of the inherent nonlinearities of such relationships. In any case, once the interrelationship has been determined, or approximated, and all boundary conditions adequately defined, the geometry of failure zones and the associated stresses can be determined by the straightforward numerical integration of Equations 2.2.25a and b and 2.2.26a and b using a modified form of the basic recurrence relationships given in Section 2.3.1. Consider the boundary conditions to be completely defined at the free surface where the coordinates are known and normal and shear stresses are zero. The boundary conditions at the soil-wheel interface then constitute a variation of the so-called "mixed boundary value problem" described by HARR (1966) and SOKOLOVSKII (1965) and discussed in Section 2.3.2. In this problem, two of the four independent variables (x, z, σ and θ) ordinarily contained in Equations 2.2.25 are defined at the boundary. In the case of a rigid wheel, for example, the definition of the boundary conditions is given by two relationships, one between the x and z coordinates at the interface, and the other defining θ at the interface. The latter relationship is conveniently obtained by defining the shear stress or the soil-wheel friction at the interface; from these, the direction (θ) of the major principal stress can be uniquely determined.

For the numerical solution, Equations 2.2.25 are written in finite difference form to yield the following recurrence relationships:

$$x_{i,j} = (z_{i-1,j} - z_{i,j-1} + \alpha_1 x_{i,j-1} - \alpha_2 x_{i-1,j}) / (\alpha_1 - \alpha_2) \qquad \text{Eq. 2.3.6c}$$

$$z_{i,j} = z_{i-1,j} + \alpha_2 (x_{i,j} - x_{i-1,j}) \qquad \text{Eq. 2.3.6d}$$

Note that the recurrence relationships for $x_{i,j}$ and $z_{i,j}$ are unaffected by consideration of inertia, however,

$$\sigma_{i,j} = [\gamma (\ddot{C}\sigma_{i,j-1} + \ddot{D}\sigma_{i-1,j}) + 2\sigma_{i,j-1}\sigma_{i-1,j}[1 + (\theta_{i,j-1} - \theta_{i-1,j})\tan\varphi]] / [\sigma_{i,j-1} + \sigma_{i-1,j}] \qquad \text{Eq. 2.3.27a}$$

$$\theta_{i,j} = [\sigma_{i,j-1} - \sigma_{i-1,j} + 2\tan\varphi\,(\sigma_{i,j-1}\theta_{i,j-1} + \sigma_{i-1,j}\theta_{i-1,j}) + \gamma(\ddot{D} - \ddot{C})] / [2\tan\varphi\,(\sigma_{i,j-1} + \sigma_{i-1,j})] \qquad \text{Eq. 2.3.27b}$$

$$\alpha_1 = \tan(\theta_{i,j-1} + \mu),$$
$$\alpha_2 = \tan(\theta_{i-1,j} - \mu)$$

$$\ddot{C} = \left[\frac{\ddot{x}_{i,j}}{g} - \left(1 + \frac{\ddot{z}_{i,j}}{g}\right)\tan\varphi\right](x_{i,j} - x_{i-1,j}) + \left[\left(1 + \frac{\ddot{z}_{i,j}}{g}\right) + \frac{\ddot{x}_{i,j}}{g}\tan\varphi\right](z_{i,j} - z_{i-1,j})$$

$$\ddot{D} = \left[\frac{\ddot{x}_{i,j}}{g} + \left(1 + \frac{\ddot{z}_{i,j}}{g}\right)\tan\varphi\right](x_{i,j} - x_{i-1,j}) + \left[\left(1 + \frac{\ddot{z}_{i,j}}{g}\right) - \frac{\ddot{x}_{i,j}}{g}\tan\varphi\right](z_{i,j} - z_{i-1,j})$$

To improve the accuracy of the numerical calculations, the coordinates x and z computed from Equations 2.3.6a and c can be considered as first approximations. An improved value of the coordinates may be computed by substituting $\theta_{j,\text{avg.}} = 0.5\ (\theta_{i,j} + \theta_{i-1,j})$ for $\theta_{i-1,j}$ and $\theta_{i,\text{avg.}} = 0.5\ (\theta_{i,j} + \theta_{i,j-1})$ for $\theta_{i,j-1}$ in a second iteration of the equations for $x_{i,j}$ and $z_{i,j}$.

The flow diagram that shows how the inertia forces in the above finite difference equations are considered in the numerical solution of the problem is given in Figure 2.23. The assumption is made in the flow diagram that the interrelationship between soil properties, stress fields and particle accelerations has somehow been defined or approximated and inputted prior to the computation of the first approximation of $x_{i,j}$ and $z_{i,j}$. The iteration indicated in blocks on the right of the flow diagram need be performed only once since experience indicates that this procedure yields satisfactory results. The change in the values of computed accelerations due to the improvement of $x_{i,j}$, $z_{i,j}$ values is minor.

Details of the application of these procedures to the analysis of soil-wheel interaction problems have been presented by KARAFIATH and NOWATZKI (1972) and are contained in Section 3.3.6.

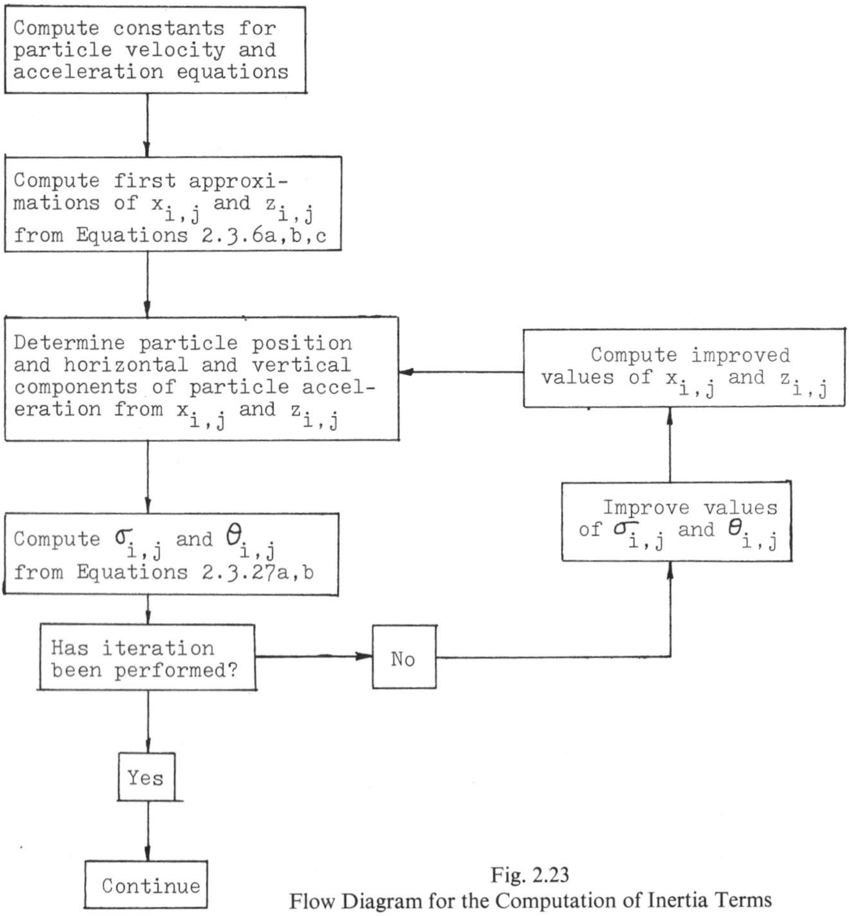

Fig. 2.23
Flow Diagram for the Computation of Inertia Terms

CHAPTER 2.4

LIMIT THEOREMS OF PLASTICITY

2.4.1 Upper and Lower Bound Solution

Limit design theorems were originally developed for the plastic analysis of indeterminate structures. These theorems establish lower and upper bounds for the "collapse load", i.e., the load at which the structure deforms appreciably while the load is maintened at a constant level. A lower bound of the collapse load is one where the stresses in the structure satisfy the equilibrium conditions and nowhere exceed the yield point. An upper bound of the collapse load pertains to a kinematically possible failure mechanism where the work done by the external loads and body forces equals the rate of energy dissipation by the stresses.

DRUCKER, PRAGER and GREENBERG (1952) extended the limit design theorems to continuous media. They found that for this purpose it was more convenient to define the collapse load as the constant load under which plastic flow occurs in the continuum. This definition allows the analysis of limit loads without the consideration of the effect of geometry changes that occur in the continuum as a result of plastic flow. The limit theorems are formulated as follows:

a) Collapse will not occur if any state of stresses can be found that satisfies the equations of equilibrium as well as the stress boundary conditions and nowhere exceeds the yield stress in the continuum (lower bound solution).

b) Collapse must occur if for any compatible flow pattern the rate at which the external forces do work on the body equals or exceeds the rate of internal dissipation (upper bound solution).

The second criterion requires the determination of kinematically possible flow patterns. The method whereby this is done is discussed in detail in Section 2.4.2 under the theory of velocity fields.

The flow pattern may be assumed to coincide with the stress characteristics (or slip lines) derived from the differential equations of plasticity.

If this flow pattern satisfies the second criterion, as it generally does in the problems of soil-wheel interaction treated in this book, then the solution obtained by the numerical integration of the differential equations of plasticity for soils is also an upper bound, that is, the solution is a unique and true solution of the problem.

The assumption that the flow pattern coincides with the slip lines or stress characteristics has been questioned by various researchers on the ground that for frictional soils an unrealistic dilation rate is associated with this assumption. The issue is a controversial one and has not yet been satisfactorily resolved. The interested reader can find pro and contra discussions in the referenced literature. From the viewpoint of the engineering solutions of the running-gear soil interaction problems the question is academic for the following reasons:

a) The interface stresses calculated by the theory of plasticity agree reasonably well with experiments. Thus, whatever the consequences of a noncoinciding flow pattern might be in regard to the calculated interface stresses, their net effect is within the range of the accuracy by which these stresses can be calculated and measured.

b) The slip line fields obtained as solutions of the differential equations of plasticity represent an instantaneous state of stresses. Because of the forward movement of the wheel this instantaneous state of stresses is valid for an infinitesimal time only, therefore, whatever dilation rate is associated with the slip line field, it would have to be maintained for an infinatesimal time only.

c) In statically determinate problems the stress and velocity characteristics coincide (SHIELD, 1954). Most of the bearing capacity and soil-wheel interaction problems are, indeed, statically determinate since the boundary conditions at the free surface and at the base of the footing or soil-wheel interface uniquely determine the solution. Note, however, that in the formulation of the problem, the interface friction angle is assumed as one of the boundary conditions at the soil-running gear interface. The development of the interface friction angle is related to the kinematic boundary conditions at the interface. Therefore, any assumption regarding the interface friction angle must be consistent with the kinematic boundary conditions for the solution to be both unique and true. Further discussion of the kinematic boundary conditions is in Chapter 2.5.

Even though the determination of flow patterns and velocity fields has little practical significance for the determination of stresses, the theory of velocity fields can be used for the calculation of velocities along the slip lines. These velocities are useful in determining the magnitude of bow waves, and for the estimation of soil inertia forces and strain rates. Therefore, the pertinent aspects of the velocity fields and methods of velocity calculation are presented in subsequent sections of this chapter.

2.4.2 The Theory of Velocity Fields

The development of the theory of velocity fields originated with the applications of plasticity theory to metal forming processes. For metals, the angle of internal friction is zero and the characteristics obtained from the solutions of the differential equations for both the velocities and stresses coincide. In the plastic state, frictionless materials actually slip along the characteristic line; hence the term "slip line field".

The theory of velocity fields was later extended to include materials exhibiting friction, such as soils (Shield, 1954). The purpose of this extension was, however, not so much to determine the flow of the material, as in the case of metal forming processes, but to enable researchers to apply the limit theorems of plasticity to various problems of plastic equilibrium in soils.

The differential equations governing the velocities and the geometry of the velocity field may be derived from the strain rates as follows (Davis, 1968). If u and v are the velocity components in the x and z directions respectively and compressive strains are positive, then:

$$\dot{\varepsilon}_x = -\frac{\partial u}{\partial x} \qquad \text{Eq. 2.4.1a}$$

$$\dot{\varepsilon}_z = -\frac{\partial v}{\partial z} \qquad \text{Eq. 2.4.1b}$$

$$\dot{\gamma}_{xz} = -\frac{\partial u}{\partial z} - \frac{\partial v}{\partial x} \qquad \text{Eq. 2.4.1c}$$

For the principal strain rates the following equations hold:

$$\left.\begin{matrix}\dot{\varepsilon}_1\\ \dot{\varepsilon}_3\end{matrix}\right\} = \frac{1}{2}\left[\dot{\varepsilon}_x + \dot{\varepsilon}_z \pm \sqrt{(\dot{\varepsilon}_x - \dot{\varepsilon}_z)^2 + \dot{\gamma}_{xz}^2}\,\right] \qquad \text{Eq. 2.4.2a and 2.4.2b}$$

If θ denotes the angle between the direction of the major principal strain and the z axis (note that for stresses θ is measured from the x axis), then

$$\dot{\varepsilon}_x - \dot{\varepsilon}_z = \dot{\gamma}_{xz} \cot 2\theta \qquad \text{Eq. 2.4.3}$$

Assuming that the ratio of the principal strain rates is the same as that of the principal stresses (associated flow rule material), i.e.

$$\frac{\dot{\varepsilon}_1}{\dot{\varepsilon}_3} = \frac{\sigma_1}{\sigma_3} \qquad \text{Eq. 2.4.4}$$

the following equation may be derived

$$\dot{\varepsilon}_x + \dot{\varepsilon}_z = -\dot{\gamma}_{xz} \sin\varphi \operatorname{cosec} 2\theta \qquad \text{Eq. 2.4.5}$$

Equation 2.4.5 is similar in form to Equation 2.2.17c in the derivation of the differential equations for stresses.

From Equation 2.4.1 and Equation 2.4.3 the following partial differential equations are obtained.

$$\frac{\partial u}{\partial x} + \cot 2\theta \frac{\partial u}{\partial z} + \cot 2\theta \frac{\partial v}{\partial x} - \frac{\partial v}{\partial z} = 0 \qquad \text{Eq. 2.4.6a}$$

$$\frac{\partial u}{\partial x} + \sin\varphi \operatorname{cosec} 2\theta \frac{\partial u}{\partial z} + \sin\varphi \operatorname{cosec} 2\theta \frac{\partial v}{\partial x} + \frac{\partial v}{\partial z} = 0 \qquad \text{Eq. 2.4.6b}$$

These partial differential equations, like their counterparts for the stresses, are hyperbolic. The velocity characteristics are governed by the equations

$$\frac{dx}{dz} = \tan\left[\theta \pm \left(\frac{\pi}{4} - \frac{\varphi}{2}\right)\right] \qquad \text{Eqs. 2.4.7a and 2.4.7b}$$

Thus, the geometry of the velocity characteristics, as far as their slopes are concerned, are governed by the same differential equations as the ones derived for the stress characteristics (Equations 2.2.20a and b). However, the differential equations for the stresses (Equations 2.2.20c and d) uniquely determine the stress characteristics. This is not the case with Equations 2.4.6 for the velocity characteristics. If v^α and v^β designate the velocities along "j" and "i" characteristics respectively, then, with reference to Figure 2.24, Equations 2.4.6 may be transformed as follows:

$$dv^\alpha + (v^\alpha \tan\varphi + v^\beta \sec\varphi)\, d\theta^\alpha = 0 \qquad \text{Eq. 2.4.8a}$$

$$dv^\beta - (v^\alpha \sec\varphi + v^\beta \tan\varphi)\, d\theta^\beta = 0 \qquad \text{Eq. 2.4.8b}$$

The above equations define the variation of velocities along characteristic lines. The velocity vectors v^α and v^β are components (projections) of the velocity vector v in the direction of the "j" and"i" lines, respectively. Note that in Figure 2.24 the vectorial sum of v^α and v^β is not v.

The u and v components of the velocity vector, v, are related to v^α and v^β as follows:

$$v^\alpha = u \sin \theta^\alpha - v \cos \theta^\alpha \qquad \text{Eq. 2.4.9a}$$

$$v^\beta = u \sin \theta^\beta - v \cos \theta^\beta \qquad \text{Eq. 2.4.9b}$$

Equations 2.4.8 express the variation of three quantities, v^α, v^β and θ, while in the stress equations only two quantities, σ and θ vary. Thus, the differential equations for the velocities are not sufficient by themselves to determine the geometry of the velocity fields, even if all of the boundary conditions that are necessary for the solution are defined. Because of this indeterminacy of the velocity characteristics it is difficult to see how upper bound solutions based on velocity fields could be meaningful for problems that are resolved by the integration of the stress differential equations of plasticity.

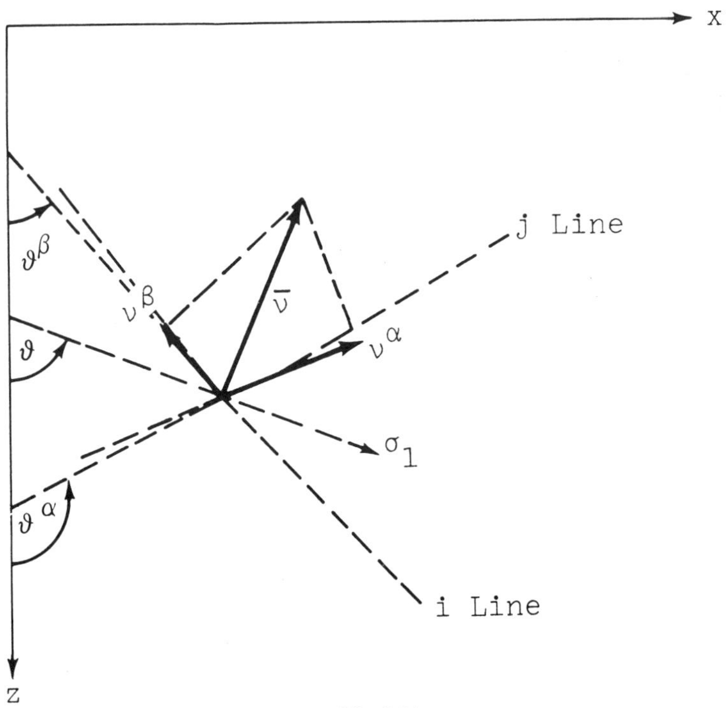

Fig. 2.24
Velocity Vectors Along Characteristic Lines

Nevertheless, Equations 2.4.8 may be useful for the computation of velocities in a given field of stress characteristics. As it is the case with differential equations in general, Equations 2.4.8 yield unique solutions only if the boundary conditions are adequately defined. The considerations that apply for the definition of velocity boundary conditions in bearing capacity type problems are discussed in the next section.

2.4.3 Kinematic Boundary Conditions

In a slip line field determined by the integration of the differential equations of plasticity for bearing capacity type problems Figure 2.25 indicates that there are three boundaries where kinematic conditions must be examined:

a) The stress free surface (AD).

b) The outermost slip line where the field adjoins the soil mass that is not in the state of plastic equilibrium ($DCBO$).

c) The surface where the external stresses are applied (OA).

At the stress free surface there are no kinematic constraints since soil particles at that surface may be displaced freely in the direction of velocities that are upward directed.

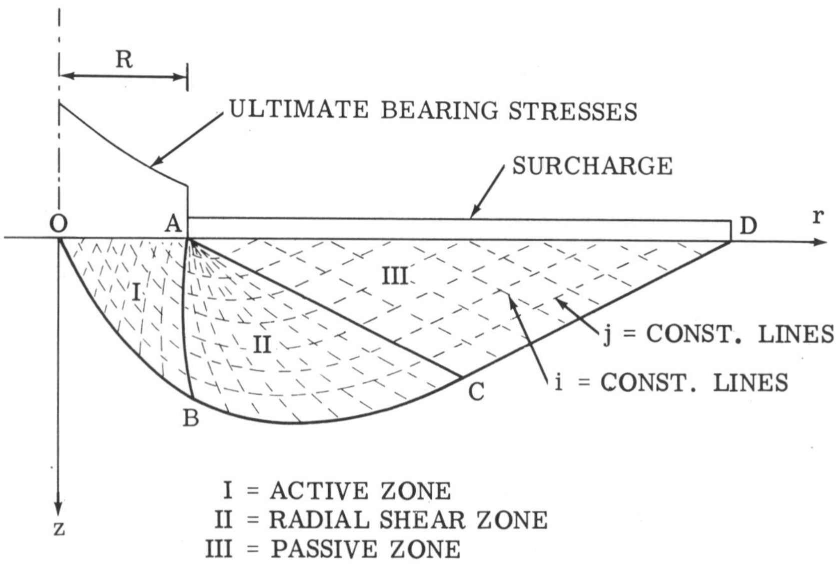

Fig. 2.25
Typical Slip Line Field

The outermost slip line constitutes a boundary beyond which the soil is not in the plastic state. Implicit in the use of the MOHR-COULOMB yield criterion is that soil deformations prior to yield are disregarded. Therefore, in this concept the soil beyond the outermost slip line acts as a rigid body. Consequently, velocities across this boundary must be zero, and the kinematic boundary condition $v^{\beta} = 0$ applies for this line. For this boundary condition Equation 2.4.8 is integrable and yields

$$v^{\alpha} = v_{0}^{\alpha} \exp\left[\tan \varphi \left(\theta^{\alpha} - \theta_{0}^{\alpha}\right)\right] \qquad \text{Eq. 2.4.10}$$

Note that for the stress computations the state of the soil outside the slip line field is immaterial. The velocity field, however, is profoundly affected by the assumption that the soil adjacent to the outermost slip line is assumed to be rigid. Experimental information on soil displacements along this boundary is scarce. It appears that while the soil mass outside this boundary undoubtedly undergoes some deformation there is an abrupt change in the displacements in a narrow band along the boundary. Thus, the theoretical boundary condition corresponding to the rigid-plastic material idealization may not be too far off from reality.

At the surface where the external stresses are applied, certain kinematic boundary conditions are imposed on the soil by the vehicular or structural footing. As discussed previously, it is at this boundary that two relations between the four variables of the stress equations have to be specified in order for the stress solution to be uniquely defined. One of these, the interface friction angle, whose magnitude and distribution along this boundary defines the relation between the normal and shear stresses at the boundary, may or may not be defined *a priori* by the conditions of the problem. In either case, the interface friction angle is related to the kinematic boundary conditions at the interface. The formulation of this relationship is, however, exceedingly difficult primarily because the plasticity theory assumes rigid-plastic stress-strain relations and ignores the strains that occur at stress levels lower than the plastic state. In actuality, however, strains and shear stresses, associated with these strains, develop in soil and at the interface. While these strains and stresses may not influence the stress computations significantly, they may be critical in the consideration and establishment of kinematic boundary conditions.

To illustrate the problem consider the application of plasticity theory to the bearing capacity problem. The interface or bearing stresses determined by plasticity theory refer to a stress state where the slip line fields are fully developed and the soil within the slip line fields is in the state of plastic equilibrium. At this state the footing has already been displaced vertically by some amount due to the volume changes that occurred in the soil while the applied stresses were increased from zero to the level corresponding to the fully plastic state. During this stress increase horizontal strains in the soil resulted in the development of interface shear stresses. From the viewpoint of the application of plasticity theory, these stresses and strains are initial ones. The theory of velocity fields, if it applies at all, applies to the strains and their associated rates that occur in addition to the initial strains. Thus, it cannot be expected that kinematic considerations based on the properties of velocity fields either influence or are useful for the determination of strains and stresses that occur prior to the development of the plastic state. In certain mobility problems, however, where instantaneous plastic slip line fields are assumed in the interaction model, these instantaneous slip line fields are superimposed on a soil that was previously strained. Also, shear stresses applied at the interface are relatively large. For both of these reasons the initial stresses and strains may only negligibly influence the kinematic boundary conditions.

A fundamental aspect of the analysis of the kinematic boundary conditions at soil-footing interfaces is that the kinematics of the footing and the adjacent soil are not identical. A useful, but by no means unconditionally valid assumption regarding the kinematic boundary conditions at interfaces is that the two surfaces comprising the interface may slide on, but may not separate from each other. This assumption leads to the boundary condition that the normal components of the velocities of the footing and adjoining soil particles are the same at any instant. This condition is, by itself, not sufficient for the determination of the boundary velocities for the soil. Some additional assumption is needed that defines the direction of the velocity vector. Such an additional assumption may be derived from the relative displacements of the footing and adjacent soil particles, if they are known or can be reliably estimated. In connection with soil-tire interaction analysis the assumption is made that the directions of the velocity vector and the major principal stress coincide. This assumption leads to reasonable slip rates and other interesting conclusions (Karafiath and Sobierajski, 1974).

2.4.4 Numerical Computation of Velocities

If the geometry of slip lines is known from the numerical integration of the differential equations of plasticity (or from any other source) then Equations 2.4.8 may be used for the calculation of velocities along these lines. For the numerical computation the differentials in Equations 2.4.8

are replaced by finite differences. The resulting difference equations are:

$$v^{\alpha}_{i,j} = \frac{(A - B \cdot C)}{(1.0 - B \cdot C)} \qquad \text{Eq. 2.4.11 a}$$

$$v^{\beta}_{i,j} = C - D \cdot v^{\alpha}_{i,j} \qquad \text{Eq. 2.4.11 b}$$

where

$$A = \frac{v^{\alpha}_{i+1,j} - \frac{1}{2} v^{\alpha}_{i+1,j} \tan\varphi\,(\theta_{i,j} - \theta_{i+1,j})}{1 + \frac{1}{2}\tan\varphi\,(\theta_{i,j} - \theta_{i+1,j})}$$

$$B = \frac{\frac{1}{2}\sec\varphi\,(\theta_{i,j} - \theta_{i+1,j})}{1 + \frac{1}{2}\tan\varphi\,(\theta_{i,j} - \theta_{i+1,j})}$$

$$C = \frac{v^{\alpha}_{i,j+1} + \frac{1}{2} v^{\alpha}_{i,j+1} \sec\varphi\,(\theta_{i,j} - \theta_{i,j+1})}{1 - \frac{1}{2}\tan\varphi\,(\theta_{i,j} - \theta_{i,j+1})}$$

$$D = \frac{\frac{1}{2}\sec\varphi\,(\theta_{i,j} - \theta_{i,j+1})}{1 - \frac{1}{2}\tan\varphi\,(\theta_{i,j} - \theta_{i,j+1})}$$

These difference equations indicate that the velocities for any grid point (i, j) can be computed if the velocities at two adjacent points $(i + 1, j$ and $i, j + 1)$ are known. The θ values are available for all grid points from the geometry computed for the stress field or can be derived from the coordinates of the grid points. Note that θ values for the directions of velocities along an α or β line differ by a constant from the θ values of the stress field. In the difference calculations this constant cancels out and θ values obtained directly in the stress field calculation may be used. The kinematic boundary conditions discussed in the preceding section provide the initial values of velocities necessary to start the computations. Since these boundary conditions define the initial values of velocities at locations where the computation of the stress field is terminated, the velocity computations must be performed in a reversed order. In the velocity computations it is convenient to retain the numbering of the i- and j-lines that was used in the stress computations. As a consequence, the computation of velocities follows a decreasing i and j sequence and the known values of velocities are at the $(i + 1, j$ and $i, j + 1)$ points, as indicated in Equations 2.4.11.

CHAPTER 2.5

APPLICATIONS OF PLASTICITY THEORY TO GENERAL SOIL-STRUCTURE INTERACTION PROBLEMS

The fundamental concepts presented in the previous chapters and to be applied in subsequent chapters to problems of soil-wheel, soil-tire and soil-track interaction are not new. Many examples of the use of plasticity theory and one of the yield criteria descriptive of soil behavior to develop solutions for the equilibrium of structures resting on or in the ground can be found in the literature. FANG et al (1974) have presented a bibliography in which most of the pertinent references are tabulated and some of which are annotated. That bibliographical data has been arranged under the following general categories:

a) Stress-strain relationships.

b) Bearing capacity.

c) Earth pressure.

d) Slope stability.

e) Miscellaneous.

This arrangement provides a good framework for our discussions here. The stress-strain relationships and the consideration of active and passive earth pressures relevant to soil-vehicle interaction studies have already been treated in general in Part 1. They will be discussed in more detail in Part 3 with reference to specific soil-running gear interaction problems.

The authors consider the soil-vehicle interaction problem to be a modified form of the bearing capacity problem. Therefore, the application of plasticity theory to bearing capacity problems will be discussed in detail in this Chapter.

On the other hand, slope stability problems and applications of earth pressure theory to rigid and/or flexible earth retaining structures, although of primary concern in many civil engineering projects, have only indirect relevance in the classical sense to soil mobility problems and will not be treated here. A specific case of interest, that of vehicles traversing a slope, will be treated as a special case of the bearing capacity problem.

Finally, other problems in terrain vehicle mechanics that are amenable to plasticity solutions and that are grouped under "miscellaneous" by FANG et al will be considered here. These include bulldozing resistance, soil cutting processes and penetration resistance.

2.5.1 Application of Plasticity Theory to the Bearing Capacity of Soils

In classical soil mechanics there are two principal modes of shear failure which have to be considered in the determination of the bearing capacity of shallow footings. One mode, the "general" shear failure, occurs in relatively dense soils and is characterized by a well-defined break in the load-deflection curve that is associated with the complete development of plastic zones of failure. The other mode, the "local" shear failure, occurs in loose and compressible soils. It is characterized by large deformations that cause failure conditions along a narrow band so that development of plastic zones does not occur. Because of the zonal character of the failure, the former mode is ideally suited for analysis by classical plasticity theory. The local shear failure, an the other hand, is not so well suited and can be analyzed only approximately by plasticity theory (J. B. HANSEN, 1952). In the discussion of bearing capacity in this chapter, only the "general" shear failure mode will be considered.

In Section 1.4.3, one rigorous and one approximate plasticity solution to the bearing capacity problem were presented. These are respectively the PRANDTL solution and the TERZAGHI solution. The former is a rigorous solution in which the stability of a strip load on the surface of a weightless soil is investigated. Although PRANDTL was the first to apply the concept of curved slip lines to the solution of the bearing capacity problem, the usefulness of the results is severely limited by the assumption of weightlessness and the fact that the bearing stresses are considered always to act perpendicularly to the loaded surface. The PRANDTL solution therefore, as shown by the field in Figure 1.44, implies that the base of the footing is frictionless.

TERZAGHI (1943) recognized the importance of base friction on bearing capacity and formulated the problem accordingly. By assuming that the friction between the footing and the soil was large enough to prevent shear displacements at the interface, TERZAGHI forced the slip surface directly beneath the footing to take the shape shown in Figure 1.45(a). The details of the development of the TERZAGHI bearing capacity theory for general shear conditions are contained in Section 1.4.3. By using super-position of the effects of cohesion, soil weight and surface loading (or surcharge), TERZAGHI derived the basic expression for the average bearing pressure or "bearing capacity" of a long, uniformly loaded strip footing of width "b". He later modified the original equation to account for the geometric shape of the bearing surface. Others further modified the TERZAGHI equation to account for inclined load, eccentricity of load, embedment, etc. The basic equation and the modifications are discussed in detail in Section 1.4.3. For the sake of continuity, the resulting general equation is repeated here

$$\sigma_u = cN_c s_c i_c d_c + \gamma \frac{b}{2} N_\gamma s_\gamma i_\gamma d_\gamma + qN_q s_q i_q d_q \qquad \text{Eq. 1.4.26}$$

where

c = unit cohesion
b = footing width
γ = unit weight of soil on which footing rests
q = surcharge or "effective" surcharge as defined in Section 1.4.3
N_c, N_q, N_γ = bearing capacity factors
s_c, s_q, s_γ = shape factors
i_c, i_q, i_γ = inclination factors
d_c, d_q, d_γ = depth factors

Actually, the theoretically correct formulation of the plane strain and axially symmetric bearing capacity problem using plasticity theory with the assumption of a rigid-perfectly plastic material and the MOHR-COULOMB failure criterion was hypothesized as early as 1909 by HAAR and VON KARMAN. The formulation consists of a pair of hyperbolic, nonlinear differential equations whose solution, except for a few special cases (one of which is the PRANDTL solution), is virtually impossible to obtain analytically. The formulations themselves, however, can accomodate almost an infinite variety of stress and geometric boundary conditions. These formulations were discussed in detail in Chapter 2.2 and are represented by Equations 2.2.20. They are repeated here for the sake of continuity:

$$dz = dx \tan(\theta \mp \mu) \qquad \text{Eqs. 2.2.20a and 2.2.20b}$$

$$d\sigma \mp 2\sigma \tan\varphi \, d\theta = \frac{\gamma}{\cos\varphi}\left[\sin(\varepsilon \mp \varphi)\, dx + \cos(\varepsilon \mp \varphi)\, dz\right] \qquad \text{Eqs. 2.2.20c and 2.2.20d}$$

However, it was not until SOKOLOVSKII (1960) presented a numerical technique based on the method of characteristics that useful solutions could be obtained. These solutions do not involve superposition as does the TERZAGHI solution and are exact solutions (within the limitations of numerical computations) for rigid-perfectly plastic materials. With the advent and widespread availability of high speed digital computers, numerical solutions of a broad spectrum of soil-structure interaction problems have emerged. In the area of bearing capacity, KO and SCOTT (1973) show that results of analyses using plasticity theory conform well with measured results. KARAFIATH (1972a) in his studies of the effect of base friction on bearing capacity showed that for both smooth and rough bases the numerical solutions of the differential equations of plasticity confirm the linear relationship among bearing capacity, footing width, and surcharge suggested by the classical bearing capacity equation of TERZAGHI. He

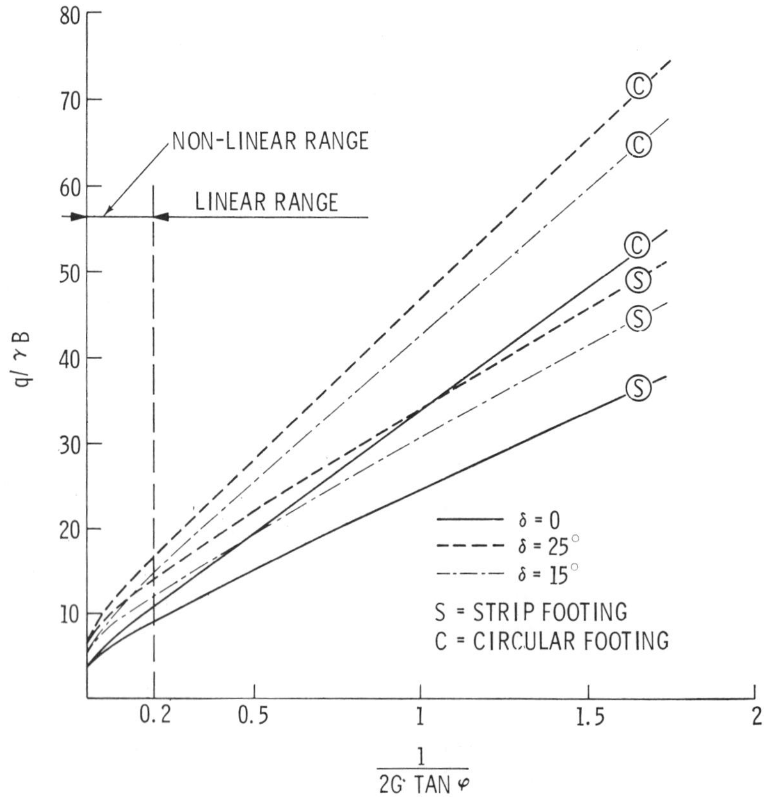

Fig. 2.26
Bearing Capacities Obtained from Numerical Solutions of the Differential Equations of Plasticity

further showed that for depth/width ratios less than about 0.2, the theory of plasticity indicates a nonlinear relationship for cohesionless soils. Figure 2.26 summarizes these results and indicates that for both circular and strip footings, base friction significantly increases bearing capacity ($1/(2\,G \tan \varphi)$ = depth/ width for cohesionless soils). Other findings of this study that are relevant to methods of analysis used in vehicle mobility investigations are:

a) Measurement of base friction is essential for proper evaluation of plate bearing tests and for comparative studies of shape factors.

b) The distribution of base friction influences the distribution of bearing stresses. For example, a base friction decreasing from edge to center of a footing results in a decrease of that part of the bearing stresses due to surcharge.

It is instructive to dwell on the first of these findings to see just how versatile plasticity theory can be in evaluating the inaccuracies of the classical approximate methods of analysis. For cohesionless soils, the classical bearing capacity relationship plots in Figure 2.26 as a straight line with a slope, N_q, intercepting the vertical axis at $N_\gamma/2$. By analogy, the bearing capacity factors resulting from numerical solutions of the differential equations of plasticity may be evaluated in the same way. Table 2.1 summarizes such an evaluation. Table 2.2 presents the bearing capacity factors according to the TERZAGHI theory, A comparison of the two tables indicates that the N_q values for the strip footing agree reasonably well, but that the N_γ values for the plasticity solution are lower than those of the TERZAGHI solution. However, the plasticity values are in agreement with those given by other approximate solutions (HANSEN and CHRISTENSEN, 1969).

TABLE 2.1
Bearing Capacity Factors Resulting from Numerical Solutions of the Differential Equations of Plasticity for Cohesionless Soil with $\varphi = 30°$ (δ = angle between resultant bearings stress and the normal to the loaded surface).

	Strip Footing		Circular Footing	
	N_γ	N_q	N_γ	N_q
$\delta = 0°$	10.2	18.6	10.2	28.2
$\delta = 25°$	17.6	23.6	17.6	38.8

TABLE 2.2
Bearing Capacity Factors According to the Terzaghi Bearing Capacity Theory for Cohesionless Soil with $\varphi = 30°$

	Strip Footing		Circular Footing	
	N_γ	N_q	N_γ	N_q
Smooth	16.5	18.3	9.9	18.3
Rough	30	22	18.0	22

In the classical bearing capacity equation, adjustments for other than the two-dimensional case are made by shape factors as indicated in Equation 1.4.26. The shape factor for circular footings is the ratio of bearing capacity factors for circular footings to those for strip footings. From Table 2.1 the shape factor s_γ according to plasticity solutions is unity for both smooth ($\delta = 0$) and rough ($\delta = 25°$) footings. On the other hand a value of $s_\gamma = 0.6$ was determined emperically by TERZAGHI and is used in convential soil mechanics analysis in Equation 1.4.26. In experiments, however, there is no way to separate the effect of shape from the effect of changes in φ due to stress-strain conditions associated with that shape. This effect is always implicitly included in experimentally determined shape factors (see, for example, DEBEER, 1970), whereas it is excluded in theoretical analyses where the friction angle is constant.

Another possible reason for discrepancies between theory and experiment is that in experiments δ is uncontrolled. If the δ angle that develops on a circular plate is lower than that which develops on a strip, an apparent s_γ lower than 1 would result. Unfortunately there have been no reported bearing capacity tests run for which base friction measurements have been taken.

From Table 2.1 the shape factor s_q for circular footings according to plasticity solutions is $s_q = 1.52$ for $\delta = 0$ and $s_q = 1.64$ for $\delta = 25°$.

The TERZAGHI solution has $s_q = 1$ for both rough and smooth footings, however such a value is inconsistent with the generally accepted values of $s_c > 1$. BENT HANSEN (1961) suggests that $s_q = 1$ for $\varphi = 0$ but that for $\varphi > 25°$, $s_q \approx s_c$. For a circular footing BENT HANSEN reports values of s_c to range from 1.2 at $\varphi = 25°$ to 1.55 for $\varphi = 40°$. Experiments performed by DEBEER (1970) confirm this range.

Numerical methods by their very nature are suitable for adaptation to problems involving almost any set of geometric and stress boundary conditions. The problem of the stability of slopes loaded over a finite area is one such problem that is of particular interest in the analysis of vehicles traversing a slope. KARAFIATH and NOWATZKI (1970) presented two methods of analysis for this problem. One method, an approximate method, is based on the assumption that a slip line field analogous to the PRANDTL solution for horizontal ground applies. The other method consists of a numerical integration of the differential equations of plastic equilibrium formulated to account for the geometric and stress boundary conditions associated with the sloping ground problem. In keeping with the assumptions of the PRANDTL solution, the former method yields the following expression for the bearing capacity of a weightless, cohesionless soil

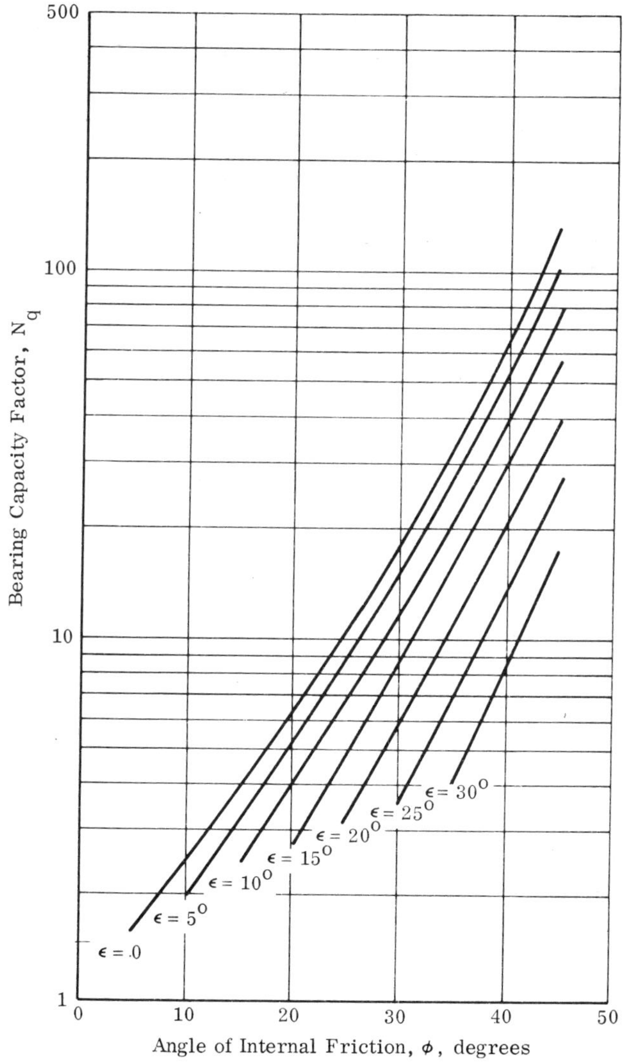

Fig. 2.27
Bearing Capacity Factor, N_q, for Sloping Ground and Vertical Strip Loading

wherein the development of PRANDTL fields occurs downslope from the loaded surface only:

$$q_{uv} = pN_q \qquad \text{Eq. 2.5.1}$$

where

q_{uv} = ultimate unit load in vertical direction relative to slope.

p = surcharge.

N_q = a bearing capacity factor determined from moment equilibrium of the various shear zones about the downslope corner of the loaded surface.

Figure 2.27 shows the values of N_q as as function of φ for various slope angles (ε). The introduction of the concept of stress gradients to express the effect of soil weight in the former method provides a unique way of modifying the PRANDTL solution and at the same time account for the possibility of upslope failure zones. Figure 2.28 shows how the effect of weight is considered and Figure 2.29 shows the nature of the various

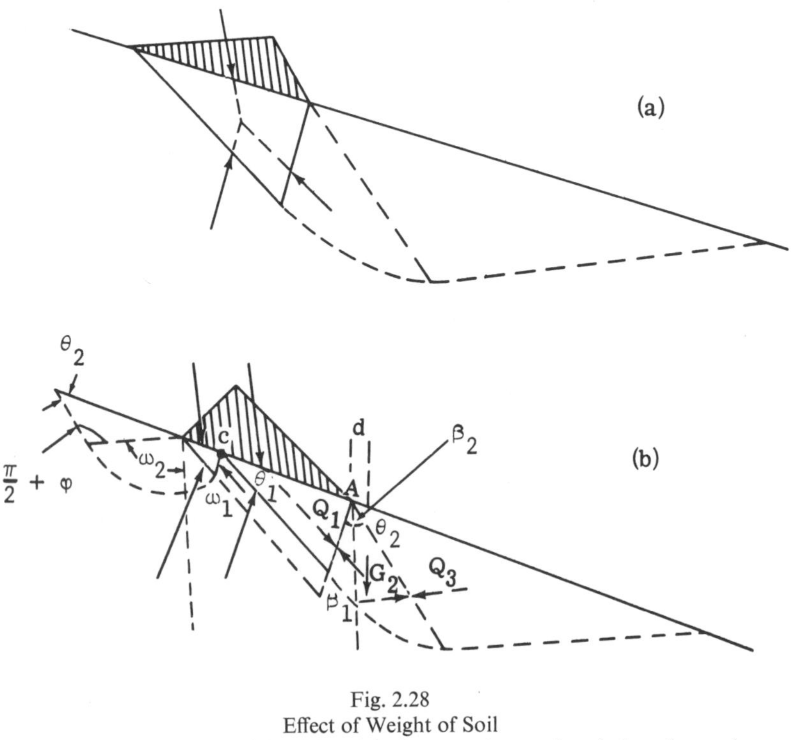

Fig. 2.28
Effect of Weight of Soil

a) Stress distribution compatible with weight forces acting on the whole active wedge

b) Stress distribution assuming two active wedges corresponding to downslope and upslope failure

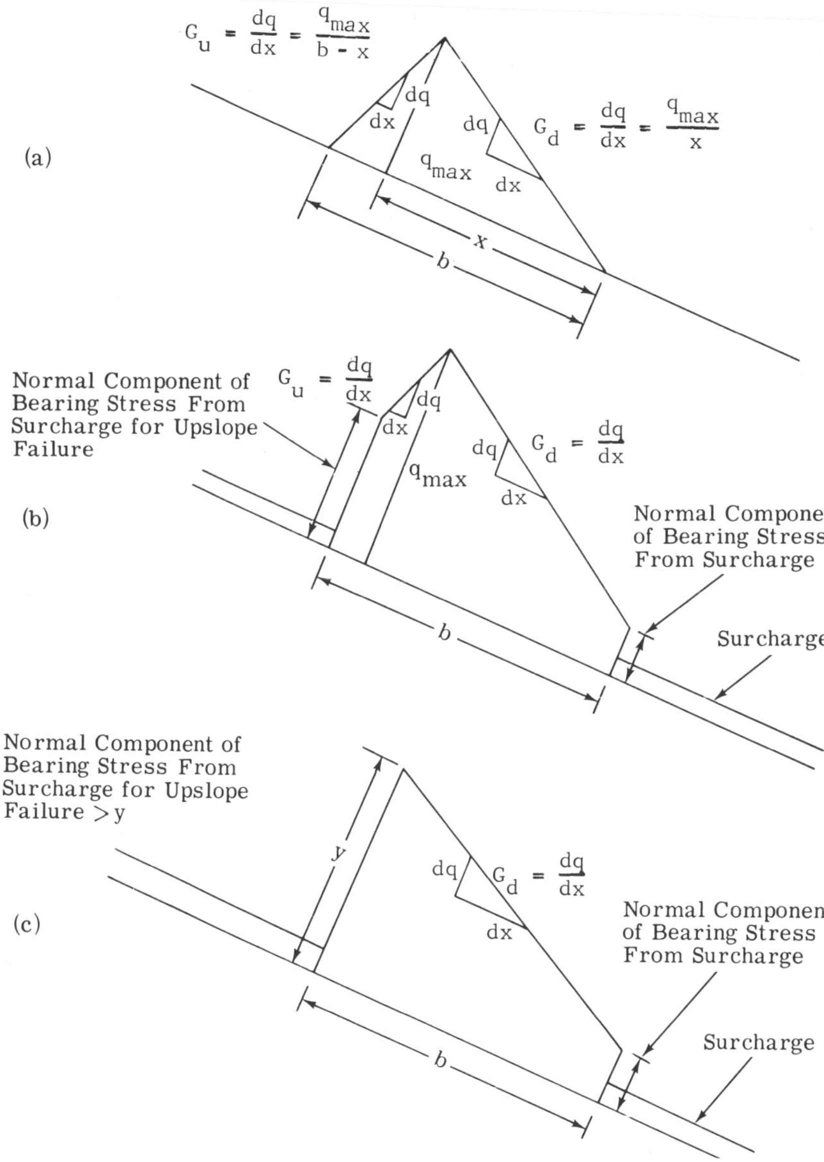

Fig. 2.29
Distribution of Bearing Stresses
a) No surcharge; b) Surcharge and upslope and downslope failure;
c) Surcharge and downslope failure only

bearing stress distributions that are subject to analysis under the modified PRANDTL solution. If there is no surcharge the maximum bearing stress is at a distance.

$$x = \frac{G_u}{G_d + G_u} b \qquad \text{Eq. 2.5.2}$$

from the downslope edge of the loading (see Figure 2.29(a)).

Its normal component is

$$q_{max} = \frac{G_u G_d}{G_u + G_d} b \qquad \text{Eq. 2.5.3}$$

where G_u and G_d are the values of the upward slope and downward slope stress gradients respectively and are determined for specific values of φ and slope angle according to the relationship shown in Figure 2.30.

The average of the normal component of the bearing stress in the two-dimensional case is $q_{avg} = q_{max}/2$; for the axially symmetric case it is $q_{avg} = q_{max}/3$. Note that the ratio of the average bearing stress in the axially symmetric case to that in the two-dimensional case is 0.66, which corresponds approximately to the shape factor for average bearing stress suggested in the classical TERZAGHI bearing capacity theory. Thus if the method of stress gradients is used, it is not necessary to consider shape factors for the various types of three-dimensional loadings. This is particularly advantageous where the loading of slopes is considered because shape factors have not yet been experimentally determined for this case.

In the case of surcharge, the stress gradients expressing the effect of soil weight on load bearing capacity are used in conjunction with the values of uniformly distributed bearing stress resulting from the surcharge and expressed by Equation 2.5.1.

In the second method of analysis in which the solution is obtained by numerical integration of the governing differential equations of plastic equilibrium, stress gradients and therefore bearing capacity are obtained directly for the assigned slope and surcharge boundary conditions. Figure 2.31 gives a graphical representation in terms of slipe line fields and stress distributions for a typical problem of a slope loaded over a finite area. KARAFIATH and NOWATZKI (1970) found that the results of the two methods compare favorably with the results of experiments performed on sand with small diameter disks.

Since the bearing capacity problem is obviously one that is of interest to many researchers, there has been a plethora of analyses, experimental

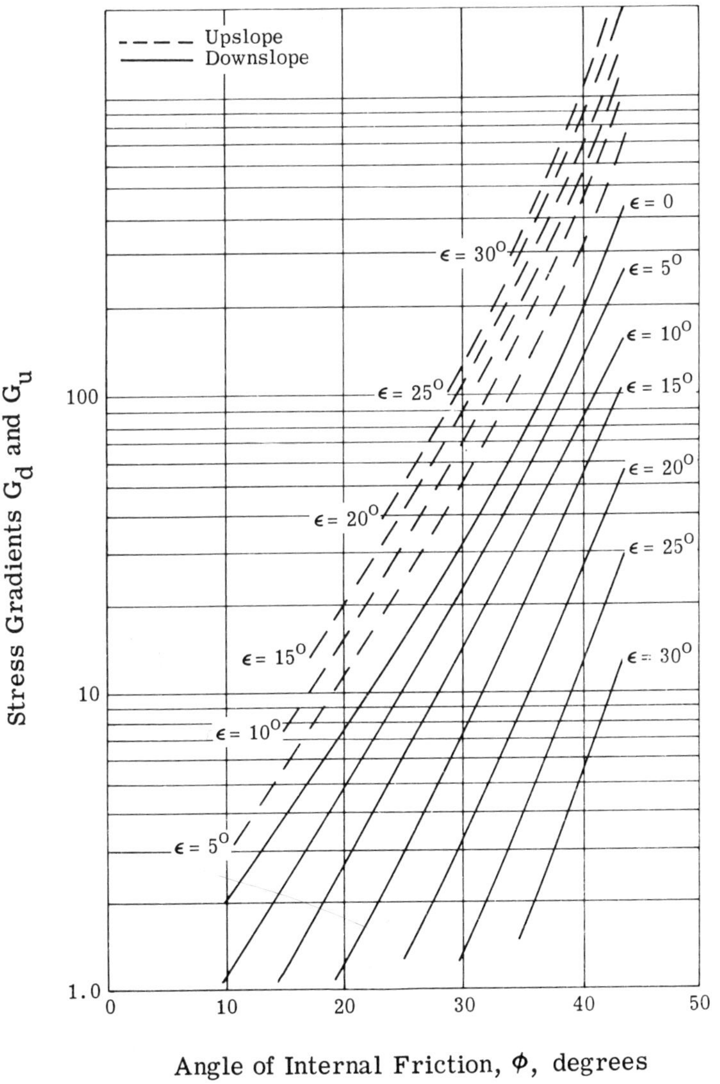

Fig. 2.30
Stress Gradients for Vertical Loading and for Slopes
Varying From $\varepsilon = 0$ to $\varepsilon = 30$ Degrees

and theoretical, of the problem. FANG et al (1974) list ninety-seven references alone that deal with bearing capacity from a plasticity viewpoint. Some of the more recent innovative analyses are found in KO and SCOTT (1973), CHEN and DAVIDSON (1973), LARKIN (1968), LIVNEH and GREENSTEIN (1974), and GRAHAM (1968).

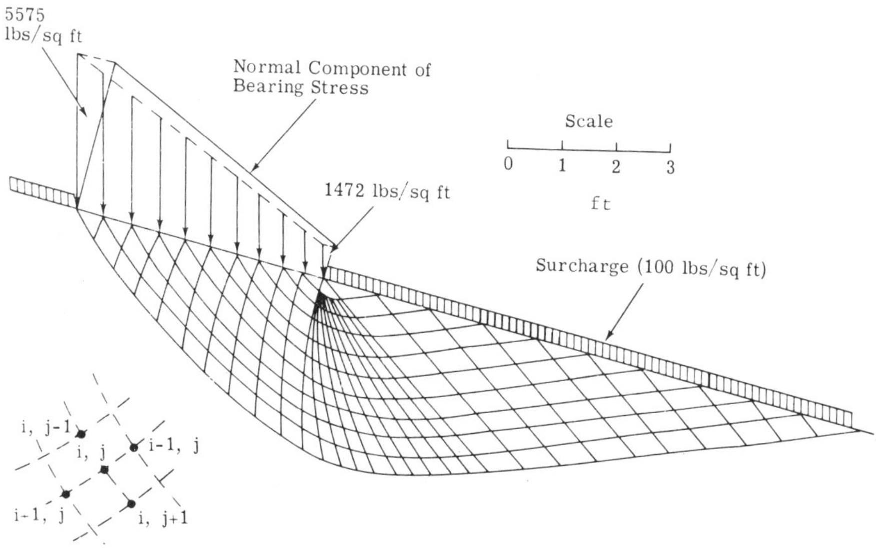

Fig. 2.31
Slip-line Field for $\varphi = 35$ Degrees, $\gamma = 100$ lb/cu ft, $\varepsilon = 15$ Degrees, $p = 100$ lb/sq ft
Determined by Numerical Integration

2.5.2 Application of Plasticity Theory to Problems Involving Bulldozing Resistance and Soil Cutting Processes

Bulldozing and soil cutting are two of the specialty areas of soil-vehicle interaction that lend themselves well to analysis by plastic theory. HETTIARATCHI and REECE (1974) have provided a tool for the solution of these problems by presenting a method of computing passive pressure based on a rigorous mathematical solution of the equations of plastic equilibrium. In their approach they start by expressing the soil resistance per unit width of interface as

$$R = f(c, \varphi, \gamma, \delta, a, z, \alpha, q) \qquad \text{Eq. 2.5.4}$$

where

c, φ = soil strength parameters of cohesion and internal friction angle.

γ = total unit weight of soil

δ = soil interface friction angle

a = actual tangential adhesion

z = depth of interface tip below soil free surface

α = rake angle of interface measured from horizontal.

q = uniform surcharge pressure

The resisting force R is broken down into a "frictional" component, P, acting at the angle δ with the normal to the interface and an "adhesive" component A, acting along the surface as shown in Figure 2.32. The magnitude and direction of the adhesive component can be determined straight-forwardly. The problem, therefore, reduces to the calculation of the magnitude and location of the frictional component.

By using dimensional analysis and the concepts of plastic equilibrium, HETTIARATCHI and REECE developed explicit relationships between P and a number of dimensionless soil restistance coefficients which, by a simple additive process, give rise to the following equation

$$P = \gamma z^2 K_\gamma + cz K_c + az K_a + qz K_q \qquad \text{Eq. 2.5.5}$$

where K_γ, K_c, K_a and K_q are dimensionless soil-resistance coefficients that

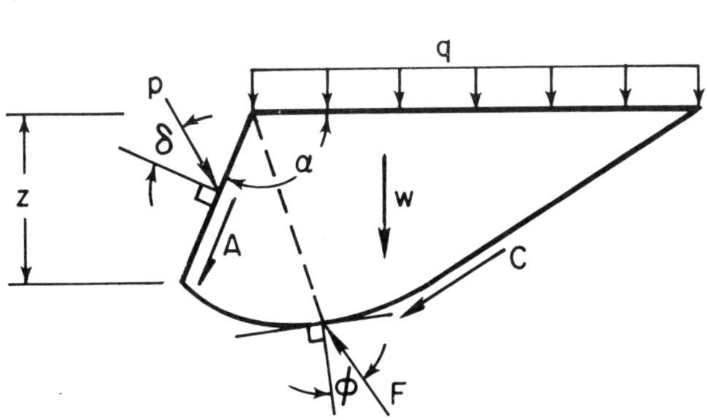

Fig. 2.32
Basic Force System for Analysis of Bulldozing and Soil Cutting Processes
(HETTIARATCHI and REECE, 1974)

account for soil self weight, cohesion, adhesion, and surcharge respectively. The general functional expression for each of these coefficients is

$$K = f(S_c, S_a, S_q, \varphi, \delta, \alpha) \qquad \text{Eq. 2.5.6}$$

where

S_c = cohesion number = $c/(\gamma z)$
S_a = adhesion number = $a/(\gamma z)$
S_q = surcharge number = $q/(\gamma z)$

Equation 2.5.5 for the soil resistance P is completely rigorous and is based on concepts developed by SOKOLOVSKII (1962). Its simple additive form reflects the fact that the relationship between P and the other four forces depends only on the plastic equilibrium of the rupture block shown in Figure 2.32. HETTIARATCHI and REECE prepared a set of charts that give computed values of each of the soil resistance coefficients in the general Equation 2.5.5 over the entire practical range of the six dimensionless parameters in Equation 2.5.6. The number of such charts was significantly reduced by the introduction of some novel interrelationships between parameters which modify the general equation as follows:

$$P = \gamma z^2 \overline{K_\gamma} + cz K_{ca} + qz K_q - \gamma z^2 K_s e^{-S} \qquad \text{Eq. 2.5.7}$$

where

$\overline{K_\gamma}$ = the resistance coefficient for a weightless soil
K_s = the resistance coefficient that accounts for the modifying effect of self weight.
K_{ca} = an amalgamate resistance coefficient that accounts for both cohesion and adhesion.
S = a "soil scale index" equal to $(S_c + S_q)$.

This value of frictional resistance is vectorially added to the value of adhesive resistance ($A = az \cdot \csc\alpha$) to yield the following expressions for total soil resistance (R) and orientation angle (δ_r):

$$R = (P^2 + A^2 + 2PA \sin \delta)^{1/2} \qquad \text{Eq. 2.5.8}$$

$$\delta_r = \delta + \sin^{-1}(A \cos \delta / R) \qquad \text{Eq. 2.5.9}$$

where

δ_r = the angle which R makes with the normal to the interface.

The point of application of the total resistive force is given approximately by

$$h = z \cos \delta \sec \delta_r [(3 P_1 + 4 P_2) / (6 R)] \qquad \text{Eq. 2.5.10}$$

where

$P_1 = cz K_{ca} + qz K_q$
$P_2 = \gamma z^2 (\overline{K_\gamma} - K_s e^{-S})$

Charts presented by Hettiaratchi and Reece enable values of the soil resistance coefficients in Equation 2.5.7 to be determined over the following range of values:

a) rake angle: $5° < \alpha < 170°$

b) internal friction angle: $0° \leq \varphi \leq 45°$

c) interface friction angle: $0° \leq \delta_f \leq \varphi$

d) soil scale number: 0 to ∞

Figures 2.33 through 2.36 are the soil coefficient charts (soil resistance coefficients as a function of rake angle) for the case where the interface friction angle is equal to the internal friction angle of the soil. In these figures β is the direction of motion of the interface with respect to the horizontal ($+\beta$ is downward, $-\beta$ is upward).

The rupture surfaces predicted by the theory occur only if the direction of translation of the interface is such that the interface tip does not enter the predicted rupture surface. In other words, for a given rake angle there is a limiting direction of translation of the interface (β) relative to the horizontal beyond which "soil cavitation" takes place and a boundary wedge is formed with continued movement of the interface. This condition is not amenable to analysis by the method presented by Hettiaratchi and Reece.

The method of analysis outlined above is applicable to problems involving bulldozing (rake angles close to 90°) and soil cutting (rake angles less than 45°). Approximate methods of solution to the problem of bulldozing and soil cutting have also been proposed by a number of researchers. Bagster (1969) used a modified Terzaghi approach to show that the assumption that a granular material fails in a logarithmic spiral surface leads to the prediction of forces close to those observed in experiments.

Luth and Wismer (1969) used dimensional analysis of a soil-blade system and a statistical curve fitting procedure on laboratory test results to formulate empirical equations for predicting the force response of cutting blades operating in sand. Wismer and Luth (1970, 1972) also applied the same methods of analysis to develop similar empirical equations for cutting blades operating in clay.

The approximate solutions to the bulldozing and soil cutting problem represented a valuable contribution to soil vehicle mechanics in their time, however, the more theoretically rigorous solution presented by Hettiaratchi and Reece now seems to be more general and therefore more attractive.

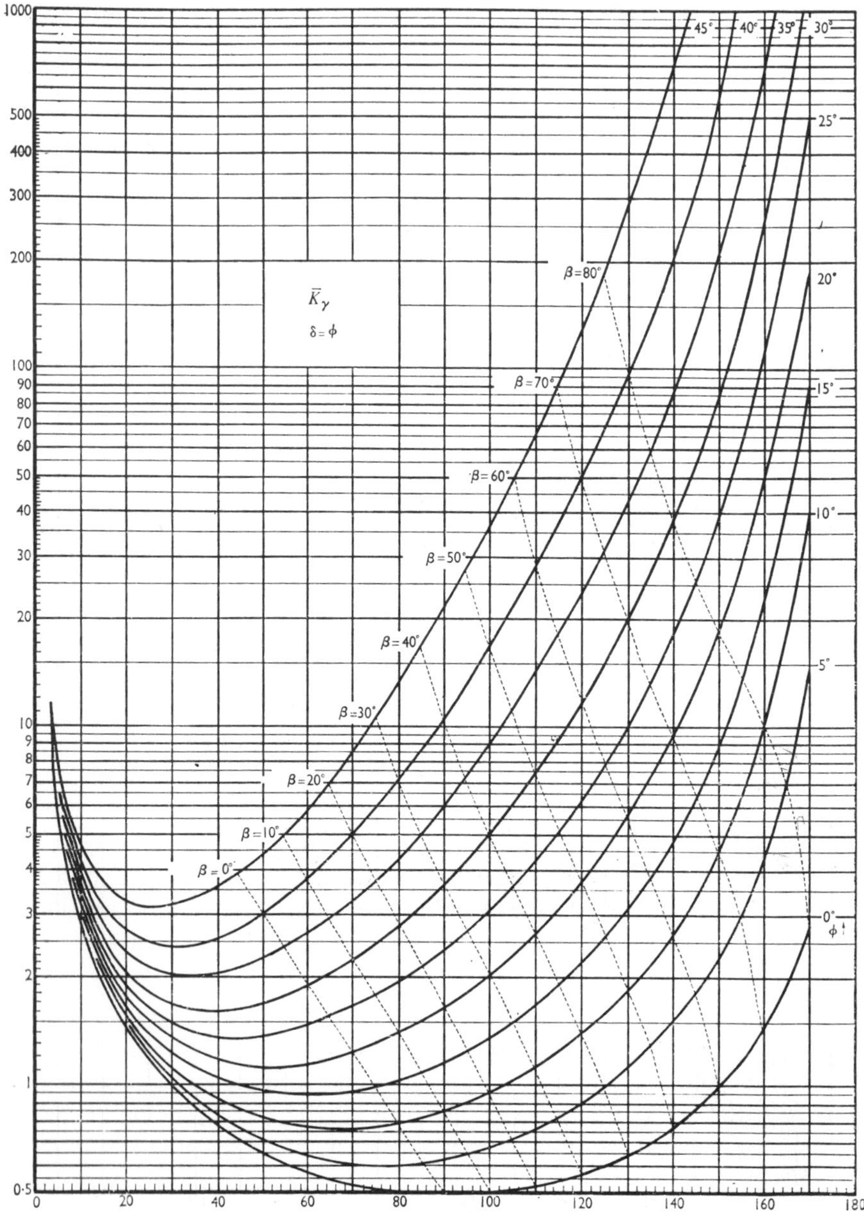

Fig. 2.33
Soil Resistance Coefficient K_γ for Interface Friction Angle (δ) Equal to Internal Friction Angle (φ)
(From HETTIARATCHI and REECE, 1974)

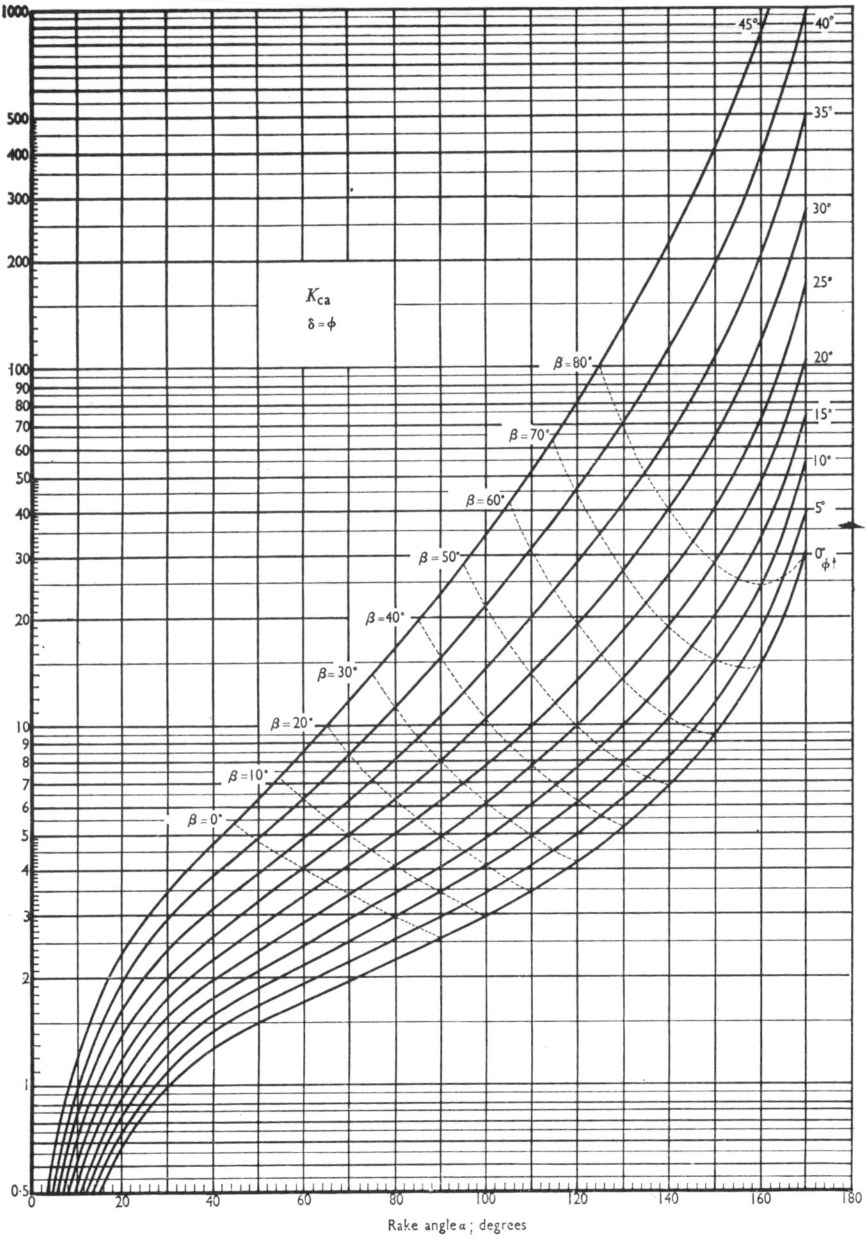

Fig. 2.34
Soil Resistance Coefficient K_{ca} for Interface Friction Angle (δ)
Equal to Internal Friction Angle (φ)
(From HETTIARATCHI and REECE, 1974)

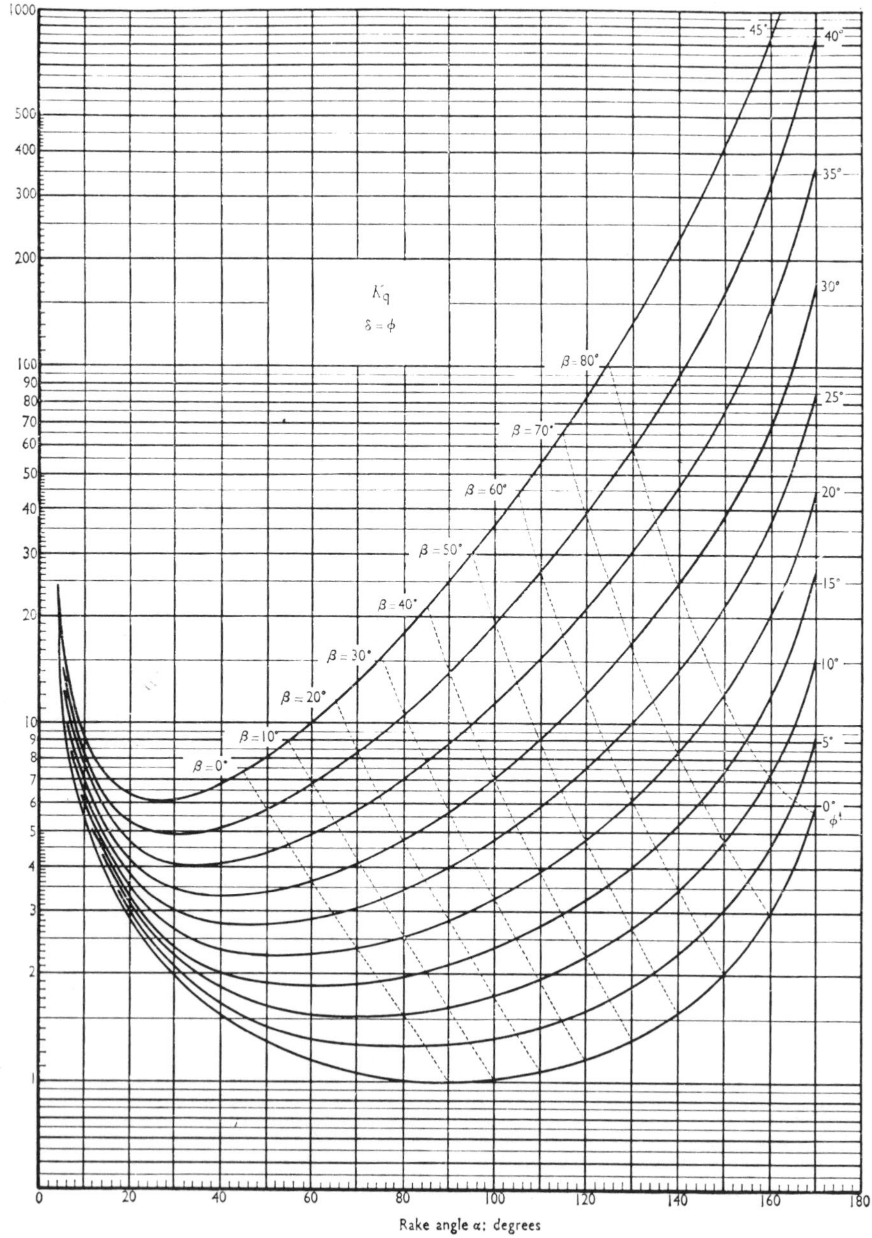

Fig. 2.35
Soil Resistance Coefficient K_q for Interface Friction Angle (δ) Equal to Internal Friction Angle (φ)
(From HETTIARATCHI and REECE, 1974)

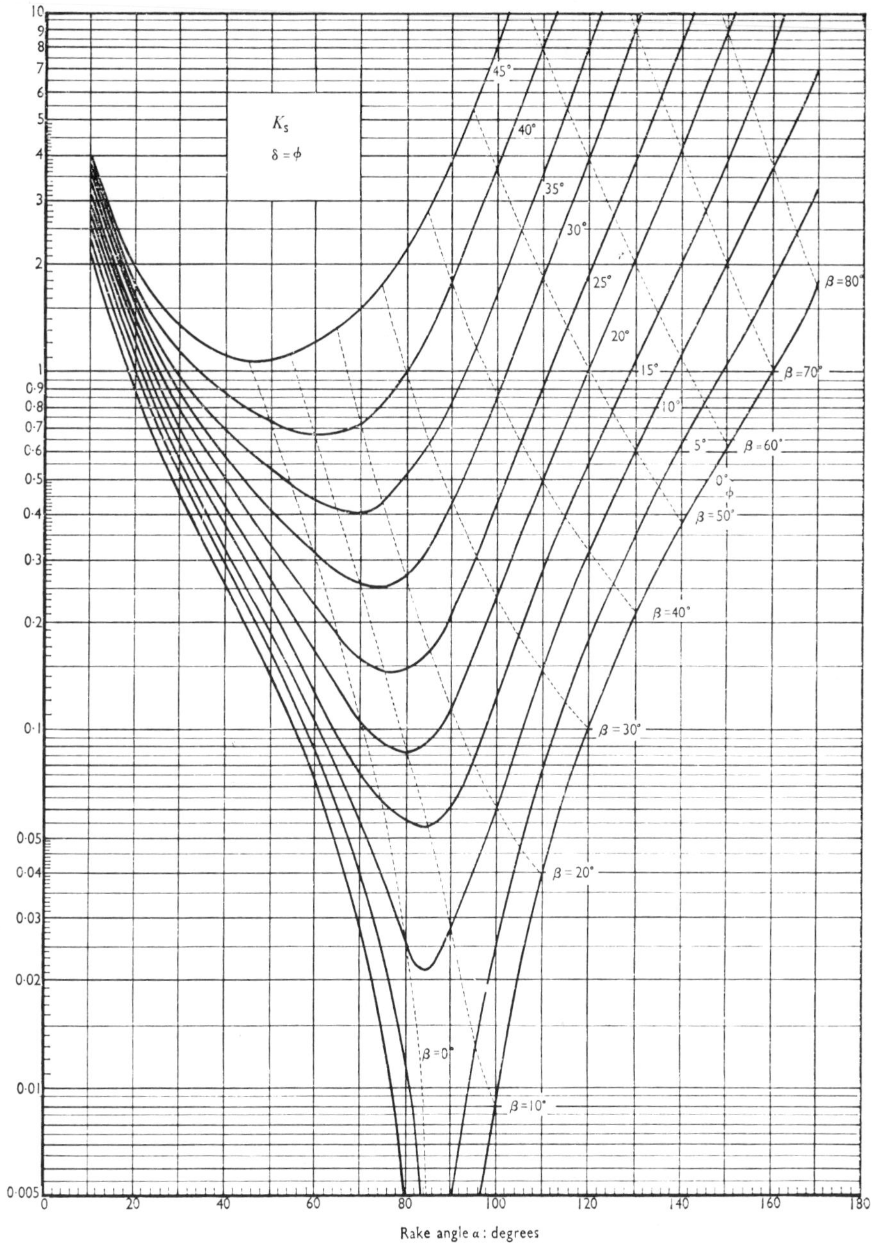

Fig. 2.36
Soil Resistance Coefficient K_s for Interface Friction Angle (δ)
Equal to Internal Friction Angle (φ)
(From Hettiaratchi and Reece, 1974)

2.5.3 Application of Plasticity Theory to Problems Involving Penetration Resistance

There are two categories of penetration tests that are widely used to measure soil resistance and, indirectly, soil strength. The first category includes all of the different types of dynamic penetration tests. The most common of these dynamic penetration tests are the Standard Penetration Test *(SPT)* that is widely used in North America and the Dutch Cone Penetration Test that is popular in Europe. Since these tests are designed to obtain information for conventional soil mechanics problems, they are usually used in conjunction with deep exploratory and/or sample borings. Consequently, they are not suitable for the near surface testing required for off-road locomotion engineering. They are, however, amenable to analysis by plasticity theory as is indicated by Figure 2.15 which was used in Section 2.3.1 to illustrate the type of problem to which the recurrence relationships for the axially symmetric case could be applied. The second category of penetration tests includes a wide variety of static plate and cone penetration tests. For off-road mobility evaluation of soil conditions, the cone penetrometer and testing procedures developed by the U.S. Army Corps of Engineers Waterways Experiment Station (WES) is most widely used. The details of the testing apparatus, the test procedure and the evaluation of results are given in Section 3.6.4.

The merits of using penetrometer data for determining soil properties have been discussed by Fletcher (1965), Meyerhof (1961), Schultz and Knausenberger (1957), Sanglerat (1972) and others. An excellent state of the art review and detailed study of the topic is contained in a report by Durgunoglu and Mitchell (1973). In much of the literature attempts are made to relate penetration resistance and other parameters of the test apparatus and procedure to soil strength properties. However, very little attention has been paid to theoretical analyses of the soil-penetrometer interaction. In this section plasticity theory as applied to the axially symmetric case (refer to Section 2.2.7) is considered in detail with respect to the cone penetrometer problem.

The cone penetrometer rather than the plate bearing test is singled out for consideration here for two reasons: first because the plate test is analogous to the general bearing capacity problem that was treated in Section 2.5.1, and second because the cone penetrometer test is being used more and more widely in the field to determine soil properties for vehicle mobility estimates. The general equations for the axially symmetric case were derived in Section 2.2.7 and the numerical forms of the recurrence relationships both for $\varphi =$ constant and for $\varphi \neq$ constant were given in

Section 2.3.1. For the sake of continuity the basic differential equations are repeated below for the case where φ = constant.

$$dz = dr \tan(\theta \mp \mu) \qquad \text{Eqs. 2.2.41 a and 2.2.41 b}$$

$$d\sigma \mp 2\sigma \tan\varphi \, d\theta - (dz \mp \tan\varphi \, dr)\gamma + \frac{n\sigma}{r}\left[\sin\varphi \, dr \mp \tan\varphi (1 - \sin\varphi) dz\right] \qquad \text{Eqs. 2.2.41 c and 2.2.41 d}$$

The corresponding recurrence relationships are:

$$\sigma_{i,j} = \left[2\sigma_{i-1,j}\,\sigma_{i,j-1}\left[1 - \tan\varphi(\theta_{i-1,j} - \theta_{i,j-1})\right] + \overline{\overline{C}}\sigma_{i,j-1} + \overline{\overline{D}}\sigma_{i-1,j} - \sigma_{i-1,j}\,\sigma_{i,j-1}\left(\frac{\overline{\overline{A}}}{r_{i-1,j}} + \frac{\overline{\overline{B}}}{r_{i,j-1}}\right)\right] \Big/ \left[\sigma_{i,j-1} - \sigma_{i-1,j}\right]$$

Eq. 2.3.9 a

and

$$\theta_{i,j} = \left[\sigma_{i,j-1} - \sigma_{i-1,j} + 2\tan\varphi(\sigma_{i-1,j}\,\theta_{i-1,j} + \sigma_{i,j-1}\,\theta_{i,j-1}) - \overline{\overline{C}} + \overline{\overline{D}} + \frac{\sigma_{i-1,j}\,\overline{\overline{A}}}{r_{i-1,j}} - \frac{\sigma_{i,j-1}\,\overline{\overline{B}}}{r_{i,j-1}}\right] \Big/ \left[2\tan\varphi(\sigma_{i-1,j} + \sigma_{i,j-1})\right]$$

Eq. 2.3.9 b

$\overline{\overline{A}} = \sin\varphi(r_{i,j} - r_{i-1,j}) - \tan\varphi(1 - \sin\varphi)(z_{i,j} - z_{i-1,j})$
$\overline{\overline{B}} = \sin\varphi(r_{i,j} - r_{i,j-1}) + \tan\varphi(1 - \sin\varphi)(z_{i,j} - z_{i,j-1})$
$\overline{\overline{C}} = \gamma\left[z_{i,j} - z_{i-1,j} - \tan\varphi(r_{i,j} - r_{i-1,j})\right]$
$\overline{\overline{D}} = \gamma\left[z_{i,j} - z_{i,j-1} + \tan\varphi(r_{i,j} - r_{i,j-1})\right]$

The expressions for r and z in this case are also given in Section 2.3.1 as:

$$z_{i,j} = z_{i-1,j} + \alpha_2(r_{i,j} - r_{i-1,j}) \qquad \text{Eq. 2.3.5 a}$$

or

$$z_{i,j} = z_{i,j-1} + \alpha_1(r_{i,j} - r_{i,j-1}) \qquad \text{Eq. 2.3.5 b}$$

$$r_{i,j} = (z_{i-1,j} - z_{i,j-1} + \alpha_1 r_{i,j-1} - \alpha_2 r_{i-1,j}) / (\alpha_1 - \alpha_2) \qquad \text{Eq. 2.3.5 c}$$

where

$\alpha_1 = \tan(\theta_{i,j-1} + \mu)$
$\alpha_2 = \tan(\theta_{i-1,j} - \mu)$

To apply the relationships to the problem of cone indentation, the geometric and stress boundary conditions must be formulated appropriately. The stress boundary conditions at the free surface and along the wall of the hole are stable, or the soil behind the hole tends to fail and failure surfaces develop toward the hole. The latter situation occurs almost exclusively in cohesionless soils, since a very small amount of cohesion is sufficient to insure stability of the hole for a small depth of penetration. The geometry of the slip line field depends on the depth of the base of the cone beneath the free surface and on the position of the intersection of the outermost slip line with the stress-free boundaries. Because of the change of the pattern of shear zones with penetration it is difficult to develop numerical solution methods where the general configuration of the shear zones would have to be *a priori* known. Therefore, with little loss of accuracy a simplified shear zone geometry is assumed as shown in Figure 2.37. The effect of shear failure above the level of the base of the cone is disregarded and the weight of the soil above the base level is included in w as an "effective surcharge". The boundary conditions at the soil-cone interface are of the GOURSAT type that require the specification of a relationship for the geometry and another one for the direction of the major principal stress. The first relationship is defined by the angle (β) that the interface makes with the horizontal, while the latter condition is satisfied by assuming that the direction of σ_1 is constant and corresponds to a specified angle of interface friction (δ). For these conditions the numerical computation of the slip line field geometry and associated stresses is straight forward. The stress boundary condition on the horizontal plane through the base of the cone is given by the surcharge (w) and the overburden soil pressure (refer to Figure 2.37). The slip-line field and associated stresses in the passive zone are computed by Equations 2.2.41 starting with these boundary values and an assumed value for the horizontal extent of the passive zone. In the radial shear zone, the same equations are used, but special consideration is given to the central point where the j-lines converge (point 0 in Figure 2.37). As indicated in Section 2.3.3 this point is a degenerated slip line, where θ changes from its value at the passive boundary to that specified at the active zone boundary. The total change in θ is divided by the number of slip lines converging at this point to obtain an equal $\Delta\theta$ increment between two adjacent slip lines. The σ values for each increment are computed from the equation

$$\sigma = \sigma_o \exp [2 (\theta - \theta_o) \tan \varphi] \qquad \text{Eq. 2.3.12}$$

Allowance must be made for the angle β as well as δ in assigning transition values of θ and σ between the active and passive zones. With these values of θ and σ for each slip line at this point, the coordinates as well as the σ and θ values for all other points in the radial shear zone can be computed by Equations 2.2.41. In the active zone the same equations are used, except for the points at the loaded surface of the cone itself. Here $\theta_{i,j}$ is assigned and the following conditions pertain:

$$z_{i,j} = z_o + (R_o - r_{i,j}) \tan \beta \qquad \text{Eq. 2.5.11}$$

$$r_{i,j} = [r_{i-1,j} \tan [(\theta_{i,j} + \theta_{i-1,j}) / 2 - \mu] - z_{i-1,j} + R_o \tan \beta + z_o] / [\tan [(\theta_{i,j} + \theta_{i-1,j}) / 2 - \mu] + \tan \beta] \qquad \text{Eq. 2.5.12}$$

$$\sigma_{i,j} = \sigma_{i-1,j} + \sigma_{i-1,j} (\theta_{i,j} - \theta_{i-1,j}) \tan \varphi + \overline{\overline{C}} - \frac{\sigma_{i-1,j} \overline{\overline{A}}}{r_{i-1,j}} \qquad \text{Eq. 2.5.13}$$

where, with reference to Figure 2.37:

β = complement to half the cone apex angle.

μ = $\pi/4 - \varphi/2$.

z_o = depth to which base of cone has penetrated.

R_o = radius of cone base.

The numerical computation is performed and adjustments made, if necessary, to the value assumed for the horizontal extent of the passive zone until the slip line field "closes" on the axis of symmetry at the apex of the cone.

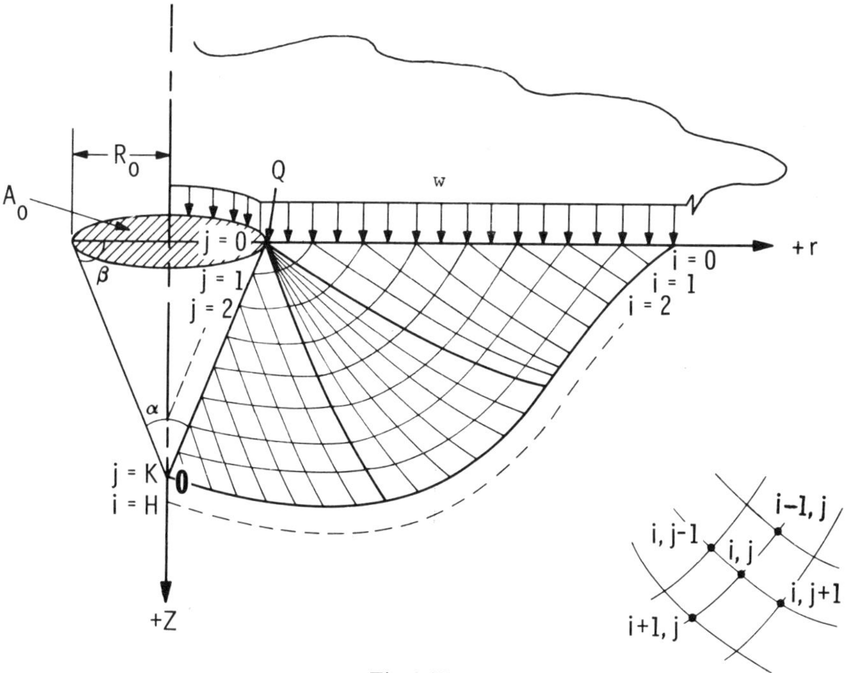

Fig. 2.37
Geometry for Axially Symmetric (Cone Identation) Problem.
Boundary Conditions and Slip-Lines Are Symmetric with the Z-Axis

The angle θ at the interface is computed for the assumed value of the interface friction angle δ from Equation 2.2.21. It is noted that the assumption of a constant value for the interface friction angle along the interface is an arbitrary one. Interface friction develops as a result of relative displacements between soil and the surface of the cone. In Section 3.3.6 a theory is propounded in connection with the analysis of the kinematic conditions at soil-running gear interfaces that predicates the coincidence of the directions of the velocity vector of a soil particle and the major principal stress. The application of this theory to the determination of the interface friction angle at the cone would require the knowledge of soil deformation during cone penetration. Any attempt to determine the deformation of soil during cone penetration would involve some assumption of the stress-strain properties. Thus, without elaborate testing and deformation analysis an uncertainty exists as to the variation of the interface friction angle along the surface of the cone and a constant value is assumed in lieu of anything better. The magnitude of the interface friction angle is also open to question. An upper limit for its magnitude may be obtained experimentally by determining the adhesion and friction forces acting between a solid surface composed of the same material as the cone and the soil. Unfortunately, there is little experimental information available on the shear stresses developing on the face of a cone at the various stages of penetration. Shear stresses on the face of a wedge were measured by BUTTERFIELD and ANDRAWES (1972) who found that the interface shear stresses developed at the face of the wedge corresponded approximately to the friction angle between the wedge material and the soil.

The angle of interface friction strongly influences cone penetration resistance in soils where the resistance is governed by plastic failure conditions. Besides its obvious effect on the shear stresses at the interface, the direction of the major principal stress also depends on the interface friction angle, influencing thereby the normal stresses at the face of the cone. The indeterminate nature of the interface friction angle makes the evaluation of strength properties from cone penetration test data uncertain, especially in the case of acute angle cones.

The resistance of the soil to cone penetration may be considered to consist of two parts: the vertical component of the resultant of the shear stresses and the vertical component of the normal stresses at the interface. If the face of the cone encloses an angle $\alpha/2$ with the vertical then the following relationship for penetration resistance, P, holds:

$$P = \int_A \left[\sigma_n \sin\left(\frac{\alpha}{2}\right) + \tau \cos\left(\frac{\alpha}{2}\right)\right] dA \qquad \text{Eq. 2.5.14}$$

where $\tau = (\sigma_n + \psi) \tan \delta$

Therefore:

$$P = \int_A \left[\sigma_n \sin\left(\frac{\alpha}{2}\right) + \sigma_n \cos\left(\frac{\alpha}{2}\right)\tan\delta + \psi \cos\left(\frac{\alpha}{2}\right)\tan\delta\right] dA \qquad \text{Eq. 2.5.15}$$

Note that when $\delta > \alpha/2$ or when $\psi = c \cdot \cot \varphi$ predominates, the share of the shear stresses resisting penetration outweighs the share of normal stresses in an acute angle cone. Therefore, in the case of acute angle cones, the penetration resistance is more a measure of interface friction than of the shear strength of the soil.

The method of computation outlined above is well suited for the analysis of the effect of various input parameters on cone penetration resistance. For example, to show specifically the effect of cone angle on the slip line field geometry, the authors (Nowatzki and Karafiath, 1972) solved the governing differential equations for a set of ideal soil conditions that describe a homogeneous, dry and purely frictional sand. These conditions are $c = 0$, $\varphi = 37°$, $\gamma = 100$ pcf, $w = 1$ psf and $\delta = 20°$. The numerical results were plotted automatically and electronically on the display tube of a Computer Displays Inc. Advanced Remote Display System. The slip line fields for $R_0 = 0.034$ ft (radius of the WES cone) and $\alpha = 15.5°$, 30°, 60°, 90°, 120° and 150° have been reproduced and are shown in Figure 2.38. The scale in Figures 2.38a, b, and c is four times that in Figures 2.38d, e, and f.

The salient feature of the slip line fields in Figures 2.38 is that they show distinctly a contraction of the radial shear zone with the decrease of the cone angle. The active, passive and radial shear zones all have curvilinear boundaries due to the three dimensional nature of the problem, an indication that the geometries obtained from the solution of the theoretically correct differential equations differ from those obtained by using the Prandtl solution for weightless soil and the log-spiral approximation in the radial zone.

Also indicated in Figure 2.38 is the fact that with decreasing cone angle the affected volume of the soil increases. For the soil and cones used in Figure 2.38 the volume of the body of revolution formed by the slip line field for cone apex angle $\alpha = 30°$ is about ten times greater than that for $\alpha = 150°$. For compressible soils, the size of the affected mass directly influences the load-penetration relationship. The material must be compressed to a state in which friction is fully mobilized and a shear failure along slip lines can take place. Therefore, the force that causes penetration is not necessarily a measure of the soil's shearing resistance if the amount of displacement corresponding to the compression of the soil allows penetration of the cone at a lower load. It follows that the larger the volume of the slip line field, the more the soil mass must be compressed to mobilize the friction fully. Therefore, cone indices obtained with cone shapes that result in large volume slip line fields are likely to be more representative of the compressibility of the material than of its Coulombic strength.

Another result of the numerical analyses is that for certain boundary conditions they show that the differential equations of plastic equilibrium may not have solutions in the axially symmetric case. Figure 2.39 shows two slip line field geometries. Both were obtained for a given soil and the same set of boundary conditions. The "normal" field is for the two-dimensional case, whereas the field showing overlapping in the passive zone is for the axially symmetric case. Overlapping of the slip line field implies that the theoretical solution is multivalued, i.e. two different stress states exist at certain locations at the same time. Such a solution is physically inadmissible.

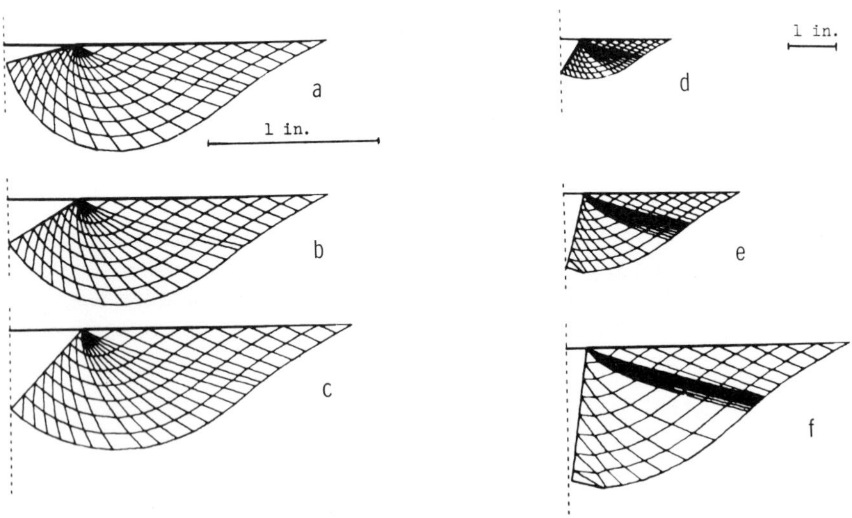

Fig. 2.38
Slip-line Fields for Cones of Various Apex Angles (α) Penetrating an Ideal Frictional Material Having $\varphi = 37°$, $\gamma_t = 100$ pcf, $\delta = 20°$ and surface surcharge = 1 psf.
a) $\alpha = 150°$; b) $\alpha = 120°$; c) $\alpha = 90°$; d) $\alpha = 60°$;
e) $\alpha = 30°$; f) $\alpha = 15.5°$

Unfortunately, there is no experimental information available that would give an insight into the behavior of soil when theory indicates multi-valued stress states. Acute angle cones are more liable to feature multi-valued solutions than right or obtuse angle cones, since the steep face of an acute angle cone compresses the three failure zones into a smaller area.

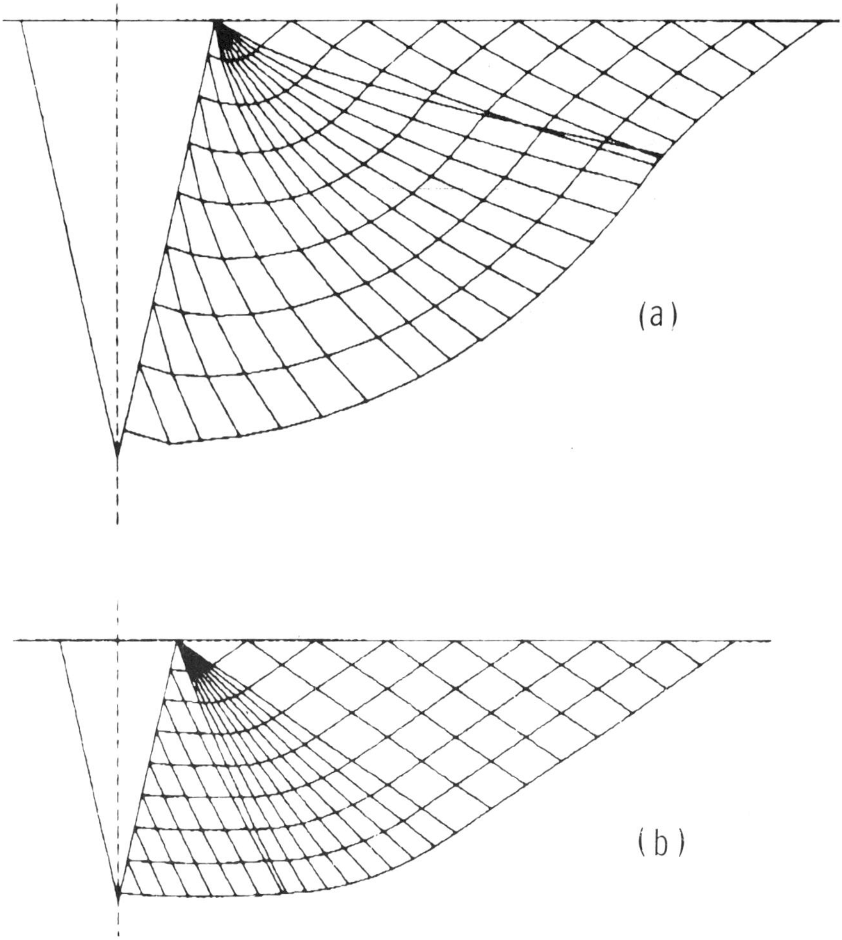

Fig. 2.39
An Example of a Non-Unique Plasticity Solution of the Cone Problem
a) "Overlapping" slip-line field for axially symmetric case
b) "Normal" slip-line field for two-dimensional case

The conclusions of the analysis of cone penetration by plasticity theory methods may be summarized as follows:

a) Cone penetration resistance is indicative of the strength properties of relatively incompressible soils. The smaller the apex angle of the cone the larger is the relative volume of the soil to be compressed so that the strength of soil may be fully mobilized. The volume affected also increases with depth. Thus, even if the full strength of soil is mobilized when the base of the cone is at the level of the surface, the same may not be the case when the base is at a lower level.

b) The penetration resistance of acute angle cones depends to a greater degree on the shear strength mobilized at the interface than on the intrinsic shear strength of the soil mass.

c) In the evaluation of cone penetration resistance by plasticity theory methods multivalued solutions may occur that are physically inadmissible.

2.5.4 Limitations of Plasticity Theory

As in the case with any other theory, the use of plasticity theory is valid only as long as none of the assumptions on which it is based are violated. In the case of soils, plasticity theory applies if the soil behaves under load at least approximately as shown in Figure 2.1. Implicit in this assumption is that failure occurs independently of load path and that stress history does not affect failure. Experiments by Wu et al (1963) have shown that load path has very little influence on failure stress. However, the discussions of soil strength properties in Chapter 1.3 suggest that this is not the case for all soils with respect to stress history. For example, plastic yielding may not occur in dry, highly overconsolidated clays because such materials tend to crack and become discontinuous at failure. The same holds true for loose sands and "sensitive" clays, although for these soils, once the structures have collapsed (a condition that is usually but not always considered failure), plasticity theory may be applied to the remolded material. Secondly, the concept of plastic failure implies that the material in the failure zone undergoes rapid displacement along a vector path making an angle φ with the slip surface. Whether or not this situation exists at failure in a soil is questionable and was discussed with reference to upper and lower bound solutions in Chapter 2.4.

In its application to soil-structure interaction problems, plasticity theory is usually combined with the Mohr-Coulomb failure criterion to develop equations that describe the behavior of the soil under load. As indicated in Section 2.2.1, the MOHR-COULOMB criterion is valid only for the condition that $\sigma_2 = \sigma_3$. There is evidence (HABIB, 1953; CORNFORTH, 1964) that at $\sigma_3 < \sigma_2 < \sigma_1$ the value of φ varies by a few degrees from that obtained by the $\sigma_2 = \sigma_3$ criterion. From the practical viewpoint, this variation is usually not important for most civil engineering problems, but in some cases where the strength of the soil is marginal and where σ_2 definitely does not equal σ_3, this small deviation from the assumptions should not be dismissed lightly.

The assumption of soil uniformity and isotropy is another factor limiting the use of plasticity theory in soil-structure interaction problems. The validity of the assumption is particularly questionable for near surface soils which is the case of interest in mobility evaluations. However, with the aid of numerical solution techniques and high speed digital computers, the limitations imposed by this assumption can be removed. This is demonstrated in Section 2.2.3 where a general set of plastic equilibrium equations are derived in which a nonlinear yield criterion is used and in Section 2.3.4 where layered soil systems are considered.

Thus, although there may be limitations to the application of plasticity theory to some soil-structure interaction problems, in most cases a plasticity analysis is valid and it provides a theoretically rigorous standard with which actual soil behavior may be compared. In fact, where soil conditions conform reasonably well with the assumptions of plasticity theory, the agreement between theoretical results and actual measurements in the case of many conventional civil engineering problems is quite good (see, for example, Chapter 8 of WU (1966)). The authors have found the same to be true in the analysis of soil running gear interactions by plasticity theory. In the next part of this book the general concepts of plasticity theory, as developed in this Part relative to soils, and the principles of soil mechanics, as explained in Part 1, will be applied to problems of mobility.

PART 2
BIBLIOGRAPHY

AURIAULT, J. and R. NEGRE (1967), "Etude des Problèmes d'Equilibre Limité a Symetrie de Revolution dans le cas d'un Materiau Pulvérulent Non Chargé," *Archiwum Mechaniki Stosowanej,* Vol. 2, No. 19.

BAGSTER, D. F. (1969), "The Prediction of the Force Needed to Move Blades Through a Bed of Cohesionless Granules," *Powder Technology,* Vol. 3.

BEREZANZEV, V. G. (1952), "The Axially Symmetric Problem in the Theory of Limiting Equilibrium of a Loose Medium," *Gostechizdat,* Moscow.

BURMISTER, D. M. (1945), "The General Theory of Stresses and Displacements in Layered Soil Systems," *Journal of Applied Physics,* Vol. 16, No. 2; No. 3; No. 5.

BUTTERFIELD, R. and K. Z. ANDRAWES (1972), "On the Angles of Friction Between Sand and Plane Surfaces," *Journal of Terramechanics,* Vol. 8, No. 4.

CHEN, W. F. and H. L. DAVIDSON (1973), "Bearing Capacity Determination by Limit Analysis," *Journal,* SMFD, ASCE, Vol. 99, No. SM 6.

CORNFORTH, D.H. (1964), "Some Experiments on the Influence of Strain Condition on the Strength of Sand," *Geotechnique,* Vol. XIV.

COULOMB, C. A. (1776), "Essais sur une Application des Rêgles des Maximis et Minimis à Quelques Problèms de Statique Relatifs à l'Architecture," *Mem Acad. Roy. Pres.* Divers, Sav. 5,7, Paris.

COX, A. D. (1962), "Axially-Symmetric Plastic Deformation in Soils – II Indentation of Ponderable Soils," *International Journal of Mechanical Sciences,* Vol. 4.

COX, A. D., EASON, G. and H. G. HOPKINS, (1961), "Axially Symmetric Plastic Deformation of Soils," *Transactions Royal Society of London,* Vol. A 254.

DAVIS, E. H. (1968), "Theories of Plasticity and the Failure of Soil Masses," *Soil Mechanics – Selected Topics,* I. K. Lee, ed., Chapter 6, American Elsevier, New York, N. Y.

DE BEER, E. E. (1970), "Experimental Determination of the Shape Factors and the Bearing Capacity Factors of Sand," *Geotechnique,* Vol. 20, No. 4.

DRUCKER, D. C., PRAGER, W., and H. J. GREENBERG (1952), "Extended Limit Design Theorems for Continuous Media," *Quarterly of Applied Mathematics,* Vol. 9.

DURGUNOGLU, H. T. and J. K. MITCHELL (1973), *Static Penetration Resistance of Soils,* Space Science Laboratory, University of California; Berkeley, Ca.

FANG, H. Y., CHEN, W. F., DAVIDSON, H. L. and J. ROSENFARB (1974), *Bibliography on Soil Plasticity,* Envo Publishing Co., Inc.; Lehigh Vallay, Pa.

FLETCHER, G. (1965), "The Standard Penetration Test: Its Uses and Abuses," *Journal,* SMFD, ASCE, Vol. 91, No. SM 4.

GRAHAM, J. (1968), "Plane Plastic Failure in Cohesionless Soils," *Geotechnique,* Vol. XVIII, No. 3.

HAAR, A. and T. VON KARMAN (1909), "Zur Theorie der Spannungszustände in plastischen und sandartigen Medien," *Nachr. Ges. Wiss Göttingen, Math-Phys Kl.*

HABIB, M. P. (1953), "Influence of the Variation of the Intermediate Principal Stress on the Shearing Strength of Soils," *Proceedings* 3rd ICSMFE (Zurich), Vol. 1.

HANSEN, BENT (1961), "The Bearing Capacity of Sand Tested by Loading Circular Plates," *Proceedings* 5th ICSMFE (Paris), Vol. 1.

HANSEN, B. and N. H. CHRISTENSEN (1969), Discussion on "Theoretical Bearing Capacity of Very Shallow Footings" by L. A. Larkin, *Journal*, SMFD, ASCE, Vol. 95, N. SM 6.

HANSEN, J. BRINCH (1952), "A General Plasticity Theory for Clay," *Geotechnique*, Vol. III, No. 4.

HARR, M. E. (1966), *Foundations ofTheoretical Soil Mechanics*, McGraw-Hill, New York, N. Y.

HETTIARATCHI, D. and A. REECE (1974), "The Calculation of Passive Soil Resistance," *Geotechnique*, Vol. 24, No. 3.

KARAFIATH, L. L. (1972), "Soil Tire Model for the Analysis of Off-Road Tire Performance," paper presented at 8th U. S. National Off-Road Mobility Symposium ISTVS, Purdue University, W. Lafayette, Ind.

KARAFIATH, L. L. (1972a), "On the Effect of Base Friction on Bearing Capacity," *Journal of Terramechanics*, Vol. 9, No. 1.

KARAFIATH, L. L. (1975), *Development of Mathematical Model for Pneumatic Tire-Soil Interaction in Layered Soils*, Final Report to U. S. Army Tank-Automotive Command, Mobility Systems Labaratory, *Technical Report* No. 12509 (LL 152)

KARAFIATH, L. L. and E. A. NOWATZKI (1970), "Stability of Slopes Loaded Over a Finite Area," *Highway Research Record Number 323*, Highway Research Board, Washington, D. C.

KARAFIATH, L. L. and E. A. NOWATZKI (1972), "Tractive Performance of Wheels in Soft Soils," paper presented at the 1972 Winter Meeting American Society of Agricultural Engineers, Chicago, Illinois, Paper No. 72–632.

KARAFIATH, L. L. and F. S. SOBIERAJSKI (1974), *Effect of Speed on Tire-Soil Interaction and Development of Towed Pneumatic Tire-Soil Model*, Final Report to U. S. Army Tank-Automotive Command, Mobility Systems Laboratory, *Technical Report* No. 11997 (LL 151).

KO, H. Y. and R. F. SCOTT (1973), "Bearing Capacities by Plasticity Theory," *Journal*, SMFD, ASCE, Vol. 99, No. SM 1.

KRAVTCHENKO, J. and R. SIBILLE (1961), "Etude des Singularites dans les Problemes D'Equilibre Limite," *C.R.A.S.*, Vol. 257.

LARKIN, L. A. (1968), "Theoretical Bearing Capacity of Very Shallow Footings," *Journal*, SMFD, ASCE, Vol. 94, No. SM 6.

LIVNEH, M. and J. GREENSTEIN (1974), "Plastic Equilibrium in Anisotropic Cohesive Clays," *Soils and Foundations*, Vol. 14, No. 1.

LUTH, H. J. and R. D. WISMER (1969), "Performance of Plane Soil Cutting Blades in Sand," Paper No. 69–115 at annual meeting ASAE, Purdue University, Lafayette, Ind. also *Transactions of ASAE*, Vol. 14, No. 2, 1971.

MEYERHOF, G. G. (1961), "The Ultimate Bearing Capacity of Wedge-Shaped Foundations," *Proceedings*, 5th ICSMFE (Paris), Vol. 2.

Nowatzki, E. A. (1971), "A Theoretical Assessment of the SPT," *Proceedings* 4th Panamerican Conference on Soil Mechanics and Foundation Engineering, Vol. 2.

Nowatzki, E. A. and L. L. Karafiath (1972), "The Effect of Cone Angle on Penetration Resistance," *Highway Research Record No. 405,* Highway Research Board, Washington, D. C.

Nowatzki, E. A. and Karafiath, L. L. (1972a), "General Yield Conditions in a Plasticity Analysis of Soil-Wheel Interaction," Journal of Terramechanics, Vol. 11, No. 1.

Nowatzki, E. A. and L. L. Karafiath (1977) Discussion of the paper "Cone Penetration of Granular and Cohesive Soils," by R. N. Yong and K. Chen, *Journal of the Eng. Mechanics Division,* ASCE, Vol 103, No EM 2.

Sanglerat, G. (1972), *The Penetrometer and Soil Exploration,* Elsevier Publishing Company, New York, N. Y.

Schultz, E. and H. Knausenberger (1957), "Experiences with Penetrometers," *Proceedings* 4th ICSMFE (London), Vol. 1.

Schuring, D. J. and R. I. Emori (1964), "Soil Deforming Processes and Dimensiona. Analysis," Paper # 897c, *Proceedings* SAE National Farm, Construction, and Industrial, Machinery Meeting.

Shield, R. T. (1954), "Stress and Velocity Fields in Soil Mechanics," *Journal of Mathematics and Physics,* Vol. 33, No. 2.

Shield, R. (1953), "Mixed Boundary Value Problems in Soil Mechanics," *Quarterly of Applied Mathematics,* Vol. 11, No. 1.

Siva Reddy, A. and G. Mogaliah (1970), "Bearing Capacity of Partially Saturated Soils," *Journal,* SMFD, ASCE, Vol. 96, No. SM 6.

Skempton, A. W. (1954), "The Pore Pressure Coefficient *A* and *B*," *Geotechnique,* Vol. 4.

Sokolovskii, V. V. (1960), *Statics of Soil Media,* 2nd ed. (translated from Russian by D. H. Jones and A. N. Schofield), Butterworths, London.

Sokolovskii, V. V. (1962), "Complete Plane Problems of Plastic Flow," *Journal Mech, Phys Solids,* Vol. 10.

Sokolovskii, V. V. (1965), *Statics of Granular Media,* Pergamon Press, New York, N. Y.

Terzaghi, K. (1925), *Erdbaumechanik,* Franz Deuticke, Vienna.

Terzaghi, K. (1943), *Theoretical Soil Mechanics,* John Wiley and Sons, Inc., New York. N. Y.

Wismer, R. D. and H. J. Luth (1970), "Performance of Plane Soil Cutting Blades in Clay," paper no. 70–120 at annual meeting ASAE, Minneapolis, Minn.

Wismer, R. D. and H. J. Luth (1972), "Rate Effects in Soil Cutting," *Journal of Terramechanics,* Vol. 8, No. 3.

Wu, T. H. (1966), *Soil Mechanics,* Allyn and Bacon, Inc., Boston, Mass.

Wu, T. H., A. K. Loh, and L. E. Malvern (1963), "Study of Failure Envelope of Soils," *Journal,* ASCE, SMFD, Vol. 89, No. SM 1.

PART 3

APPLICATIONS OF SOIL MECHANICS THEORIES TO PROBLEMS OF MOBILITY

CHAPTER 3.1

INTRODUCTION

The mechanical properties of the terrain are undoubtedly among the most important factors that affect off-road mobility. Nevertheless, when soil mechanics theories are applied to the various problems of off-road mobility, the soil mechanics aspects of the problem have to be viewed in the broader context of man-terrain-vehicle interaction that ultimately determines mobility. It is in this context that decisions have to be made as to what properties of the soil are significant for the off-road mobility problem in question, how can these properties be determined or adequately estimated and which of the many soil mechanics theories is best suited to describe soil behavior under the loading conditions of interest. The problem is compounded by the fact that it is usually necessary for the essential soil properties to be quickly and accurately determined in the field. It would be a fatal fallacy, however, if soil mechanics considerations were allowed to be influenced by the limitations of field testing techniques. Theories that evolved from overrating the importance of field tests often failed to recognize fundamental soil mechanics aspects of the problem and have turned out to be conceptually inadequate to cope with the complex problems of mobility.

The logical approach to the various problems of mobility requires a reversed order of the development of theories and field techniques. The first step in such an approach is the definition of the mobility problem with respect to the basic parameters involved. Then a concept of the interactions among vehicle, running gear and soil has to be developed and a soil mechanics theory that applies to the determination of soil behavior in this concept has to be formulated within the framework of reasonable assumptions that make the solution tractable. The properties of soil associated with the soil mechanics theory have to be defined and methods for their determination in the laboratory established. At this stage, validation of the theoretical concepts under controlled laboratory conditions is in order. The development of field techniques is the *last* step in this approach that should be undertaken only after the validation of the theoretical concepts have been performed in the laboratory. It is essential that the field techniques be suitable for the determination of those soil properties that are required in the theory. Procedures for the evaluation of these properties from the results of field tests should be developed and validated in the laboratory. It is also essential that such field tests be simple without sacrificing accuracy, otherwise their advantage over laboratory testing is greatly diminished.

In a very general sense, even without clearly formulated theoretical concepts, workers in the field of off-road mobility have recognized that the shear strength of soil is the most important property that governs mobility. In extremely adverse soil conditions the mobility of cross-country vehicles is, indeed, limited by the shear strength of soil. In such "no go" situations soil failure prevents the development of the traction necessary to overcome whatever motion resistance has been created by the sinkage caused by soil failure. Obviously, the shear strength of the soil is the controlling factor in these critical cases of immobilization. While this "no go" situation is of great importance in the trafficability evaluation of the terrain, equally important is the evaluation of vehicle performance under "go" conditions. The role of shear strength of soil in "go" conditions depends on the nature of the interaction between the running gear of the vehicle and the soil. Experimental observations as well as theoretical considerations indicate that the performance of rigid wheels is always controlled by the shear strength of soil since soil failure develops in practically all loading conditions of interest. This state of stresses is brought about by the ability of the rigid wheel to impart sufficiently high stresses to the soil even under low loads. Since it does not deform, the rigid wheel transmits its loads to the soil through as small a contact area as the soil strength allows. In this respect pneumatic tires are fundamentally different from rigid wheels in that their contact area in soils is at least as large as that on a rigid surface under the same load. Thus, the soil is not necessarily in the plastic state of failure beneath pneumatic tires. Nevertheless, in most cases of interest, soil failure conditions govern the performance of pneumatic tires, as will be discussed in detail in Chapter 3.4.

In off-road mobility engineering the distinction is made between "soft soil" and "hard surface" performance of tires. These terms have not been precisely defined but, by implication, one may assume that "soft soil" refers to soil conditions where tire performance is governed by the strength properties of soil, while "hard surface" performance refers to soil conditions where the strength of the soil is high enough to have only minor, if any, influence on tire performance.

The same concepts apply to the design of tracked vehicles where the ground pressure beneath the track is sought to be minimized within the limitations of steerability so that the vehicle might be able to operate on weak terrain. As a result of the low ground pressure purposely designed into tracked vehicles, the bearing capacity of the soil beneath the track is generally not exceeded and the soil is not in failure condition. However, the bearing capacity of soil is substantially reduced by the application of the horizontal thrust that provides traction. Ultimately, the tangential load on the track generated by the thrust causes the soil to fail beneath the track. Thus track performance is controlled by the shear strength of soil alone only in conditions requiring the development of ultimate traction. In other cases volume change properties of the soil as well as its strength influence the performance of tracks.

Interestingly, the recognition of the strength properties of soil as the governing factor in mobility has not found consistent application in the various theories proposed by others for the solution of mobility problems. The drawbacks arising from this inconsistency became apparent when an estimate of the trafficability of lunar terrain was needed for the space program. Soil parameters based on terrestrial field tests were evidently not applicable to lunar conditions. At the same time reasonably good estimates of the soil strength properties were available from the evaluation of Surveyor missions data. The need for a theoretical approach where this information could be utilized by consistent application of soil mechanics principles motivated the authors in the development of their concept of interaction between rigid wheel and soil. In this concept the soil is modeled by its strength parameters c and φ and the theory of plasticity for soils is applied for the computation of stress states in the soil beneath the rigid wheel. The major portion of this chapter deals with the application of plasticity theory methods to mobility problems previously labeled as too complex to be amenable to theoretical treatment. The solutions obtained to these problems constitute a major breakthrough. At the same time it must be emphasized that the application of the plasticity theory is not a panacea to mobility problems. This point will be made in each instance when the problem cannot be satisfactorily solved by plasticity theory methods.

The application of plasticity theory to the problem of running gear-soil interactions requires the solution of the differential equations of plasticity for soils by numerical methods. While it would desirable to have closed formula solutions for the various problems of running gear-soil interaction, the complexity of the problem is such that with the conditions imposed to obtain closed formula solutions the results become meaningless. If simplicity is the overriding consideration in a mobility analysis then, as a first approximation, performance curves developed on the basis of dimensional analysis and cone penetrometer tests as given in the various WES reports are the answer. An example of such a curve is shown in Figure 3.1. As long as soil conditions are close to those used in the experimental determination of these performance curves the approximation of the actual performance is naturally fairly good. The limitation of this method, however, would become apparent as soon as soil conditions are not in the category of either purely frictional or purely cohesive soils. The results of cone penetration tests in frictional-cohesive soils may leave doubt about whether performance curves for purely frictional or purely cohesive soils should be used. Even worse, the non-homogeneity of natural soil and moisture content variations with depth may cause cone penetration measurements to be erroneously interpreted as indicative of purely frictional or purely cohesive soils. The point is that cone penetration resistance is not a unique measure of soil strength and the results of cone penetrometer tests are highly dependent on subjective interpretation. Thus, over-simplification of the complex problem of running gear-soil

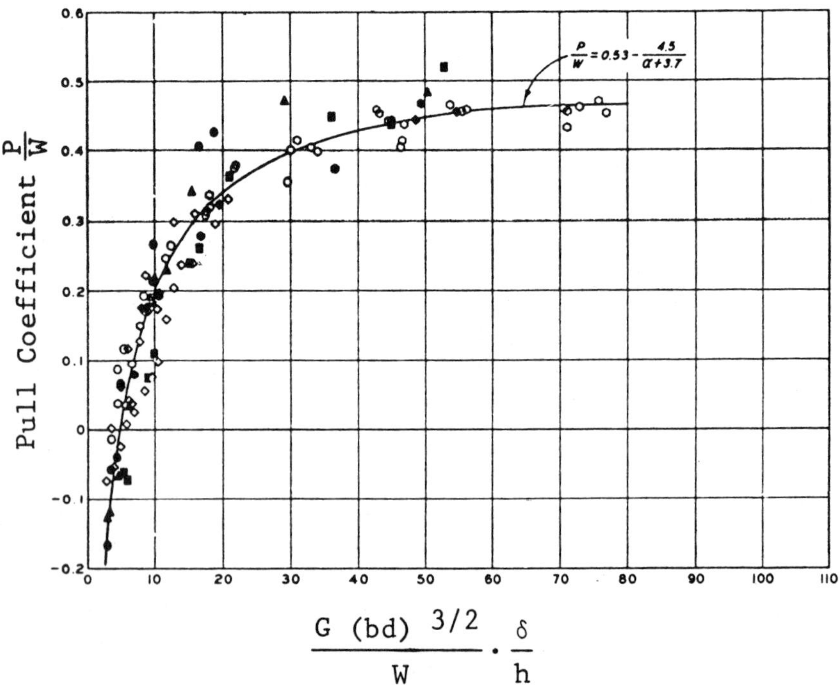

Fig. 3.1
Relationship Between Pull Coefficient and Sand Number (See Eq. 3.6.4)
for Pneumatic Tires
(TURNAGE, 1972)

interaction by relating running gear performance to results of cone penetration tests may be attractive at the first glance but cannot be considered as an absolute solution of the general problem.

The models of running gear-soil interaction to be presented later in this section are based on the applied mechanics approach that considers the equilibrium of free bodies. In mobility problems the free body is the running gear. The boundary where stresses and displacements are to be determined is the running gear-soil interface. In this approach the resultant of the integral of interface stresses over the contact area yields the forces and the torque that is the solution of the mobility problem for an assumed boundary geometry. The solution of the mobility problem for a given load can be found by trial and error methods that would require the use of a computer even if a closed formula solution were available for the computation of interface stresses. The computer programs that were developed for the solution of the various running gear-soil interaction problems presented in this chapter require only a modest computer capacity. Most of the programs can be accommodated on so-called mini-computers. For the development of the pneumatic tire-soil model a large scale analysis of experimental data was performed on a Data General Corporation Nova 800 computer. Other programs were run on Hewlett-Packard 2000 and 3000 computers. Although the solution of running gear-soil interaction problems requires more computer time, and sometimes substantially more on these mini-computers than on large capacity computers, in most cases this may be a secondary consideration compared to the economy of operation. In fact, acquisition of a mini-computer that could be dedicated to mobility problems would cost only a fraction of that of a well equipped running gear testing facility with the added attraction that the mini-computer could be used to investigate the full range of mobility problems whereas a testing facility is usually limited in its scope of investigation.

Although the solutions of the mobility problems presented in this chapter require the use of a computer, complete listings of the programs that the authors developed have not been included. However, the program development as well as the experiences with the various computational schemes are discussed in detail so that those who have a basic knowledge of computer programming should be able to write their own programs without too much difficulty. There are various reasons why the authors decided on this course. In the first place, we consider the programs we developed as starting points rather than ultimate solutions of the running gear-soil interaction problem. The algorithms are based on relatively simple models of running gear-soil interaction; for certain problems more sophisticated models may be needed. The use of computer programs obtained by copying program listings would freeze the model in its first stage of development, whereas writing a computer program for the model on the basis of directives would endue the programmer with a familiarity with the program that is indispensable for intelligent use and further development of the model. Also, writing of the program and obtaining intermediate results develops a "feel" for the problem that may become one of the most important assets to the user.

Another reason for encouraging people to write their own programs is that transferring programs from one computer to another always involves some program modifications even if the computer language is common to both computers. Such program modifications are generally time consuming when the new user is not familiar with the existing program logic. If the language of the existing program is not common to the receiving computer the time involved in making modifications is usually comparable to that of writing the program from scratch.

The solution methods presented in this Chapter for the various mobility problems are intended as engineering solutions rather than solutions aimed at solving hypothetical problems with ultimate precision. A guiding principle for the development of these engineering solutions has been the truism that no computer output is more accurate than its least accurate input. The accuracy with which input soil properties, as well as some tire characteristics, can be determined per se precludes the realization of accuracies in the end result that computers would otherwise be capable of. Another criterion applied in the development of concepts and models has been that material constants and other input parameters be available or determinable by existing methods. All in all, the proposed engineering solutions are believed to represent a sound balance between theoretical exactness and practicability, as well as between economies of computer operation and obtainable accuracy of the solution.

CHAPTER 3.2

THE ROLE OF RUNNING GEAR-SOIL INTERACTION IN OFF-ROAD MOBILITY

The soil mechanics aspects of the various off-road mobility problems apply principally to the interaction between the soil and that part of the running gear that is in direct contact with the ground. Often the term "*vehicular footing*" will be used for this part of the running gear (in lieu of anything better) and thereby the basic similarity between the mechanics of footings for structures and vehicles will be emphasized.

In many civil engineering design methods interaction between the structure and the soil is completely disregarded. A typical example is the method of settlement computations that assumes a hypothetical uniform stress distribution beneath the footing irrespectively of the soil response to the footing loads. On the other hand, as early as in the nineteen-thirties TERZAGHI recognized the significance of interaction between retaining wall structures and the distribution and magnitude of earth pressures. His experiments where he demonstrated the controlling influence of wall movements on the development of earth pressure are classic. Just as interaction between structure and soil is crucial in the case of retaining walls, interaction between vehicular footings and soil is the key to the solution of problems in mobility.

For a clear presentation of the issues in vehicular footing-soil interaction it is necessary to consider this complex interaction in an idealized way. To this end the interactions between vehicle and running gear, brought about by the suspension system, have to be disregarded. This simplification allows the consideration of running gear performance in an uncoupled way, without interference from the vehicle. The uncoupling of running gear-soil interaction from the man-vehicle-terrain system involves the following basic assumptions.

a) The load on the running gear is constant.

b) The terrain is even.

c) There is no interaction between vehicle power train and the driving force (torque, thrust) applied to the running gear.

d) The travel velocity is constant and sufficiently low so that a "steady" or "quasi static" state may be assumed to exist in the soil.

Under these hypothetical conditions the interaction between vehicular footings and soil comes into play primarily through the following three features of soil response and footing characteristics:

a) *Geometry of the vehicular footing* – The normal stresses at the interface are limited by the ability of the soil to carry the load in the plastic state of equilibrium. The limit stresses are affected by the geometry of the contact area and by the changes in the geometry due to deflection.

b) *Shear stresses at the footing interface* – Shear stresses generated at the interface by the torque or thrust applied to the running gear significantly affect the limit of normal stresses that can be developed in the soil.

c) *Balancing of the load* – The load on the running gear must be balanced by the interface stresses. Thus when the interface normal stresses are affected by either the geometry of or shear stresses on the interface, balancing of the load requires a change in the size of the contact area of wheels and tires. This is accomplished by sinkage. In the case of tracks this effect is minor since both the contact area and the interface normal stresses are practically constant.

As it can be seen from this brief description of the processes that play a predominant role in running gear-soil interaction, the dependence of the soil response on the boundary conditions at the interface is a major factor in these processes. Since in the other branches of soils engineering the significance of this feature of the soil response is suppressed by the application of a quite large safety factor, it is useful to discuss this aspect of soil behavior in more detail.

3.2.1 The Effect of the Geometry of the Contact Area on Footing-Soil Interaction

The ultimate load that the soil can carry at incipient soil failure is termed bearing capacity. The effect of the size and shape of the footing on bearing capacity has been discussed in general in Chapter 1.4.3. Evidently, the degree of influence of the size and shape of the vehicular footing on the interaction with the soil depends on the range of the variation in the size and shape of the contact area that the vehicular footing exhibits. This range is the widest for rigid wheels, is moderate for pneumatic tires, and very small for tracks.

In the case of vehicular footings there is another geometric feature that significantly affects the response of the soil. The curvature of the footing in the vertical plane and the inclination of footing elements to the horizontal have an appreciable effect on soil response to the loading. Since the soil-foundation interface of most structures is linearly planar, this effect is of little interest to civil soils engineering and, therefore, not much can be learned about it from conventional soil mechanics textbooks. For the significance of this effect on running gear-soil interaction to be fully appreciated, some of the results of computations for rigid wheel-soil interaction problems are anticipated here. Figure 3.2 shows how the entry angle, α_e, affects the soil response when the wheel load produces a stress field in the front that is in the state of plastic equilibrium with it. This

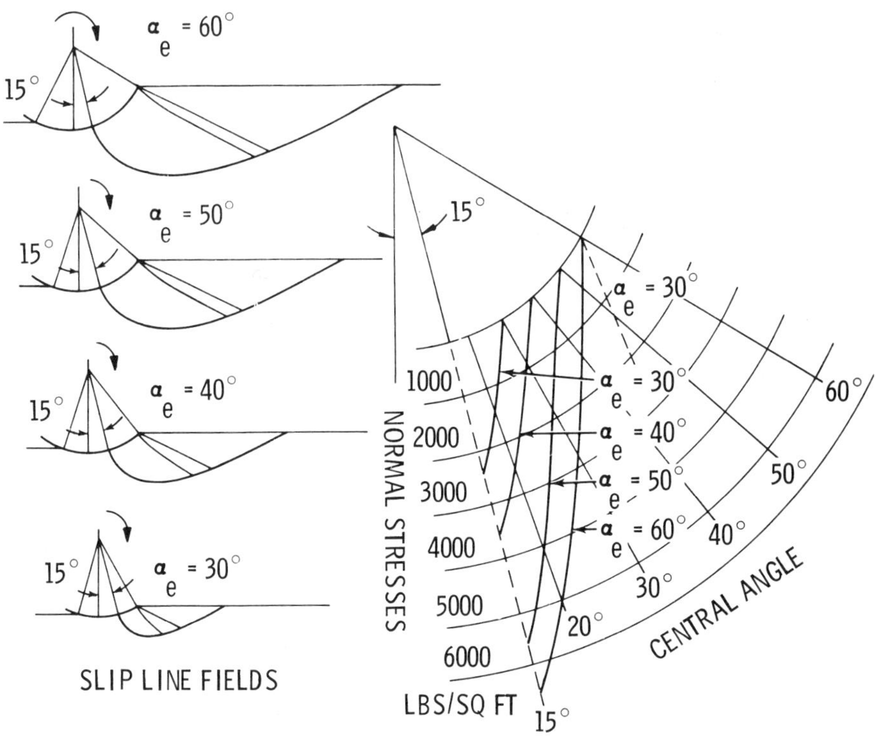

Fig. 3.2
Slip Line Fields and Associated Normal Stresses for Various Entry Angles

figure shows outlines of slip line fields in the front of rigid wheels for a $\varphi = 41°$ material, assuming various entry angles. The inner end of the slip line field corresponds to a central angle of $\alpha = 15°$ in all cases. The normal stresses corresponding to these slip line fields are plotted radially in the right side of the figure. In this radial plot the normal stresses pertaining to the various entry angles appear as essentially parallel lines. Nevertheless, the rate of increase of the normal stresses with the angular distance represented by these parallel lines in the radial plot varies considerably, as for example the dashed line for $\alpha_e = 30°$ shows. This line shows the same rise of the normal stresses with the angular distance as the full line, but with the entry point shifted from $\alpha_e = 30°$ to $\alpha_e = 60°$. Another illustration of this relationship is shown in Figure 3.3 where the normal stress-angular distance relationships for various entry angles are directly comparable. It is seen that at a distance corresponding to a 10° difference in central angle the normal stress for an entry angle of $\alpha_e = 60°$ amounts to about 500 lb/sq ft, while for an entry angle of $\alpha_e = 30°$ the normal stress rises to about 1800 lb/sq ft over the same distance.

In Figure 3.4 the normal stress at the entry angle that can be developed in purely cohesive soils is shown as a function of the entry angle.

Clearly, the entry angle considerably influences the normal stresses that the soil can develop at the wheel-soil interface. Actually, the decrease of the rise rate of the normal stresses with the entry angle can be offered as an explanation for the bogging down of wheels in many instances.

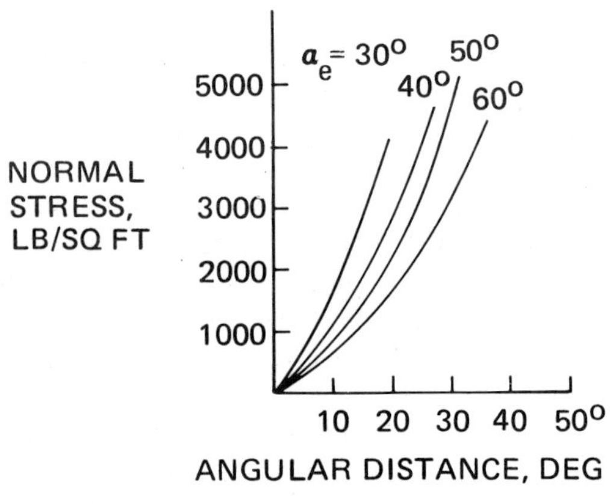

Fig. 3.3
Effect of the Entry Angle on the Interface Normal Stresses in Frictional Soils

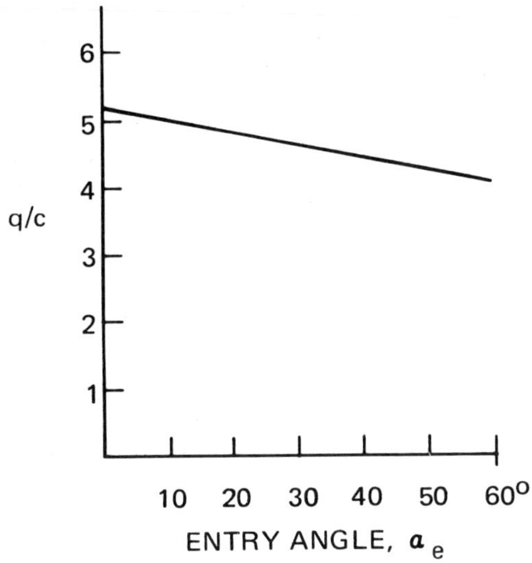

Fig. 3.4
Variation of the Ratio q/c with the Entry Angle in Cohesive Soils
(q = interface normal stress at entry angle, c = cohesion)

3.2.2 The Development of Interface Shear Stresses

Since the interface shear stresses play a major role in running gear-soil interaction it is worthwhile to consider some aspects of their relation to the applied thrust or torque that generates them and to the slip that is concomitant to their development.

In the case of rigid wheels the relation between interface shear stresses and applied torque is straightforward: equilibrium requires that the integral of shear stresses over the contact area multiplied by the wheel radius be equal to the applied torque. In the case of pneumatic tires no such clear relation exist since the line of action of the interface normal stresses generally bypasses the axle because of the deflection of the tire. Thus, the interface normal stresses enter into the equilibrium equations for the applied torque. Nevertheless, the major portion of the driving torque is transmitted to the soil in the form of interface shear stresses. In either case, equilibrium requirements set a condition only for the magnitude and position of the resultant of the interface stresses and in no way restrain the distribution of the shear stresses along the interface. An infinite variety of shear stress distributions exists that satisfy the requirement for equilibrium with the applied forces.

There are, however, other limitations on the interface shear stresses that have to be considered in the interaction between running gear and soil. The interface shear stresses may not exceed either the adhesive strength between the surface of the running gear and the soil or the shear strength of the soil. In the design of running gears for off-road vehicles different types of traction devices, such as various patterns of treads, lugs or grousers, are employed to insure that in the development of traction the adhesion and friction between the surface of the running gear and soil should not be a restraint and as high interface stresses as the shear strength of the soil permits may be developed. Thus, for all practical purposes the only limitation on the interface shear stresses is the one imposed by the shear strength of the soil, which, in the Coulombian concept (as has been shown previously in Part 1), is directly related to normal stress as follows:

$$s = c + \sigma_n \tan \varphi \qquad \text{Eq. 1.3.24}$$

Alternatively, the following expression may be used

$$s = (\psi + \sigma_n) \tan \varphi \qquad \text{Eq. 3.2.1}$$

where $\psi = c \cot \varphi$ and all other terms are as defined previously.

It is convenient to express the interface shear stress in a similar form as follows

$$\tau = (\psi + \sigma_n) \tan \delta \qquad \text{Eq. 3.2.2}$$

where δ is defined as the angle of interface friction.

Figure 3.5 shows the definition of the angle δ in relation to the Mohr-Coulomb strength envelope and the mobilized interface shear stress, τ_{mob}. The development of shear stresses at the interface is associated with slip, and mathematical formulations for the relationship between shear stress and slip have been proposed by various researchers. Of these, the most useful is the empirical one proposed by Janosi and Hanamoto (1961) on the basis of analogy with the direct shear test. This relationship, proposed for tracked vehicles, is as follows

$$\tau_{mob} = \tau_{max} (1 - e^{-j/K}) \qquad \text{Eq. 3.2.3}$$

Slip in this expression, and throughout this book is defined as

$$j = (1 - v/v_t) \qquad \text{Eq. 3.2.4}$$

where

v = actual travel velocity

v_t = theoretical travel velocity

For compressible soils that are of primary interest in off-road locomotion, this equation properly describes the relationship between shear stress and slip. When this relationship is applied to the rigid wheel or pneumatic tires a constant, j_o, must be included in the slip term to account for the fact that a threshold perimeter shear exists, at which the movement of the wheel starts. Thus, Eq. 3.2.4 is modified as follows

$$\tau_{mob} = \tau_{max}\,(1 - e^{-(j+jo)/K}) \qquad \text{Eq. 3.2.5}$$

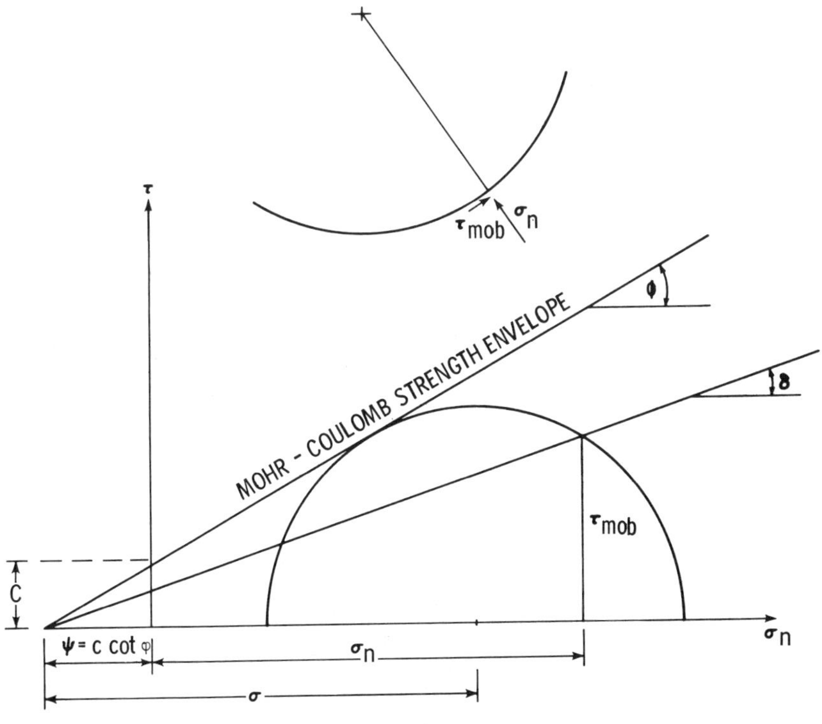

Fig. 3.5
Mohr Circle, Mobilized Shear Strength and Interface Friction Angle (δ)

From Figure 3.5 the following relationship is seen to exist between the shear strength mobilized at the interface and the angle of interface friction.

$$\tan \delta = \frac{\tau_{mob}}{\sigma_n + \psi} \qquad \text{Eq. 3.2.6}$$

Combination of Eqs. 3.2.6 and 3.2.5 yields

$$\tan \delta = \tan \delta_{max} (1 - e^{-(j + jo)/K}) \qquad \text{Eq. 3.2.7}$$

Since it is derived from JANOSI and HANAMOTO's equation, this relation between the developed interface friction angle and slip is an empirical one. Further discussion of slip and a theoretical analysis of slip and its relation to the kinematic boundary conditions at the running gear-soil interface are presented in Section 3.3.6.

3.2.3. The Effect of Interface Shear Stresses on Vehicular Footing-Soil Interaction

The effect of interface shear stresses on the development of interface normal stresses is enormous. In Section 2.5.1 where the bearing capacity of soils under inclined loads was discussed, it was already pointed out that the bearing capacity decreases tremendously as the angle of inclination of the load from the vertical approaches the friction angle. When a driving torque or thrust is applied to the running gear, shear stresses are generated at the running gear-soil interface and the angle of the inclination of the resultant stresses changes. For a qualitative appreciation of this effect it is shown in Figure 3.6 how the angle of the inclination of the resultant stress to the normal of the interface affects the normal stresses that can be developed in the rear portion of a rigid wheel. On the left side of the figure the outlines of the slip line fields are shown that yield the normal stresses shown in the radial plot on the right side. The curves showing the distribution of the normal stresses in this plot refer to the same conditions except for the δ angle. It is easy to visualize that the tangential components of the stress vector act in the direction of soil failure and tend to facilitate this failure. In effect they reduce the normal stresses that would otherwise be necessary to cause failure. This reduction, as can be seen from the radial plot in Figure 3.6, becomes significant as the angle approaches the friction angle of the soil ($\varphi = 41°$). Thus, the application of shear stresses reduces the normal stresses at the interface and necessitates an increase in the contact area to balance the wheel load. This is the fundamental process in the interaction between driven wheels and soil.

3.2.4 Running Gear-Soil Interaction and Concepts of Traction

In the solution of off-road mobility problems one cannot overemphasize the importance of understanding the fundamental processes of running gear-soil interaction as described above. Failure to account for these phenomena has led to erroneous concepts in mobility theory. A typical example of such an erroneous concept in mobility theory is found

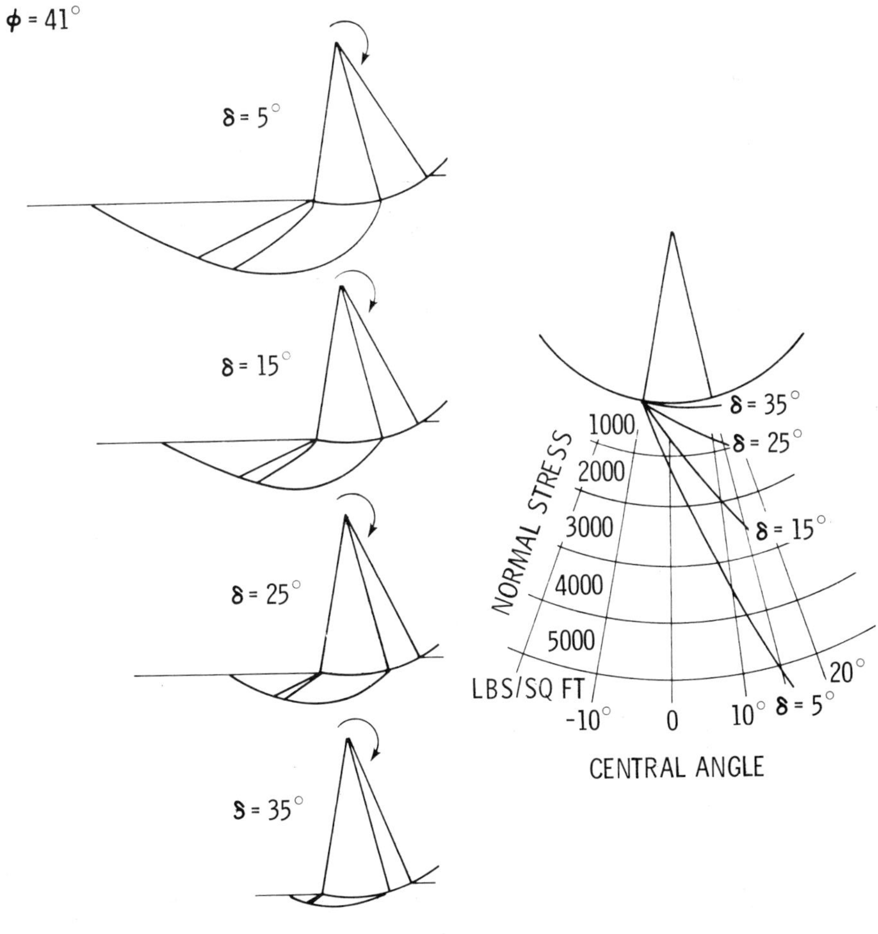

Fig. 3.6
Effect of the Interface Friction Angle (δ) on the Geometry of the Rear Slip Line Field and the Associated Normal Stresses

in the following equations advocated by BEKKER (1969) for the determination of the drawbar pull of powered wheels:

$$DP = H - R \qquad \text{Eq. 3.2.8}$$

where

DP = drawbar pull

H = soil thrust

R = motion resistance.

This equation implies that the motion resistance is independent of the soil thrust. In this equation soil thrust is defined as the sum of the components of the interface stresses in the direction of travel. The processes of interaction, as explained briefly in the preceding paragraphs, clearly show that the interface shear stresses comprising the soil thrust profoundly affect the magnitude of interface normal stresses and thereby the size of the contact area. In the case of rigid wheels and tires, an increase in the size of the contact area is closely associated with the sinkage, and, as a consequence, with an increase of the motion resistance. Thus, the proper formulation of Equation 3.2.8 should read as follows

$$DP = H - R(H) \qquad \text{Eq. 3.2.9}$$

where the parenthesis represents functional dependence on the enclosed variable.

It is interesting to note that in the literature of off-road mobility one is hard pressed to find a definition of motion resistance. If motion resistance is defined as the force required to pull a free rolling running gear, then the fallacy of Equation 3.2.8 is readily apparent for all mobility problems where there is a significant interaction between running gear and soil. Since this interaction is weakest in the case of tracks where the contact area varies but little as a function of load and sinkage, Equation 3.2.8 in its original form coincidentally yields acceptable results.

CHAPTER 3.3

APPLICATIONS OF PLASTICITY THEORY TO SOIL-WHEEL INTERACTION PROBLEMS GOVERNED BY FAILURE CONDITIONS IN SOIL

3.3.1 Concept of Rigid Wheel-Soil Interaction

In the development of mobility theories, the behavior of soil beneath rigid wheels has been a favored starting point since the simple geometry of the rigid wheel eases the mathematical problems as well as the performance of experiments. Measurements of interface stresses generated beneath rigid wheels under various loading conditions and the determination of soil deformation patterns by photographic methods contributed greatly to our present understanding of this specific interaction phenomenon. Perhaps the earliest experiments in which soil deformation patterns were measured under the loading by a rigid wheel are those performed in 1948 and reported by BEKKER (1969). A more extensive experimental investigation of deformation patterns was carried out by WONG and REECE (1966). In these experiments it was clearly established that failure zones develop in the soil beneath the wheel and that the extent and form of the failure zones vary with loading conditions and slip. Figure 3.7 shows outlines of failure zones beneath an $8^1/_4$ in. diameter wheel determined by WONG and REECE. The existence of failure zones is consistent with the view that the shear strength of soil is the controlling factor in mobility problems since failure zones, or in another terminology, slip line fields, are those areas where the combination of normal and shear stress is such that the shear strength of soil is everywhere exceeded. The field itself is usually shown as consisting of a number of intersecting lines called slip lines along which the failure conditions pertain.

The existence of failure zones beneath wheels has not found recognition in theoretical considerations of the problem until the authors proposed the application of plasticity theory for the determination of the geometry of the slip line fields and the stress states assosiated with the geometry. Advances in numerical computation techniques and the availability of high speed digital computers made it possible to formulate the theoretical concept of rigid wheel interaction in a form suitable for solution on the computer and, thereby, for practical use.

The rigid wheel-soil interaction concept developed by the authors and presented for the first time in 1970 is illustrated in Figure 3.8. The principal features of this concept are as follows.

Generally, two separate zones of failure or slip line fields develop beneath rigid wheels, a forward field, where the soil tends to fail in the direction of travel and a backward, or rear field, where the soil tends to fail in the opposite direction. In each field there are three zones corresponding to different states of stress. Just as in the case of bearing capacity there is an active zone, a transitional or radial zone, and a passive zone. The wheel interface adjoins the active zone conforming with the wheel's role of applying stresses to the soil and causing the soil to move toward the free surfaces in the front and back of the wheel. If passive zones were to adjoin the wheel interface, then the soil would have to move toward the wheel interface. This is mentioned here to clarify the proper place of these zones since the reader may encounter some concepts proposed in the literature where the passive zone adjoins the wheel interface.

Continuity of the interface stress distribution requires that at the common point of the two slip line fields (defined in terms of central angle as α_m in Fig. 3.8) the interface normal and shear stresses be the same for

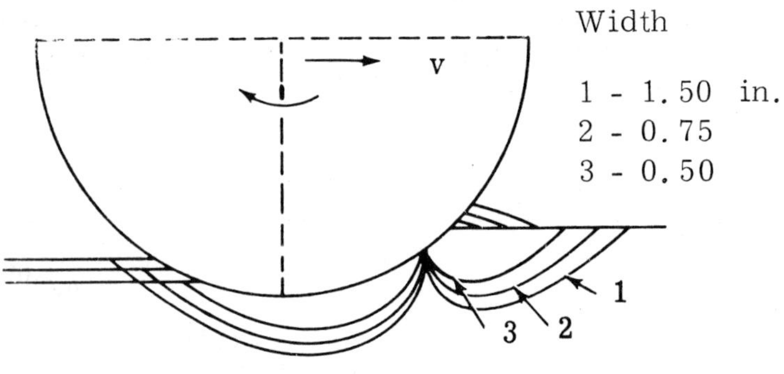

Fig. 3.7
Failure Zones Beneath a Model Rigid Wheel
(After WONG and REECE, 1966)

both the forward and backward fields. This condition cannot always be met in the computations. In certain cases when the interface stresses associated with one of the slip line fields are lower for the whole range of central angles between the potential entry and exit angles, there is only a single slip line field. In reality such a case exists for driven wheels in highly cohesive soils when the single slip line field is the rear one. Also, in the case of braked wheels a single forward slip line field develops under certain conditions.

The concept of wheel-soil interaction illustrated in Figure 3.8 is a two-dimensional one; the slip line fields are thought to be in the vertical plane of travel. In certain cases lateral displacement was observed in the front of the wheel, suggesting three-dimensional failure conditions. For the proper assessment of the significance of three-dimensional failure conditions and the magnitude of error that may be introduced by using a two-dimensional model of the interaction the following considerations are pertinent.

Figure 3.8 shows that in the idealized rigid wheel problem, all applied forces are in the vertical plane of travel. The vectors of the normal and shear stresses at the interface that balance these forces are also in that vertical plane. If these interface stresses are now considered as stresses

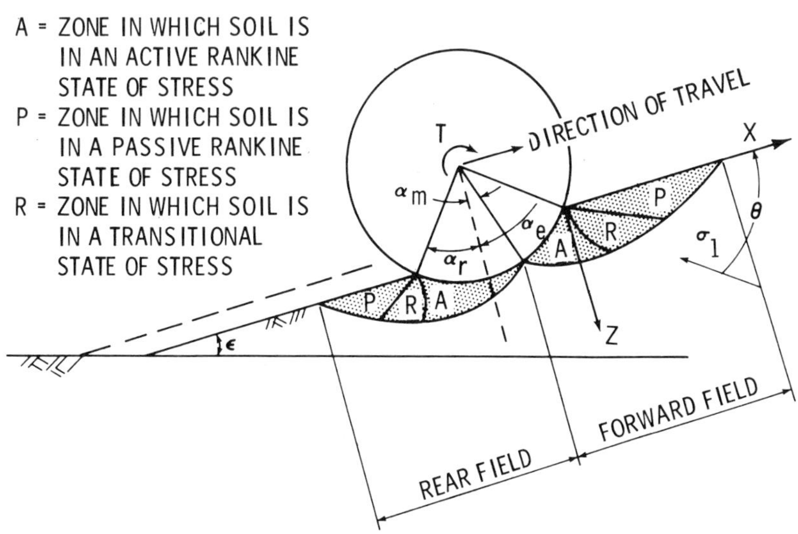

Fig. 3.8
Concept of Rigid Wheel-Soil Interaction

applied to the soil mass, then the stress states in the vertical plane can be determined on the assumption that the soil is in failure condition. Such calculations show that both the major and minor principal stresses in the vertical plane increase with the increase of the applied shear stresses.

If the stresses perpendicular to the vertical plane of travel are also considered, then a three-dimensional stress state, characterized by the three principal stresses and their orientation, is present. The third principal stress may be called lateral stress to distinguish it from the others in the vertical plane. At least in the center plane the third principal stress must be perpendicular to that plane since there are no shear stresses across that plane because of symmetry. According to the MOHR-COULOMB theory, the failure plane is perpendicular to the plane in which the major and minor principal stresses lie. This is the vertical plane as long as the smaller principal stress in that plane is less than the lateral stress. With an increase of the applied stresses, however, the lateral stress may become the minor principal stress, changing the $\sigma_1 - \sigma_3$ plane to an oblique one, as shown in Figure 3.9. Just before this situation occurs and at the limit when the lateral stress and the smaller principal stress in the vertical plane are equal, ($\sigma_3 = \sigma_1$), failure conditions in the vertical plane govern the interface stresses; with lateral failure this condition still has to be maintained, otherwise the failure mode would revert to that in the vertical plane. Thus, the effect of lateral failure is a limitation on the applied shear stresses; at the limit the stress can be calculated on the basis of two-dimensional failure conditions. A suggestion how to take these limiting lateral failure conditions into account by using a hybrid – partially three-dimensional – model of wheel-soil interaction is presented in Section 3.3.7.

An important feature of the authors' concept of rigid wheel-soil interaction is that the geometry of the slip line fields and the stresses associated with that geometry vary with the applied torque. This, of course, follows from the corollary of the concept that the slip line fields shown in Figure 3.8 represent solutions of the differential equations of plasticity for soils. For these solutions to be uniquely determined two relations among the four principal variables (x, z, σ, θ) of the differential equations (Equations 2.2.20) have to be specified at the boundary represented by the wheel-soil interface. One relation is given by the geometry of the interface. The other one expresses a relationship between the shear and normal stresses at the interface. The integral of the interface shear stresses, however, must equal the applied torque. Thus, the magnitude of the shear stresses, although not necessarily their distribution, depends on the applied torque. The shear stresses at the interface directly influence the geometry of the slip line fields, as was shown in Figure 3.6. This variation of the slip line field geometries with the applied torque is the expression of the interaction between applied torque and soil response.

In many experimental and theoretical treatments of mobility problems, slip is considered as an independent variable that governs wheel performance. Although wheel performance undoubtedly varies with slip, the authors' view is that slip is not a causative factor but a result of the interaction that takes place between wheel and soil. Interaction is governed by stresses applied to the interacting bodies and by the deformations of these bodies under these stresses. Slip is the result of the geometry of rolling and relative displacement of the interfaces. Thus, in the authors' concept the problem consists of determining the combination of interface shear and normal stresses that satisfy the equilibrium of forces applied to the wheel and that are compatible with the behavior of soil as postulated by the plasticity theory. When the interface stresses are known, slip may be estimated on the basis of the developed interface shear stresses.

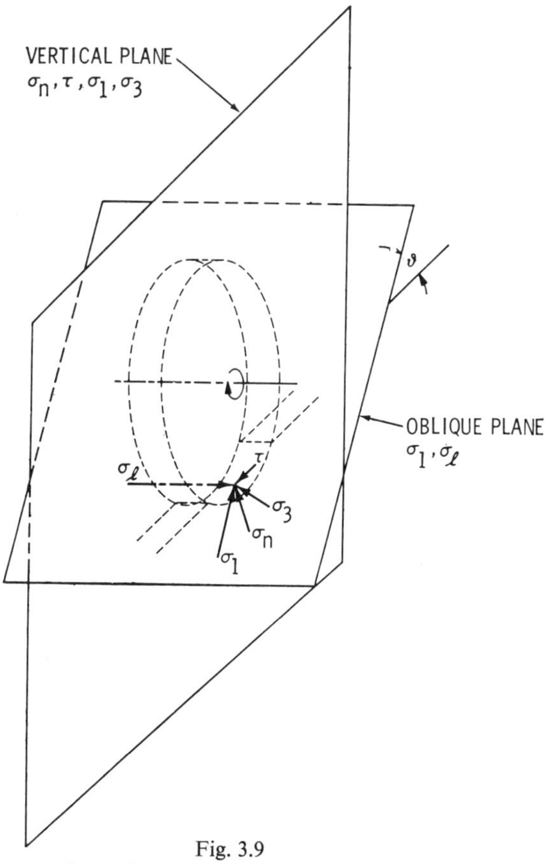

Fig. 3.9
Stress State beneath a Rigid Wheel.
Applied stresses in the vertical plane: σ_n, τ.
Principal stresses in the vertical plane: σ_1, $\sigma_3 < \sigma_l$

3.3.2 Performance of Single Rigid Wheel in Homogeneous Soil

The concept of rigid wheel-soil interaction discussed in Section 3.3.1 is suitable for the solution of practical problems of mobility. The solution methods, however, will vary for the loading conditions specified in the particular problem. In Chapter 3.2 the uncoupling of the running gear from the vehicle was discussed and the idealized conditions for the analysis of the running gear-soil interaction were described. Under these idealized conditions the vertical load on the running gear, which in the present case is a rigid wheel, is assumed to be constant. In addition to the vertical load the total force system applied to the wheel includes the torque and the tangential load. In the various problems of mobility the specification of loading conditions with respect to the torque and tangential load vary. Combinations of these loads yield all possible variations of loading conditions. These are illustrated in Figure 3.10 where, in addition

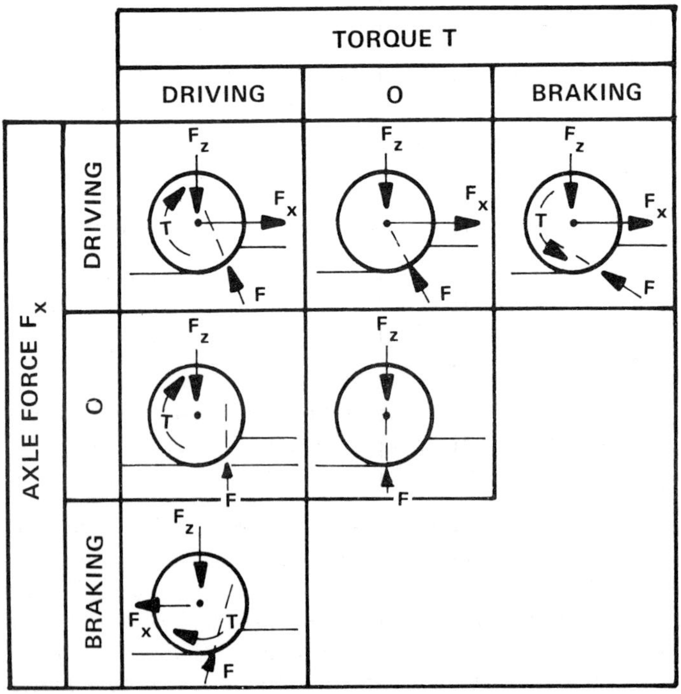

Fig. 3.10
Combinations of Torque T and Horizontal Axle Force F_x Acting on a Rigid Wheel.
F = soil reaction
(After SCHURING, 1966)

to the loads applied to the wheel, the resultant *(F)* of the stresses acting on the interface is also shown. The magnitude and position of this resultant force is generally unknown. In the authors' concept the integration of the horizontal and vertical components of the interface stresses yields the respective components of the resultant force. The position of the resultant force vector may be computed from the equilibrium conditions for the torque.

From the viewpoint of solution methods the loading conditions indicated in Figure 3.10 represent the following three basic problems.

a) Driven wheel – Determine the drawbar pull (tangential force) for given load and torque, or alternatively determine the torque for given drawbar pull and load.

b) Free rolling or towed wheel – Determine the drag (tangential force) for given load and zero torque.

c) Braked wheel – Determine the drag or drawbar pull for a given load and torque applied opposite to wheel rotation.

In applying the rigid wheel-soil interaction concept for the solution of these problems some additional assumptions have to be made regarding the boundary conditions at the interface and the relative positions of the slip line fields.

Assumptions Regarding the Interface Friction Angle

For the slip line fields in these problems to be uniquely defined it is necessary to specify the relationship between the normal and shear stresses at the interface. The interface friction angle, as defined by Equation 3.2.6, is well suited for this purpose.

For the three basic problems of rigid wheel performance enumerated above, various considerations apply regarding the assumption of the maximum value and variation of interface friction along the contact area.

For driven wheels δ may be assumed as constant. Its evaluation is obtained from measurements of interface normal and shear stresses, a typical example of which is shown in Figure 3.11. In most cases δ varies but little along the contact area. There are, however, exceptions when the angle decreases appreciably toward the center of the contact area. A preliminary theory for the relationship between kinematic constraints at the wheel-soil boundary and the variation of the δ angle is advanced in Section 3.3.6. Undoubtedly, this is an area in wheel-soil interaction where further theoretical and experimental research could bring fruitful results. Until that time only the simplest of the assumptions, namely that δ is constant, is supportable. This assumption is consistent with the tacit assumption of the slip being constant for every point along the wheel perimeter.

For a free rolling or towed wheel the torque and the moment of shear stresses about the axis are zero. If δ were assumed as constant then its value would have to be zero for there to be no moment due to interface shear stresses. Consequently, the interface shear stresses would vanish, a condition contrary to the experimental results shown in Figure 3.12. If there are shear stresses, then their sign has to change along the contact area to satisfy the requirement that the moment of shear stresses about the axis be zero. It is reasonable to associate opposite signs to shear stresses in the forward and rear slip line fields. In this book the convention is that shear stresses in the forward slip line field are positive and those in the rear field are negative. A δ angle that decreases linearly from the entry and exit

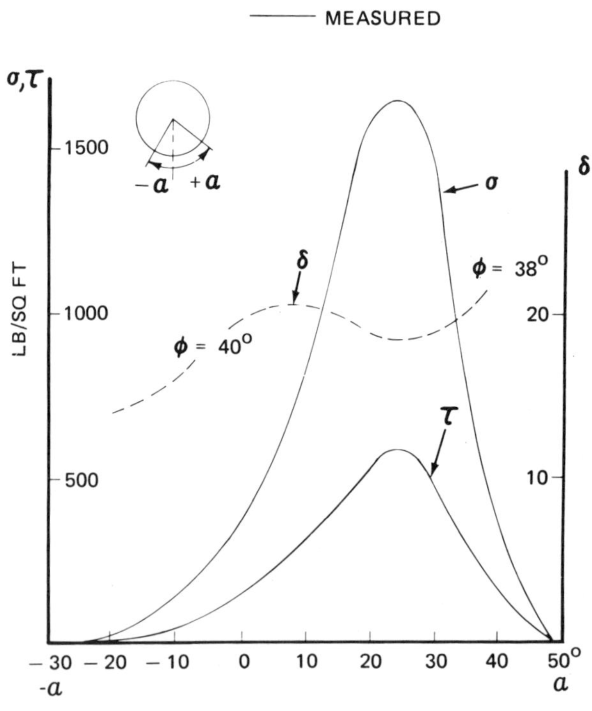

Fig. 3.11
Variation of the Interface Friction Angle, δ, With the Central Angle, α, at the Interface of a Driven Rigid Wheel. Evaluated from Normal and Shear stresses Measured by SELA (1964)

points toward the center and becomes zero at the angle of separation results in a shear stress distribution similar to that shown in Figure 3.12. The value of the δ angle may be assumed in the range of 1/2 to 1/3 φ at the entry point. The same value with opposite sign may be assumed for the exit point.

It is noted that for very small values of torque, the distribution of shear stresses may be in between that shown for driven wheels in Figure 3.11 and in Figure 3.12 for towed wheels. The variation of the δ angle may be assumed accordingly.

For braked wheels there is but little information available on shear and normal stress distribution. In lieu of anything better, analogy can be made with the driven wheel and a constant δ angle with a sign opposite to that of the driven wheel may be assumed.

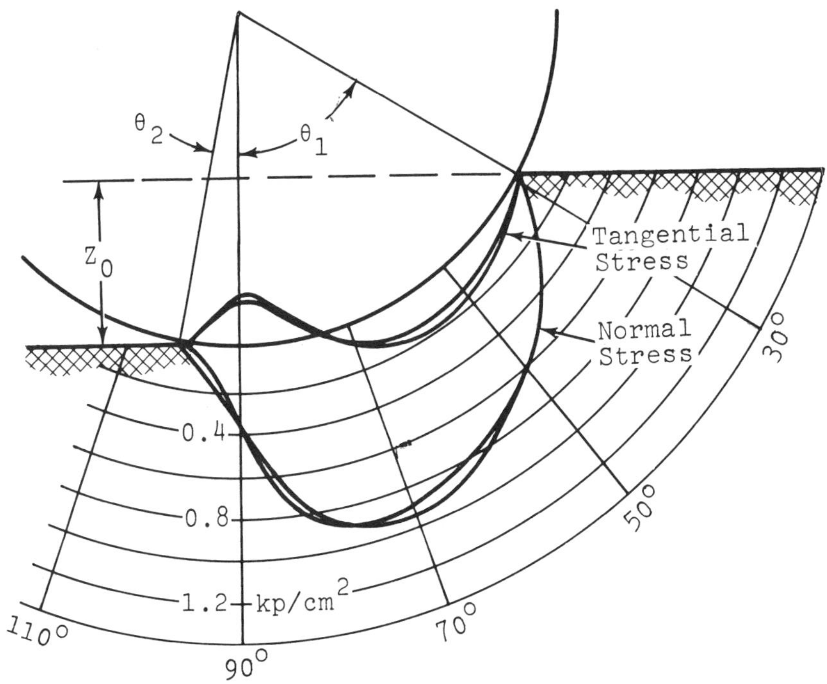

Fig. 3.12
Distribution of Normal and Shear Stresses Beneath a 0.88 m Diameter Towed Rigid Wheel, Averaged Over the Width for Two Tests. Wheel Load = 640 kg.
(After KRICK, 1969)

Assumptions Regarding the Angle of Separation

The position of slip line fields generated beneath rigid wheels is defined by the following three central angles (Figure 3.8):

α_e = entry angle

α_r = rear or exit angle

α_m = angle of separation (of slip line fields)

None of these angles is known beforehand; each of them has to be determined for the solution of the rigid wheel-soil interaction problem. In the authors' concept of interaction the following two conditions exist that establish two relationships among these three angles.

a) Force equilibrium requires that the vertical components of interface stresses integrated over the contact area must equal the load. Since the integration limits are the entry and exit angles, this condition is equivalent with a relationship between these angles.

b) Continuity requires that the magnitude of the normal and shear stresses at the joint point of the forward and rear slip line fields (at the angle of separation) must match.

A study of the available information on interface stress measurements shows that the angle of separation for driven wheels is closely related to the developed interface friction angle. SELA (1964) found that for dry sand the angle of separation approximately equals the developed interface friction angle, δ. This finding is consistent with the concept that the forward failure zone extends over that part of the wheel perimeter where the component of the normal and shear stresses *(ΔD)* in the direction of motion is negative (i.e., resisting the motion), and that the backward zone extends over that part of the wheel perimeter where this component is positive.

Applying this concept to soils with friction and cohesion the angle of separation (α_m) may be determined on the assumption that $\Delta D = 0$ at $\alpha = \alpha_m$. The following relations hold:

$$\Delta D = \tau_{mob} \cos \alpha - \sigma_n \sin \alpha$$

$$\tau_{mob} = (\sigma_n + \psi) \tan \delta$$

$$\Delta D = (\sigma_n + \psi) \tan \delta \tan \alpha = 0$$

$$\alpha_m = \text{arc tan} \left(\frac{\sigma_n + \psi}{\sigma_n} \tan \delta \right) \qquad \text{Eq. 3.3.1}$$

These equations define the position of slip line fields for driven wheels completely. However, the relationship between the load and the entry and exit angles is not known *a priori*. Therefore, the value of one of these angles must be assumed and trial and error computations performed until the solution satisfies all equilibrium and boundary conditions. In the computation scheme developed by the authors the value of the rear angle is assumed and an inversion scheme is applied to find the value of the α_r angle that yields the load. This inversion scheme is discussed in Section 3.3.1.

For towed wheels Equation 3.3.1 does not apply since δ varies along the interface. Experiments show that the rear angle for towed wheels varies little and is generally small. Thus, instead of making an assumption regarding α_m, one can assume that α_r is constant and equals an arbitrarily selected small angle, say 5°. Inaccuracies in the towed force calculation due to this arbitrary selection of the rear angle are within the tolerance limits corresponding to the magnitude of errors from other sources such as the determination of soil properties, etc.

3.3.3 Computational Methods

The concept of rigid wheel-soil interaction illustrated in Figure 3.8 together with the additional assumptions discussed in Section 3.3.2 can be easily adapted to numerical computation. In the numerical computation there are essentially two problems: the computation of the geometry and associated stresses of a slip line field and the solution of the interaction problem using the interface stresses determined from the slip line field computations. Since the solution is a trial and error type, the computation of slip line fields occurs at least two (forward and rear) and more likely several times in an interaction problem. Therefore, it is practical to arrange the computations of a slip line field in the form of a subroutine in the computer program.

Computation of a Single Slip Line Field

For the computation of a single slip line field in a wheel-soil interaction problem the following input data are needed:

Soil properties: c, φ,

Interface friction angle: δ

Wheel geometry: R, α_e (or α_r) and α_m

For the computations a grid is set up, as shown in Figure 3.13. This grid consists of "*i*" and "*j*" lines (characteristics of the differential equations) and the variables x, z, σ and θ are computed for each of the nodal points in the grid. The difference equations for the computation of these variables at a general i, j point are the same as those given in Chapter 2.3 for the general plane strain condition with ϑ = constant (Equations 2.3.7).

For wheel-soil interaction problems there are the following two choices in regard to the selection of grid size:

a) Grid with a constant number of "*i*" and "*j*" lines (Figure 3.13)

b) Grid with constant number of "*i*" lines and variable number of "*j*" lines (Figure 3.14)

If the computer program has to be accommodated on a mini-computer then it may be necessary to choose the first option. For larger computers, the second option is preferable because an appreciable reduction in com-

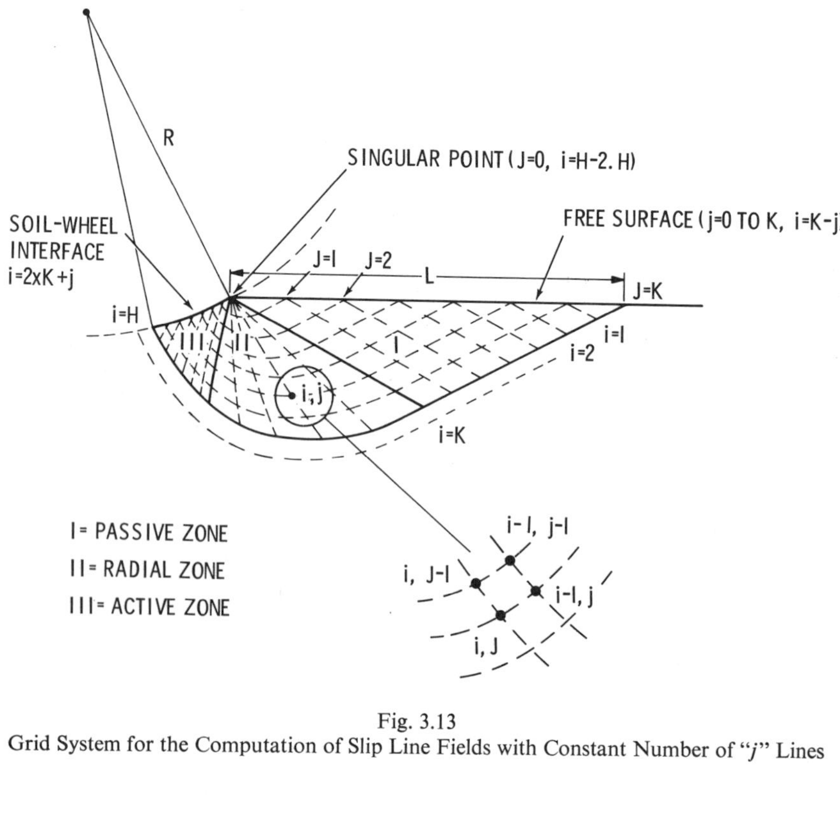

Fig. 3.13
Grid System for the Computation of Slip Line Fields with Constant Number of "*j*" Lines

puting time may be achieved by using the variable "*j*" line method. This is brought about by the greater latitude in finding the proper size slip line fields as explained below.

If "*H*" is the number assigned to the last "*i*" line and "*K*" is that assigned to the last "*j*" line in the slip line field, then in the authors' experience the following grid sizes are satisfactory for accuracy and reasonable computing time.

	"*H*"		"*K*"
Constant "*j*" option	30		10
Variable "*j*" option	48	up to	16

In this numbering system "0" is assigned to the singular point (Figure 3.13). Note that if a "0" subscript in arrays is not allowed in the computer language, then the above numbers change appropriately. By writing the program in terms of variables *H* and *K* and by dimensioning sub-

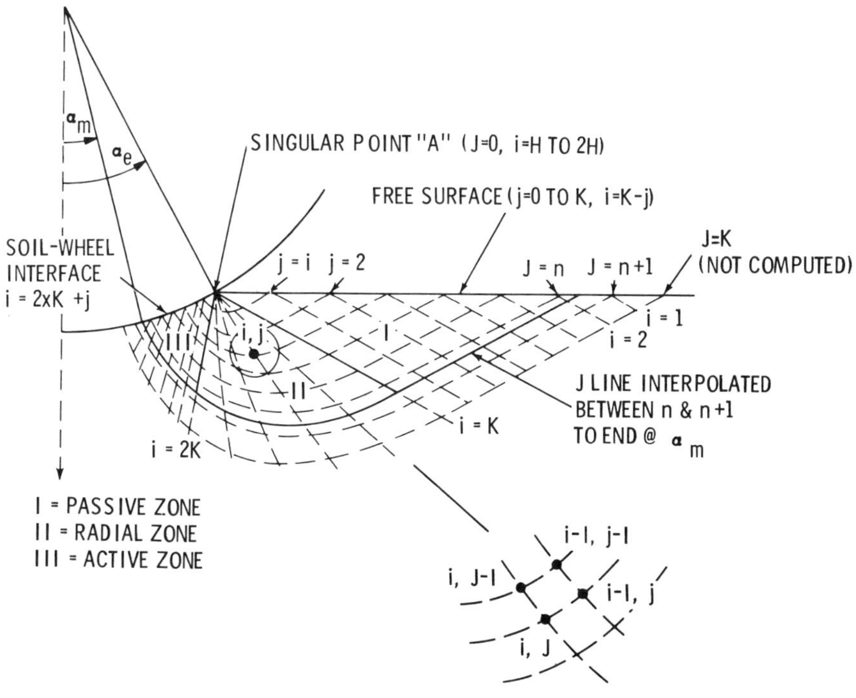

Fig. 3.14
Grid System for the Computation of Slip Line Fields with Variable Number of "*j*" Lines

script variables large enough (or by using dynamic dimensioning techniques) the grid size can be varied simply by varying the input values of *H* and *K*.

The consideration behind the choice of the grid system is the method of finding the size of the slip line field that will have its last "*j*" line end at the interface at the angle α_m. The computations start from the free surface where the length of the passive zone *(L)* is assumed (Figure 3.13). The *L* value determines the size of the slip line field and the location where the last "*j*" line joins the surface. Since the value of *L* that meets the aforesaid condition is not known beforehand, an iterative procedure has to be devised to find the "*L*" value that meets this condition within an allowed tolerance, ξ.

With the constant "*j*" option as many iterations on *L* have to be performed as necessary to match the specified arc length of the active zone at the interface. In each iteration a complete computation of a trial slip line field with the 30 x 30 grid is necessary to find the location of the last "*j*" line at the interface. In this option, all variables may be computed first in the passive, then in the radial and finally in the active zone. This sequence of computations would allow the use of an even smaller (20 x 10) grid if only level free surfaces are considered, since the variables along the boundary of the passive zone may be directly computed.

With the variable "*j*" option, core locations for a larger grid (48 x 16) are allocated but actual computations are carried out only for as many "*j*" lines as necessary. To this end, a sequence of operations, different from that outlined above for the constant "*j*" option, is employed, as shown in the flow diagram in Figure 3.15. Instead of computing the variables first in the passive, then in the radial and finally in the active zone, the variables are computed along the first "*j*" line in all three zones and then along subsequent "*j*" lines until a "*j*" line ends farther than the point defined by α_m. Then a "*j*" line is interpolated so that it ends up at α_m within the limits of tolerance. This method eliminates most of the time consuming trial and error procedure of finding the length of the passive zone that matches the length of the arc of the active zone. The length of the passive zone in this procedure is initially overestimated so that the last "*j*" line is likely to overshoot the α_m angle. Some iteration on *L*, however, may be necessary if with the initial estimate of *L* the last "*j*" line falls short of the specified end or if the number of "*j*" lines is too low to be acceptable for the desired accuracy. In this scheme, a minimum number of 8 or 9 "*j*" lines is satisfactory.

The length of the passive zone may be estimated by assuming that the

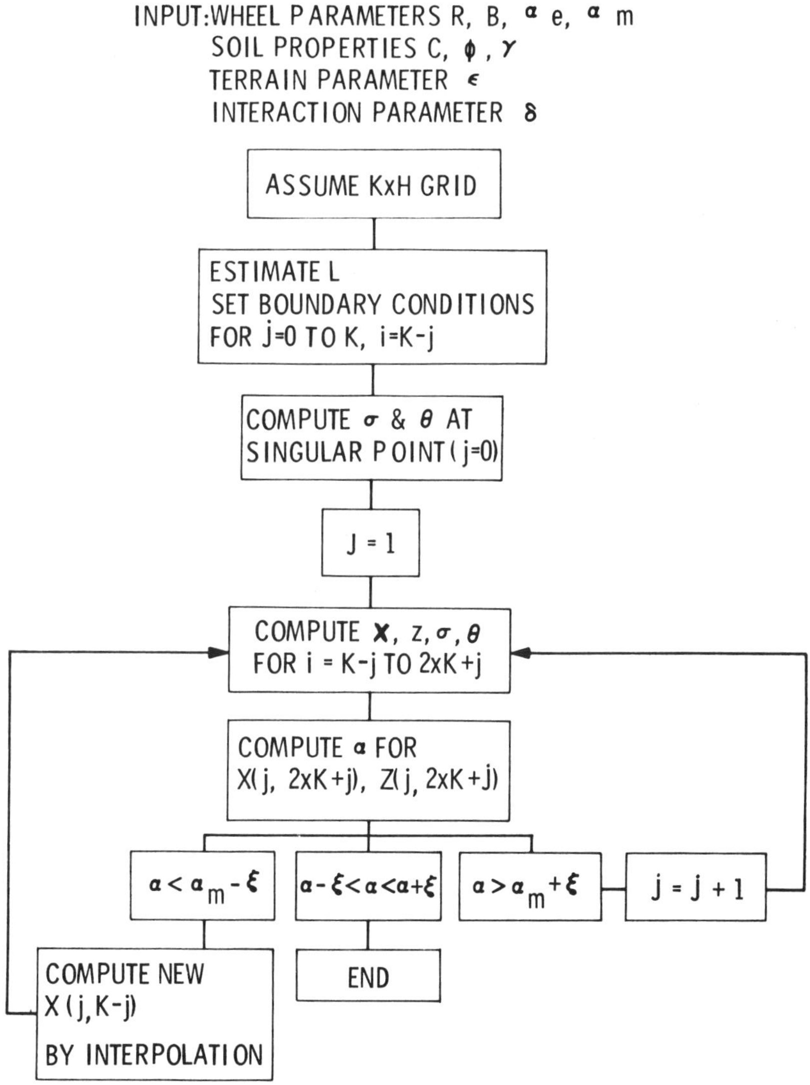

Fig. 3.15
Flow Chart for the Computation of Slip Line Fields with a Variable Number of "*j*" Lines

"j" lines are logarithmic spirals in the radial zone. This assumption yields the following expression for L:

$$L = 2R\,(\alpha_e - \alpha_m)\, e^{(\theta_e - \theta_o)\tan\varphi} \cos\mu \cos(\theta_1 - \varphi) / \cos\varphi$$

$$\theta_1 = \frac{3}{4}\pi + \frac{1}{2}\varphi - \theta_e + \theta_o - \alpha_o \qquad \text{Eq. 3.3.2}$$

where
$\theta_o = \theta$ at the free surface
$\theta_e = \theta$ at the entry point at the interface

For a level unloaded free surface $\theta_o = 0$ and θ_e is computed as follows:

$$\theta_e = \frac{1}{2}\pi + \frac{1}{2}(\Delta + \delta) - \alpha_e \qquad \text{Eq. 3.3.3}$$

where

$$\Delta = \arcsin \frac{\sin\delta}{\sin\varphi}$$

The L length is generally overestimated by Equation 3.3.2. For the constant "j" option it is expedient to use an initial value of L smaller than that given by Equation 3.3.2 by a factor of 0.75, and for the variable "j" option a larger one by a factor of 1.5.

The computations start at the free surface, where boundary conditions for all four variables have to be specified. In the grid system shown in Figures 3.13 and 3.14, the points at the free boundary are designated by the following subscripts:

$$i = K - j$$
$$j = j$$

In the coordinate system shown in the figures, the "z" coordinates of all points at the free surface equal zero. (If the free surface is not level, as in the case of bow waves, z varies.) The x coordinates of the i, j points at the surface are obtained by assuming equal spacing within the L distance. For increased accuracy in the neighborhood of the singular point it is advantageous to use half spacing for the first two "j" lines.

The value of θ may be assumed as zero for all points on an unloaded free surface. The value of σ equals

$$\sigma = c\cot\varphi/(1 - \sin\varphi) \qquad \text{Eq. 3.3.4}$$

The singular point (Figures 3.13 and 3.14) is common to both the free surface and the wheel-soil interface. It may be considered as a degenerate "j" line with vanishing length. Along this degenerate "j" line the θ value changes from its value at the free surface to that at the entry point at the interface. This latter θ value, designated as θ_e, has been determined previously for the purpose of estimating the L length by Equation 3.3.2. For the purpose of numerical computations the total change of θ along the degenerate "j" line is divided by K, the number of "i" lines in the radial zone so that the θ increment between subsequently numbered "i" lines may be obtained. The value of σ for each of these "i" lines is computed from the incremented θ value the same way as in the case of bearing capacity from equation

$$\sigma = \sigma_o \, e^{2 \tan \varphi \, (\theta - \theta_o)} \qquad \text{Eq. 3.3.5}$$

where the subscript zero denotes values at the free surface. (It is noted that there is no compelling reason to have the same number of "i" lines in the radial zone than in the other zones. Actually, it would be possible to devise computational schemes where the number of "i" lines in the radial zone would change according to the change in the value of θ at the singular point.)

The case $c = 0$ presents difficulties for the computation of the stresses at the singular point. To circumvent this problem it is practicable to assign a small minimum value for c, such as 0.2 lb/sq ft. Since even so-called cohesionless soils exhibit a very small, often hardly measurable, cohesion due to capillary water forces, the assumption of a very small cohesion is reasonable and eliminates a problem in the numerical calculation.

The wheel-soil interface is the boundary where the normal and shear stresses have to be determined for the solution of the interaction problem. According to the numbering system established in Figures 3.13 and 3.14, the following i, j values pertain to the interface:

$$i = j + 2K$$
$$j = j$$

The boundary conditions for these points are of the mixed boundary value type where two of the four variables have to be specified. However, in the wheel problem instead of the "z" coordinate being specified, as in the bearing capacity problem, the relation between "x" and "z" is specified by the condition that they must lie on the circle with radius R.

For numerical computations the circle is approximated by its tangent allowing the use of the following difference equations:

$$x_{i,j} = \frac{1}{1+a_o F}\, x_{i-1,j} + a_o F\, x_{i-1,j-1} + a_o\,(z_{i-1,j-1} - z_{i-1,j})$$

$$z_{i,j} = z_{i-1,j-1} + F\,(x_{i-1,j-1} - x_{i,j})$$

$$\sigma_{i,j} = \sigma_{i-1,j} + 2\tan\varphi\,\sigma_{i-1,j}\,(\theta_{i,j} - \theta_{i-1,j}) + \gamma C \qquad \text{Eqs. 3.3.6}$$

where

$$a_o = \operatorname{cotan}\left(\frac{1}{2}(\theta_{i,j-1} + \theta_{i,j}) - \mu\right)$$

$$F = \tan a_{i-1,j-1}$$

$$C = \frac{\sin(\varepsilon - \varphi)}{\cos\varphi}(x_{i,j} - x_{i-1,j}) + \frac{\cos(\varepsilon - \varphi)}{\cos\varphi}(z_{i,j} - z_{i-1,j})$$

In these equations, $\theta_{i,j}$ is the direction (with reference to the free surface) of the major principal stress at an i, j point at the interface. The value of $\theta_{i,j}$ at the interface is determined from the following equation:

$$\theta = \frac{\pi}{2} + \frac{1}{2}(\Delta + \delta) - \alpha \qquad \text{Eq. 3.3.7}$$

where

$$\Delta = \arcsin\left(\frac{\sin\delta}{\sin\varphi}\right)$$

The θ value for $\alpha = \alpha_e$ or $\alpha = \alpha_r$ obtained from Equation 3.3.3 is also used for the computation of the stresses at the singular point by Equation 3.3.5.

Computation of a Matching Set of Slip Line Fields for Wheel-Soil Interaction Problems

There are several ways to compute a pair of slip line fields that meet the conditions set forth in the concept of interaction and additional assumptions discussed in Section 3.3.2. The authors found the most expedient way to be the one discussed below.

The value of the rear angle α_r is assumed and the rear field computed first. The rear field is the mirror image of the slip line field shown in Figure 3.13. The α_m angle is negative for this case. The absolute value of the α_m angle is computed from Equation 3.3.1 and the normal stress q_{mr} at this angle determined. The coordinates of the wheel axis are computed and preserved to serve as a common reference point for both the forward and rear slip line fields. As noted above, the rear slip line field's coordinate system is a mirror image of the front one shifted in the "z" direction by the rut depth. An entry angle α_e is assumed and the front slip line field is computed. The normal stress at α_m computed from the front field (q_{mf}) is compared to that computed from the rear field (q_{mr}) and an iteration on the entry angle is performed until q_{mf} matches q_{mr} within a specified tolerance limit. The scheme of the computation is shown in Figure 3.16. A reasonable tolerance has been found to be $\pm$ 5 % of q_{mr}. Once the entry angle has been determined, the slip line field computations have been completed. The numerical integration of the interface stresses yields the load, drawbar pull and torque. The corresponding slip is computed from the interface friction angle δ by inverting Equation 3.3.6 as follows:

$$j = -K \text{ lognat} \left(1 - \frac{\tan \delta}{\tan \delta_{max}}\right) - j_0 \qquad \text{Eq. 3.3.8}$$

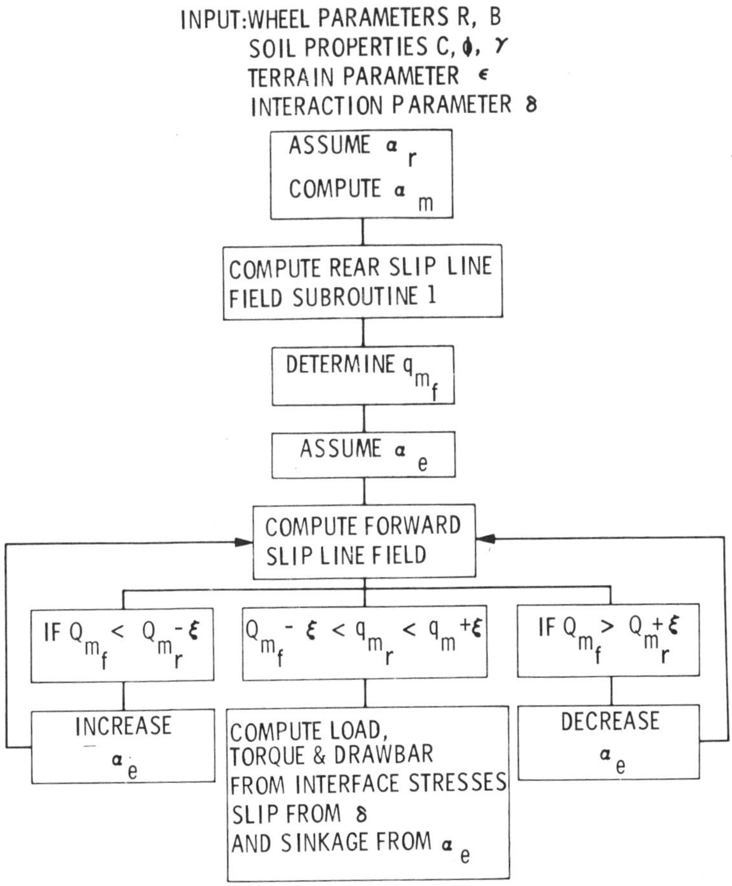

Fig. 3.16
Flow Chart for the Computation of a Matching Set of Slip Line Fields

The sinkage and rut depth are determined from the entry and rear angles.

The difference Equations 3.3.6 yield the value of σ at the i, j points at the interface. For the interaction problem the normal and shear stresses are needed at these points. These are computed as follows:

$$\sigma_n = (\cos\delta + \sqrt{\cos^2\delta - \cos^2\varphi})\cos\delta\cdot\sigma - \psi \qquad \text{Eq. 3.3.9a}$$
$$\tau = (\sigma_n + \psi)\tan\delta \qquad \text{Eq. 3.3.9b}$$

If the computation of a single slip line field (forward and rear) is performed in a subroutine, then it is convenient to transmit only the values computed for the interface to the main program where these data can be stored until the data from the matching slip line field becomes available.

Geometries of matching sets of slip line fields, as determined for the various conditions shown in Table 3.1 by the computing procedure outlined previously, are shown in Figure 3.17. The figures shown were obtained directly from a computer graphics system. In an optional subroutine program the x, z coordinates of the nodal points of the final slip line fields were recorded, in an appropriate sequence, in data files. A plotting program projected the slip line fields represented by these nodal point coordinates on the screen of an advanced remote control visual display terminal, manufactured by Computer Displays, Inc. The pictures of the slip line fields shown in Figure 3.17 are photographic reproductions of the displays.

The use of computer graphics is strongly recommended for the display of slip line field geometries obtained in the computer programs. They provide the user with a visual perceptiveness of a problem's solution as well as a check on numerical computations. Displays of slip line fields are an excellent tool in program developing since errors in the numerical computations usually result in irregularities in the slip line field that are easily detected by visual inspection. The costs in time and material of obtaining numerical printouts are also circumvented.

The slip line fields indicate zones in the soil mass where the soil is in the state of plastic equilibrium and conditions of incipient failure pertain. Another way to illustrate the stress state in the soil within the slip line field is to show the variation of principal stresses and their directions. Vectorial representations of the principal stresses and their directions at selected nodal points of a matching set of slip line fields beneath a rigid wheel is shown in Figure 1.38. The directions of the major principal stresses are obtained directly in the computer program, while the magnitudes of the major and minor principal stresses are readily computed from

TABLE 3.1
Loading Conditions and Soil Properties for the Slip Line Fields Shown in Figure 3.17

			Slip Line Fields					
			a	b	c	d	e	f
Wheel Radius		ft	1.67	1.67	1.67	2.04	0.87	0.87
Wheel Width		ft	1.0	1.0	1.0	1.0	0.5	0.5
Load		lb	1460	700	480	2085	300	300
Drawbar Pull		lb	200	27	68	–880	5	10
Soil Strength	c	lb/sq ft	10	10	10	14.4	0	0
in	φ	degree	35	35	35	34	38	39
Front Field	γ	lb/cu ft	96	96	16*	100	100	100
Soil Strength	c	lb/sq ft	10	10	10	2.9	0	0
in	φ	degree	38	38	38	31	40	40
Rear Field	γ	lb/cu ft	96	96	16*	100	110	110
Interface Friction Angle	δ	degree	24	30	24	N.A.	24	14

* lunar conditions.

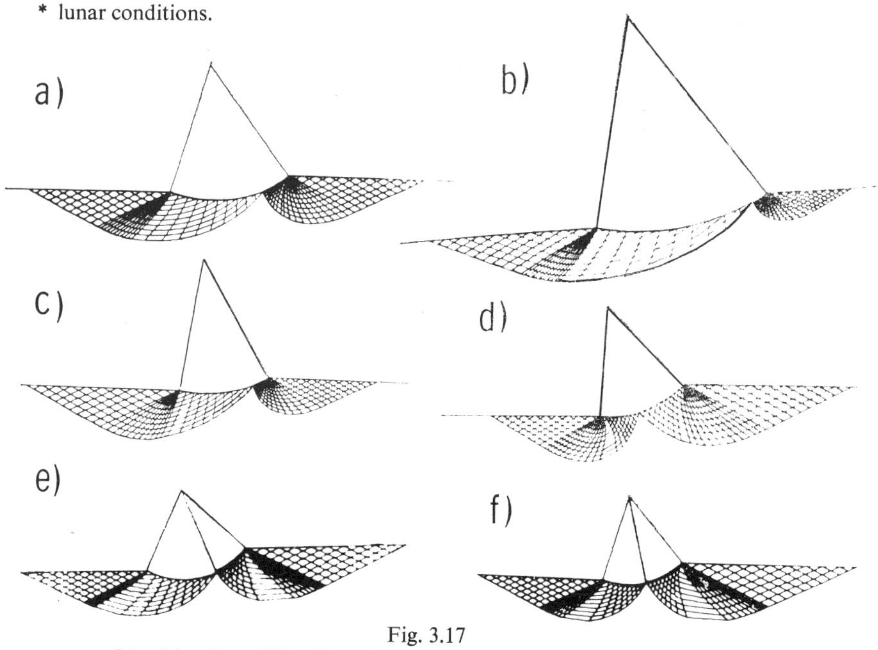

Fig. 3.17
Matching Set of Slip Line Fields for Conditions Shown in Table 3.1.
a), d) through f) = level terrain b) = 12° slope, c) = lunar conditions, level terrain

the σ value. The figure has also been prepared by using computer graphics. Note the growth of the major principal stress vector from the free surface toward the wheel as its direction changes from the horizontal to nearly normal orientation with the rigid wheel surface along the interface. The orientation at the interface is a function of δ, as has been discussed previously.

Solution of the Wheel-Soil Interaction Problem for a Given Load

A complete solution of the wheel-soil interaction problem for a constant load is usually presented in parametric form as a function of slip. Figure 3.18 shows a typical parametric plot of pull and torque performance for a constant load and for the full range of slip of interest. Indicated in the figure are often used terms of wheel performance: the self propelled point (zero pull), the free rolling point (zero torque), the maximum pull and zero slip points. Since the interface friction angle, δ, and slip are related by Equation 3.2.8, the slip axis may be substituted by a δ axis. As an example, δ values corresponding to $\varphi = 35°$, $j_o = 0.05$ and $K = 0.20$ are shown on the lower scale in the plot.

In an actual case, the performance curves are curve fittings to points determined by experiments or theory. Whether the problem involves the determination of the drawbar pull for a given torque or vice versa, if the performance curves are available, one can proceed from the value given to the respective curve, determine the corresponding slip and read the performance value sought from the other curve. If points of these performance curves are determined by a computer program, it is natural to elect an iteration procedure for the solution of a particular problem instead of making a plot of these performance curves. In regard to devising such an iteration scheme the following comments are pertinent.

The computation of a matching set of slip line fields for a wheel-soil interaction problem yields the interface stresses and, by integration, the wheel load, torque and drawbar pull values for an assumed rear angle α_r and interface friction angle δ. Thus the load, torque and drawbar pull are parametric functions of α_r and δ and may be expressed as follows:

$$L = f_1(\alpha_r, \delta) \qquad \text{Eq. 3.3.10a}$$
$$DB = f_2(\alpha_r, \delta) \qquad \text{Eq. 3.3.10b}$$
$$T = f_3(\alpha_r, \delta) \qquad \text{Eq. 3.3.10c}$$

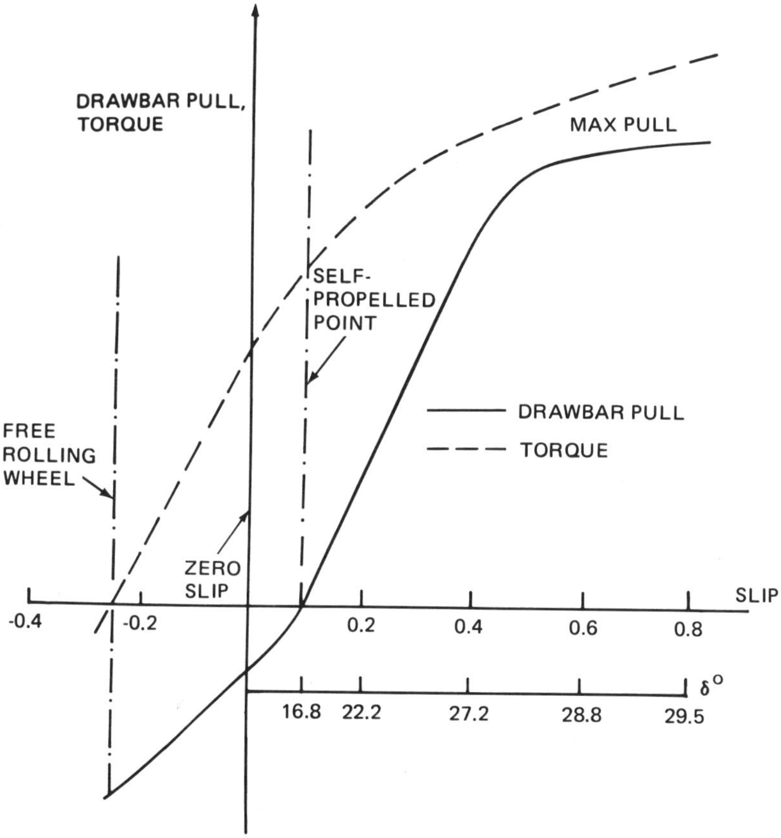

Fig. 3.18

Pull and Torque Performance as a Function of Slip (Example)

The functions f_1, f_2 and f_3 are not closed form functions. Even if they were, finding α_r and δ for given L and DB (or alternatively for T) would require the solution of a system of two nonlinear equations. Since there is no generally valid theorem for the solution of this problem, and convergence criteria for iterative solutions cannot be established unless the derivatives of f_1, f_2 (or for the alternative problem f_3) are known, it is necessary to make use of some features that these functions exhibit.

There are two properties of the wheel performance relationships expressed by Equations 3.3.10 that are useful for the solution of the inverted problem, that is finding the α_r and δ values if two of the three dependent variables in Equations 3.3.10 are given. First, the wheel load increases monotonically with the rear angle for a constant angle of interface friction. Second, the pull coefficient $\omega = DB/L$, often used as a dimensionless parameter in wheel performance studies, was found to increase monotonically with the angle of interface friction within the range of δ values of interest. In the inversion procedure, these two relationships constitute the basis for the iteration scheme that is shown schematically in Figure 3.19. The λ values in the figure are load coefficients defined as $\lambda = L/L_o$, where L_o is the design load.

In the iteration scheme ξ denotes the tolerance that is expressed in terms of the pull and load coefficient, and as such is a dimensionless number. For the load coefficient a tolerance limit of $\xi = \pm 0.05$ is usually appropriate since a 5 % difference in load is not likely to cause a major change in the pull coefficient. The proper selection of the tolerance limit for the pull coefficient is a more difficult problem. If the expected value of the pull coefficient is low, say less than 0.2, then a tolerance limit of $\xi = \pm 0.02$ may be appropriate. A tolerance limit of $\xi = \pm 0.05$ may be selected when the pull coefficient is expected to be above 0.2. These values were found to represent a good balance between computer run time and accuracy. These figures serve for general information only; in each case the tolerance limits should be determined on the basis of their merits for the particular computation.

The "*o*" subscript designates the values for which the solution is to be found in the iteration scheme. The λ_o value generally equals one, although exceptionally $1 - \xi$ may be used, if convergence from one direction is desired.

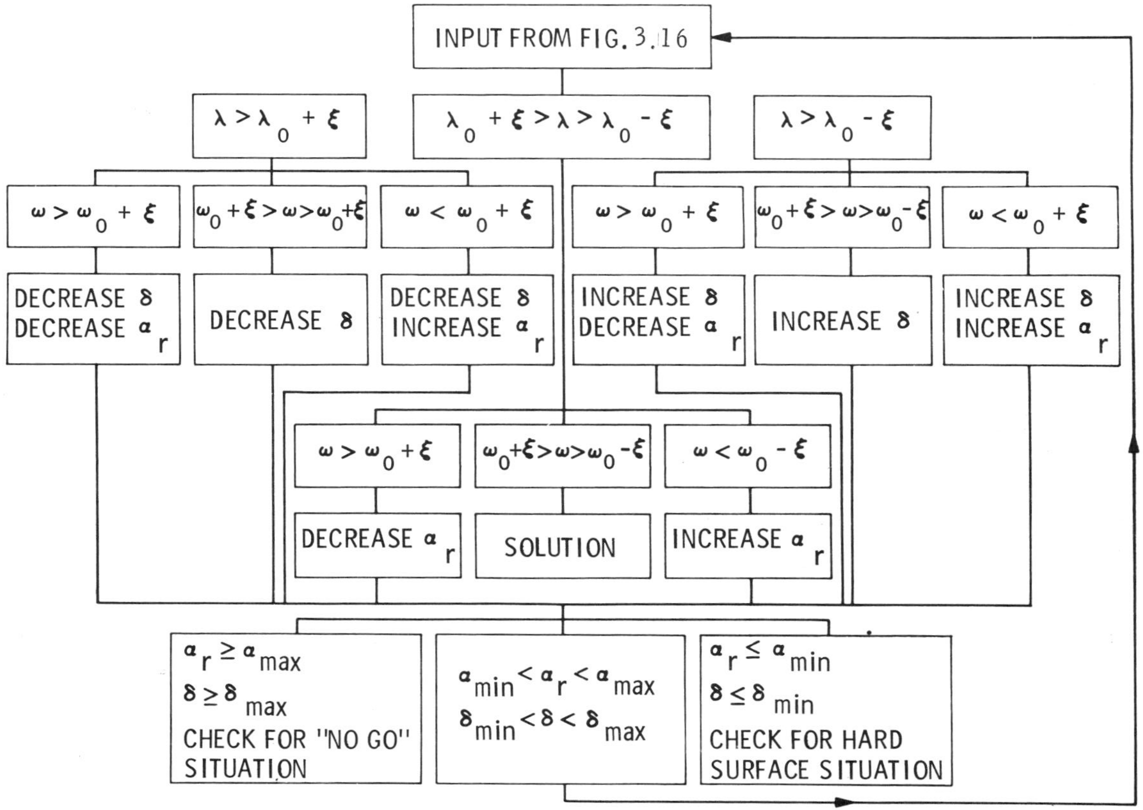

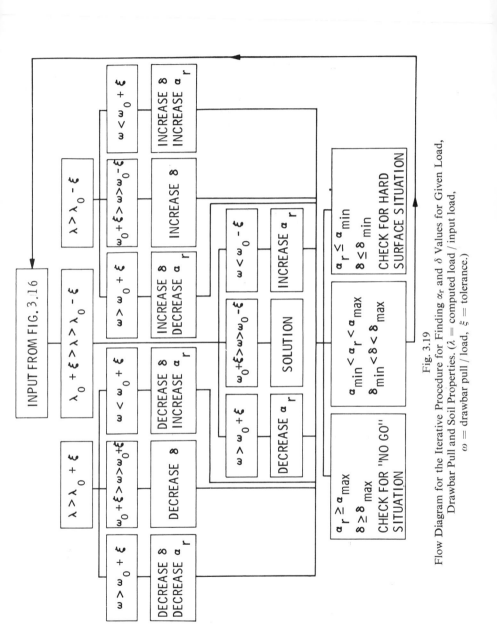

Fig. 3.19
Flow Diagram for the Iterative Procedure for Finding α_r and δ Values for Given Load, Drawbar Pull and Soil Properties. (λ = computed load / input load, ω = drawbar pull / load, ξ = tolerance.)

3.3.4 General Relationships Between the Applied Wheel Loads and the α_r and δ Angles

Performance relationships as shown in Figure 3.18 can be easily established by the computerized wheel-soil model for any desired combination of the input parameters. Such relationships are shown for a variety of conditions in Chapter 3.4.3 for the illustration of the performance of pneumatic tires.

For the appreciation of the role of the α_r and δ angles in rigid wheel-soil interaction another form of presentation of the general relationships that exist among the wheel forces and these angles is called for. In Figures 3.20 and 3.21 the relationships $L = f_1\ (\alpha_r, \delta)$ and $DB = f_2\ (\alpha_r, \delta)$ are shown, respectively, in isometric presentation for the following conditions:

Wheel geometry:	Radius	$R = 1.5$ ft
	Width	$B = 0.36$ ft
Soil Properties:	Forward Field:	$c = 0$, $\varphi = 38°$,
		$\gamma = 100$ lbs/cu ft
	Rear Field:	$c = 0$, $\varphi = 41°$,
		$\gamma = 110$ lbs/cu ft

The axes in the horizontal plane are the interface friction angle, δ, and the rear angle α_r. The vertical axis shows the load in Figure 3.20 and the drawbar pull in Figure 3.21. The δ axis can also be thought of as a slip axis, since δ and slip are related by Equation 3.2.8.

The figures help to understand the complicated parametric relationships $L = f_1\ (\alpha_r, \delta)$ and $DB = f_2\ (\alpha_r, \delta)$ referred to in the previous section. The surface shown by its contourlines in Figure 3.20 represents the variation of the load with the δ and α_r angles. A constant load is represented by a plane, as shown for a load of $L = 250$ lbs in Figure 3.20. The intersection of a plane for a constant load with the load surface is a curve in that plane. Each point of this curve represents a combination of the δ and α_r values that yield the constant load that the plane indicates.

The following features of the relationship $L = f_1\ (\alpha_r, \delta)$ illustrated in Figure 3.20 are noted:

a) Each of the contourlines of the load surface yields a lower load for any given δ angle than the contourline drawn for the next positively incremented α_r angle. This indicates that the load increases monotonically with the α_r angle.

b) There is an optimum δ angle for which the load carrying capacity of the wheel is highest. With the increase of the α_r angle this

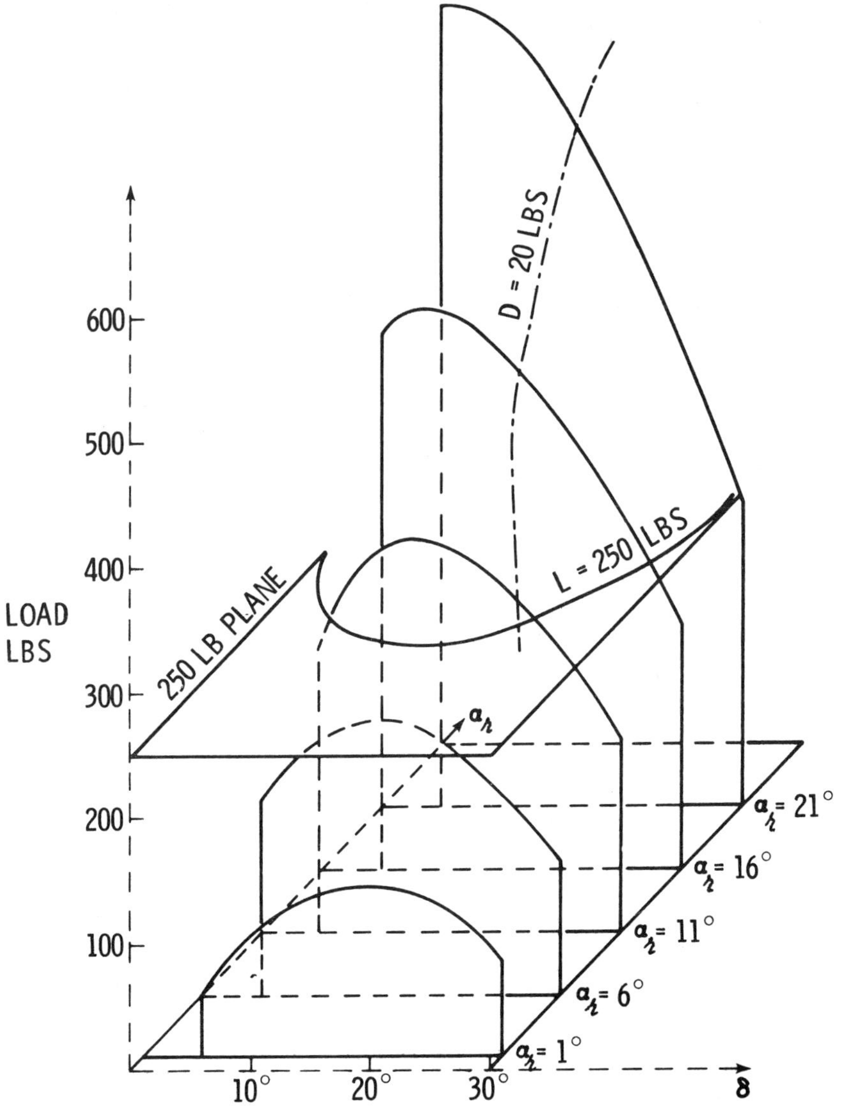

Fig. 3.20
Isometric View of the $L = f_1(\alpha_r, \delta)$ Relationship

optimum value of the δ angle becomes smaller. An examination of the drawbar pull values illustrated in Figure 3.21 shows that δ angles that are smaller than the optimum value yield a negative drawbar pull and, therefore, are not relevant to the problem of driven wheel performance for conditions beyond the self-propelled point. Thus, it can be said that for all practical purposes the load carrying capacity of a driven wheel decreases with an increase of the interface friction angle, δ, or slip.

c) The load-rear angle relationship shown in parametric form in Figure 3.20 also demonstrates that the assumption of an $\alpha_r = 0$ angle, often proposed for the convenience of computations, is an untenable simplification. The load carrying capacity of the wheel is profoundly affected by the rear angle; restricting the value of α_r to zero is an unacceptable limitation that would result in serious underestimation of the wheel performance.

From the isometric view of the $DB = f_2(\alpha_r, \delta)$ relationship shown in Figure 3.21 the following general conclusions may be drawn:

a) The surface represented by the contourlines of drawbar pull drawn for constant α_r values is a warped one. However, the drawbar pull generally increases with the δ angle except when the values of both δ and α_r are high (upper right corner of the figure).

b) A plane representing in the isometric view a constant value of the drawbar pull (in Figure 3.21 20 lbs) intersects the drawbar pull surface along a curve. Each point of this curve denotes a combination of the δ and α_r values that yields that particular drawbar pull. It is interesting to note that, at least for the conditions the figure was prepared for, a minimum α_r angle of about 15° is needed to realize the 20 lbs drawbar pull. Evidently, any wheel-soil interaction concept based on the assumption of $\alpha_r = 0$ is unsuitable for the prediction of drawbar pull in this range.

The graphical illustration of the parametric relationships $L = f_1(\alpha_r, \delta)$ and $DB = f_2(\alpha_r, \delta)$ shows the problems involved with iteration schemes designed to solve the inverse problem of finding the α_r and δ values for given L and DB. In Figure 3.20 the curve obtained by intersecting the load surface with the 250 lb plane was shown, while in Figure 3.21 a similar curve was shown for $DB = 20$ lbs. Both of these curves may be plotted in the same α_r, δ coordinate system as shown in Figure 3.22. The solution for the inverted problem is the intersection of these curves. The curve for $DB = 20$ lbs was also plotted in Figure 3.22 by a dash-dot line representing the loci of those points at the load surface that pertain

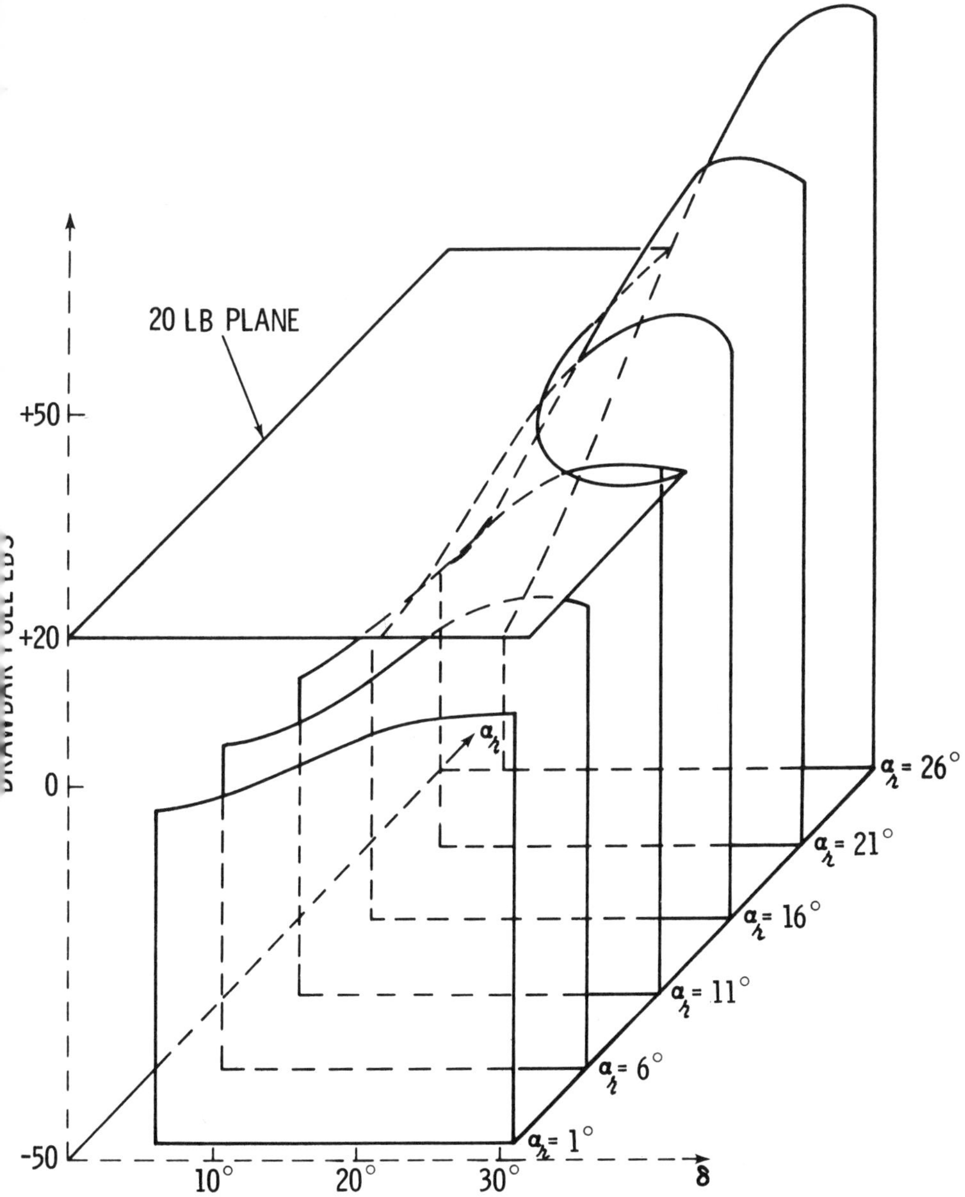

Fig. 3.21
Isometric View of the $DB = f_2\ (\alpha_r,\ \delta)$ Relationship

to the α_r and δ values defined by the $DB = 20$ lbs curve. In this figure the solution of the inverted problem appears as the intersection of the dash-dot and solid curves.

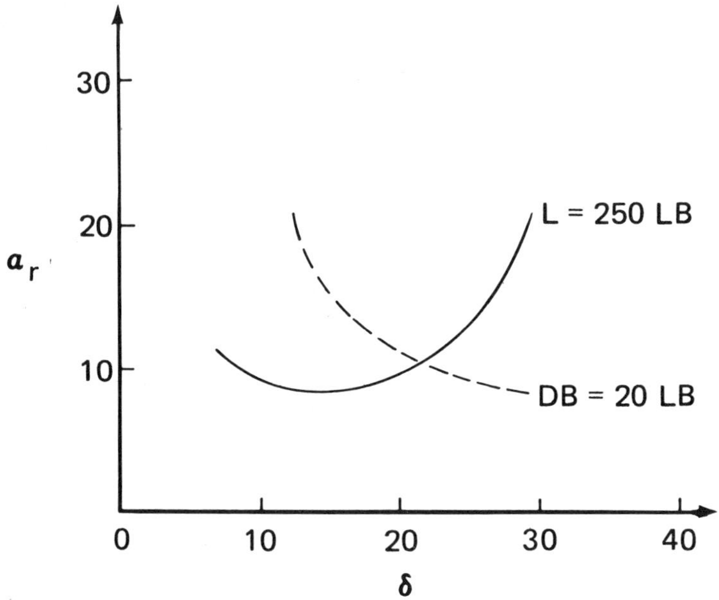

Fig. 3.22
The Relationship $L = 250$ lb $= f_1(\alpha_r, \delta)$ and $DB = 20$ lb $= f_2(\alpha_r, \delta)$

3.3.5 Comparison of Wheel Performance Predictions with Experiments

In the development of the concept of wheel-soil interaction much reliance was placed on the experimental information available *a priori* from various sources. In adapting the concept to a working model of wheel-soil interaction suitable for computer programming, interim results of computations obtained at various stages of the adaptation were regularly compared with experimental data. Furthermore, certain assumptions were applied to the original concept on the basis of experiments to facilitate the solution procedures for the various problems of mobility. Since these experiments were performed for purposes different from that of concept validation, it is understandable that direct data on parameters essential to the evaluation of the concept were often not available. Therefore information, such as strength properties of the soil, either had to be estimated from other data or determined subsequently, as was done for the Detroit sand used in SELA's experiments (SELA (1964); KARAFIATH et al (1973)). An experimental program set up for the purpose of validating the concept was obviously called for. Such a program was performed at the Stevens Institute of Technology, Hoboken, New Jersey, under the sponsorship of TACOM in 1972. Results obtained in this experimental program have been reported in detail for 56 validation tests by KARAFIATH et al (1973). A summary evaluation of these results is given here.

In the validation test program slip-controlled wheel performance tests were conducted in the 40 ft. long mobility bin of the Stevens Institute of Technology. In the tests wheel load, torque and drawbar pull were measured by dynamometers. Interface normal and shear stresses were also measured by strain gauges specifically designed for this purpose. These were installed on the perimeter of the 28 in. diameter, $4^1/_2$ in. wide plywood wheel as shown in Figure 3.23. With this arrangement of the strain gauges it was possible to measure both the longitudinal and lateral distribution of stresses during wheel movement through the soil. The recorded interface stresses were integrated numerically by a computer program and the resultants compared with the total applied forces measured by the dynamometers.

The following three types of soil beds were used in the tests:

a) Loose sand

b) Dense sand

c) Loam.

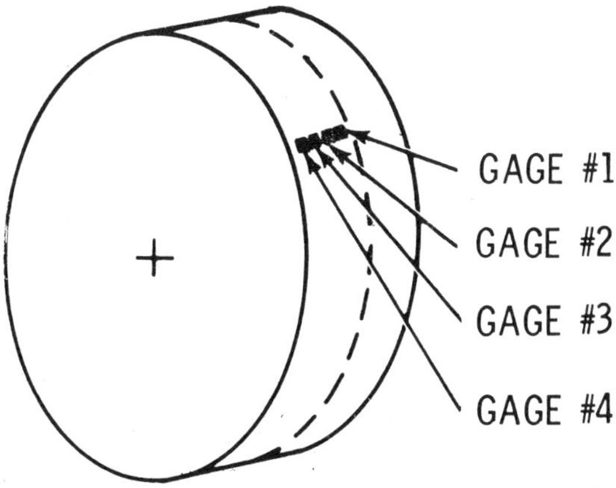

Fig. 3.23
Arrangement of Strain Gages at the Perimeter of the Test Wheel for the Measurement of Normal and Shear Stresses

The sand beds were prepared in air dry condition and the loam beds at a moisture content of approximately 16 % at which the loam exhibited sufficient cohesion and friction to qualify as a cohesive-frictional soil. The strength properties of the soil were determined by triaxial tests for various densities and moisture contents in the Soils Research Laboratory at the Grumman Aerospace Corporation, Bethpage, New York. Cone penetrometer tests were performed both in the laboratory under controlled density and moisture conditions and in the soil bed before and after each wheel performance test. The strength properties of the soil bed for any

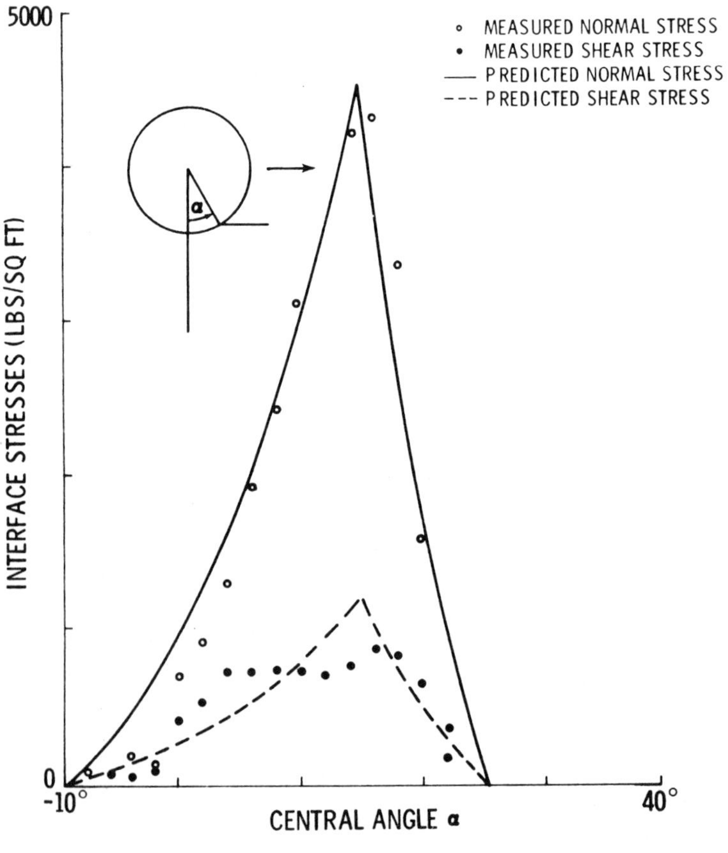

Fig. 3.24
Comparison of Measured and Computed Interface Stresses for a 1.15 ft. Diameter, 0.36 ft. Wide Driven Wheel in Sand (28 % Slip)

particular density were established by correlation to the cone penetrometer test data.

The 56 validation tests performed in this testing program offered a comparison not only between the predicted and measured wheel forces, but also between the predicted and measured interface stresses. The latter comparison served as a general validation of the use of plasticity theory for the determination of stress states in soil in general, and also as a particular validation of the authors' method of computation of interface stresses in wheel-soil interaction. Typical results of this stress distribution comparison are shown in Figures 3.24 and 3.25 where the average of the

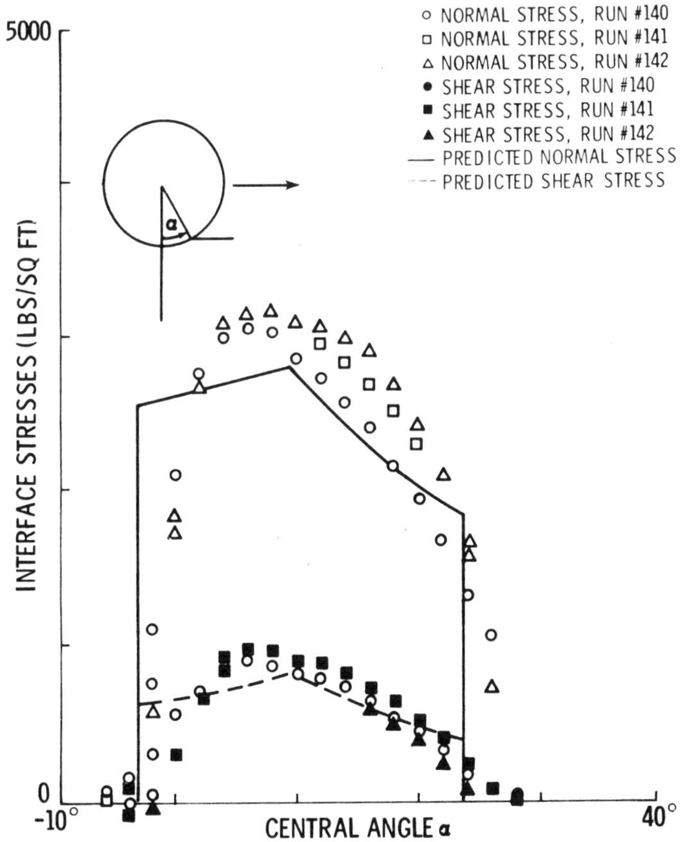

Fig. 3.25
Comparison of Measured and Computed Interface Stresses for a 1.15 ft. Diameter, 0.36 ft. Wide Driven Wheel in Clay (—6% Slip)

interface normal and shear stresses measured by the four strain gauges is compared with the predicted values for cohesionless and cohesive-frictional soils, respectively. These figures show good agreement between experiment and theory. A detailed examination of all test results showed that there were two areas where discrepancies between predictions and measurements consistently occurred that were not attributable to random experimental or computational errors. The causes and significance of these discrepancies in these two areas are evaluated as follows:

a) The predicted stress distribution curves for the front and rear field join in a cusp at the angle of separation. The stress distribution curves obtained in the experiments show a rather smooth transition at this point. Whether this smoothness is due to some inertial lag in the instrumentation or some adjustment in the soil that is not accounted for in the theory could not be ascertained. Since the observed discrepancies between predicted and measured values are confined to a small area and since the "point" discrepancy becomes rather insignificant when integration is performed to obtain computed wheel forces, the question is mainly of academic interest and does not affect prediction results appreciably.

b) In cohesive soils, the theory predicts an instantaneous rise of the interface stresses at the entry and rear angles (Figure 3.25). The observed stress rise, though rapid, is not instantaneous. This discrepancy between theory and experiments is the consequence of using the MOHR-COULOMB yield criterion in plasticity theory irrespective of the volumetric strain that is associated with the yield strength of soil. In the prediction method, a stress distribution that features an instantaneous rise of stresses in cohesive soils results in a somewhat smaller entry angle than what occurs with the actual distribution. Fortunately, this discrepancy causes but minor inaccuracies in the computed wheel forces. The use of a nonlinear strength envelope obtained by the method of strain dependent chamber pressure type triaxial tests, discussed in Chapter 1.3.5, would at least partially eliminate this problem. The use of nonlinear strength envelopes in wheel-soil interaction problems is discussed in Section 3.3.8.

The results of the validation tests were also analyzed with respect to the basic assumptions of the theoretical concept. Specifically, the measurements of the stresses in these tests made it possible to examine how well the assumption of two-dimensional conditions and that of a constant interface friction angle approximated the actual conditions. The use of four strain gauges across the width of the wheel allowed the evaluation of the transverse distribution of interface stresses; a comparison with the uniform transverse distribution postulated in the two-dimensional model could threreby be made. The simultaneous measurement of the interface normal and shear stresses allowed the evaluation of the interface friction angle for the various central angle positions of the strain gauges; the variation of this angle along the contact area could thereby be determined. The results of these evaluations are summarized as follows.

In the tests performed in loose sand, the distribution of stresses across the wheel was reasonably uniform. A typical example of such a distribution is shown in Figure 3.26.

In the tests performed in dense sand, the transverse distribution of stresses was found to conform with the hypothesis that there is a limiting

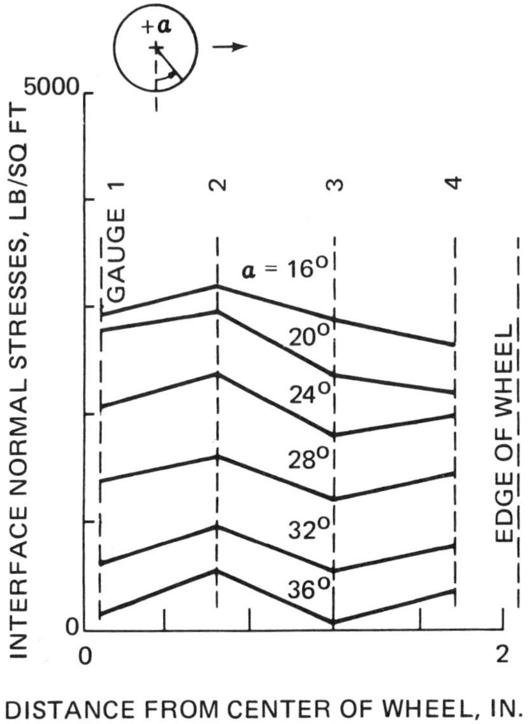

Fig. 3.26
Transverse Distribution of Normal Stresses at Central Angles from 16° to 36°.
Loose Sand

transverse distribution governed by potential lateral failure. This hypothesis is illustrated in a simplified way in Figure 3.27 and is discussed in more detail in connection with the problem of dual wheels in Section 3.3.7. In granular soils, this limit is approximately linear and varies with the depth of the cross section beneath the surface. Stresses computed from the conditions in the plane of travel may not exceed this limit set by the transverse conditions. Figure 3.28 shows an example where the transverse limiting condition governs the stresses across the full width of the wheel and Figure 3.29 exemplifies a case where the transverse limiting conditions govern in that portion of the wheel that is close to the side while in the center portion the longitudinal conditions govern.

In the tests performed in the loam, the transverse distribution of stresses was found to have been influenced by the condition of uniform vertical displacement in any vertical transverse cross-section, as shown in Figure 3.27, imposed on the soil by the rigidity of the wheel. These conditions require that the stresses at the edges of the loaded area be higher than in the center. A typical transverse distribution of normal stresses in loam is shown in Figure 3.30. This type of transverse distribution also indicates that in this direction the soil is far from being in the failure state; transverse limiting conditions in cohesive soils are rarely critical.

The consideration of lateral failure conditions and the ensuing non-uniform transverse distribution of stresses is especially important in the case of dual or multiple wheel arrangements. Conceptual formulation of

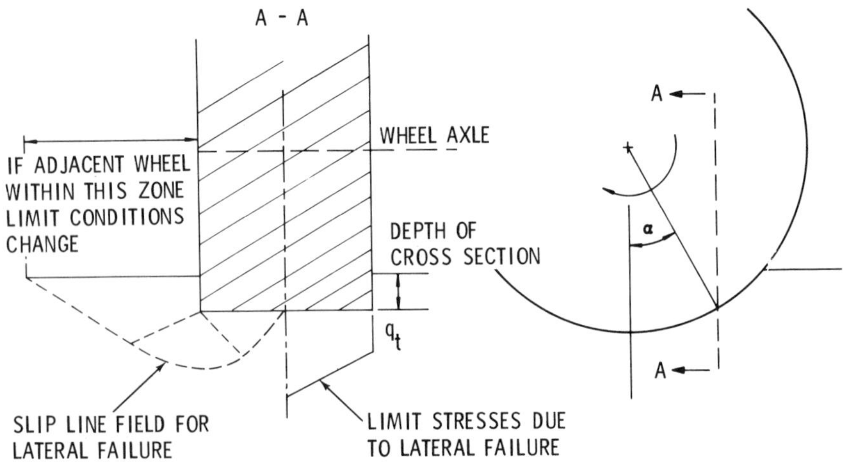

Fig. 3.27
Limiting Normal Stresses Due to Lateral Failure

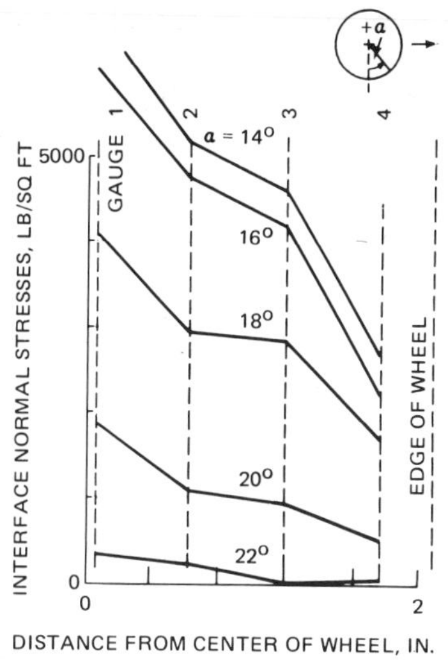

Fig. 3.28
Transverse Distribution of Normal Stresses at Central Angles from 14° to 22°.
Driven Wheel in Dense Sand
Load = 486 lb., Drawbar Pull = 51 lb.

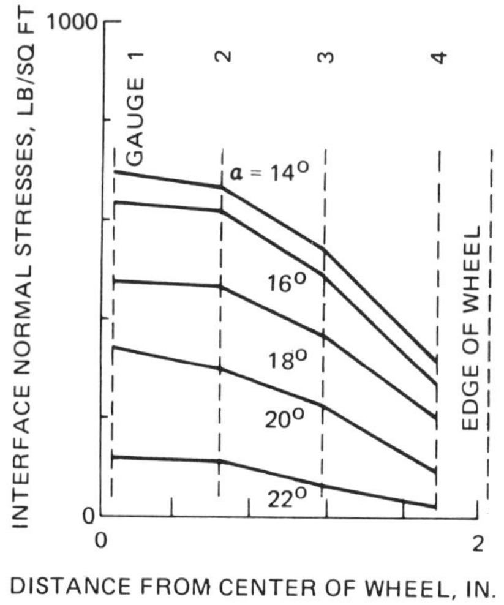

Fig. 3.29
Transverse Distribution of Normal Stresses at Central Angles from 14° to 22°.
Driven Wheel in Dense Sand
Load = 576 lb., Drawbar Pull = 2 lb.

the consideration of lateral failure conditions in wheel-soil interaction is discussed in that context in Section 3.3.7.

From the evaluation of the variation of the interface friction angle observed in the validation tests the following general conclusions may be drawn. In loose sand, with some exceptions, the assumption of a constant interface friction angle appears to be a reasonable approximation. A typical case is illustrated in Figure 3.31. No curve is drawn in but the general "constant" trend is apparent. The exceptions are where the interface friction angle decreases from the entry and rear angles toward the center, a distribution that was found typical of the tests performed in dense sand. A typical example of such a variation of the interface friction angle is shown in Figure 3.32. In the loam, the variation of the interface friction angle along the contact area was found to be different from either that typical of loose sand or that typical of dense sand. The characteristic feature of the variation of the interface friction angle in loam, an example of which is shown in Figure 3.33, is that the highest value of δ occurs at $\alpha = 0°$, the bottommost part of the wheel. A tentative explanation of this feature is that the development of interface friction in the highly compressible loam is associated with the volumetric straining of the soil that is obviously greatest at the bottom part of the wheel.

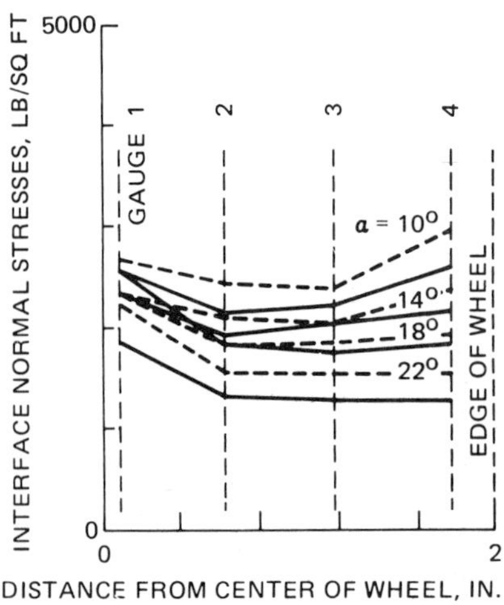

Fig. 3.30
Transverse Distribution of Normal Stresses at Central Angles from 10° to 24°. Driven Wheel in Loam

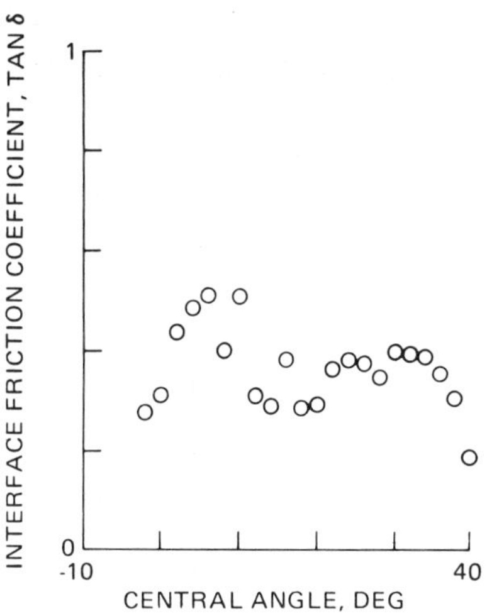

Fig. 3.31
Variation of the Interface Friction Coefficient, tan δ, Along the Wheel Interface in Dense Sand. Load = 402 lb. Drawbar Pull = 6 lb. Torque = 157 ft-lb.

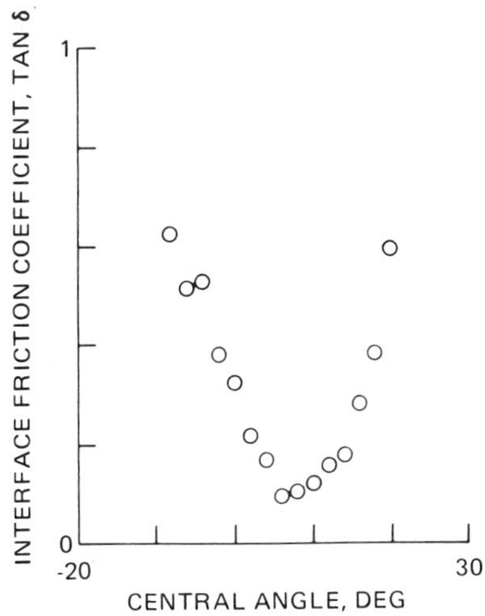

Fig. 3.32
Variation of the Interface Friction Coefficient, tan δ, Along the Wheel Interface in Dense Sand. Load = 535 lb. Drawbar Pull = 25 lb. Torque = 124 ft-lb.

These experimental data indicate that the interface friction angle, δ, is approximately constant only in certain cases while in other cases it varies along the interface. While it would not present any difficulties to include provisions in the numerical computation of the slip line fields that would allow for either a linear or a nonlinear variation of the δ angle along the interface, the experimental information on this variation is not sufficiently well defined to formulate meaningful empirical relationships between the variation of δ and soil properties for the various loading conditions. Consequently, at this time, the assumption of a constant δ angle is recommended for predictive purposes in lieu of anything better. Theoretical research is in progress, however, to lay the basis for the development of such relationships by establishing the kinematic boundary conditions at the interface. Interim results of this research are presented in Section 3.3.6.

Another reason for further research in this area is the connection between the angle δ and the angle of separation, α_m. In the computations the assumption is made that α_m is defined by Equation 3.3.1 which, in the case of cohesionless soils, reduces to $\alpha_m = \delta$. In the development of this equation δ was tacitly assumed as constant. If δ varies along the interface, then the value of α_m may become indefinite and difficulties would arise in the computational scheme. A review of performance predictions based on a constant δ and α_m calculated from Equation 3.3.1 indicated that in most cases where prediction accuracy was not good, the maximum normal stress occurred at an angle that deviated from the hypothesized separation angle.

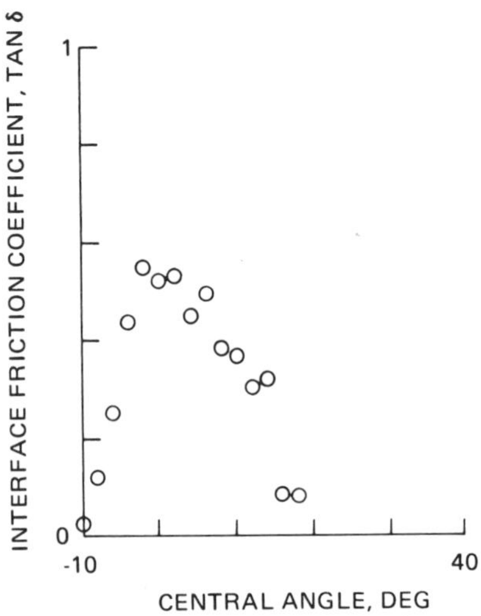

Fig. 3.33
Variation of the Interface Friction Coefficient, tan δ, Along the Wheel Interface in Loam. Load = 303 lb. Drawbar Pull = 100 lb. Torque = 166 ft-lb.

3.3.6 Kinematic Boundary Conditions, Slip and Interface Friction Angle

In the discussions of the applications of plasticity theory to bearing capacity and wheel-soil interaction problems, the point was made that for adequately defined stress boundary conditions the problem is statically determinate and, therefore, the solution is a true one according to the fundamental theorems of plasticity. The requirement of an adequate definition of stress boundary conditions at the interface is satisfied with the specification of the δ angle at the interface. Thus, as long as the specification of the δ angle corresponds, at least with a good approximation, to the actual conditions, the validity of the solutions by the plasticity theory cannot be questioned. Since the experimental evidence indicates that the assumption of a constant δ angle is an unsatisfactory approximation in certain cases, it is important to analyze this problem in more detail and formulate theoretical concepts that can lead to a better understanding of the relationships among the δ angle, slip and other variables in the problem.

The turning wheel stresses the soil along and in proximity to its contact area. These stresses impose certain strains in the soil which result in displacements that are a function of the geometry of the rolling. The instantaneous displacement velocity vector at a point on the wheel perimeter is perpendicular to the instantaneous center of rotation (Figure 3.34). On account of the travel reduction due to slip the location of the instantaneous center of rotation has been related to slip by the following equation:

$$j = \frac{h}{R} \qquad \text{Eq. 3.3.11}$$

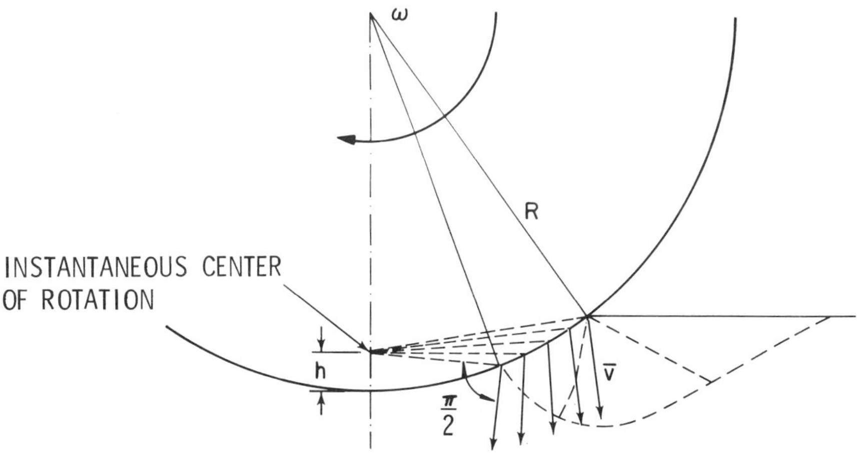

Fig. 3.34
Instantaneous Velocity Vectors for a Slipping Rigid Wheel

The magnitude of the instantaneous velocity vector is

$$\bar{v} = \omega R \qquad \text{Eq. 3.3.12}$$

Obviously, for a rigid body there is only one instantaneous center of rotation at one time. Therefore, a variable slip that would follow from a variable δ angle on account of Equation 3.2.8 is inconceivable in this concept of displacement velocity vectors. A closer examination of the kinematic boundary conditions at the interface reveals, however, that the displacements of the soil are by no means identical with that of a point at the wheel perimeter indicating, therefore, that a variable slip is indeed possible. For the proper formulation of the kinematic boundary conditions at the interface, distinction must be made between the kinematics of a point that is attached to the wheel and the kinematics of a point in the soil (or a soil particle) that is displaced by the rotation of the wheel. In subsequent discussions the problem of kinematic boundary conditions will be treated in a general way that is not restricted to the rigid wheel but that allows for the deformation of the vehicular footing such as occurs along soil-tire interfaces. This approach will be taken because the variation of the δ angle apparently affects the performance characteristics of tires also. Unfortunately, experimental information on the δ variation has not yet become available for tires because of the difficulties of obtaining shear stress measurements on elastomeric materials.

The fundamental factor in the analysis of kinematic conditions at the vehicular footing-soil interfaces is that the interface must be considered as consisting of two faces: that of the vehicular footing and that of the soil. For the analysis of interface kinematics the key assumption is made that the two faces of a vehicular footing-soil interface may slide on but may not separate from each other. (Note that in the case of certain tires and tracks this assumption may be questioned.)

This assumption leads to the boundary condition that the normal components of the velocities of adjoining points at the interface must be equal. This boundary condition, however, is by itself insufficient for the determination of soil particle velocities at the interface. The authors propose the following hypothesis as a complement to their concept of vehicular footing-soil interaction: The direction of the velocity vector of a soil particle at a point on the interface coincides with the direction of the major principal stress in the slip line field at that point.

In many cases of footing-soil interaction the coincidence of the directions of the velocity and major principal stress vectors is self-evident, as for example, in plate sinkage tests where both are vertical. In the case of wheel-soil interaction it would be desirable to prove by experimental research that the assumption of this coincidence is realistic.

Since the direction of the major principal stress is known from the computation of the appropriate slip line field, the proposed hypothesis together with the key assumption stated previously allows the determination of the velocity vectors for the soil particles at the interface. These velocity vectors constitute the kinematic boundary conditions for the soil at the vehicular footing-soil interface. These kinematic boundary conditions are also valid for the differential equations (Equations 2.4.8) that govern the velocity fields associated with slip line fields (Section 2.3.2).

The velocity vector for a point at the surface of a vehicular footing may be determined by vectorially adding the forward velocity vector ($\bar{v}_f$) and the tangential velocity vector ($\bar{v}_t$) as shown schematically in Figure 3.35. In the case of rigid wheels the tangential velocity vector $\bar{v}_t$ is identical with the peripheral velocity vector $\bar{v}_p$ and its magnitude can be computed as follows:

$$\bar{v}_p = \omega R = \bar{v}_f \,/\, (1 - j) \qquad \text{Eq. 3.3.13}$$

In the case of tires $\bar{v}_t$ is the component of $\bar{v}_p$ in the direction of the deflected surface of the tire. Since $\bar{v}_p$ is perpendicular to the radius, the angle that $\bar{v}_p$ encloses with the horizontal equals the central angle α. The vector $\bar{v}_t$ acts tangential to the deflected surface and encloses the angle α' with the horizontal. Thus,

$$\bar{v}_t = \bar{v}_p \cos(\alpha - \alpha') \qquad \text{Eq. 3.3.14}$$

In the case of tracks similar relationships may be established between $\bar{v}_t$ and the nominal velocity of the track.

The horizontal and vertical components of the resultant velocity vector $\bar{v}$ are:

$$\bar{v}_x = \bar{v}_f - \bar{v}_p \cos(\alpha - \alpha') \cos\alpha' \qquad \text{Eq. 3.3.15a}$$

$$\bar{v}_z = \bar{v}_p \cos(\alpha - \alpha') \sin\alpha' \qquad \text{Eq. 3.3.15b}$$

The normal component of the velocity vector, $\bar{v}_n$ is computed as follows:

$$\bar{v}_n = \bar{v}_x \sin\alpha' + \bar{v}_z \cos\alpha' = \bar{v}_f \sin\alpha' \qquad \text{Eq. 3.3.16}$$

This last equation expresses the fact that the component of the velocity vector normal to the deflected surface of the vehicular footing depends only on the forward velocity of the wheel and is independent of the slip.

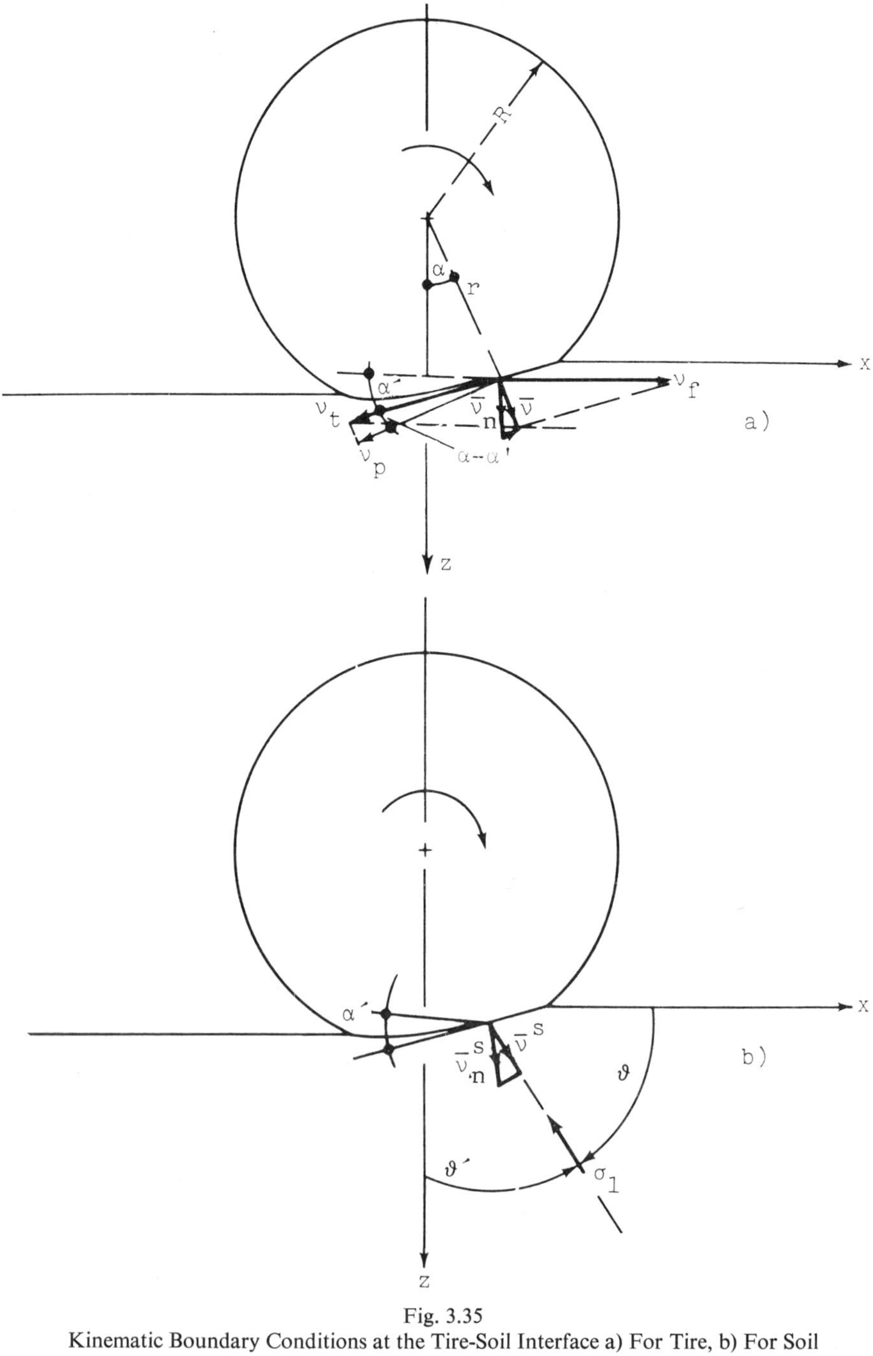

Fig. 3.35
Kinematic Boundary Conditions at the Tire-Soil Interface a) For Tire, b) For Soil

Equations 3.3.13 through 3.3.16 refer to velocities of a point that is attached to the surface of the vehicular footing. The velocity of a soil particle is computed as follows (velocities referring to a soil particle are distinguished by the superscript "*s*")

$$\bar{v}_n^s = \bar{v}_x^s \sin \alpha' + \bar{v}_z^s \cos \alpha' = \bar{v}_f \sin \alpha'$$
$$\frac{\bar{v}_x^s}{\bar{v}_z^s} = \tan \theta' \qquad \text{Eqs. 3.3.17a and 3.3.17b}$$

From Eqs. 3.3.17 the horizontal and vertical components of the velocity vector of a soil particle at the interface can be expressed as

$$\bar{v}_x^s = \bar{v}_f \frac{\sin \alpha'}{\sin \alpha' + \operatorname{cotan} \theta' \cos \alpha'}$$
$$\bar{v}_z^s = \bar{v}_x^s \operatorname{cotan} \theta' \qquad \text{Eqs. 3.3.18a and 3.3.18b}$$

In the equations θ' denotes the angle that the velocity vector encloses with the z axis (See Figure 3.35). Its value is $\frac{1}{2}\pi - \theta$, where θ is the direction of the major principal stress as defined in the stress field computations.

The velocity vector of a soil particle can also be thought of as being composed of the forward velocity vector and a tangential velocity vector. The latter can be computed from the following equation:

$$\bar{v}_t^s = \bar{v}_f \frac{1}{\sin \alpha' \tan \theta' + \cos \alpha'} \qquad \text{Eq. 3.3.19}$$

The tangential velocity computed from Equation 3.3.19 for a soil particle is, in the case of driven wheels and tires, generally less than the tangential velocity computed from Equation 3.3.14 for a point attached to the surface of the wheel or tire. This indicates that a relative displacement occurs between the surface of the vehicular footing and the soil. From the value of the tangential velocity of a soil particle a hypothetical slip value may be computed as follows

$$j' = 1 - \cos (\alpha - \alpha') \cdot (\sin \alpha' \tan \theta' + \cos \alpha') \qquad \text{Eq. 3.3.20}$$

(Recall that $j = h/R$ according to Equation 3.3.11)

It is interesting to note that this hypothetical slip value is independent of the translational velocity of the wheel or tire, at least for the assumed steady state concept of vehicular footing-soil interaction.

At this point it is worthwhile to consider the meaning of the hypothetical slip value determined by Equation 3.3.20. If the tire or wheel actually turned with an angular velocity that resulted in a slip equal to j then there would be no differential displacement between the surface of the wheel or tire and the soil. The hypothetical slip j' may be termed as "contact" slip, since j' is brought about only if the soil particles stay in contact with the same point of the wheel rim as the position of that point changes with the revolution of the wheel. Obviously, the difference between j and j' is the result of differential displacement between wheel and tire surface and the soil. The quantity $j - j'$ may be designated as "spin", since this term conveys the idea of a tire rotating relative to a non-yielding surface. It also expresses the relative motion between a tire and a yielding surface, such as the surface of the soil.

To elucidate the meaning and significance of the concept of contact slip a track element may be considered (Figure 3.36). If a track element displaces the soil by ΔL but stays in contact with the soil while the vehicle travels a distance L (the total length of track in contact with the soil) then the "contact slip" equals

$$j' = 1 - \frac{L - \Delta L}{L} = \frac{\Delta L}{L} \qquad \text{Eq. 3.3.21}$$

However, if the track element slides over the soil and at the end of vehicle travel ΔL is displaced by ΔX relative to its original position (Figure 3.37) then the total slip is:

$$j' = \frac{\Delta X + \Delta L}{L} \qquad \text{Eq. 3.3.22}$$

In the case of a track element it is easy to visualize the meaning of the two slip values j and j'. In the case of wheel-soil and tire-soil interaction the assumption of a steady state in the soil leads to the concept that the slip line fields move with the wheel or tire while the soil particles are displaced from their original position with respect to a coordinate system that is fixed to the ground. This concept makes it somewhat difficult to visualize the relative displacement of wheel or tire surface to the soil. However, the meaning of the terms indicated by Equation 3.3.20 is essentially the same as explained for a track element.

The kinematic boundary conditions and Equation 3.3.20 derived from these conditions allow the computation of contact slip for every point at the interface of a vehicular footing of known geometry in interaction problems where the slip line fields have been determined for some assumed variation of the δ angle along the interface. Conversely, it is possible to determine the kinematic boundary conditions for a given value of contact slip and the δ angle corresponding to that slip for each nodal point at the interface. More research is needed to formulate the various interaction problems according to this concept and to develop relationships between the value of contact slip and conventional slip.

3.3.7 Dual, Tandem and Multiple Wheel Arrangements

Dual or tandem wheel arrangements are favored for many types of off-road vehicles that carry heavy loads. Many military vehicles that are designed for off-road operation have multiple drive wheel arrangements. Special purpose military trailers often need groups of free rolling wheels

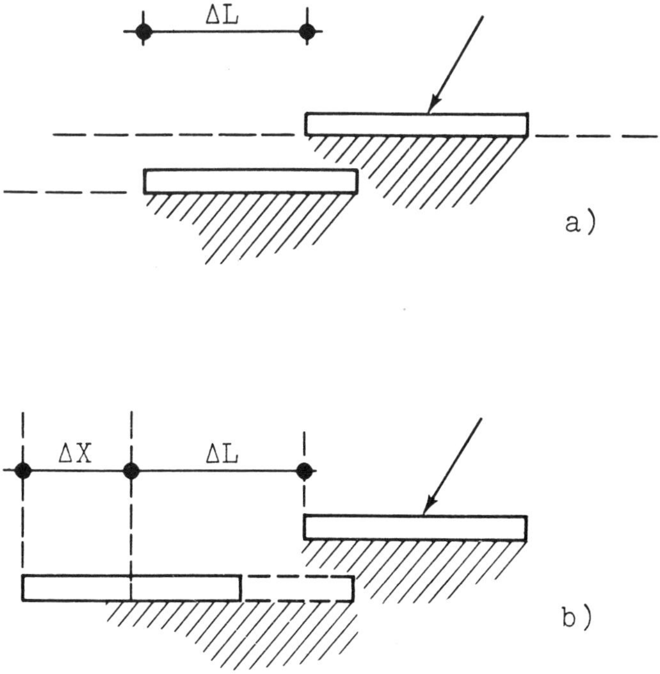

Fig. 3.36
Contact Slip (a) and Total Slip (b) of a Track Element

to support their heavy load both off-road and on paved roadways. In heavy construction, rubber tired rollers are employed for fill compaction; these come with multiple wheels as a rule.

Landing gears of medium and large aircraft contain a number of wheels in a variety of configurations. The analysis of the capability of such aircraft to land on or take off from unprepared airfields and the determination of soil requirements for such an operation to take place without unacceptable structural damage to the aircraft are among the most challenging tasks in the field of off-road mobility. The fact that the wheels of aircraft landing gear are free rolling simplifies the interaction problem, but consideration of the effect of the grouping of the wheels in clusters, the high velocities, braking and turning, rut formation and repetitive use of the airfield makes the problem very difficult to model mathematically.

For the parametric analysis of the various multiple wheel arrangements available to the designer as well as for the evaluation of the mobility of off-road vehicles with multiple wheel units, an interaction concept is needed that considers both the effects of close spacing of wheels on the soil response and the potential load transfer among the wheels of the multiple wheel unit. In such an interaction concept the multiple wheel unit is considered as the running gear on which, analogously with the single wheel interaction concept, the load is assumed to be constant. Otherwise, all basic assumptions are the same as was set forth for the concept of single wheel-soil interaction. This technique is used regularly in conventional soil mechanics in the analysis of pile foundation problems where, although rigorous theories have been developed for single pile-soil interactions, none exists for pile clusters.

Dual Wheels

Dual wheels are mounted on the same axle, therefore, assuming the axle has an adequate suspension system, there is no torque transfer between the wheels and any load transfer is minimal. Differences in the performance between a single wheel and a member of a dual wheel arrangement is solely due to their different interaction with the soil. Obviously, the two-dimensional concept of wheel-soil interaction that assumes the same conditions in the soil in all planes parallel to that of travel is unsuitable for the analysis of dual wheel performances. Therefore, an interaction model that considers the effect of an adjacent, closely spaced wheel on the soil response has to be formulated. A concept of such a model of dual wheel-soil interaction, based on both the observed transverse distribution of normal stresses in experiments and theoretical considerations, is outlined in the following discussions. This concept is also applicable to the problem of dual pneumatic tire-soil interaction if the transverse deformation of the tires due to the different transverse interface normal stress distributions is disregarded. In this case the interaction model becomes a hybrid one, since the consideration of three-dimensional effects in the interaction is restricted to the soil response.

In Figure 3.9 an alternate mode of soil failure beneath wheel loads is illustrated. In this alternate mode, soil failure is governed by the MOHR-COULOMB yield criterion (just as in the case of failure in the plane of travel), but, due to changes in the relative magnitude of the three principal stresses the plane of failure is no longer in the plane of travel but is an oblique one, as shown in Figure 3.9. For the hybrid model of running gear-soil interaction the criteria for such a lateral failure in an oblique plane have to be established and methods for the estimation of its effect on soil response have to be developed.

Generally, stress states in the soil at failure can be computed by plasticity theory, if failure is governed by the MOHR-COULOMB yield criterion. These computations, however, are strictly valid only for plane strain or plane stress conditions. In the case of failure in the oblique plane, as shown in Figure 3.9, the component of the weight of the soil gives rise to shear stresses in that plane so that plane strain considerations no longer prevail. However, analyses of cases, including those where non-uniform transverse distribution of the interface normal stresses was observed in the validation tests, indicated that lateral failure was critical only in that portion of the forward slip line field where the obliquity of the alternate plane of failure was relatively small, less than about 15° from the vertical. Thus, as an approximation, it may be assumed that lateral failure occurs in the vertical plane as shown in Figure 3.27. The interface stresses for this condition can be computed according to the theory of plasticity. The slip line fields are essentially the same type as for the two-dimensional bearing capacity case shown in Figure 3.37. As in the case of slip line fields in the direction of travel, an assumption as to the value and variation of the interface friction angle has to be made in order for the solution to be defined and unique. In the case of transverse failure the value of δ must be zero at the center because of symmetry. Thus, a linear variation of δ from the edges toward the center is indicated. Normalized stress distributions for various values of the δ angle are shown in Figure 3.38 as a function of the similitude parameter G. At this time there is no experimental information available on the value of δ in the transverse direction beneath wheels or in the bearing capacity case. As is often done in soil mechanics analysis of retaining wall-soil interaction, $\delta = \varphi/3$ may be assumed.

The interface normal stresses computed on the basis of these assumptions for lateral failure conditions have to be compared with those computed for failure conditions in the plane of travel. Whichever is lower is the maximum of the interface normal stresses that can be developed in the soil and is, therefore, the interface normal stress that controls the wheel-soil interaction. The resulting interface normal stress distribution in a typical case is illustrated in Figure 3.39. When an integration of the

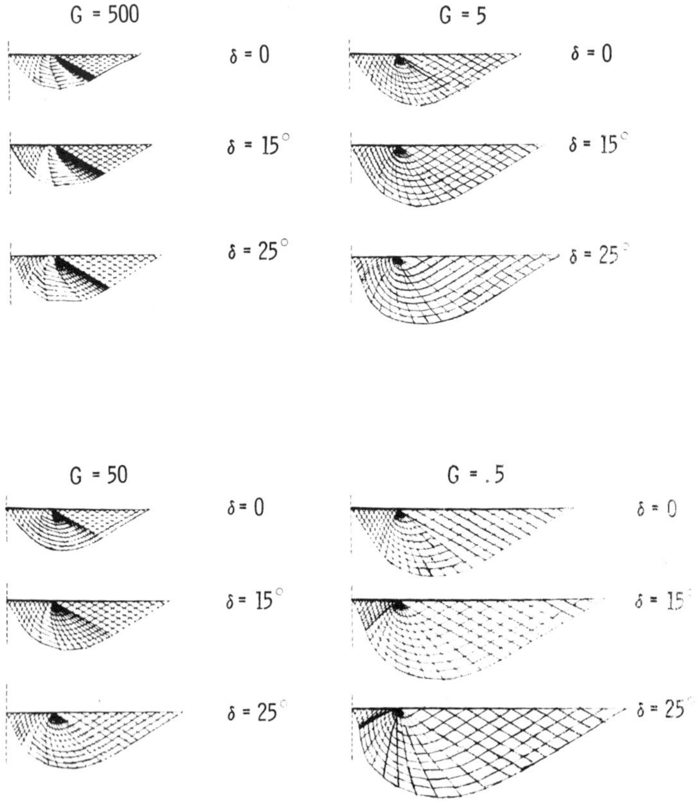

$$G = \frac{\gamma L}{c + w \tan \varphi}.$$

Fig 3.37
Slip Line Fields for Various Values of the Similitude Parameter G, and Interface Friction Angle, δ. Strip Footings

interface stresses is carried out for the determination of wheel load, torque and drawbar pull, the effect of lateral failure, if any, makes itself manifest in commensurately lower wheel load than what would be obtained with the two-dimensional model for the same central angles.

The hybrid model of single wheel-soil interaction outlined in the foregoing is suitable for the analysis of dual wheel-soil interaction if the effect of the second wheel on the lateral failure conditions beneath the first wheel (and vice versa) is taken into consideration. A second wheel is, in

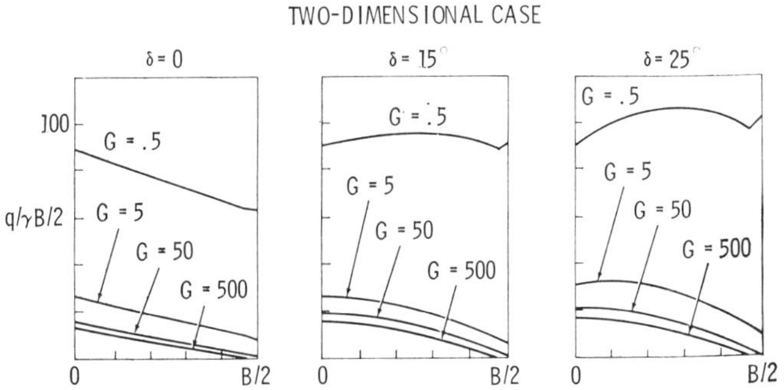

Fig. 3.38
Distribution of Normalized Bearing Stresses, $2q/\gamma B$, Beneath Strip Footings for Various Values of the Similitude Parameter $G = \gamma L/(c + w \tan \varphi)$ and Interface Friction Angle, δ

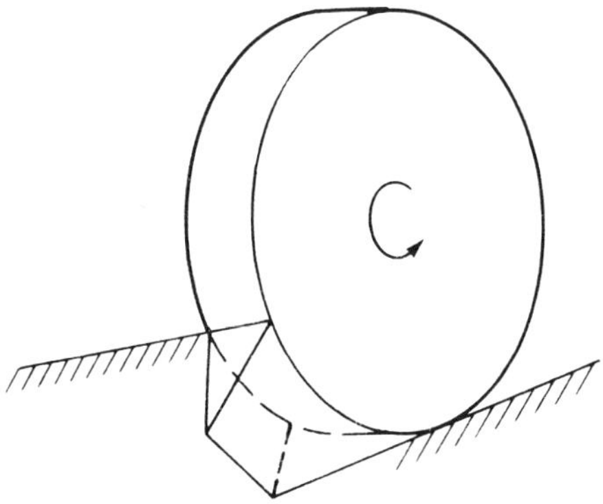

Fig. 3.39
Spatial Distribution of the Interface Normal Stresses Beneath a Rigid Wheel

effect, equivalent to a surcharge load on the passive zone of the slip line field for lateral failure beneath the first wheel. The interface normal stresses beneath the first wheel that correspond to this surcharge load are, in all likelihood, larger than those associated with failure in the plane of travel and are, therefore, not critical. Lateral failure toward the second wheel is effectively prevented from underneath that area of the first wheel where potential slip lines in the passive zone end beneath the second wheel. The situation is illustrated in Figure 3.40 (a) where outlines of potential slip line fields are shown. The slip line fields that unquestionably control the transverse distribution of normal stresses are shown by continuous lines while extensions of these slip line fields that may or may not control are shown by dashed and dotted lines. The normal stresses cor-

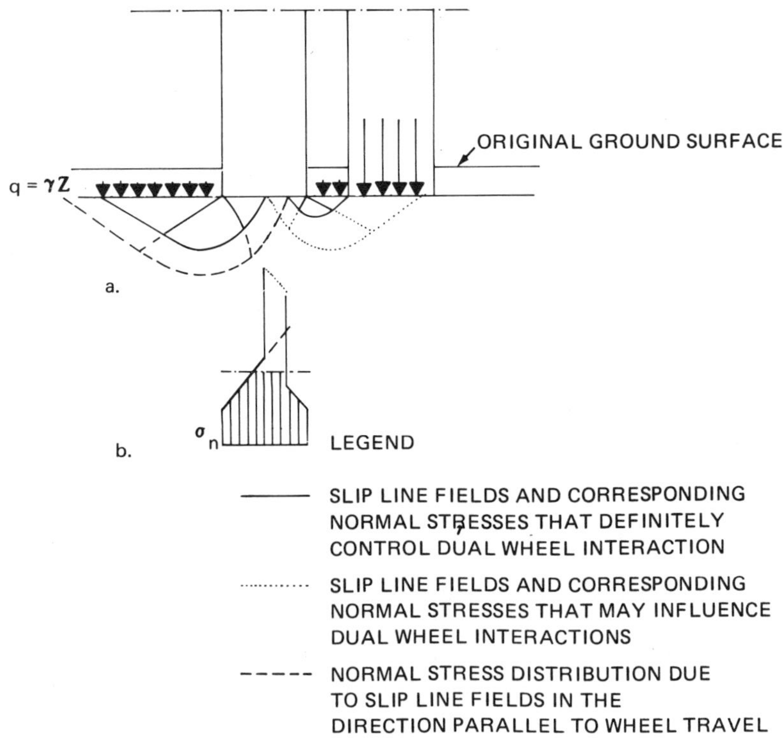

Fig. 3.40
Lateral Failure Conditions
a) Slip Line Fields Beneath Dual Wheels
b) Distribution of Normal Stresses

responding to these slip line fields are shown by the same convention in Figure 3.40 (b). In addition, the uniform normal stress corresponding to the slip line field in the plane of travel is also shown by dash-dot line. All these lines indicate limits for the interface normal stresses; the actual distribution controlled by these limits is shown by the shaded area. These limits, and with them the actual distribution of the interface normal stresses across the wheel, vary in each cross-section with the central angle that defines the location of the cross-section. The limit controlled by lateral failure conditions depends, among other things, on the surcharge $q = \gamma z$ that varies with the depth of the cross-section beneath the original surface and, consequently, with the central angle. The limit controlled by the longitudinal failure conditions, indicated by the dash-dot line in Figure 3.40 also varies with the central angle. Thus, the actual transverse distribution of interface normal stresses has to be computed for every central angle for which the normal stresses are computed in the two-dimensional model. The consideration of such limiting conditions in a computer program is routine.

The concept of dual wheel-soil interaction outlined in the foregoing discussion has not yet (1977) been translated to a computerized model. Therefore, comparisons of performance predictions with the meager experimental data are not yet available. However, tentative calculations indicate that seemingly contradictory experimental results, such as SWANSON's (1971) who found no difference between single and dual wheel performance, and MELZER's (1971) who found appreciable differences between the performance of single and dual tires, could be explained by the proposed concept. Indeed, preliminary evaluation of these tests showed that transverse failure conditions as described above were probably not controlling in SWANSON's experiments, while they were in MELZER's.

Tandem Wheels

The most common arrangement to accomodate tandem wheels is the bogie suspension system that enables tandem axles to function together as load carrying and driving axles. In the bogie suspension system the tandem axles are usually interconnected by so-called walking beams (often leaf springs serve as walking beams). These are joined at their midpoint by a single cross support (trunnion axle) that serves as a pivot point for the entire unit. The purpose of this arrangement is to distribute the load on the trunnion axle evenly over the wheels. Torque arms are usually employed to prevent the driving and braking torques from producing spring windups that would result in unequal axle loadings.

Tandem wheels are most often drive wheels that are powered either by independent propeller shafts or by a tandem drive with some means to allow differential action between the axles.

At first glance it appears that the load equalization mechanism of a bogie suspension system insures that each axle carries the same load and, thereby, performs the same way. However, the trailing wheel runs in the rut of the lead wheel and therefore encounters the soil at a different level. In addition, since the soil has been compacted by the lead wheel, it may react differently to the loads imposed by the trailing wheel (i.e., its strength properties have been modified by the pass of the lead wheel). Thus, even though the suspension system equalizes the load on the two wheels, their combined performance cannot be calculated simply as the performance of two single wheels. Thus, proper consideration must be given to the differences between the lead and trailing wheel in their interaction with the soil and also to the interaction between the axles brought about by the torque transfer mechanism of the power train. A running gear-soil interaction model is needed that simulates both the interaction of the wheels with the soil and the mechanical interaction of the axles. In this book only the features of the former interaction problem are discussed since modeling of vehicle components is outside the scope of the book.

The close spacing of tandem wheels may result in a situation where the passive zone of the rear slip line field of the lead wheel interferes with the passive zone of the front slip line field of the trailing wheel, as shown in Figure 3.41. Theoretically, this overlapping of the slip line fields could be

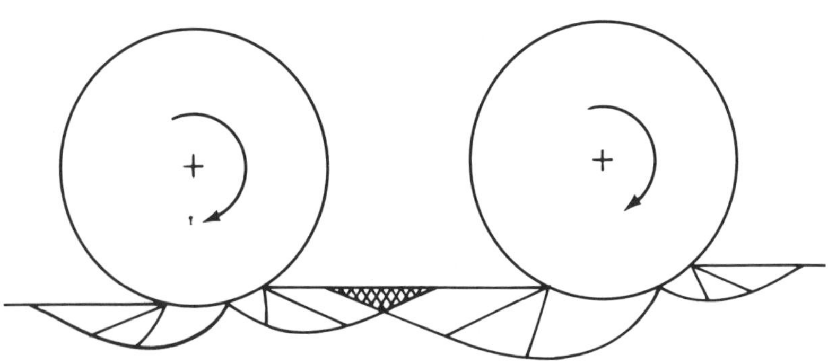

Fig. 3.41
Slip Line Fields for Rigid Wheels in Tandem. Cross-hatched Area Indicates Interference Between Slip Line Fields

treated by assigning only one half of the σ value at the free boundary for each field where the overlap occurs. However, in the computations an iteration scheme would be necessary because the extent of the overlap is not known beforehand and the allocation of half of the σ value may itself change the extent of the overlap. It is questionable whether the theoretical improvement in the prediction accuracy that may be achieved by such a cumbersome iteration scheme could be realized when other factors that affect the boundary conditions at the free surface between the wheels are completely disregarded in the two-dimensional model. The overlap of slip line fields occurs in the rut of the lead wheel where the soil failure postulated by the interaction of the passive zones of the two slip line fields is restrained by the surcharge effect of the soil that is at the original surface outside the rut. This surcharge effect increases with depth toward the rut. Thus, the hypothetical effect of the overlapping of slip lines fields may be offset by these conditions not considered in the two-dimensional model. Unless all these conditions are taken into account in a more elaborate model of tandem wheel-soil interaction, the overlapping effect may as well be disregarded.

The most significant interaction effect between wheels in tandem arrangement is brought forth by the change in soil properties as the lead wheel works its way through the soil. In the interaction of the trailing wheel with the soil, these changed soil properties have to be taken into account. The lead wheel compacts the soil beneath it; a measure of the compaction is the rut depth. The trailing wheel encounters soil that has been compacted by the lead wheel. Therefore, in the analysis of the interaction of the trailing wheel with the soil, the properties of the soil as compacted by the lead wheel have to be considered. These properties may be best determined in the laboratory by triaxial tests. In principle, it is possible to duplicate the stress path in the triaxial tests that the soil beneath the lead wheel experiences. One of the advantages of the authors' interaction concept is that the stress states in the soil, and thus the stress paths in an interaction situation, can be determined. In extending this concept to tandem wheel arrangements, the stress path in the soil for the wheel is first determined by the single wheel-soil interaction concept. The strength properties of soil for this path are then obtained from triaxial tests and applied in the analysis of the trailing wheel-soil interaction.

While the procedure outlined previously is recommended for specific cases, an approximate but more general relationship that expresses the change in the soil strength properties in terms of the original strength parameters is desirable for parametric studies and a broad evaluation of the effects of tandem wheel interaction. The establishment of such relationships requires great care and soil engineering judgment and is possible only for certain types of soils. A very approximate description of the changes in strength characteristics of various types of soils due to the compacting action of the lead wheel is summarized in Table 3.2.

TABLE 3.2
Changes in Soil Strength Upon Passage of a Wheel

Soil Type	Category	Degree of Saturation	Effect on Soil Properties
SEDIMENTARY	a	0–30%	Cohesionless loose soils gain in strength due to compaction. Very dense cohesionless soils (unlikely to occur in nature) lose strength due to reworking. Friable silt and clay is likely to gain strength. Loess is likely to lose its cohesion.
	b	30–90%	Partially saturated soils generally gain in strength due to compaction. Gain is most at optimum moisture content. Information on compaction (available in civil soils engineering literature) is applicable. See Section 1.2.3.
	c	90–100%	Highly saturated soils are unlikely to gain strength since for practical purposes the compacting effect is negligible. Clays with structure are likely to experience collapse or reorientation of particles (See Section 1.2.2) and lose strength in reworking.
RESIDUAL	d	0–100%	Residual soils usually exhibit some cohesion due to their structure. If wheel load breaks the structure (lead wheel sinks significantly), cohesive strength is likely to be lost in reworking.

The significance of the changes in the strength of various types of soils summarized in Table 3.2 is illustrated in Figures 3.42 through 3.44 where these changes, as experienced in the validation tests for rigid wheels and reflected in cone penetration resistance measured in the rut are shown. Figure 3.42 shows a significant increase in cone penetration resistance in loose sand, while Figure 3.43 shows a decrease in dense sand after the passage of the wheel. Note that the cone penetration resistances measured in the rut are about of the same magnitude, whether the sand bed was loose or dense originally. This is in accordance with the concept that cohesionless soils tend to achieve a characteristic void ratio when stressed to failure, no matter what the initial void ratio was. Figure 3.44 shows a significant increase in the cone penetration resistance in loam after the passage of the wheel. The loam bed, as prepared for the test, falls in category "b" in Table 3.2. This category is the only one where a general estimate of the increase of soil strength due to the compaction by the lead wheel may be made. In partially saturated soils it may be assumed that the stresses applied to the soil are effective stresses and once the soil acquired some strength in its effective stress history, a major portion of this strength remains "locked in" even after the stresses are released. For the application of this concept to the estimation of strength increase due to wheel action, it is necessary to know, at least approximately, the maximum normal stress that the soil experiences beneath the wheel. Then the strength of soil for subsequent stressing may be estimated as shown in Figure 3.45. The factor K_s applied for the determination of the friction angle of the compacted soil should be chosen on the basis of judgment; its value may be anywhere between 0.1 and 0.9.

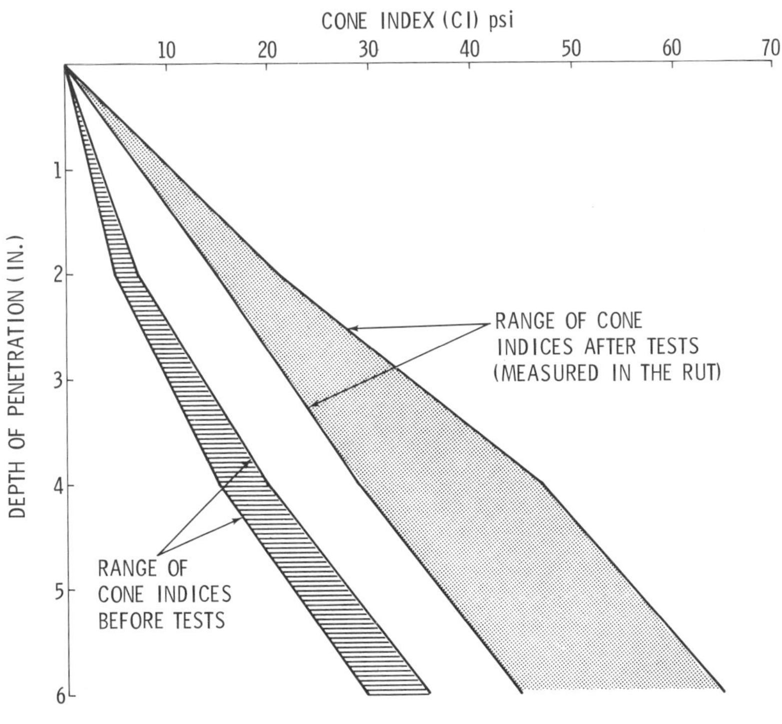

Fig. 3.42
Cone Penetration Resistance in Loose Sand Before and After Passage of Wheel

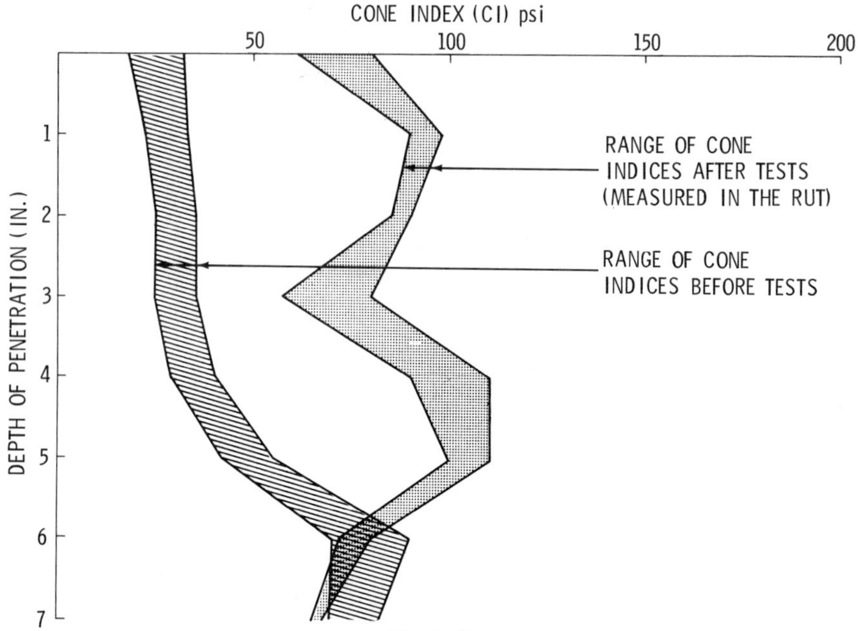

Fig. 3.43
Cone Penetration Resistance in Dense Sand Before and After Passage of Wheel

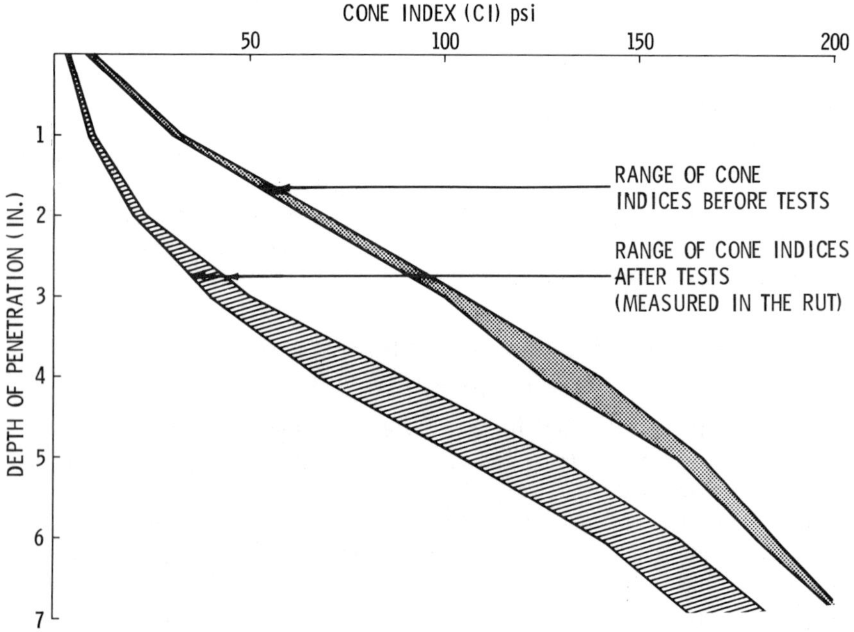

Fig. 3.44
Cone Penetration Resistance in Loam Before and After Passage of Wheel

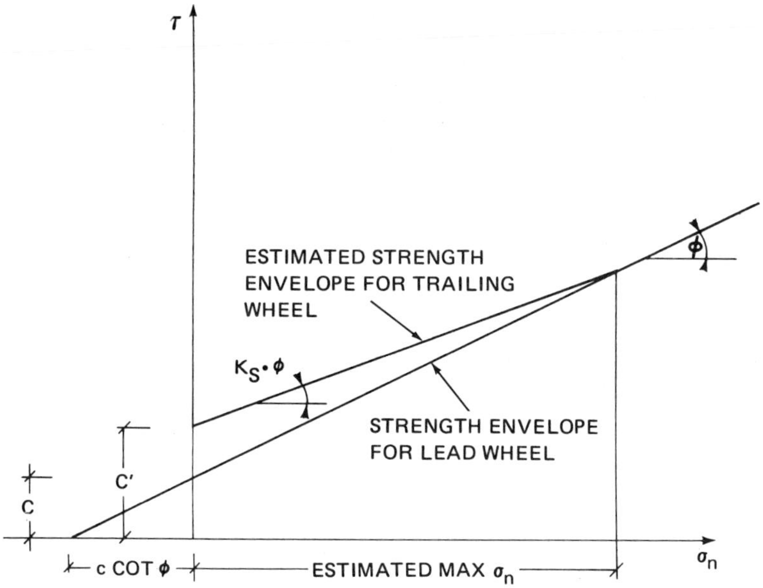

Fig. 3.45
Estimation of the Effect of Compaction by the Lead Wheel on the Strength Properties of Soil Encountered by the Trailing Wheel

Multiple Wheel Arrangements

The basic concept of dual and tandem wheel interaction applies to arrangements where more than two wheels are mounted on the same axle or travel in the same path. Interaction concepts for multiple wheel arrangements are combinations of dual and tandem interaction effects discussed previously in this section.

3.3.8 Wheel-Soil Interaction in Soils Exhibiting Nonlinear Strength Properties

The linear relationship between shear strength and normal stress postulated by the Mohr-Coulomb failure criterion (Equation 3.2.1) is an approximation of the nonlinear relationship that soils generally exhibit over a wide range of normal stresses. The linear approximation is usually very close if only a limited range of normal stresses have to be considered. However, where the error introduced by the linear approximation may be significant, the use of a nonlinear strength envelope is advisable.

The implication of using a nonlinear strength envelope in the solution of the differential equations of plasticity on the nature of the stress distributions beneath rigid wheels is best shown with reference to Figure 3.46. In Figure 3.46 two Mohr circles, A and B, corresponding to the nonlinear failure envelope are shown together with a $\varphi =$ $=$ constant $= 41°$ envelope. This envelope is a linear approximation corresponding to Circle A for a cohesionless material. In plasticity theory, normal stresses are related to the intersection of tangents to the failure envelope with the σ axis. In the case of a cohesionless material having a linear envelope, this intersection coincides with the origin of the τ–σ coordinate system. For the same material, the use of a nonlinear envelope may result in a ψ intercept on the σ axes (refer to Figure 3.46) depending on the normal stress level, i.e. where on the nonlinear envelope a tangent is drawn.

Even though the Mohr circle for the stresses at points A and D in Figures 3.46 (b) and (d), respectively, is the same for both the linear and nonlinear failure envelope (Circle A), the shear and normal stresses developed at the interface, assuming the same angle of interface friction

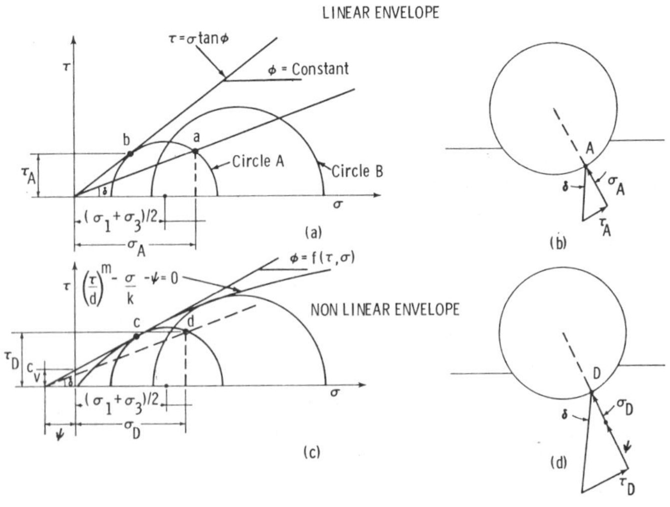

Fig. 3.46
The Effect of a Nonlinear Mohr Failure Envelope on the Magnitude and Nature of the Interface Stresses

(δ), are different in the two cases (refer to point "*a*" and "*d*" in Figure 3.46 (a) and (c), respectively). Since shear stresses at the interface are the major contributors to drawbar pull, the importance of using a nonlinear envelope for the wheel-soil interaction problem is evident.

The failure envelope is conveniently defined in general terms by the equation

$$\left[\frac{\tau}{d}\right]^{m} - \frac{\sigma_n}{k} - c = 0 \qquad \text{Eq. 2.2.22}$$

where m, d, k = constants that define the curvature of the failure envelope.

For the linear case ($d = m = 1$ and $k = \cot\varphi$) Eq. 2.2.22 reduces to the conventional Mohr-Coulomb form represented by Equation 1.3.24.

While there is no inherent difficulty in the solution of the differential equations of plasticity for soils with nonlinear strength properties, in the numerical computations it is necessary to include additional iterative procedures to take the variation of φ and ψ with τ and σ into account. Another complication arises with the specification of the interface friction angle, δ, at the active zone boundary. If a constant δ is assigned, then care should be exercised lest δ exceed the frictional angle that decreases with the normal stress. Equation 3.2.6 that defines the relationship between mobilized shear stress and δ is obviously not applicable to nonlinear strength envelopes and a variable δ value, corresponding to a constant ratio of τ_{mob}/τ_{max} is clearly the logical choice. However, a variable δ would involve a variable a_m and, therefore, another iteration scheme.

At the singular point the value of θ_0 in Equation 3.3.5 is not available directly from Equation 3.3.3 since the normal stress at this point of the interface, needed for the determination of φ, is not known beforehand. Thus, another iteration procedure is needed for the determination of θ_0. A more detailed discussion of these problems is presented by Nowatzki and Karafiath (1974). This refinement clearly requires more elaborate programming, a larger computer core and considerably longer computer run times for execution of the numerical computations. The question arises whether the gain in prediction accuracy is worth the additional effort and computer operating expenses. Obviously, the nonlinear strength envelope has to be reliably determined for the soil in question, otherwise there is no point in applying sophisticated computing procedures with crude input data. Results of computations made for the purpose of laboratory research may best illustrate the effects of nonlinear strength properties on wheel performance and prediction accuracy. All results relate to an 8 inch diameter, 2 inch wide rigid wheel being driven over medium dense (100 lbs/cu. ft), dry Jones Beach sand. The failure criteria used in the analyses are based on triaxial tests and are expressed as follows.

$$\left(\frac{\tau}{1.0}\right)^{1.0} - \frac{\sigma_n}{1.1504} - 0 = 0 \qquad (\varphi = 41°)$$

Lower bound linear envelope:

$$\left(\frac{\tau}{1.0}\right)^{1.0} - \frac{\sigma_n}{1.3764} - 0 = 0 \qquad (\varphi = 36°)$$

Nonlinear envelope:

$$\left(\frac{\tau}{1.0}\right)^{1.027} - \frac{\sigma_n}{1.1605} - 0 = 0 \qquad (\varphi - \text{variable}) \qquad \text{Eqs. 3.3.24}$$

where τ and σ_n are in units of pounds per square foot.

Values of the interface friction angle ($\delta = 15°$, $\delta = 21°$, and $\delta = 25°$) were combined with the φ angles to yield a range of slips from 18 to 52 percent. Slips were calculated by Eq. 3.3.8 with empirically determined values of the constants K and j_0.

Figure 3.47 shows the slip line fields for these failure envelopes and an assumed angle of interface friction of 15°. For the purpose of comparison, a rear angle of 5° was chosen. It is clear from Figure 3.47 that the entry angle (α_e) in each case is about the same and equals approximately 22°. What is different is the geometric extent of the slip line field; it is the largest for $\varphi = 41°$ and about the same for $\varphi = 36°$ and $\varphi =$ variable. This means that in the former case, more soil material is affected and more frictional resistance is mobilized than for the other two cases. Consequently, the vertical load that the wheel can carry is greater for $\varphi = 41°$ than for the other two cases. A summary of the performance characteristics of the wheel for the three cases is given in Table 3.3. Obviously, a $\varphi = 41°$ approximation in this case would have seriously overestimated the performance of the wheel.

The performance parameters computed by using Equation 3.3.24 for the characterization of the nonlinear strength properties of the Jones Beach sand were spot checked in the laboratory. The mobility bin at Grumman, where these check tests were made, is equipped with a spreader that deposits sand in the bin at a uniform density, a prerequisite of duplicating in the experiments the hypothetical conditions assumed in the computations. Figure 3.48 shows the comparison of test results with performance relationships established by the computations. The agreement is, indeed,

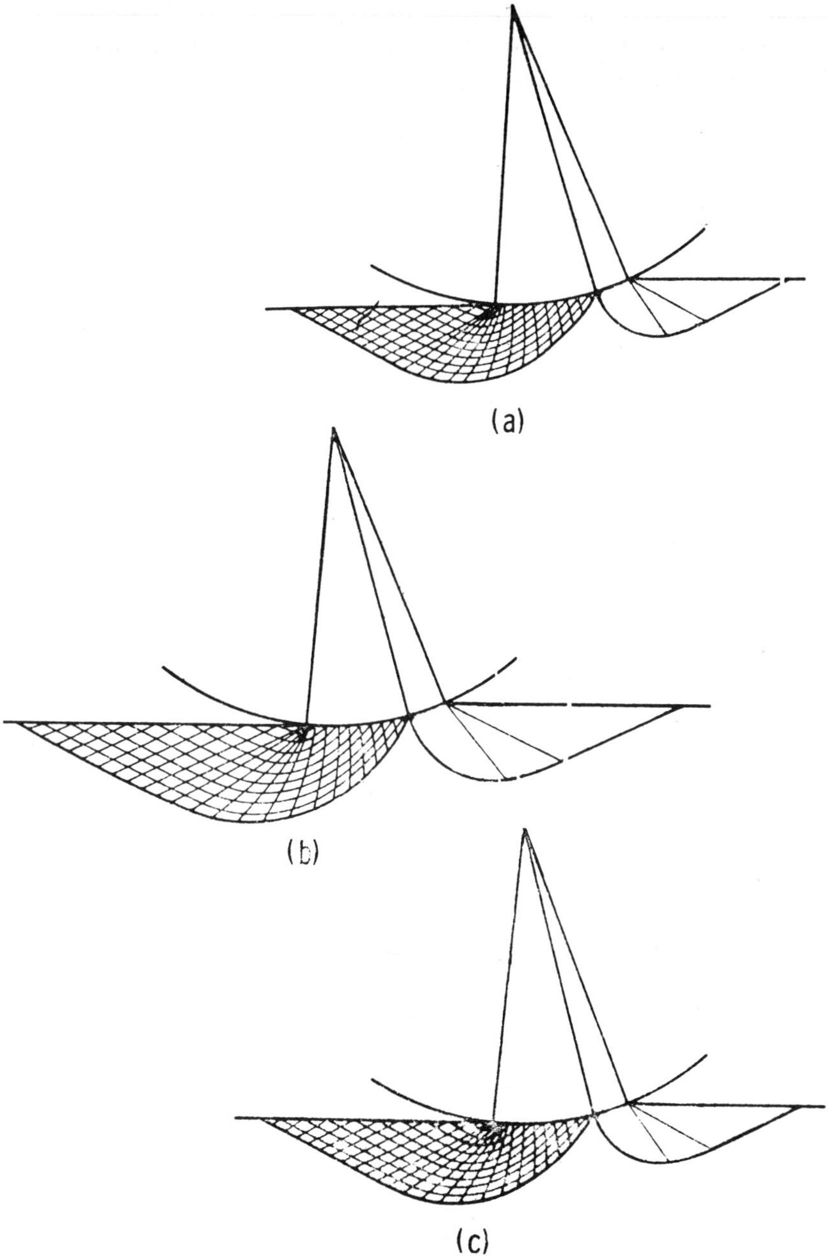

Fig. 3.47
Variation of Slip Line Field with Friction Angle ($\delta = 15°$)
a) $\varphi = 36°$ b) $\varphi = 41°$ c) $\varphi =$ variable

TABLE 3.3
Summary of Performance Characteristics for Driven Rigid Wheel in Jones Beach Sand

φ (deg)	δ (deg)	α_r (deg)	α_e (deg)	W (lb)	DB (lb)	T (ft–lb)
41	15	5	23.1	9.81	0.61	0.85
36	15	5	22.0	3.96	0.29	0.34
Var.	15	5	22.0	5.34	0.41	0.47

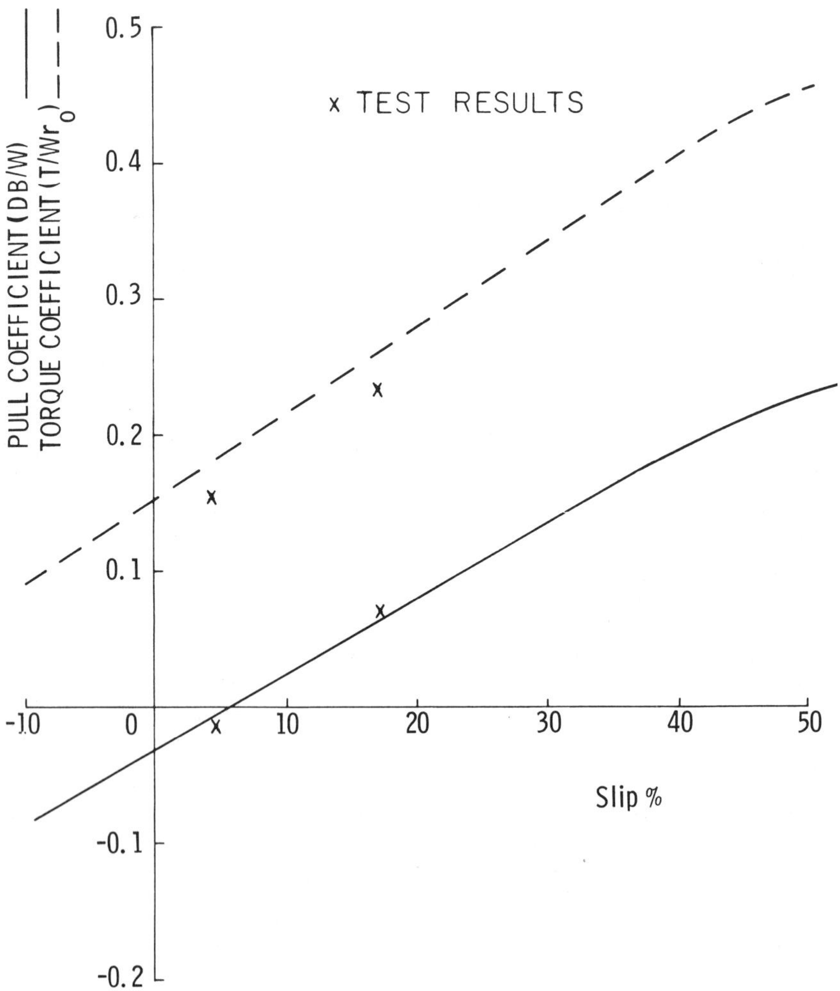

Fig. 3.48
Relationship of Performance Coefficients to Slip for Jones Beach Sand

very good and could not have been achieved if linear approximations of the strength properties had been used.

In summary, the consideration of nonlinear strength envelopes improves the prediction accuracy, but the additional effort and computing time is justified only if strength properties are also determined with extra care and soil conditions are sufficiently uniform, as in the case of research projects.

3.3.9 Wheel-Soil Interaction in Submerged Soils

From time to time, off-road vehicles are required to operate on inundated land where their mobility may be seriously impaired. Other vehicles are designed to cope with the problem of developing traction in submerged soils; agricultural machinery working in rice fields or amphibians egressing from or ingressing into water encounter submerged conditions in the regular course of their opeations. The exploration of sea floor by underwater vehicles is another challenging task in off-road mobility where not only the running gear but the whole vehicle works under water.

Even though submerged soil is undoubtedly more critical for mobility than soil above groundwater level there is but little experimental information available on running gear-submerged soil interaction. If one can speak of the theoretical concepts of this interaction, they certainly do not go beyond the assumption that field tests, if performed under water, would yield parameters that could be simply inserted in the formulas developed for above water soil conditions.

Undoubtedly, wheel-soil interaction in this case is governed by the strength of the soil in the submerged condition. However, soil strength in this case is no longer independent of the drainage conditions, as has been assumed for above water interactions. The implication is that the strength properties may change with the degree of drainage that the soil experiences during passage of the wheel and they may have to be calculated for each interaction problem by means of an effective stress analysis.

In view of these complicating factors it is all the more important to use a theoretical approach that allows proper consideration of the effects of submergence on soil behavior. The basic concept of wheel-soil interaction discussed in the previous chapters applies to submerged conditions too. The application of the theory of plasticity for the computations of stress states in the soil allows the direct consideration of the reduction of the unit weight of soil due to buoyancy. In Chapter 2.2.5 the concept of effective stresses has been applied in conjunction with plasticity theory and the differential equations of plasticity have been developed in terms of effective stresses. This formulation provides a powerful tool for the analysis of submerged conditions.

At this point it is necessary to digress from the problem of wheel-soil interaction and discuss submergence in relation to drainage and groundwater conditions. True submergence exists if the water covering the terrain is continuously connected with the groundwater and there are no interconnected air channels in the soil. Temporary flooding of a terrain often results in a situation where surface water seeps downward and entraps the air that was present in the pores of the soil above the groundwater level before the flooding. In this case the upper water stratum is held by capillary tension and the weight of the soil is not relieved by buoyancy. Instead, the weight of the soil is actually increased by the water that displaces the pore air. The effect of such an apparent submergence can be represented by a variable strength soil model, possibly by a two-layer model for the purposes of wheel-soil interaction analyses.

In the case of true submergence of soils, such as submerged soils making up the floor of natural bodies of water, the principal effects on soil behavior are as follows.

Buoyancy

For the computation of stress states in the soil by plasticity theory, the buoyant unit weight of soil, as computed by the formulas given in Section 1.2.3, applies. The buoyant unit weight is much less than the total unit weight of soil. Independently of any other effect that submergence may have on wheel performance, the effect of buoyancy is always present and impairs wheel performance. This impairment is appreciable in cohesionless soils and relatively minor in soils with high cohesive strength.

Saturation

Even though submergence tends to saturate the soil, the fact that a soil layer lies under water cannot be identified with 100% saturation. In the process of saturation air bubbles remain enclosed in the pore water preventing complete saturation unless the water pressure is very high, as in the case of deep sea floors. Nevertheless, it may be assumed that in submerged soils the degree of saturation is high and within a certain layer there are no air channels through which pore air can escape and precipitate instantaneous volume changes in the soil. Under these circumstances, pore water pressure are generated when the soil tends to compress under the applied load, and suction (or negative pore water pressure) is generated when the soil tends to expand under the applied state of stresses.

Pore Water Pressures

The effect of pore water pressures on the strength properties of soil was discussed in detail in Chapter 1.3. The generation of pore water pressures in submerged soils and its effect on the strength properties of soil is the most important factor that has to be evaluated by the methods discussed in Chapter 1.3 for the appropriate analysis of wheel-soil interaction in submerged soils.

A direct way of assessing the effect of pore water pressures on wheel-soil interaction is the application of effective stress analysis methods to the problem. These methods are particularly useful when dissipation of pore water pressure may in some degree occur during passage of the wheel and the estimation of the degree of dissipation by consolidation theory is of interest. In an effective stress analysis of wheel-soil interaction the differential equations of plasticity in terms of effective stresses, derived in Section 2.2.5, are used with the techniques of numerical computation discussed in Section 2.3.5.

Pore Water Pressures and Development of Traction

In wheel-soil interaction in submerged soils the interface shear stresses, that are the instrument of traction development, are directly affected by the pore water pressures that arise at the wheel-soil interface. For the analysis of this effect it is useful to apply the principle of effective stresses, discussed in Section 1.3.1, to the concept of the development of interface shear stresses. The maximum value of the interface shear stress, τ_{max}, is determined by the effective normal stress, $\bar{\sigma}_n$, and equals (Figure 3.49):

$$\tau_{max} = (\psi + \bar{\sigma}_n) \tan \bar{\varphi}$$

In Figure 3.49 the effective stress circle touches the effective strength envelope and, therefore, represents a failure state of stresses. The total stress circle that includes the pore water pressures is of the same size but shifted toward the right by the amount of pore water pressure. The maximum shear stress for the total stress circle is the same as for the effective stress circle. The shear stress, τ_{mob}, that an effective interface friction angle, δ, mobilizes is less than that without pore pressures for the same interface friction angle by $\Delta\tau$. When the wheel is considered as a free body, the equilibrating stresses at the interface are the total stresses. Pore water pressures do not affect the normal stresses but reduce the interface shear stresses appreciably. Thus, pore water pressures in the soil may not affect the sinkage that depends primarily on the normal stresses but they may impair the development of traction seriously. Pore water pressures that reduce the interface shear stresses need not extend further than the immediate vicinity of the interface. Thus, saturation of a thin upper layer of a clay is sufficient for the wheel loads to generate pore water pressures and reduce traction resulting in a condition commonly known as slipperiness.

Results of Sample Computations

To illustrate the results obtained by the application of the principle of effective stresses to plasticity theory and wheel-soil interaction and to compare wheel performance in soils with and without pore water pressures, sample computations were performed for the following conditions (Karafiath, 1972b):

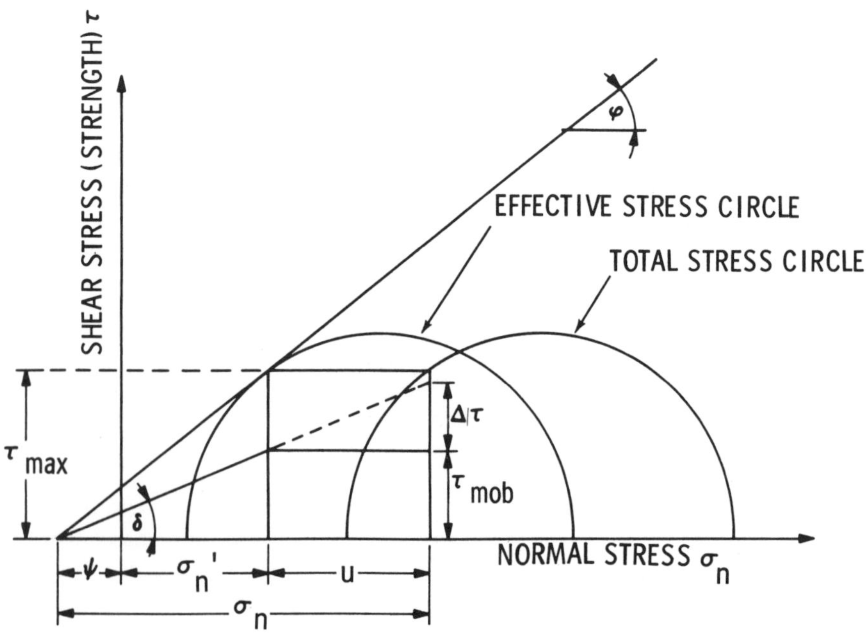

Fig. 3.49
Interface Shear Stresses in the Case of Pore Water Pressures

Wheel Geometry:			
	Radius (ft)	1.25	
	Width (ft)	0.54	
	Rear Angle (degree)	10	
Soil Properties:		Front	Rear
	Unit weight (lb/cu ft)	100	100
	Friction angle (degree)	35	37
	Cohesion (lb/sq ft)	50	50
Slip Parameters:		$j_0 = 0.1, K = 0.5$	
Pore Pressure Parameters: (Refer to Equation 1.3.14 and Table 1.22)			
	Case 1 (No pore water pressure)	$A = 0$	$B = 0$
	Case 2 (Pore water pressure)	$A = 0.1$	$B = 0.1$

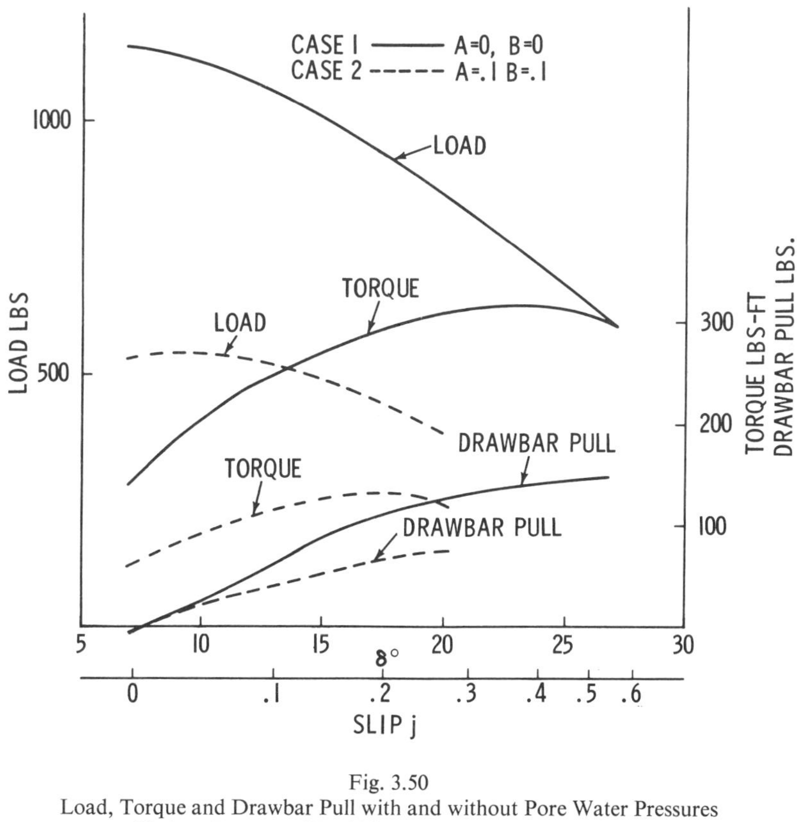

Fig. 3.50
Load, Torque and Drawbar Pull with and without Pore Water Pressures at Various Degrees of Mobilized Interface Friction Angle (δ)

Results of the computations, in which the angle δ, representing the mobilization of interface shear, was taken as the principal variable while the rear angle was kept constant, are summarized in Figure 3.50. It can be seen that with increasing δ the load carrying capacity of the wheel decreases, while the torque and drawbar pull increase. In Case 2, the load carrying capacity of the wheel is half of that in Case 1; an enormous decrease, considering that the assumed pore pressure parameters represent a very weak pore water pressure response to applied stresses. In Figure 3.51 the slip line fields for $\delta = 12°$, 16° and 20° are shown for both Case 1 and 2. For clarity, some of the slip lines computed in the program have been omitted.

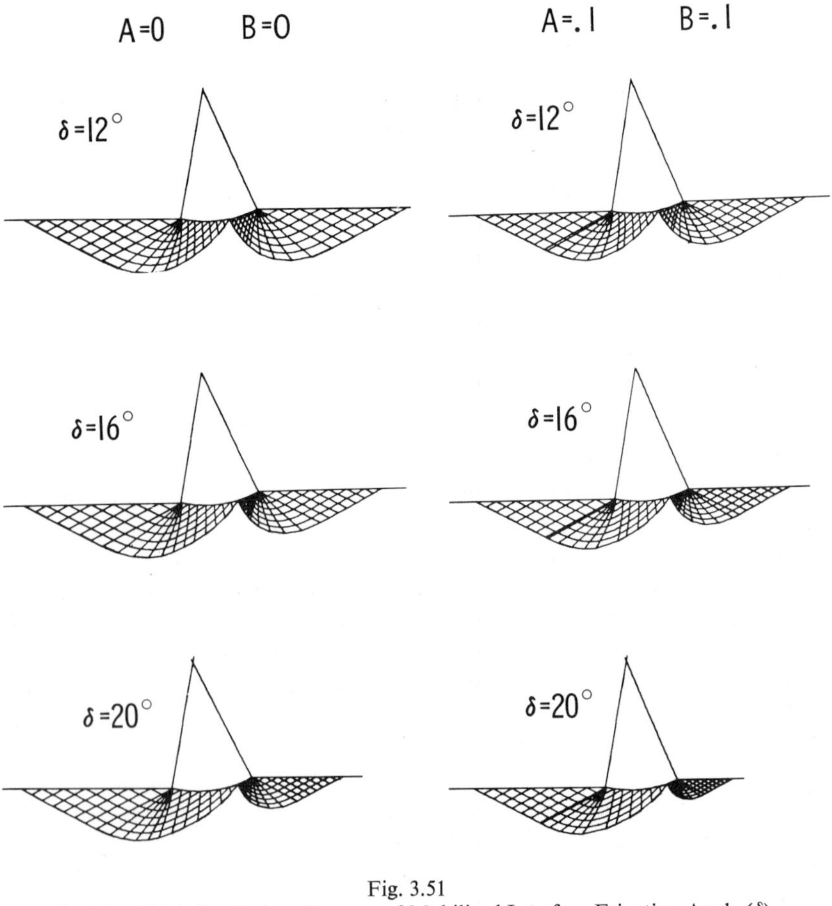

Fig. 3.51
Slip Line Fields for Various Degrees of Mobilized Interface Frinction Angle (δ) and Pore Pressure Parameters A and B

CHAPTER 3.4

PNEUMATIC TIRE-SOIL INTERACTION PARTIALLY CONTROLLED BY SOIL FAILURE CONDITIONS

3.4.1 Pneumatic Tire-Soil Interaction

In Chapter 3.2 general problems of the mathematical formulation of running gear-soil interaction were discussed. It was pointed out that certain idealizations are necessary to make the problem of running gear-soil interaction amenable to mathematical simulation. These idealizations, however, must not affect the fundamentals of the interaction between running gear and soil that govern running gear performance and make such simulation useful. In the case of pneumatic tires these fundamentals include the changes in the geometry of the contact area due to tire deflection. These changes affect tire performance profoundly and must, in some way, be taken into account in the mathematical simulation of tire performance.

Many theoreticians propose to use the rigid wheel as a model of the pneumatic tire and state that the pneumatic tire behaves as a rigid wheel. Such statements are suspect of being made more in the interest of promoting a rigid wheel theory than in the interest of disseminating valid information on tire behavior. While under certain conditions pneumatic tires indeed behave as rigid wheels, these conditions would have to be defined for practical applications to prevent the misuse of the rigid wheel model. Obviously, the definition of these conditions would require a validated deflecting tire-soil model, obviating per se the usefulness of the rigid wheel representation of pneumatic tires.

The consideration of the geometry changes in pneumatic tire-soil interaction is one of the most difficult problems of the mathematical simulation of this interaction. The elastomeric properties of rubber and chord materials and the laminated structure of tire carcasses present such problems for the determination of tire deflections that the application of sophisticated finite element methods is necessary for the mathematical solution of the problem. Even so, up to now the solutions obtained by finite element methods have been restricted to specific and relatively simple loading conditions.

In the case of pneumatic tire-soil interaction the interface stresses are not known beforehand and, therefore, an iterative application of the finite element method would be necessary to determine tire deflection under given loading conditions. Since finite element methods require considerable computer time and core capacity, their iterative application for the solution of tire-soil interaction problems is unacceptable for reasons of economy. Clearly, a compromise between refined tire deflection computations and the simplistic approach of rigid wheel representation is needed for the engineering solution of the tire-soil interaction problem. A basis for such compromise solution is the experimental information on tire behavior in soft soils. Tire deformation and interface stress measurements that are useful for this purpose are discussed next.

Deformation of Tires on Rigid Surfaces and in Yielding Soils

A measure of the deformation of tires is the shape and size of the contact area. On rigid surfaces, tire deflection defines the contact area and, thereby, the intensity of ground pressure. The contact area of tires may be approximated by a rectangle, an ellipse, or a torus section; for these shapes relationships between deflection and contact area have been derived for various inflation pressures (EBERAN-EBERHORST, 1965). Variations in the length of the contact area with the speed of rolling and with slip have also been studied both experimentally and theoretically (CLARK, 1971). From the viewpoint of tire-soil interaction the significance of contact area determinations on rigid surfaces is that it establishes a lower limit for the contact area in yielding soils.

The deflection (δ) of a tire on a rigid surface is defined as the difference between the unloaded and loaded section height (Figure 3.52) and percentage deflection (100. δ/h) as the percentile ratio of the deflection to unloaded section height. This measure of tire flexibility was introduced by FREITAG (1965) as a tire deformation characteristic in the dimensional analysis of tire performance.

While the deflection of the tire one a rigid surface is a useful measure of tire flexibility, it does not allow the calculation of tire deflection under other than vertical loads or in yielding surfaces. Various models have been proposed (CLARK, 1965; DODGE, 1965) for the analysis of tire deflections. One such model consists of a cylindrical shell; another of springs acting on a cylindrical shell from the inside. Although the deformation of the

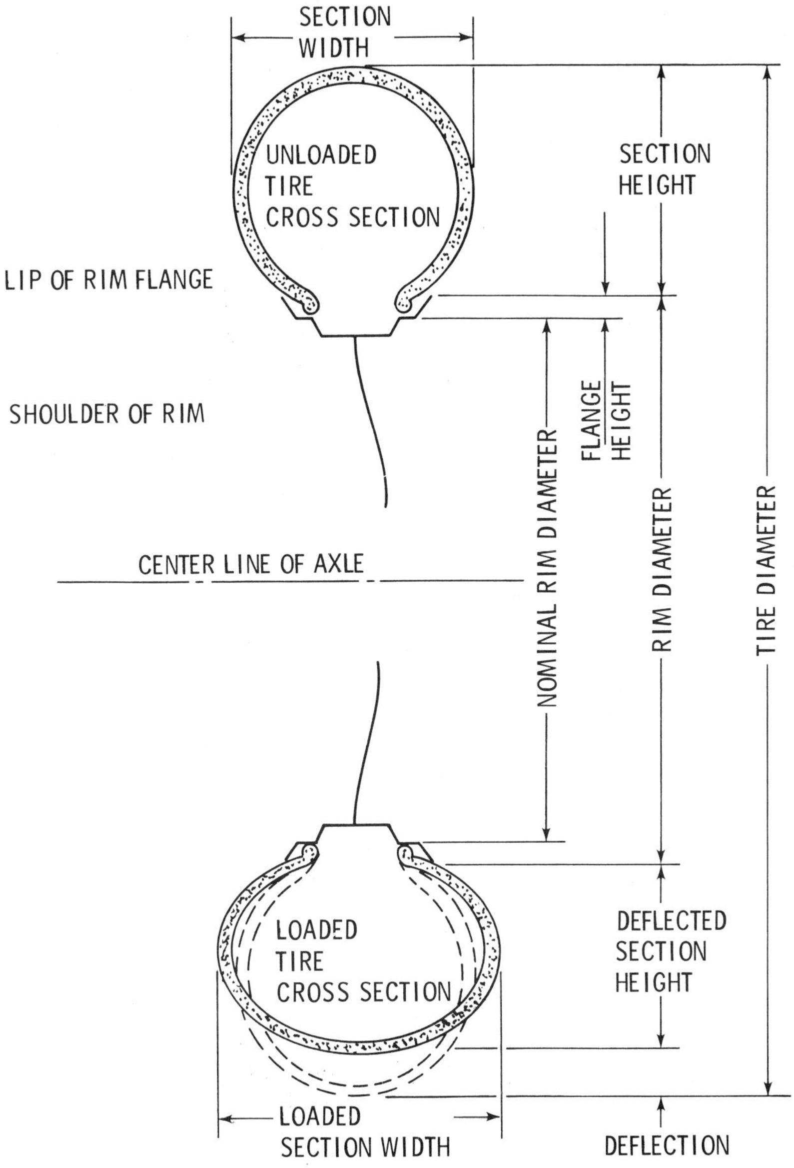

Fig. 3.52
Pneumatic Tire Terms
(After FREITAG, 1965)

tire may be reasonably approximated by these models under the conditions for which each was developed, the elastic and other constants used in the models are not generally available for tires. Computation of tire deformation on a yielding surface using the cylindrical shell, or any other model would be possible only if the response of the yielding surface could be adequately represented by a spring model. This is not the case with soils in failure condition when interacting with wheels or tires.

Measurements of tire deformation in yielding soils have been undertaken by several investigators. FREITAG and SMITH (1966) presented a comprehensive evaluation of the centerline deflections of tires measured under a variety of soil strength, inflation pressure, loading and slip conditions. A typical result of their investigations is shown in Figure 3.53 where centerline deflections of a 9.00—14 tire in Yuma sand are shown for various percentages of slip. The figure shows that with increasing slip, higher and higher shear stresses are transmitted to the soil at the tire-soil interface. These shear stresses decrease the capacity of the soil to carry loads. The stiffness of the tire relative to the ground increases with increasing slip and the tire shape approaches that of a rigid wheel. Other experiments by FREITAG and SMITH point to the same qualitative conclusion: the shape of the deflected tire depends on the stiffness of the tire relative to the ground. Deflection and tire imprint measurements by KRICK (1969, 1971) generally confirm the above conclusions.

Effect of Tire Deflection on the Development of Stresses at the Tire-Soil Interface

Tire deformation affects tire-soil interaction in two ways: it changes the geometry of the tire-soil interface, and it relieves the stresses that would develop in the soil if the interface were undeformable. Experiments in which stresses at the tire-soil interface were measured not only confirm this latter effect but also give an indication of the magnitude of the stress relief, as the following discussions show.

The interface stresses generated by the tire load on a given surface are influenced not only by the size and shape of the tire and by the applied inflation pressure but also by the type of tire construction and by the geometry and properties of the tread. To eliminate variations in stresses due to the tire tread, tests at the U.S. Waterways Experiment Station (WES) have generally been performed with treadless or buffed tires (see, for example, TURNAGE, 1972). Even though a considerable number of experiments were performed for the purpose of interface stress measurements, only very general conclusions can be drawn from these experiments because of the wide variety of tires and soil conditions. In the following paragraphs these conclusions will be discussed first from the viewpoint of tire deflection on rigid surfaces and then from the viewpoint of tire deflection on yielding surfaces.

At the Waterways Experiment Station tire interface stress measurements were first made on unyielding surfaces that allowed the placement of sensors in the unyielding surface rather than the tire (WES, 1964). Results of these measurements are of interest for tire-soil interaction studies because stresses measured on an unyielding surface represent the upper limit of stresses that would develop in a soil that yields relatively little under the tire load. Normal stresses developing on a rigid surface in the contact area of stationary and slowly rolling tires were measured in an experimental program at WES in 1961 as a first step in gaining information on the pressure distribution at the tire-soil interface. The general pattern of stress distribution observed in these tests showed a fairly uniform stress distribution over the center portion of the contact area, and stress concentra-

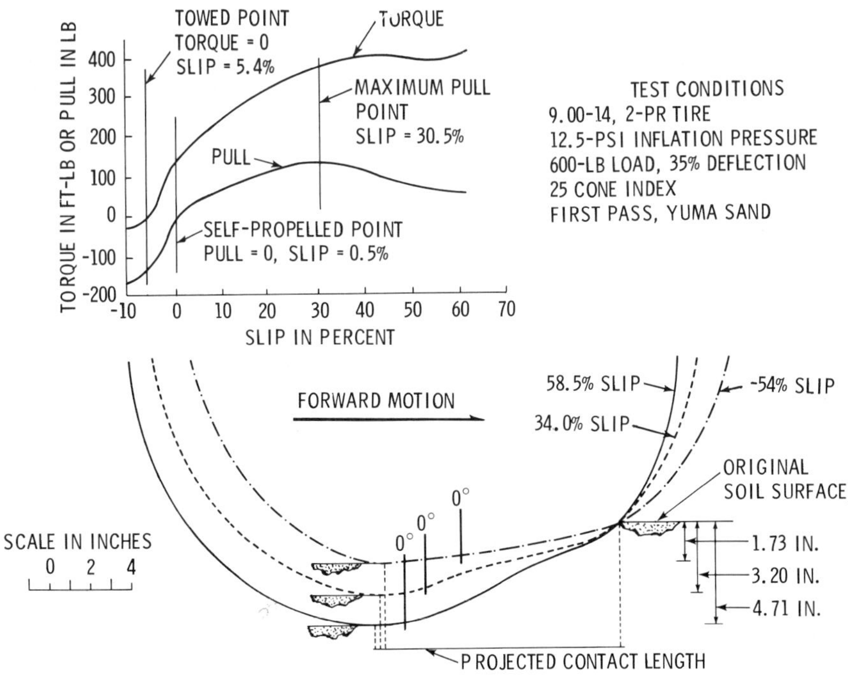

Fig. 3.53
Centerline Deflection of a 9.00–14 Tire Under Various Loading Conditions
(After FREITAG and SMITH, 1966)

tions called "edge stresses" at the perimeter of the contact area. These edge stresses are related to the sidewall stiffness of the tire while the magnitude of the average center portion stresses is related to the inflation pressure of the tire. Experiments performed by SEITZ (1969) at the Munich Polytechnic generally confirmed these findings. BODE (1962) investigated the distribution of shear stresses at the tire-roadway interface at various values of tractive and braking forces. A review of these and other contact stress measurements on rigid surfaces is given by CLARK (1971), Chapter 5.

The magnitude and distribution of normal and shear stresses that develop in the contact area between a tire and a rigid surface as a reaction to the tire load are of interest not only because they constitute a limit to the interface stresses that may develop in soils but also because they are indicative of the general pattern of stress distribution. Naturally, as the soil yields under the tire load, the contact area increases and a general reduction of the average value of the contact stresses results. Yielding of the soil also flattens out the high peaks in the contact stress distribution at the perimeter of the contact area where stress concentrations occur. The effect of soil yielding on the stress distribution was investigated by many researchers. VANDEN BERG and GILL (1962) measured the interface stresses that develop in the soil beneath tractor tires. Figure 3.54 shows typical stress distribution patterns obtained in their experiments. The general pattern of stress distribution is similar to that obtained on rigid surfaces. Stress concentrations occur at the perimeter, while over the center portion of the contact area the pressure is quite uniform and varies with the inflation pressure. FREITAG et al (1965) made extensive investigations to determine the stress distribution in the contact area of both towed and powered tires under a wide variety of loading conditions, inflation pressures and soil conditions. A typical result of their measurements is indicated in Figure 3.55. The vertical components of the normal stresses measured in the centerline and 3.75 inches off-center of a 11.00—20 tire, inflated to 19 psi are shown for powered and towed conditions. The maximum stress in each case exceeds only sligthly the inflation pressure. The resultant of the normal stresses in all of the 32 tests performed in this experimental program passed within 0.5 inch of the axle centerline, indicating that tire deflections were such that normal stresses did not generate any moment about the axis, a condition that is characteristic of rigid wheels. All these tests were performed with buffed tires. The question arises whether or not the peripheral stiffness of treaded tires shifts the normal stress distribution relative to the tire axis and generates moments about the axis. Since such a moment would increase the engine torque requirement in a wasteful way, the question is of more than academic interest and deserves further research.

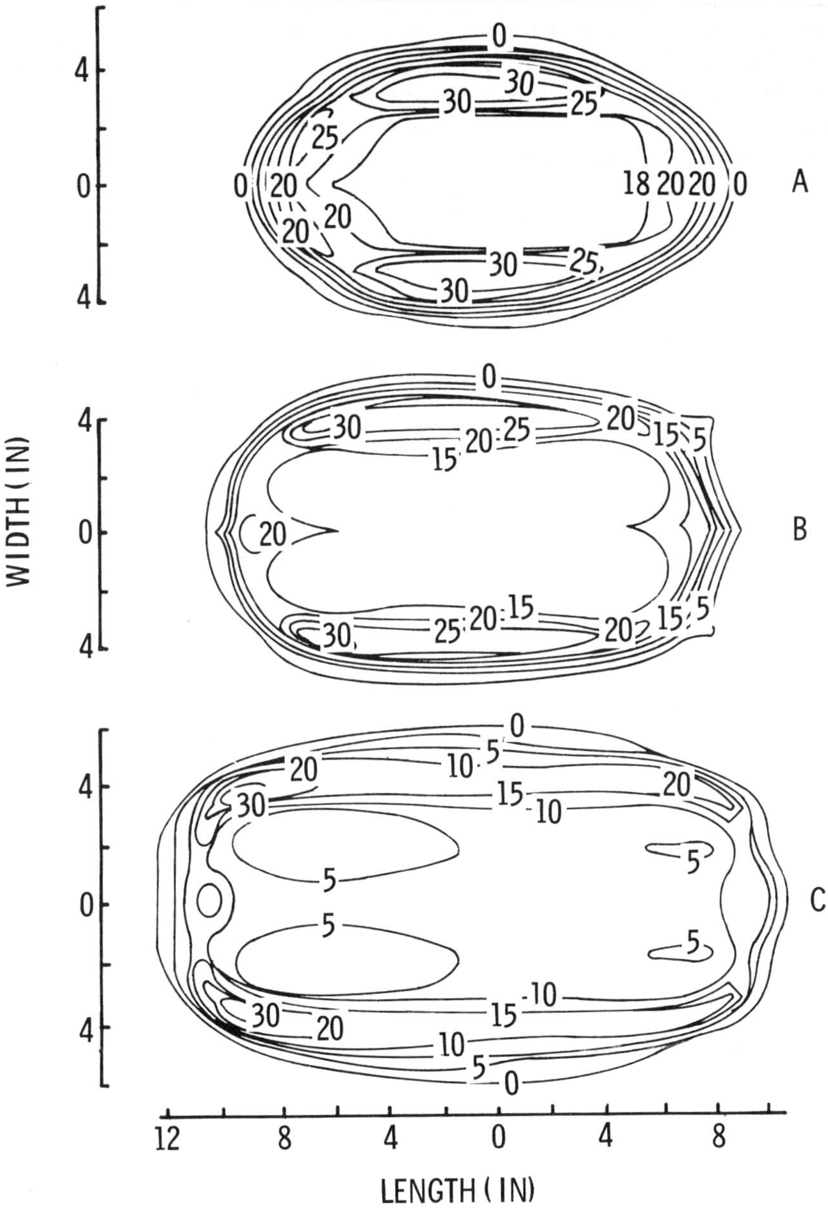

Fig. 3.54
Contour Maps of Pressure Distribution Under a 11.0–38 Smooth Tire on Firm Sand Inflated to: A) 14 psi; B) 10 psi; C) 6 psi. The direction of travel of tire was from right to left. Numbers indicate pressure in psi
(From VANDEN BERG and GILL, 1962)

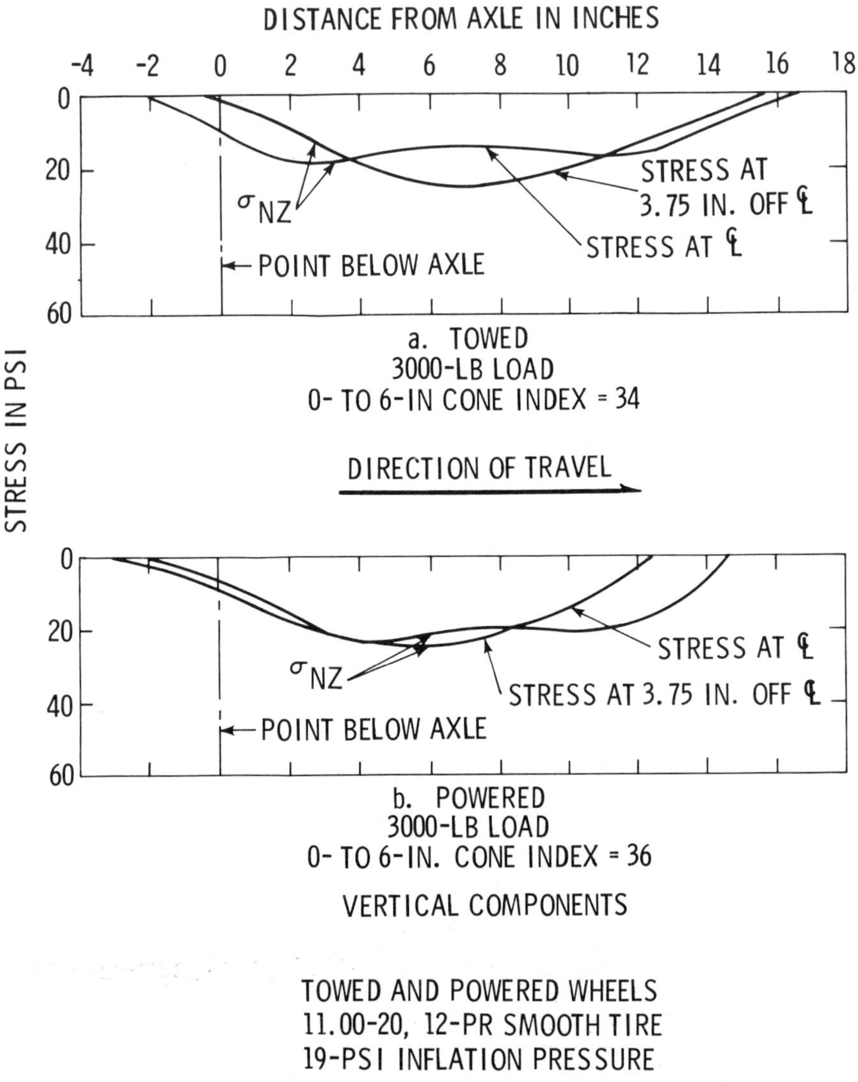

Fig. 3.55
Vertical Components of Normal Stresses Measured in Sand
(After FREITAG et al, 1965)

KRICK (1969) also measured normal and shear stresses on the interface of both rigid wheels and tires in sandy loam. Figure 3.56 shows the results of one of his experiments, referenced to the undeflected tire, obtained at 40% slip. The effect of tire deflection on restraining the maximum normal stress is evident if normal stresses measured on tires are compared with those on rigid wheels under the same loading conditions.

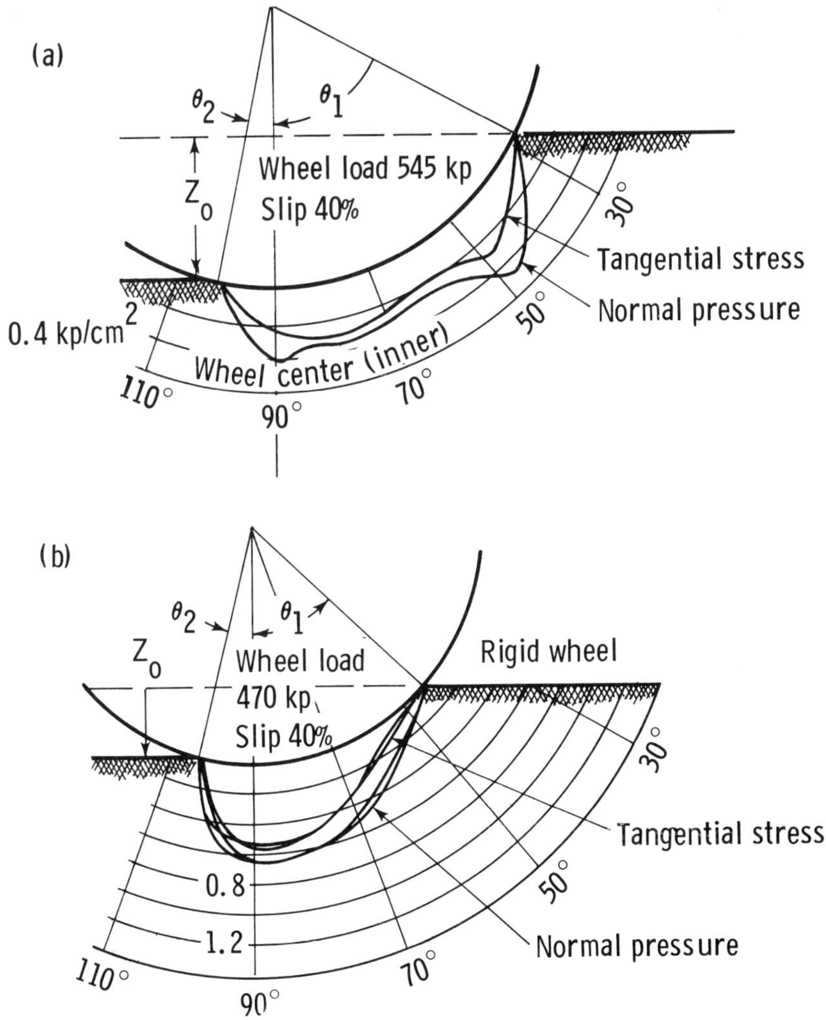

Fig. 3.56
Distribution of Normal and Tangential Stresses Beneath Tire (a) and Rigid Wheel (b) in Sandy Loam. Tire deflection not shown.
(After KRICK, 1969)

TRABBIC et al (1959) measured tire-soil interface pressures on the undertread, lug face and trailing lug side of tractor tires at various drawbar pulls and inflation pressures. Stress concentrations on the lug faces as opposed to the undertread were observed. The general trend of stress distribution reflected the effect of tire inflation pressure as found by other investigators.

Concept of Pneumatic Tire-Soil Interaction

The deformation and stress measurements discussed briefly in the preceding paragraphs indicate the complexity of the tire-soil interaction problem. The shape of the tire and the geometry of the contact area depend not only on the properties of the tire, but on the properties of the soil and the loads applied. The stresses measured over the full contact area are far from uniform. Stress concentrations occur at the edges of the contact area. Obviously, all these variations cannot be considered in a tire-soil interaction concept that is to yield practical solutions of problems occurring in off-road vehicle engineering practice. Even if unlimited computer usage were available for the solution of these problems, a refined interaction concept that would reflect all these variations in the geometry of the contact area and in the interface stresses would undoubtedly require generally unavailable input parameters with regard to tire characteristics and soil properties. Thus, an appropriately simplified tire-soil interaction concept is needed that uses readily available input parameters to yield sufficiently accurate results for the purposes of off-road vehicle engineering.

To decide what simplifications can be undertaken in a concept without jeopardizing its accuracy and usefulness, it is expedient to consider the tire as a free body and to assess the effect of possible simplifications on the performance of the tire. The edge stresses in the contact area, as experiments indicate, are symmetrical both crosswise and lengthwise (refer to Figure 3.54). This symmetry allows one to consider average stresses across the tire without any significant loss of accuracy in the performance calculations. Likewise, edge stresses may be averaged lengthwise and the resulting torque, load and drawbar pull still may be reasonably close to the actual values. Conversely, it is important to duplicate the deflected shape of the tire and its orientation to the ground surface as closely as possible. In the summation of the interface stresses for the computation of the drawbar pull, the inclination of the interface elements to the ground surface cannot be neglected. Depending on the inclination of the element, normal stresses on the interface yield a component (plus or minus) in the direction of the drawbar pull that may or may not be significant relative to the component of the shear stresses.

To treat the tire-soil interaction two dimensionally, it is necessary to assume that the width of the contact area is constant. This assumption is reasonable for certain types of tires; for others it may be necessary to allow for a change of the width of the tire with a change in the loading conditions.

The assumption of a constant tire width and two dimensional conditions simplifies the consideration of tire deformation since the tire may then be represented by its centerline geometry. A measure of the general inclination of the centerline in the contact area is the sinkage of the tire. From the tire deformation and interface stress measurements discussed in Section 3.4.1, only very general conclusions can be drawn as to the combined effect of the tire stiffness and soil reaction on the geometry of the centerline. These general conclusions are portrayed schematically in Figure 3.57. Tire deformation is negligible, and the tire behaves as a rigid wheel if the tire stiffness is great relative to the ground (right corner of the diamond scheme in Figure 3.57). In the other extreme (left corner), soil deformation is negligible and the centerline geometry approaches that on a rigid surface, if the stiffness of the ground relative to that of the tire is great. The deflection and sinkage for intermediate combinations of tire stiffness and soil strength is found by constructing the intersection of lines starting from the qualitatively estimated tire stiffness and soil strength and paralleling the sides of the diamond (dashed lines). The intersection projected vertically to the horizontal diagonal indicates qualitatively the magnitude of sinkage and tire deflection that can be expected under this combination of tire stiffness and soil strength. It is essential that a well conceived tire-soil concept reflects this qualitative relationships, preferably in such a way that quantification of the relationship by experiments be realizable with state of the art methods.

The effect of tire deformation on soil reaction is another important factor that has to be considered in a tire-soil interaction concept. As discussed in Chapter 3.3, soil reaction stresses on rigid wheels are controlled by the failure conditions in the soil that develop beneath towed or driven rigid wheels under the applied wheel load. In the case of rigid wheels, there is no limit to the interface stresses other than that imposed by soil failure criteria. As it was pointed out before, experiments with tires indicate that except for local stress concentrations, tire deformation does not allow the development of normal stresses higher than a certain limit. This limit is related to the inflation pressure of the tire. In this respect, it is of interest to review the data on the average contact stresses obtained with stationary or slowly rolling tires on a rigid surface and the relationships proposed to relate these average contact stresses to the inflation pressure of the tire. Since the contact area in yielding soils is always greater than on a rigid surface, the average stresses must be lower for the same load than those obtained on a rigid surface, all other conditions being the same. Thus, the average stresses measured on rigid surfaces represent an upper limit to the average stresses in yielding soils. The general form of the

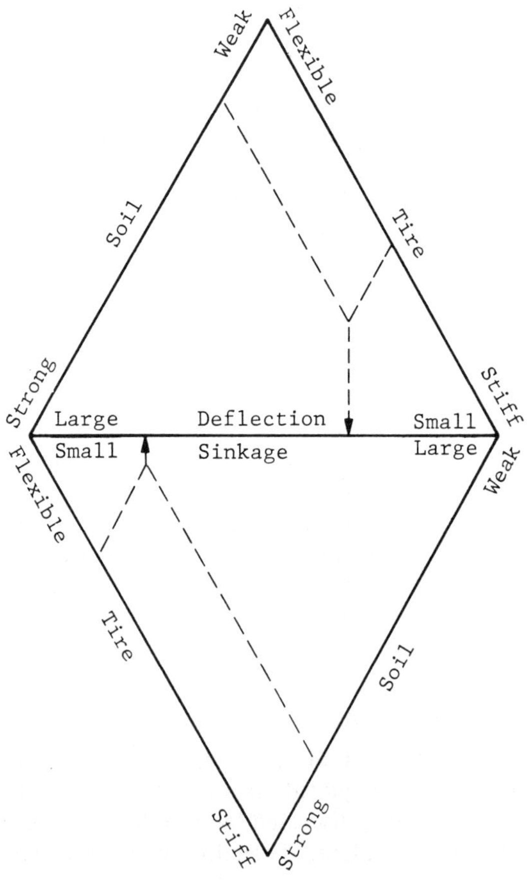

Fig. 3.57
Schematic Representation of Tire-Soil Behavior
(Based on WES experiments)

equations proposed by various researchers for the relationship between the average contact stress and inflation pressure is as follows:

$$p = c_1 p_i + p_c \qquad \text{Eq. 3.4.1}$$

where

p = average contact stress
p_i = inflation pressure
p_c = average pressure transmitted by the carcass at $p_i = 0$
c_1 = constant expressing the effect of the carcass stiffness of the tire

Bekker and Janosi (1960) found that p_c is independent of the inflation pressure, as postulated in Equation 3.4.1 and concluded that Equation 3.4.1 holds true for both yielding and unyielding surfaces. For a 7.00—16 tire, p_c was found to vary from 2.4 psi at 300 lb load to 4.8 psi at 700 lb load with $c_1 = 1$. Other experiments performed to determine the contact pressures beneath tires of earth compacting equipment (Simon, 1964) indicate that c_1 may be as low as 0.6 for high inflation pressures. Ageikin (1959) suggested a value variying from 0.9 to 1.0 for c_1 and 6 to 10 psi for p_c; in his notation, however, p is the mean pressure in the flattened portion of the tire and not the average pressure over the whole contact area.

The effect of tire deformation on the development of interface stresses in the center portion of the contact area may also be expressed as a limit pressure that is related to the inflation pressure by the same type of relationships as Equation 3.4.1. The interface normal stress would equal this limiting pressure whenever the soil reaction stresses computed on the basis of plastic state of stresses in the soil exceeds this limit. Whenever these stresses are lower than the limit pressure, the plastic state in the soil governs the interface stresses. The magnitude of the area over which the limit pressure controls the interface stresses depends on the equilibrium conditions for the vertical components of the interface stresses that must equal the tire load.

Pneumatic Tire-Soil Model

The conceptual definition of the requisites for a workable tire-soil model discussed previously, guided the authors in the development of their tire-soil model. This model, discussed later in detail, represents the results of extensive studies of available deflection and interface stress measurements as well as tire performance tests. In the early stages of the development deflections and interface stresses computed by various versions of the tire-soil model were compared with experimental data. Later, those versions of the model that were capable of duplicating the measured deflections and interface stresses satisfactorily with appropriate imput parameters were tested against a broad range of tire performance tests. This approach was chosen because laborious deflection and interface stress measurements were available only for a few types of tires and for limited combinations of loading and soil conditions. On the other hand, the results of routinely performed tire performance tests were available that covered a wide variety of tire sizes, loading and soil conditions. Even though this experimental information was utilized as much as possible in the model development, the tire-soil model presented here is considered by the authors only as a first generation model that is suitable for further development and improvement.

The prototype tire-soil model from which the model versions for driven, towed and braked tires were derived, is shown in Figure 3.58. Regarding the geometry of the tire the following assumptions were made:

a) The width of the tire is constant in both the deformed and undeformed state.

b) The interface stresses across the width of the tire are uniform.

c) The shape of the tire is the same in all planes parallel to the plane of travel.

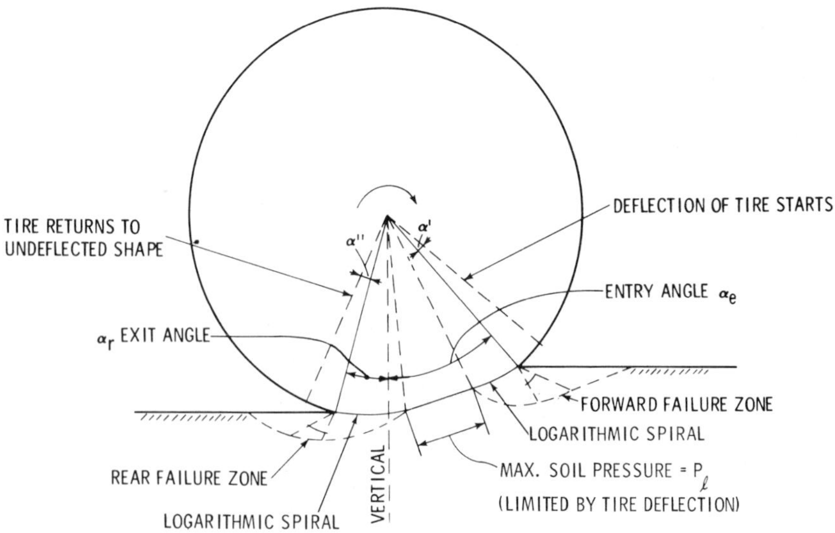

Fig. 3.58
Prototype Tire-Soil Model

d) The centerline geometry consists of two curvilinear segments separated by a linear, or flat section. It is assumed that the tire starts to deform ahead of the entry angle, α_e, and reaches its original form past the exit angle, α_r, as shown in Figure 3.58.

The curvilinear segments are logarithmic spirals with the radii decreasing according to the following relationship (Figure 3.59)

$$r = Re^{\beta(\alpha-\alpha_0)} \qquad \text{Eq. 3.4.2}$$

where

R = radius of the unloaded tire
r = deflected radius
β = constant
α = central angle
α_0 = initial central angle.

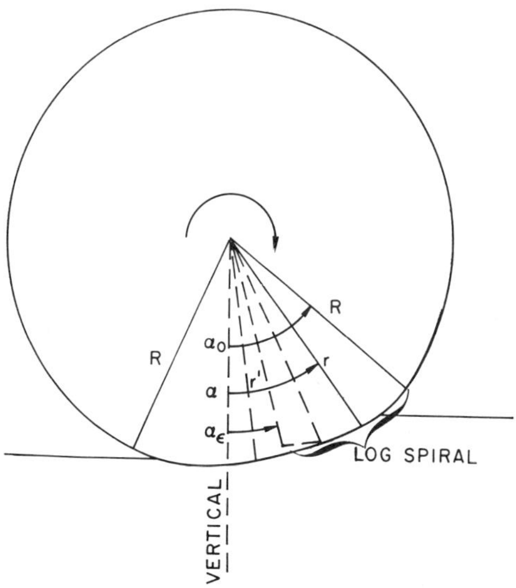

Fig. 3.59
Assumed Tire Centerline Geometry in the Front Portion of Tire

The effect of tire deflection on soil reaction comes into play in the prototype model in the following two ways:

a) Soil failure conditions, as indicated by the failure zones in Figure 3.58, govern the interface stresses along the length of the forward and rear failure zone. Deflection of the centerline affects the magnitude of these stresses; this effect is taken into account by using the deflected geometry as the boundary condition in the numerical computations. The assumed geometry of the curvilinear portion of the deflected centerline, corresponding to a logarithmic spiral, is very convenient in the numerical computation in that its tangent makes a constant angle with the radius.

b) Tire deflection is assumed to limit the normal stresses that may arise at the interface. The magnitude of this limiting pressure depends on the inflation pressure and carcass stiffness but otherwise it is constant. This limit pressure, p_l, defines the extent of the forward and rear failure zones, since the inner end of these zones is determined on the condition that the interface stress computed on the basis of stresses in the failure zones equals the limit pressure.

Another important factor in tire-soil interaction is the shear stresses generated at the interface by a driving or braking torque. The effect of these shear stresses is implicit in the model in that the geometry of the failure zone, or slip line fields depends on them. Shear stresses that are directed toward the free surface contribute to failure in that direction and, therefore, a lesser magnitude of interface normal stresses is sufficient to cause failure. A driving torque generates outward directed shear stresses in the rear and reduces thereby the interface normal stresses in the rear portion of the tire. A braking torque produces the same effect in the forward failure zone. This role of shear stresses constitutes the major difference among the driven, towed and braked versions of the interaction model.

The key feature of the prototype tire-soil model is the evaluation of the constant β in Equation 3.4.2. This constant determines the curvature of the logarithmic spiral and is a measure of tire deflection. As pointed out previously, tire deflection in soils depends on the relative stiffness between the tire and soil, as illustrated schematically in Figure 3.57. Tire stiffness depends primarily on the inflation pressure, while soil stiffness is directly related to the strength of the soil. The coefficient β in Equation 3.4.2 should reflect the combined effect of tire and soil stiffness. In the mathematical formulation of the model this is accomplished in the following way: The arc length of the interface of the forward failure zone depends on both the limiting pressure (which is related to the inflation pressure) and the soil strength. In strong soils the rise of normal stress is steep and the limiting pressure is reached over a short arc length, whereas in weak soil a longer arc length is needed to reach the same limiting pressure. On the other hand, for given soil conditions, the arc length depends on the limiting pressure; low limiting pressure (soft tire) results in short arc length, while high limiting pressure (hard tire) results in long arc length. Thus, the arc length of the forward failure zone is governed, at least qualitatively, by the same interrelationship that governs tire deflection in yielding soils. In order to incorporate this interrelationship into the mathematical formulation of the tire-soil model, a deflection coefficient, ε, is introduced that defines the shortening of the tire radius by deflection at a specified central angle (α_ε), as follows (Figure 3.59)

$$r' = \varepsilon R \qquad \text{Eq. 3.4.3}$$

The coefficient β is calculated for any given ε value from Equation 3.4.2. By this method of calculation, β depends on the arc length of the front failure zone and reflects, at least qualitatively, the desired interrelationship between tire deflection and soil and tire stiffness. The angle α_ε has been defined in connection with the development of the computational schemes for the driven, towed and braked versions of the prototype model and is discussed together with the relationship between the coefficient ε and the deflection measured on a rigid surface in Section 3.4.2.

3.4.2 Computational Methods

The tire-soil interaction concept described in the preceding section provides the basis for the solution of the various tire performance problems occurring in off-road vehicle engineering. The mathematical formulation of these problems as well as the solution techniques depend on the magnitude and distribution of the interface shear stresses generated by the applied torque. Therefore, it is expedient to develop separate mathematical models for driven, towed (free rolling) and braked tires. These mathematical models are but slightly different versions of the prototype model. The differences in these versions from the prototype model are discussed together with the appropriate computational techniques in the subsequent sections.

Tire-Soil Model and Computational Scheme for Driven Tires

In the prototype tire-soil model shown in Figure 3.58 certain geometric characteristics, as for example the entry and rear angles and the centerline geometry associated with these angles, are assumed and certain principles are established that allow the determination of the interface stresses for these assumed geometric conditions. The tire forces (load, drawbar pull and torque) may then be computed by appropriate integration of the interface stresses. In off-road vehicle engineering the tire performance problems are posed differently: usually two of the tire forces are given and the problem is to find the third one. Incidental to the problem solution is the determination of the entry and rear angles and the sinkage associated with these angles. Slip is another parameter that is usually calculated in some way. Obviously, the mathematical model is not a direct answer to the problem as posed in off-road vehicle engineering and some inversion procedure is needed to find the solution for a given loading condition. Such a procedure usually consists of iterative calculations that converge toward the solution. These, as well as the numerical solutions of the differential equations of plasticity require the use of a computer with moderate capacity.

Drawbar pull and torque values obtained as a result of either tire performance calculations or tire performance tests are often presented in parametric from as a function of slip. If these values are available for the full range of slip then the solution of any tire performance problem is easily found by reading off corresponding values of drawbar pull and torque. The computational scheme presented here for the determination of the performance of driven tires has been devised to calculate one point of both the drawbar pull-slip and the torque-slip relationship per computation. Other computational schemes may be directed toward the determination of drawbar pull for given torque, or vice versa. All the essential information that is needed to devise such computational schemes is included in the subsequent description of the mathematical model for driven tire-soil interaction. Otherwise, the comments on the general relationships among the principal variables in rigid wheel-soil interaction, made in Section 3.3.4, apply.

In the prototype tire-soil model certain parameters were introduced, as for example the limit pressure, that have to be defined or related to measurable characteristics of tire and soil if the tire-soil model is to be used for performance prediction. Other variables, as for example the entry and rear angles, may be determined in the course of computations from the overall equilibrium of the tire as a free body, or from the continuity condition for the interface stresses. To define these parameters, or relate them to available information, an extensive computer analysis was made of all available tire performance test data. Many of the parameter values and approximate relationships among input data and tire-soil model parameters that are specified in the following description of the driven version of the tire-soil model are based on this extensive analysis of experimental data.

The objective of the development of the computational scheme is the calculation of drawbar pull, torque and sinkage from the following input data.

Tire characteristics:
- Radius, width (nominal, in the unloaded state)
- Inflation pressure
- Deflection (measured on rigid surface under the given load)

Soil characteristics:
- Cohesion
- Friction angle
- Unit weight

Loading conditions:
- Load
- Slip

The following discussions summarize the various relationships and parameter values that are needed in the tire-soil model for prediction purposes.

Interface Friction Angle and Slip. In the case of driven tires the torque generates shear stresses at the interface. As in the case of rigid wheels, these shear stresses may be related to the normal stresses by the interface friction angle, δ, that represents the degree of mobilization of the shear strength of the soil at the interface. In the driven version of the tire-soil model it is assumed that δ is uniform throughout the length of the contact area. The few experiments where shear stresses at tire-soil interfaces have been measured show that this assumption yields reasonable approximations for the shear stresses. Theoretical considerations, including analyses of the kinematic boundary conditions at the interface, discussed in Section 3.3.6, also indicate that the assumption of a constant interface friction angle is a reasonable one. The only qualification that may be made in connection with this assumption is that at very low torque values the distribution of shear stresses may resemble some sort of a transition between the one for a free rolling tire and the one for a driven tire at high torque that corresponds to a uniform interface friction angle. Such a transitional distribution could be simulated by a superposition of a uniform and a linearly varying δ angle. Since the torque in practical problems is generally large enough to suppress the shear stress distribution of the free rolling case, the special case of a low torque is not included in the further discussions.

In the concept of the tire-soil model, the angle of the developed interface friction, δ, is the independent variable that enters into the computation of the slip line fields. The angle δ is related to slip by the same equation as in the case in rigid wheels. This equation is

$$\tan \delta = \tan \delta_{max} (1 - e^{-(j+j_o)/K}) \qquad \text{Eq. 3.2.7}$$

The slip-shear parameters j_o and K in this equation depend on the soil properties and the tire characteristics. Originally, BEKKER (1956) proposed that these parameters be determined by direct shear tests in the laboratory. However, in the direct shear test the developed shear resistance that is related to the interface friction angle is measured as a function of the horizontal displacement of the shear box that has the dimension of length. To obtain slip, a dimensionless quantity, the measured displacement is sometimes divided by the length of the shearbox. The validity of this procedure is open to question. It appears that the differences in the scale of the laboratory test and the contact area of the running gear to which the laboratory results are applied affect the value of these parameters as the correlation studies, made in connection with the large scale computer analysis of tire performance tests, indicate. The results of these analyses are as follows.

The slip parameters depend not only on the properties of soil but also on the dimensions of the tire and the applied load. A correlation was found to exist between the dimensionless tire performance prediction terms developed at WES and the slip-shear parameters. Tentatively the following relationships are proposed for the determination of slip-shear parameters.

For frictional soils, based on tire tests in Yuma sand:

$$j_o = 0.046 - 0.0006\, N_s$$

$$K = e^{-0.58 \log 2 N_s}$$

where

$$\text{Sand number} = N_s = \frac{CGR\,(bd)^{3/2}}{W} \cdot \frac{\delta}{h} \qquad \text{Eq. 3.4.4}$$

For cohesive soils, based on tire tests in Buckshot clay:

$$j_o = -0.065 + 0.49/N_c$$
$$K = -0.06 + 0.66/N_c$$

where

$$\text{Clay number} = N_c = \frac{CI\,(bd)}{W}\;\frac{\delta^{1/2}}{h} \qquad \text{Eq. 3.4.5}$$

where

b = tire width
d = tire diameter
h = tire section height
δ = tire deflection
W = load
CI = cone index
CGR = cone index gradient

These relationships are entirely empirical and are not intended to represent causative relationships. For that purpose theoretical modeling of the slip-shear phenomenon in both shear strength tests in the laboratory and in full scale tire-soil interaction would be necessary.

Of the two types of soils for which these empirical relationships were established, the Yuma sand is typical of a purely frictional soil, while the Buckshot clay is typical of a purely cohesive soil. Slip parameters may be reasonably well estimated by Equation 3.4.4 for other purely frictional soils and by Equation 3.4.5 for other purely cohesive soils. However, there is but little useful information available on slip parameters for other, cohesive-frictional type soils. Where no experimental information is available for the estimation of slip parameters, the following procedure may be applied. Performance parameters are computed for equal increments of the interface friction angle, δ, and the pull performance curves are constructed for the full range of interface friction angles. It is not too difficult to assign slip percentages to certain characteristic points of the pull performance curve. Peaks in the pull performance curve are likely to occur at about 20 % slip. Pull performance curves that increase monotonically over the whole range of the interface friction angle are likely to show a break in their curvature at about 20 % slip. The self-propelled point (zero pull) is likely to occur at 2—4 % slip in frictional soils, while in cohesive soils the likely range of slip at this point is between 5 and 10 %. As the value of the interface friction angle approaches the friction angle of the soil, the slip approaches 100 %. From these estimated values it is possible to recalculate approximate values of the slip parameters.

Limit Pressure (p_l) and Inflation Pressure (p_i). In the tire-soil interaction concept the limit pressure is a measure of the effect of tire deflection on the development of interface normal stresses. As a conceptual quantity, it is closely tied to the tire-soil model and meaningful only in the context of the model. Therefore, even though the limit pressure is related to the average normal stresses in the center portion of the contact area, it is not amenable to direct measurement. Nevertheless, for a tire-soil model to be a working model for prediction purposes, it is necessary to establish relationships between the limit pressure and measurable tire characteristics. This has been done by a large scale computer analysis that resulted in the following relationship

$$p_l = 0.64\, p_i + 4 \text{ (psi)} \qquad \text{Eq. 3.4.6}$$

In the computer analysis tire diameters ranging from 7 to 20 inches and tire widths ranging from 4 to 9 inches were considered. Inflation pressures varied from 2.5 to 52 psi. Interestingly, the analyses showed that the tire pull performance was not overly sensitive to the value of limit pressure. It is probably on this account that it was possible to establish a single relationship, Equation 3.4.6, for several tire sizes and loading conditions. Nevertheless, for tire sizes outside of the range of this analysis Equation 3.4.6 is not necessarily the best approximation and it may be advantageous to perform a small rumber of tire tests and adjust the value of p_l, if necessary, on the basis of these tests.

Deflection Coefficient ε and Tire Deflection on Rigid Surface. In the driven version of the tire-soil interaction model the deflection coefficient is the parameter that, together with the angles α_d and α_r (Figure 3.60) defines the geometry of the centerline of the tire. The coefficient ε would be directly measurable had the angle α_ε been defined for the case of deflection on a rigid surface. If $\alpha_\varepsilon = 0$ is assumed for the deflection on rigid surface, then the deflection coefficient may be computed from the deflection measured on rigid surface as follows

$$\varepsilon = K \qquad \text{Eq. 3.4.7}$$

where

$$K = 1 - \frac{2\delta}{d}$$

and

δ = deflection on rigid surface

d = nominal tire diameter

In lieu of anything better, Equation 3.4.7 may be used to estimate the deflection coefficient. Nevertheless, it should be remembered that deflection on a rigid surface represents an extreme of the tire-soil stiffness ratio.

The large scale computer analysis of tires performance tests referred to earlier was also useful for the determination of α_ε and ε values that resulted in the best simulation of the pull performance of driven tires. It was found that for driven tires α_ε may be determined from the following equation:

$$\alpha_\varepsilon = \frac{1}{2}\,\alpha_d \qquad \text{Eq. 3.4.8}$$

where α_d = central angle at the end of the forward slip line field.

In conjunction with the determination of this relationship for α_ε, the ε coefficients that correlated with the best simulation were also determined for various tire sizes and inflation pressures. These ε values are given in Table 3.4 and are shown graphically in Figure 3.61 as a function of the deflection measured on the rigid surface.

Determination of the α' and α'' Angles. In the model the angle α' defines that point on the perimeter of the tire where the tire starts to deform and the angle α'' the point where the tire returns to its original shape (Figure 3.60). It was found that $\alpha' = \alpha'' = 5°$ yields sufficiently good approximation of the centerline geometry in both the front and rear portion and further refinement of these angles is not necessary.

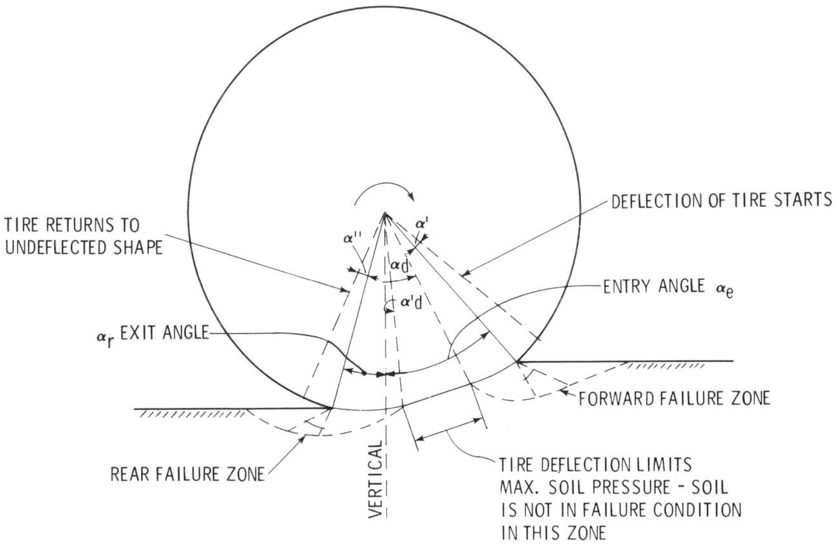

Fig. 3.60
Driven Version of Tire-Soil Model

Table 3.4
Estimation of the Deflection Coefficient ε for Various Tire Sizes

Tire Size	Relationship for Estimation, $\varepsilon =$
9.00–14	$1.24K - 0.195$
6.00–16	$1.62K - 0.59$
4.00–7	$1.14K - 0.115$
4.00–20.0	$0.91K + 0.085$
31 × 15–13	$0.98K + 0.065$

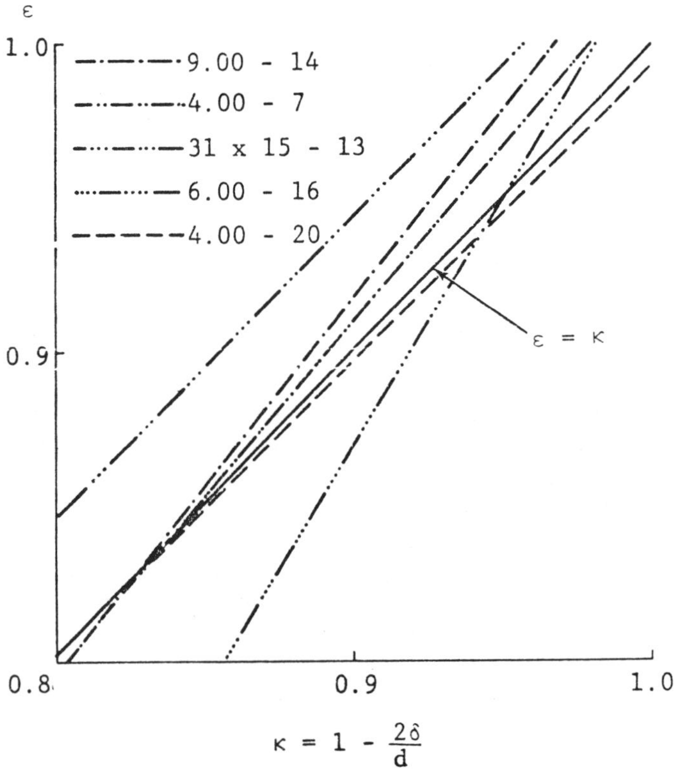

Fig. 3.61
Relationship Between the Deflection Parameters ε and K for Various Tire Sizes

Determination of the β coefficient for the tire-soil model. The curvilinear segments of the centerline are determined by the equation

$$r = R e^{\beta(\alpha - \alpha_0)} \qquad \text{Eq. 3.4.2}$$

In this equation α_o equals $\alpha_e + \alpha' = \alpha_e + 5°$, whereas $\alpha' = \alpha''$, according to the preceding discussions. The equation for the shortening of tire radius,

$$r = \varepsilon R \qquad \text{Eq. 3.4.3}$$

combined with Equation 3.4.2 yields for β the following relationship

$$\beta = \log \varepsilon \,/\, (\alpha - \alpha_e - 5°) \qquad \text{Eq. 3.4.9}$$

In the model, provisions are made to insure that the curvilinear segments of the front and rear portion should not result in a concave curvature (away from the interface). To this end the following limitations apply to the logarithmic spiral segments:

a) In the front field, the β coefficient is limited to such a value that the z coordinates of the spiral be always positive (below the surface).

b) In the rear field, the angle of inclination to the horizontal of the tangent to the logarithmic spiral at a particular nodal point is limited to the angle of a straight line from that point to the end of the forward field (no double curvature in the center portion).

If both of these limitations apply, then the centerline geometry reverts to that of a tire on a rigid surface.

Computation of a single slip line field. A detailed discussion of two methods that may be applied to the computation of a single slip line field in the case of rigid wheels was given in Section 3.3.3. In the case of pneumatic tires, either of these methods may be used with minor modifications required to adapt the computation method to the assumed centerline geometry of the tire. The finite difference equations used for the computation of the coordinates of the nodal points at the interface and the associated stresses are as follows (horizontal surface):

$$x_{i,j} = \frac{1}{1 + \alpha_o F} x_{i-1,j} + \alpha_o F x_{i-1,j-1} + \alpha_o (z_{i-1,j-1} - z_{i-1,j})$$

$$z_{i,j} = z_{i-1,j-1} + F(x_{i-1,j-1} - x_{i,j}) \qquad \text{Eqs. 3.4.10}$$

$$\sigma_{i,j} = \sigma_{i-1,j} + 2 \cdot \tan \varphi\, \sigma_{i-1,j} \cdot (\theta_{i,j} - \theta_{i-1,j}) + \gamma C$$

where

$$\alpha_0 = \text{cotan}\left(\frac{1}{2}(\theta_{i,j-1} + \theta_{i,j}) - \mu\right)$$

$$C = z_{i,j} - z_{i-1,j} - \tan\varphi \cdot (x_{i,j} - x_{i-1,j})$$

$$F = \tan(\alpha_{i-1,j-1} - \alpha_{sp})$$

In these equations α_{sp} denotes the angle between the tangent of the logarithmic spiral and the tangent to a circle with the same radius as the logarithmic spiral. This angle equals

$$\alpha_{sp} = \arcsin\beta \qquad \text{Eq. 3.4.11}$$

Computational scheme for the determination of tire performance parameters. The preceding discussions contained all information necessary for the determination of model parameters that sufficiently define the driven version of the tire-soil model so that for a set of initial values of certain central angles the interface stresses may be computed and the load, drawbar pull and torque determined by appropriate integration of the interface stresses. In the computational scheme the values of these angles are varied in a prescribed manner and their final values determined by an iteration process on the condition that the tire load computed for the tire geometry defined by these angles equals the input load within a given tolerance.

The determination of the entry and rear angles in a tire-soil interaction problem is one of the objectives of the solution procedure. However, in the computational scheme it was found more expedient to start the computations with the initial value of the angle α_d that defines the position of the inner end of the front slip line field (instead of α_e, the entry angle that defines the outer end of that field), and the rear angle α_r that defines the position of the singular point of the rear slip line field. In the driven version of the tire-soil model the following initial values are used for these angles:

$$\alpha_d = \arctan((p_l + \psi)\tan\delta/p_l) \qquad \text{Eq. 3.4.12}$$
$$\alpha_r = 10°$$

The main reason for choosing a procedure in which the computation is started with the initial value of the angle α_d is that for this angle it can be established by a relatively simple computation whether the tire load produces a forward slip line field under the soil conditions or not. Unnecessary iterations of forward slip line field computations can be omitted in the computational scheme by determining first the normal stress (q_m) that pertains to a hypothetical, infinitely small forward slip line field. This normal stress can be computed on the same basis as the stresses at the singular point where the θ angle changes from that at the free surface (θ_o) to that at the interface (θ_f) along an infinitesimal "*j*" line. Thus, the following equations hold:

$$\sigma_f = \sigma_o \, e^{2(\vartheta_f - \vartheta_o) \tan \varphi}$$

where

$\theta_o = 0$ (at the free surface)

$\sigma_o = c \cdot \text{cotan}\, \varphi / (1 - \sin \varphi)$

$\theta_f = \frac{1}{2} \pi + \frac{1}{2} (\Delta + \delta) - \alpha_d + \alpha_{sp}$

$$q_m = \sigma_f \cos \delta \left(\cos \delta - \sqrt{\cos^2 \delta - \cos^2 \varphi}\right) - c \cdot \text{cotan}\, \varphi \qquad \text{Eq. 3.4.13}$$

If q_m is greater than p_l, the limit pressure, then there can be no forward slip line field, since even for the generation of an infinitesimally small forward field higher normal pressures than p_l would be needed. In other words, the soil is too strong in this case to fail in the forward direction under the tire load. This, by itself, does not preclude the generation of a rearward directed slip line field by the tire load, since in the rear field the outward directed shear stresses reduce the normal stresses needed to produce failure in the soil. As a matter of fact, as δ approaches φ, the friction angle, the associated normal stresses approach zero and, therefore, for a sufficiently high, outward directed interface friction angle there is always a rear failure zone and slip line field.

In the case of $q_m < p_l$ both a forward and a rear slip line field are generated by the tire load. The computation starts with the forward field. The coefficient β is calculated for the logarithmic spiral for an assumed entry angle and the variables in the forward field are calculated using the subroutine for the calculation of a single slip line field in an iterative manner. In this subroutine the normal stress q_d at the angle α_d is calculated. An iteration on the entry angle, α_e, is performed until the normal stress q_d at angle α_d equals p_l within the allowed tolerance. A reasonable tolerance limit for these calculations is $\pm$ 5 % of the p_l value. Since the concept of limit pressure itself is only an approximation of the effect of tire deflection on the normal stresses, there is no point in setting a close tolerance limit and lengthen the calculations unnecessarily. When the forward slip line field meets the condition of $q_d = p_l \pm 0.05\, p_l$, then the entry angle, α_e, is set and the coordinates of the deflected geometry of the centerline as well as the associated normal and shear stresses are final for this condition. The results are stored, so that when the calculations for the rear field are completed, they are available for the summation of interface stresses over both the front and rear portion of the interface.

The extent of the rear slip line field is determined by the condition that it should end at the central angle α'_d, where the normal stress equals p_l. Between the angles α_d and α'_d (Figure 3.60) the interface normal stress equals p_l as postulated by the tire-soil model. Should, however, the interface normal stress computations in the rear field show that they are less than p_l even if the rear field extends up to the inner end of forward field at α_d, then p_l is made equal to q_d, the normal stress at α_d computed from the rear field, and the computation with the updated p_l value is repeated from the start. This situation may occur at high slip values when the relatively large outward directed interface friction angle reduces the bearing capacity of soil and the resulting normal stresses are lower than p_l over the contact area from α_r to α_d. In such cases the tire geometry resembles that of a rigid wheel, since the limit pressure no longer affects the interface stresses.

When both the forward and the rear field meet the conditions set for the normal stress at the inner end of the field, then the load, torque and drawbar values are calculated by summation of the respective horizontal and vertical components of the interface normal and shear stresses. Generally, the load obtained from this summation will not equal the input load within the tolerance limits. To offset the inaccuracies in the drawbar pull and torque calculations caused by the differences in the calculated load within the tolerance limits, it is practical to calculate pull and torque coefficients rather than drawbar pull and torque values. When this is done, a higher tolerance limit may be set for the load calculations.

If the calculated load is not within the allowed tolerance and is lower than the input load, then the angles α_r and α_d are increased, each by the same $\Delta\alpha$ value. If the calculated load is higher then the input value, then the angles α_r and α_d are decreased, again each by the same $\Delta\alpha$ value. Once the input load is bracketed by the loads calculated for the various α_r and α_d angles, finding the final values for these angles, at which the calculated load equals the input load within the allowed tolerance, is a routine matter of applying a convergent iteration scheme.

In the computations a lower limit is set for α_r and an upper one for α_e. Recommended limits are zero for α_r and 60° for α_e. Obviously, if the calculated load is higher than the input load at the minimum value of α_r, then the soil is too strong for failure to occur under the tire load and a "hard surface" situation exists. On the other hand, if the calculated load is lower than the input load at the maximum value of α_e, then the soil cannot support the tire load even at a very high sinkage of the tire and a "no go" situation exists.

In the case when $q_m > p_l$ there is only a rear slip line field. The rear field is computed by the subroutine for the calculation of a single slip line field. The initial value of the rear angle is set at 10°. In this case it is necessary to make an additional assumption as to the value of the entry angle. It was found from computer simulation studies of tire performance tests in cohesive soils that the assumption: $\alpha_e = 1.5\ \alpha_r$ yields reasonable approximations of pull performance. The rear field extends to the entry angle if the normal stress there is less than p_l; otherwise it ends at an angle where the normal stress equals p_l.

Tire-Soil Model and Computational Scheme for Towed Tires

The determination of drawbar pull that a powered tire can develop under various soil conditions is of prime importance for cross-country mobility. However, it is often necessary to evaluate the performance of off-road vehicles towing trailers or of all wheel drive vehicles when the front wheel drive is disengaged or inoperative. Another important tire-soil interaction problem is the determination of the drag force acting on the free rolling wheels of aircraft landing gears during landing on or taking off from unprepared airfields. For these purposes a towed version of the prototype model is needed.

The first tire-soil model that considered tire deflection was developed by Janosi (Bekker and Janosi, 1960) for towed tires. Many features of his model were incorporated in the prototype tire-soil model presented here. The towed version of this model, shown in Figure 3.62, differs from the driven version primarily in the magnitude and distribution of the interface shear stresses. The following concepts of towed tire-soil interaction are incorporated in the model:

a) Tire deflection is related to the arc length of the front slip line field in the same way as in the driven version of the model.

b) The interface friction angle, δ, that governs the shear stress distribution is assumed to vary linearly from the entry and exit points to a central angle, α_τ, where its sign changes. This assumption results in a shear stress distribution similar to that obtained for towed rigid wheels shown in Figure 3.12.

c) For the shear stresses the criterion has been adopted that their moment about the tire axis is zero. While at the first glance this criterion appears to be self-evident for a towed tire where the applied torque is zero, it should be borne in mind that in the case of a deflecting tire normal stresses may also produce moments about the axis. In such a case the moment produced by the normal stresses would have to be balanced by a moment due to shear stresses, thus resulting in a different shear stress distribution. The lack of experimental information on the interface shear stresses developing beneath towed tires precludes at this time the formulation of a concept that would take this contingency into account.

d) For the driven version of the tire-soil model, relationships were developed between slip and interface friction angle. In the case of towed tires a certain amount of negative slip, or skid develops. This is, however, of minor importance, since it does not, *per se,* affect travel efficiency or power consumption. Therefore, skid-interface friction relationships are not considered in the model. The interface friction angle, which has its maximum value at the entry and exit points is assumed on the basis of shear stress measurements with towed rigid wheels as $\varphi/4$ at these points. In the development stage

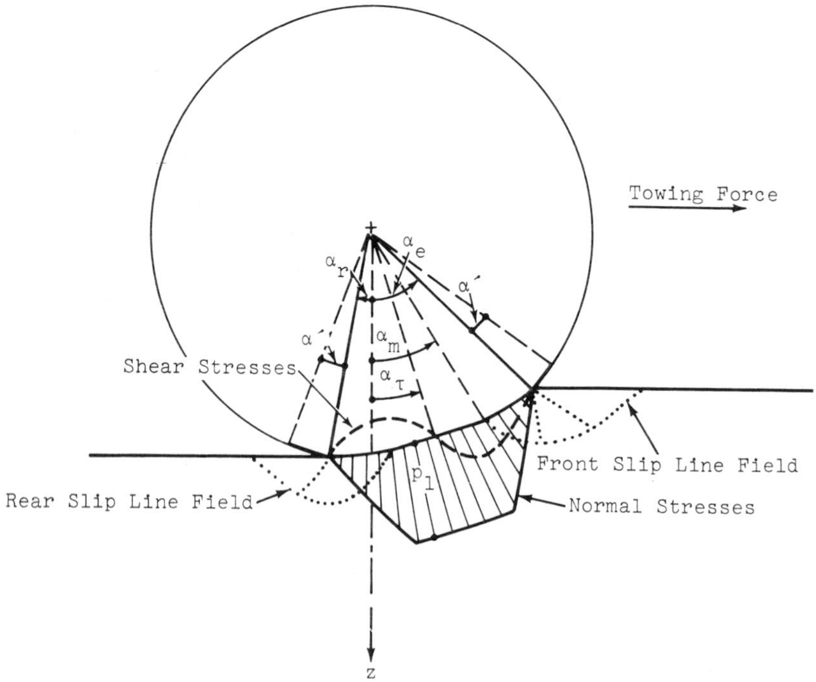

Fig. 3.62
Towed Version of Tire-Soil Model

of the towed version of the tire-soil model, analyses of tire tests were made with various values of the model parameters. These analyses indicated that the α_τ angle, the angle at which the shear stresses become zero, may be assumed as

$$\alpha_\tau = \frac{1}{2}\alpha_d \qquad \text{Eq. 3.4.14}$$

Limit pressure (p_l) and inflation pressure (p_i). In the towed version of the prototype tire-soil model the limit pressure plays the same role as in the driven version. However, analyses of a large number of tire tests showed that in the towed version the relationship between limit pressure and inflation pressure is different from that in the driven version. For tire sizes ranging from 4.00—7 to 31 x 15—13 the following relationship is recommended:

$$p_l\,(\text{psi}) = 0.82\,p_i + 6\,(\text{psi}) \qquad \text{Eq. 3.4.15}$$

Computation of a single slip line field. For the computation of a single slip line field the subroutine used for the driven version may be used with the minor modification that the interface friction angle, δ, varies from a maximum value at the entry and rear angles to zero at angle α_τ.

Deflection coefficient ε and angles α' and α''. Assumptions and computations are the same as in the driven version.

Computational scheme for the determination of the towing (drag) force. The foregoing explanations of the model parameters and the relationships introduced for the estimation of some of the parameters from readily available information sufficiently define the towed version of the tire-soil model so that the computation of the interface stresses becomes straightforward for a given initial geometry. This initial geometry is defined by the initial values of the following angles:

Initial value of the rear angle $\alpha_r = 10°$

Initial value of the angle at inner end of front field $\alpha_d = 20°$

The final values of these angles are determined in the course of computations from the load equilibrium conditions. Starting with the initial values of these angles, the interface stresses are computed and the load determined by the summation of the vertical components of all stresses. If the computed load is outside the tolerance limits of the input load, then the values of these angles are changed so that the following relationship holds:

$$\alpha_d = 1.5\,\alpha_r + 5° \qquad \text{Eq. 3.4.16}$$

To avoid unnecessary iterative computations it is convenient to include the computation of the normal stress at angle α_d for an infinitely small forward slip line field. If this normal stress, q_m, computed by Equation 3.4.13 is greater than p_l, then the soil conditions are such that no failure zone develops in the front of the tire under the tire load. While in the case of driven tires this condition did not exclude the development of a rear failure zone (since the torque-generated shear stresses promote rearward directed failure), in the case of towed tires the condition $q_m > p_l$ is prohibitive in regard to a rear failure zone too. In the case of towed tires the rise of normal stresses in the rear field is generally steeper than in the front since there is no difference in the magnitude and direction of the interface friction angle in the two fields, but the inclination of the interface is less steep in the rear than in the front. Thus the condition $q_m > p_l$ signifies a situation where the tire load is too small to cause failure in the soil. The towed (drag) force coefficient in such cases is very small, probably only slightly higher than on a rigid surface and, therefore, is of no particular interest in off-road mobility evaluation.

If $p_l > q_m$, then there are two slip line fields, one in the front and another in the rear. The computations start with the front slip line field so that the β coefficient and the entry angle may be determined. To this end the size of the front slip line field has to be found that is associated with a normal stress at the inner end of the field that equals p_l within the allowed tolerance. The iteration schemes developed for this purpose for the driven version assume that the normal stresses increase from the entry point toward the inner points at the interface. While this is generally true for a constant δ angle of interface friction assumed in the driven version of the model, it is not necessarily so when the δ angle decreases from the entry point toward the inner points, as it is assumed in the towed version. It was found that in certain cases in cohesive soils with a low friction angle the normal stress is unchanged or even decreases from the entry point for a certain rate of decrease in the δ angle. Measurements of normal stresses at the interface of a rigid wheel in clay by UFFELMANN (1961), shown in Figure 3.63, indicate that in highly cohesive soils this is, indeed, possible. This feature of the normal stress distribution in cohesive soils makes it necessary to employ provisions in the computation scheme that account for this situation. The main problem to be resolved is the determination of the size of the front slip line field for nearly constant normal stresses. In principle, this problem has been resolved by the assumption that in the case of nearly constant normal stresses, the size of the front field for entry angles between 30 and 60 degrees is determined by the condition that the vertical components of all normal stresses be equal to the load. The rear angle is assumed as 10 degrees for entry angle variations from 30 to 60 degrees. For entry angles assumed between these values, all interface stresses are computed and the final entry angle is determined by iteration on the condition that the vertical components of interface stresses equal the load. For entry angles less than 30 degrees the rear angle is reduced by half of the difference between the entry angle and 30 degrees.

Tire-Soil Model and Computational Scheme for Braked Tires

In the development of the driven and towed versions of the prototype tire-soil model the available tire performance tests were extensively studied and used both for the evaluation of the effects of the various model parameters and for the validation of the final model. The braked condition, although significant in such cases as the drag force estimation for aircraft landing on unprepared airfields, has not been extensively tested in the laboratory. Therefore, the values of model parameters for the braked condition could not be determined by large scale analyses, as was

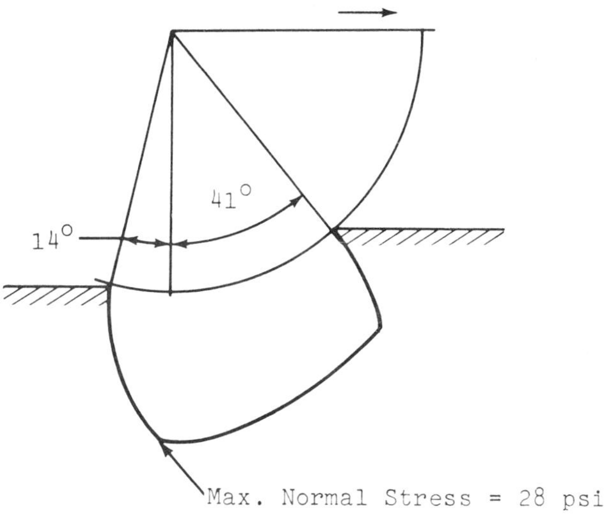

Fig. 3.63
Distribution of Normal Stresses Beneath a 54 inch Diameter Rigid Wheel Towed in Heavy Clay. Load: 6750 lb.
(After UFFELMANN, 1961)

done for the driven and towed versions. Consequently, the proposed model discussed here is largely a conceptual one and is based only on the authors' experiences with the driven and towed versions of the model.

The effect of braking can be considered as a negative torque applied to the tire. This negative torque must be balanced by interface stresses. Experimental evidence indicates that in the case of driven tires the driving torque is balanced primarily by the interface shear stresses, since the resultant of the normal stresses produces but a negligible torque. In the absence of any experimental evidence to the contrary, it is reasonable to assume for braked tires that a negative torque is also balanced primarily by the interface shear stresses and that the torque due to the normal stresses is negligible.

To consider the effect of shear stresses on braked tire-soil interaction, some assumption has to be made as to their distribution along the contact area and their relation to the normal stresses. In the driven tire-soil model the interface friction angle, δ, was introduced to define the relationship

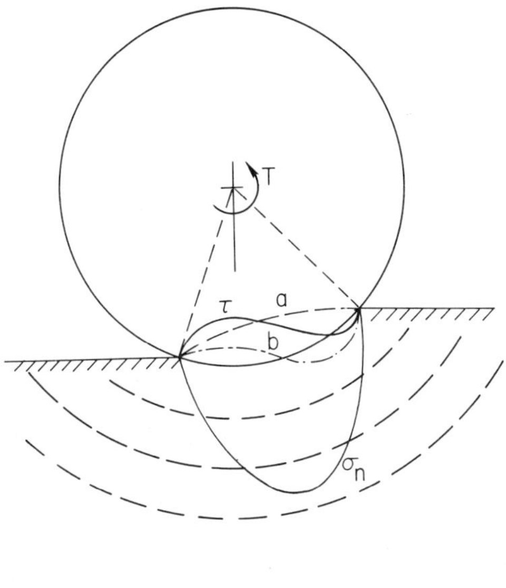

Fig. 3.64
Distribution of Shear Stress (τ) Beneath a Braked Wheel Results from the Superposition of Shear Stresses from Uniform Interface Friction Angle (a) and for Towed Condition (b)

between shear and normal stresses. This angle was assumed to be constant over the length of the contact area. In the case of towed tires δ was assumed to decrease linearly from the entry point, reach zero in the center where the normal stress is maximum, and decrease further to reach $-\delta$ at the exit point. Experiments with braked rigid wheels (Sela, 1964; Krick, 1969) indicate that the shear stress distribution results from the superposition of shear stresses that would be obtained for a towed wheel with those that would be obtained assuming a constant negative δ over the length of the contact area to balance the negative torque. A typical resultant shear stress distribution is shown in Figure 3.64 together with the distribution of the component shear stresses.

The shear stress distribution and the associated variation of the interface friction angle is the fundamental feature of the braked version of the tire-soil model. The shear stresses due to a negative interface friction angle are forward directed and promote the development of a forward slip line field. The angle α_d that defines the inner end of the forward slip line field may be taken as equal to the rear angle, α_r. If the normal stress for an infinitely small rear field is higher than the limit pressure, then there is no rear field. In such a case the front field extends as far back as necessary to have a normal stress equal to the limit pressure at its inner end, but not farther back than the rear angle. The final values of the entry and rear angles are determined from the load equilibrium conditions.

3.4.3 Use of the Tire-Soil Model for the Analysis and Simulation of Tire-Soil Interaction

The engineering uses of the various versions of the tire-soil model presented in the previous section are manifold. Perhaps the most important application of the model is for the parametric analysis of tire performance. The independent and dependent variables in tire-soil interaction constitute a multivariate system where the evaluation of the interrelationships among the variables is essential to the understanding of the problem. Experiments, however useful and necessary, do not serve this purpose as effectively as a validated model. Because of the multivariate relationships involved in tire-soil interaction, a large number of experiments is required to explore the effect of just one variable on the resulting performance for all the combinations of other variables. In addition, in tire tests it is especially difficult to prepare soil beds repeatedly so that their strength is the same. In contrast, with a computerized model the effect of any variation in the input data can easily be analyzed in a matter of minutes at a fraction of the cost of comparable physical experiments.

Other engineering uses of the model include performance prediction. In this respect the model is valuable not only for the prediction of the performance of a single tire, but also as a submodel in vehicle performance models. Ultimately, the vehicle performance is of interest; the tire is only a component in the vehicle system.

Typical examples of the simulation of the pull performance of tires driven in sand are shown in Figures 3.65 and 3.66. An interesting feature of the pull performance simulation by the model is that for slip values greater than about 20% it shows a drop in the pull coefficient with increasing slip. The shape of the pull coefficient versus slip curve in frictional soils is similar to that of the shear stress-displacement curve in direct shear tests experienced in dense soils (Figure 1.37). The decrease in

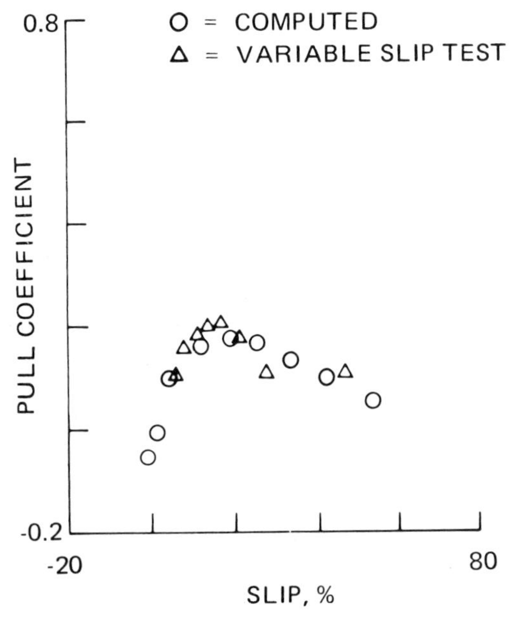

Fig. 3.65
Simulation of Pull Performance of Tire Driven in Sand. Tire: 9.00–14. Load: 450 lb. Inflation Pressure: 16.4 psi. Deflection: 15%. Deflection Coefficient (ε): 0.97. Cone Index Gradient: 8.9 lb/cu in. Friction Angle: 42.4°. Slip Parameters: $j_0 = 0.047$, $K = 0.184$

pull coefficient was frequently attributed to the decrease in mobilized shear stress with slip. However, the mobilized shear stress-slip curve used with the driven version of the tire-soil model, represented by Equation 3.2.5, does not show a peak but increases monotonically. Thus, the decrease of the pull coefficient at high slip rates cannot be attributed to this effect, but is the consequence of tire-soil interaction. When the shear stress at the interface approaches its maximum value, the normal stresses in the rear field that are controlled by soil failure conditions rapidly decrease. The tire-soil model responds to this decrease by an increase of the entry and rear angles and of the sinkage associated with these angles. The average inclination of the contact area to the horizontal increases as does the horizontal component of the normal stresses acting on this area. The net result is a decrease of the pull coefficient even though the mobilization of the shear strength at the interface is close to its maximum.

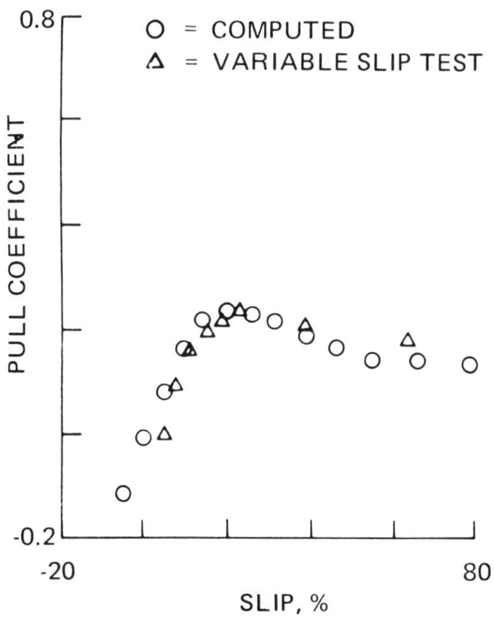

Fig. 3.66
Simulation of Pull Performance of Tire Driven in Sand. Tire: 4.00–7. Load: 225 lb. Inflation Pressure: 14.2 psi. Deflection: 25%. Deflection Coefficient (ε): 0.92. Cone Index Gradient: 13.0 lb/cu in. Friction Angle: 44.3°. Slip Parameters: $j_0 = 0.02$, $K = 0.15$

The use of the model in this case leads to a new and correct interpretation of pull performance curves. This new interpretation is significant inasmuch as strain softening of the interface shear strength may be discounted as the cause of drawbar pull decrease at high slip rates. Strain softening is characteristic of the shear strength properties of dense granular materials where part of the shear strength is derived from the necessity that particles override each other. When the dense material loosens, shear may occur without much override and the shear strength decreases. At the interface the mechanism of shear strength mobilization is different from that described above in that the failure surface is a solid one where shear may occur without particle overriding. Thus, the monotonical increase of shear strength mobilization, intuitively suggested by Janosi and Hanamoto (1961), is more representative of the mechanism of shearing than other relationships that show a peak.

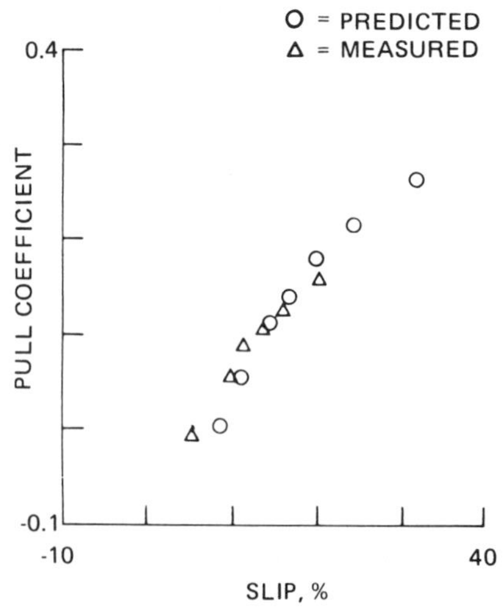

Fig. 3.67
Simulation of Pull Performance of Tire Driven in Clay.
Soil: Clay. Cone Index: 42 psi. Tire: 4.00–7. Load: 335 lb.

Figure 3.67 shows an example of pull performance simulation in clay. Note that the measured pull coefficient-slip curve does not show a peak nor does the simulation. The model rightly senses that in cohesive soils the decrease of interface normal stresses in the rear field due to the interface shear stresses is relatively small, therefore, the increase in traction due to greater mobilization of the interface shear strength dominates the pull performance curve.

Figure 3.68 shows an example of simulation in frictional-cohesive soils. This figure shows results of tests performed at the National Tillage Machinery Laboratory, Auburn, Alabama, in Vaiden clay for the purpose of determining the effect of lug angle on the performance of tractor tires (TAYLOR, 1973). The reference tests in this testing program performed with smooth tires were selected for the simulation. Best fitting second

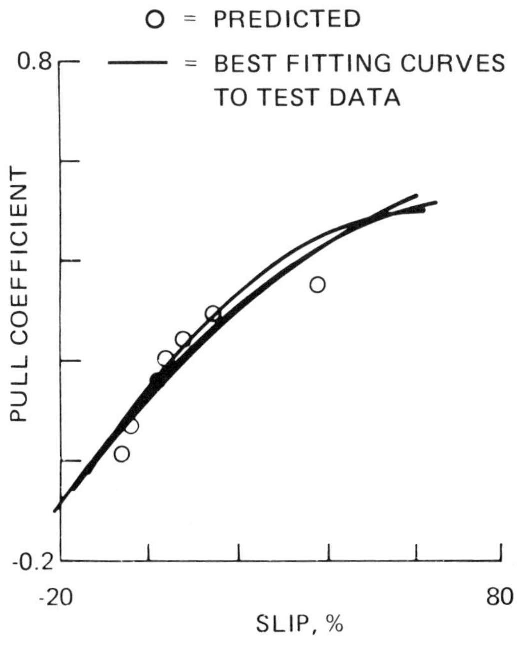

Fig. 3.68
Simulation of Pull Performance of Tire Driven in Frictional-Cohesive Soil.
Soil: Vaiden Clay. Tire: 11.0–38. Load: 2185 lb.

degree curves were applied to the well over 100 digital data points obtained in each of the four reference tests. For the clarity of comparison these curves are shown, instead of the data points, in Figure 3.68. The closeness of the best fitting curves obtained in four separate tests indicates the good control over testing conditions and the reproducibility of the tests. In this testing program the moisture content of the soil bed increased with depth, a condition intended to duplicate that occurring in the agricultural use of the tractors. The simulation shown in the figure was obtained with the driven version of the tire-soil model in which uniform conditions were assumed. The COULOMB strength parameters were estimated on the basis of cone penetration tests and correspond to the moisture conditions observed in the top layer. An analysis of variable soil strength conditions performed with a later version of this model, expanded to accomodate linearly varying strength parameters, confirmed that the

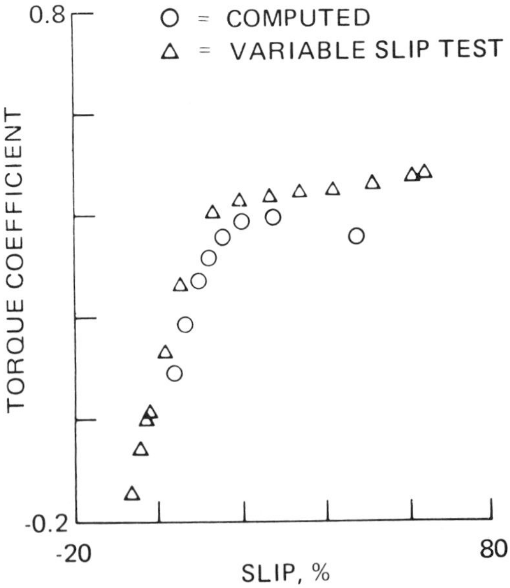

Fig. 3.69
Simulation of Torque Coefficient. Tire Driven in Sand.
Tire: 9.00–14. Load: 859 lb. Inflation Pressure: 16.4 psi. Deflection: 25%. Deflection Coefficient ε: 0.88. Cone Index Gradient: 15.0 lb/cu in. Friction Angle: 45.2°. Slip Parameters: $j_0 = 0.015$, $K = 0.14$

strength condition at the surface is the predominant controlling factor in the pull performance of tires. This explains the good simulation shown in Figure 3.68 obtained by using the strength properties of the top layer.

Figure 3.69 shows the simulation of torque coefficient for a 9.00—14 tire driven in sand. Note that while the drop in the pull coefficient was well reproduced in the model, the simulation of the torque coefficient did not follow the torque coefficient points at high slip rates. In other tests, where both the pull and torque coefficients decreased at high slip rates, the simulation of both were good. The most likely cause of this discrepancy in the simulation of the rise of the torque coefficient at high rates of slip is that in the model it was assumed that the moment of interface normal stresses about the tire axle is zero, while in actuality this was not the case. The general validity of the conclusion that the moment of normal stresses is zero, drawn from a limited number of experiments (FREITAG et al, 1965) does not seem to be warranted. In some instances the center of the tire axis may shift at high slip rates in such a way that normal stresses generate a torque about the axis. Until this geometry problem can be clarified by either appropriate tests or a reasonable theory, torque simulation at high rates of slip will necessarily be uncertain.

The tire-soil interaction simulation shown in these figures are just a few examples of comparisons between predictions by the model and experiments. Many more are presented in the detailed reports on the development of the tire-soil model that conclusively show the superiority of this model over other prediction methods. The clue to the good performance prediction achieved by the model is the good simulation of tire geometry. Figure 3.70 shows the tire geometries and outlines of slip line fields postulated in the model for three different slip rates. Although tire geometry measurements are not available for these simulations, it is clear that the changes in the geometry as indicated in the figure are both realistic and essential to good performance prediction.

The typical examples as well as the detailed report on the development of tire-soil model (KARAFIATH, 1974) show that the prediction of tire performance by the driven version of the model is exceptionally good, much better than might be expected from a two-dimensional model that neither takes bow waves into account nor considers soil failure in the lateral direction. If these phenomena occur, and they do in many instances, then they must affect tire performance in some degree. Thus, it is of interest to analyze the conditions under which these phenomena occur and to determine their importance for tire performance prediction. In the case of rigid wheel-soil interaction it was demonstrated by theory and experiments

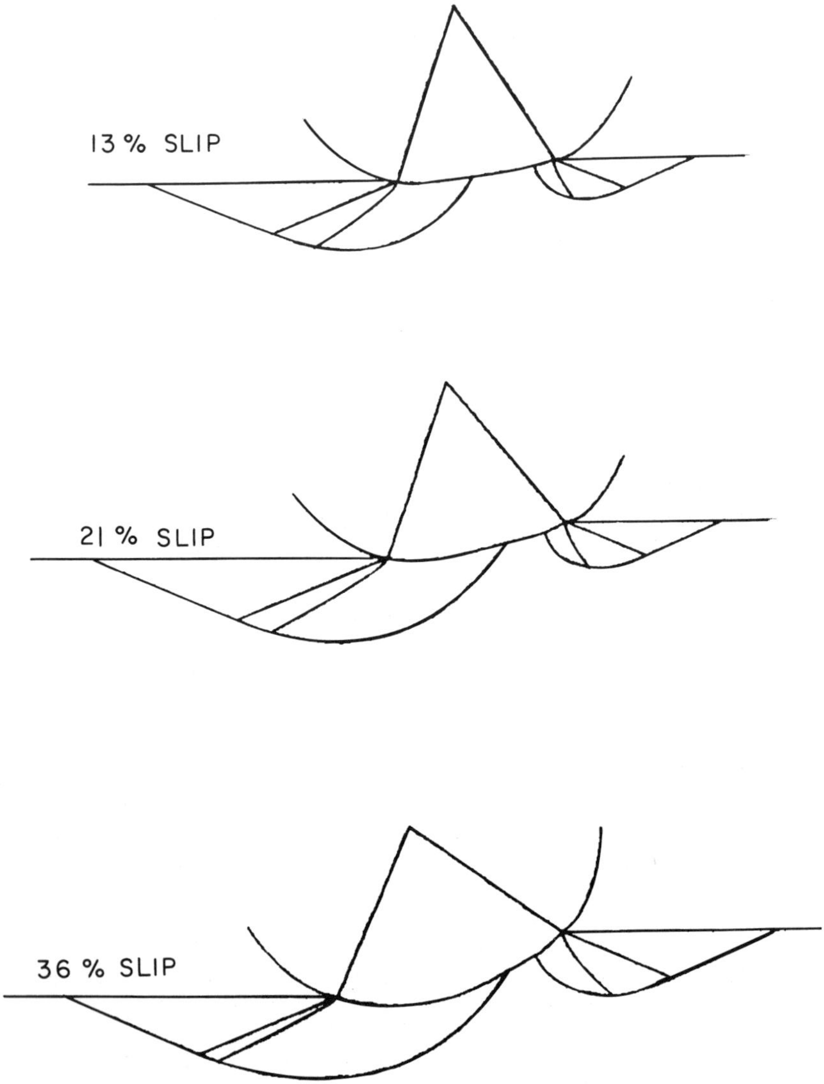

Fig. 3.70
Tire Centerline Geometries and Outlines of Slip Line Fields at Various Rates of Slip as Obtained by Computer Graphics.
Tire: 4.00–7. Load: 225 lb. Inflation Pressure: 14.2 psi. Deflection: 25%. Deflection Coefficient ε: 0.92. Soil: Sand. Cone Index Gradient: 13.0 lb/cu in.

that soil failure in the lateral direction controls the transverse distribution of normal stresses. Lateral failure conditions thus constitute a limitation of the normal stresses that would otherwise arise at the interface. The situation is essentially the same in the case of tire-soil interaction. The limitation on the transverse distribution of normal stresses is most pronounced in the case of frictional soils, where the normal stress at the outside edge of the tire would be zero were it not for the surcharge effect brought about by the sinkage of the tire. The surcharge corresponds to the depth of tire perimeter at a particular point beneath the original surface. The normal stress due to lateral failure may be approximately calculated on the assumption that all stresses are in the vertical plane. An example of edge stresses in frictional soils is shown in Figure 3.71 by dashed lines, whereas full lines show the normal stresses calculated from conditions in the plane of travel. It is seen that edge stresses due to lateral failure limit the normal stresses in the front portion of the tire; in the rear, where the tire edge is deeper beneath the original surface, there is no limitation of the normal stresses. In the case of small sinkage, the average inclination of the contact area to the horizontal is minimal and does not have any appreciable effect on the pull coefficient since the horizontal component of the normal stresses is negligible. In this case the pull coefficient approximately equals the τ/σ_n ratio. Thus, the tire-soil model predicts the pull coefficient accurately, even though the computed arc length of the front field is shorter than it would be had the limitation of normal stresses due to lateral failure been considered in the model. With increasing sinkage, lateral failure conditions become less significant and their effect on the normal stresses and performance prediction is minimal. Even though this fortuitous situation allows a satisfactory prediction of tire performance by the two-dimensional model, consideration of three-dimensional effects in the model is believed to result in the following advantages:

a) The relationships established in Section 3.4.2 for the estimation of the coefficient ε vary with the type of the tire. In all likelihood a uniform relation for ε could be established in a three-dimensional model.

b) The two-dimensional tire-soil model is not very well suited for the analysis of the effect of width/diameter ratios on tire performance, or for the simulation of the performance of dual tires with respect to their spacing. It is essential to take the effects of lateral failure into account for these type of analyses.

The formation of bow waves in the front of tires has intrigued many workers in the field of off-road vehicle engineering. The physical appearance of bow waves suggests an appreciable influence on tire-soil interaction. Nevertheless, up to now no theory has been advanced on their formation or on their effect on tire performance. The problem is twofold: how to determine the size of the bow wave and how to take the effect of a given size bow wave into account. The formation of a bow wave is an expression of volumetric imbalance in tire-soil interaction. The stresses imposed on the soil by the tire load compress the soil until the plastic state is reached. In the plastic state plastic flow occurs without significant volumetric changes. The net result of the volumetric changes due to compression is the permanent deformation of the soil after the passage of the tire. A measure of the volume changes associated with this permanent deformation is the formation of a rut.

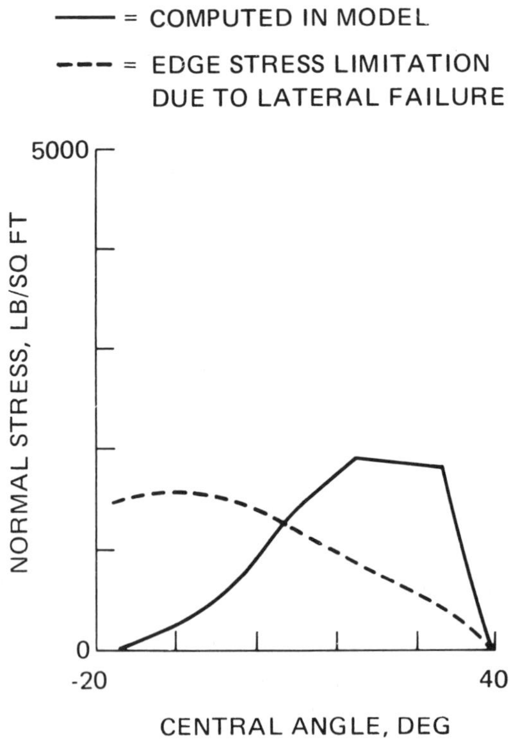

Fig. 3.71
Limitation of Interface Normal Stresses Imposed by Lateral Failure Conditions. Tire: 4.00–7. Load: 210 lb. Inflation Pressure: 10.0 psi. Deflection: 25%. Deflection Coefficient ε: 0.092. Soil: Sand. Cone Index Gradient: 13 lb/cu in. Slip: 21%. Sinkage: 0.8 in.

In an experimental program performed at WES (1973) for the purpose of studying the formation of slip line fields in tire-soil interaction, densely packed wooden pegs were used as a two-dimensional soil model. Motion pictures were taken of the movements of the pegs during passage of the tire by a camera rotating with the tire. The interaction of the tire with the two-dimensional soil model required a certain sinkage and a volume change that could not be balanced by the further densification of the wooden pegs. Consequently, sizable bow waves developed in these tests even at high slip rates. Since the volume change of the soil model was practically nil, and no lateral displacement occurred in the two-dimensional model, no volume balance could be achieved and the size of the bow waves did not stabilize in the tests. In actuality, the conditions are never rigorously two-dimensional and significant bow waves occur only with towed and relatively wide tires.

The versatility of the tire-soil model allows the estimation of the effect of bow waves on tire performance, if so desired. The geometry of the bow waves may be either assumed or estimated from the velocity fields associated with the front slip line field (see Section 3.4.4). Figure 3.72 shows a front slip line field for an assumed bow wave geometry. Preliminary analyses of tire performance with assumed bow wave geometries indicate that the effect of bow waves on interface stresses and tire performance is minor and certainly not as great as the physical appearance of some of the bow waves would suggest.

The simulation of tire performance by mathematical models is advantageous not only for performance predictions, as discussed previously, but

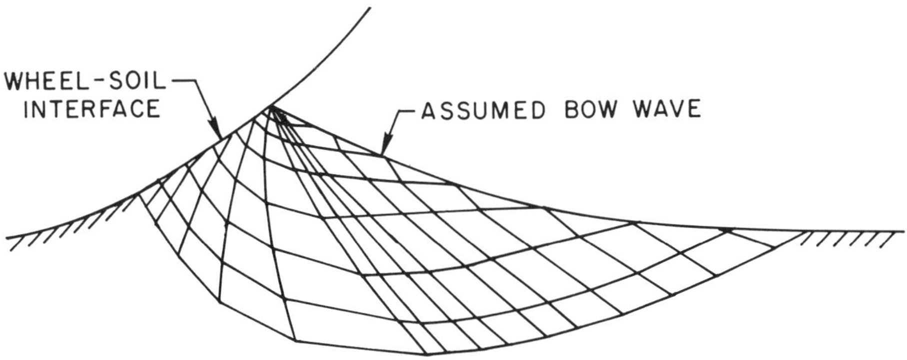

Fig. 3.72
Geometry of Front Slip Line Field for an Assumed Bow Wave

also for the analysis and understanding of the significance of the various factors that influence tire-soil interaction. Some examples of the use of the tire-soil model for the analysis of special problems, such as bow waves and three-dimensional effects, have already been presented. The value of the tire-soil model as an analytical tool can be best appreciated if the effect of changes in any one of the input variables on tire performance is to be evaluated. For example, the maximum drawbar pull that a tire can exert in sand can be easily analyzed and determined for various tire loads. Figure 3.73 shows the results of such an analysis for a 9.00—14 tire inflated to 16.4 psi. The soil is Yuma sand with a cone index gradient of 13.8 pci. It can be seen that there is a maximum drawbar pull that cannot be exceeded by increasing the tire load even if the available torque is unlimited. Another way of presenting the effect of tire load on pull performance is shown in Figure 3.74 which shows, over the whole range of slip, the decrease of the pull coefficient as the tire load increases.

Parametric analysis of design variables is another important task that can be solved easily by the mathematical tire-soil model. In Figure 3.75

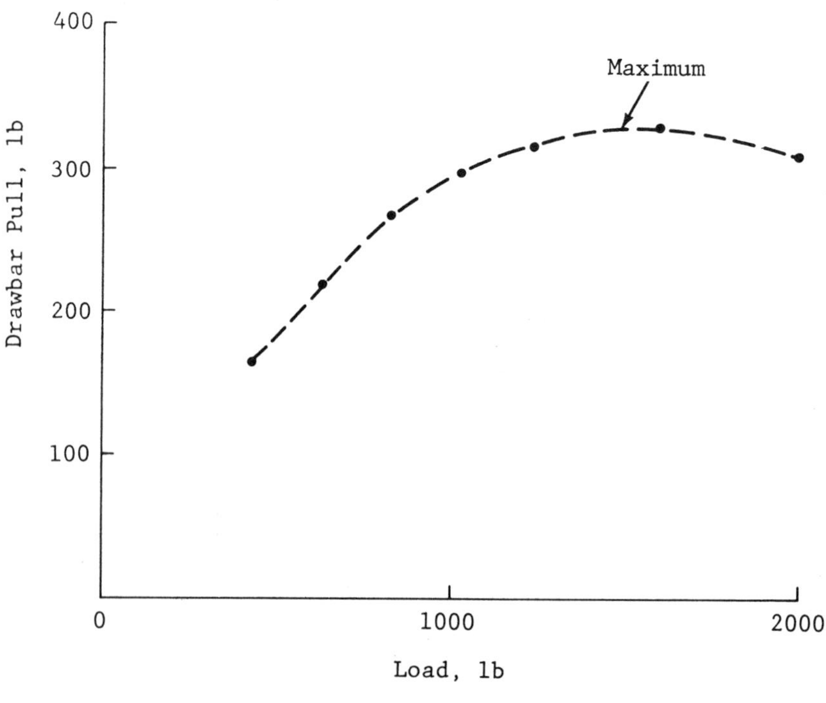

Fig. 3.73
Maximum Drawbar Pull at Various Tire Loads. Tire: 9.00–14.
Inflation Pressure: 16.4 psi. Soil: Sand. Cone Index Gradient: 13.8 lb/cu in

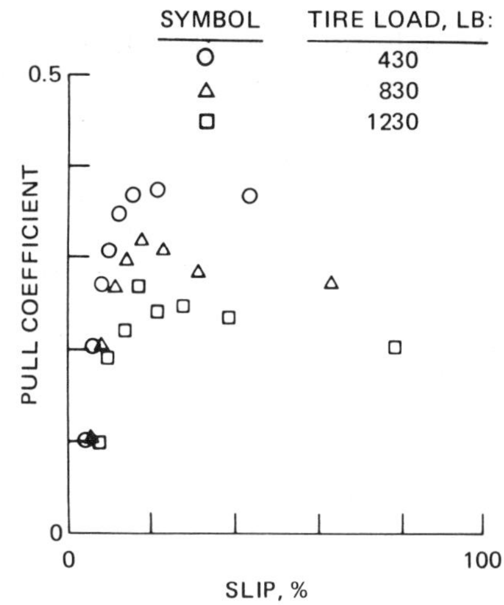

Fig. 3.74
Effect of Tire Load on Pull Performance. Tire: 9.00–14.
Inflation Pressure: 16.4 psi. Soil: Sand. Cone Index Gradient: 13.8 lb/cu in.

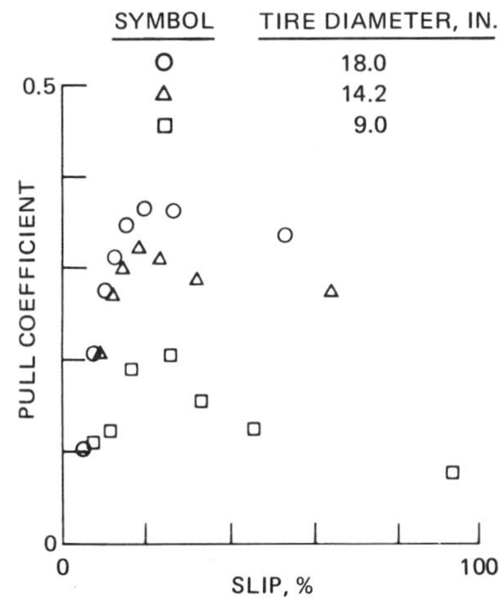

Fig. 3.75
Effect of Tire Diameter on Pull Performance. Tire Width: 8.5 in. Inflation Pressure: 16.4 psi.
Load: 830 lb. Soil: Sand. Cone Index Gradient: 13.8 lb/cu in.

the pull coefficients for various tire diameters are shown, all other variables being constant. The fact that larger diameter tires work better in sand than smaller one is, of course, well known. The mathematical model confirms this fact in quantitative terms over the whole range of slip. The respective torque and sinkage values are obtained simultaneously in the computer program.

The effect of inflation pressure on pull performance is shown in Figure 3.76. The inflation pressures shown correspond to 15, 25 and 35 percent deflection (of section height), respectively. The analysis confirms the well-known beneficial effect of lowering the inflation pressure on traction in quantitative terms.

The effect of soil properties on tire performance may also be easily analyzed. An example of such an analysis is shown in Figure 3.77 where pull performances are compared for various values of the unit weight, γ, all other conditions are the same. It is seen that a slight increase in γ improves tire performance by three percent in the pull coefficient. Such a

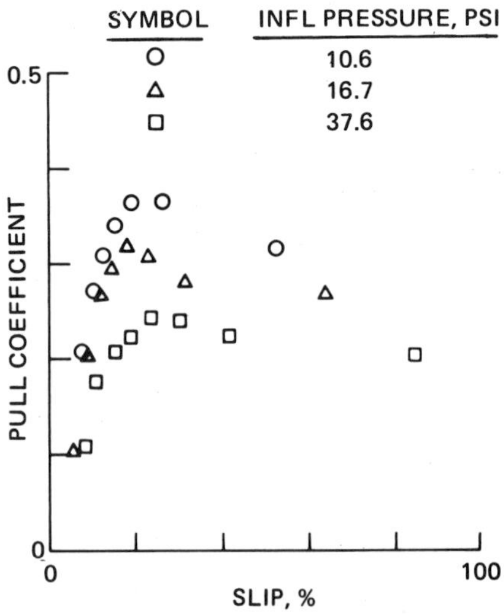

Fig. 3.76
Effect of Inflation Pressure on Pull Performance. Tire: 9.00–14. Load: 830 lb. Soil: Sand. Cone Index Gradient: 13.8 lb/cu in.

difference may remain obscured in an experimental program where data scatter occurs for many reasons and a detailed statistical analysis would be necessary to show that such observed differences are statistically significant. However, in an analysis by a mathematical model the effect can be studied further, all other variables being kept exactly the same. For example, in Figure 3.77 the computed pull coefficients are also shown for the case of $\gamma = 67$ lbs/cu ft that corresponds to the submerged unit weight of soil. It is seen that submergence affects tire performance appreciably even if only its effect on unit weight is considered. In this analysis pore water pressures are assumed to be neutral. Pore water pressures may either decrease or increase soil strength, depending on the density of soil. In the case of submergence this effect may override the effect of the change in unit weight.

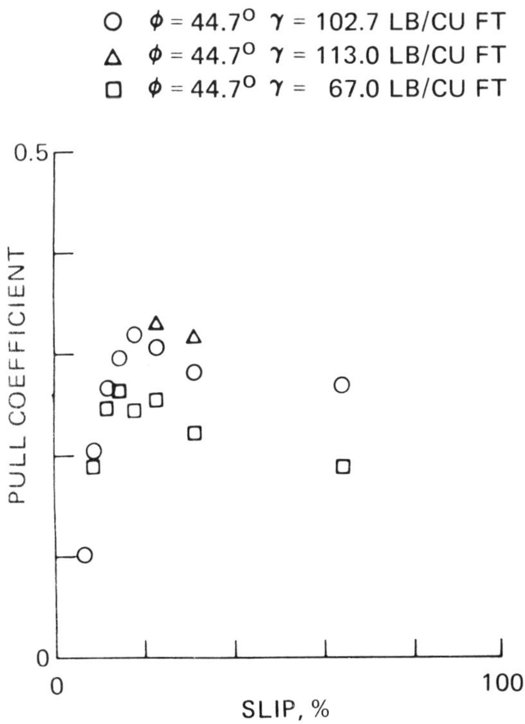

Fig. 3.77
Effect of Unit Weight of Soil on Pull Performance. Tire: 9.00–14. Inflation Pressure: 16.4 psi. Load: 830 lb. Soil: Sand. Cone Index Gradient: 13.8 lb/cu in.

The effect of soil strength on pull performance is shown in Figure 3.78 where changes in pull coefficient are shown as a function of cone index gradient, all other conditions being equal. Soil strength, as this comparison and many other performance analysis indicate, is the most crucial single factor in vehicle mobility.

Figure 3.79 shows the effect of a small amount of cohesion on pull performance. A cohesion of 10 lbs/sq ft, which is indeed very small and could be the result of a slight dampness in frictional soils, improves the pull performance appreciably. Generally, the effect of cohesion on pull performance, if it acts in conjunction with a high friction angle, is great.

As these examples indicate, the tire-soil model is excellently suited for the parametric analysis of many design variables. These analyses can be performed at a fraction of the cost of experiments and once the computer codes have been developed, in a matter of minutes. The use of such mathematical models of vehicle-soil interaction is indispensable in optimizing the design of off-road vehicles.

The towed version of the prototype tire-soil model is equally useful for the analysis and prediction of drag forces acting on free rolling tires.

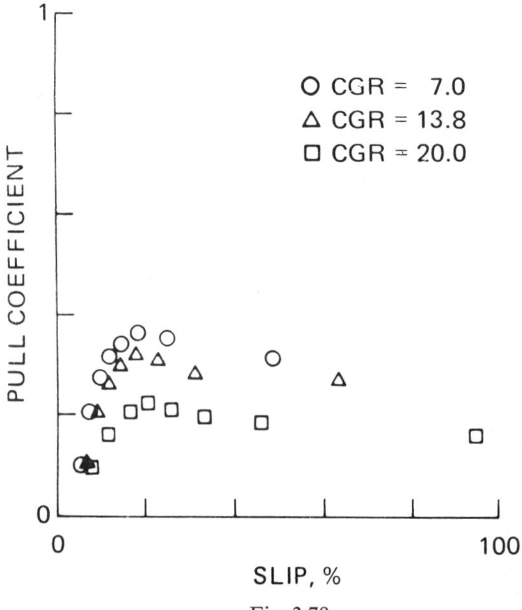

Fig. 3.78
Effect of Soil Strength on Pull Performance. Tire: 9.00–14. Inflation Pressure: 16.4 psi. Load: 830 lb. Soil: Sand

Table 3.5 shows a comparison of towed (drag) force coefficients measured in an experimental program at WES (Turnage, 1972) with those predicted by the towed version of the mathematical model.

It is seen from Table 3.5 that the predictions are acceptable, even though the differences between the measured and predicted towed force coefficients are generally greater than those experienced with the pull coefficients. One reason for this less accurate simulation of the experiments lies in the sensitivity of the towed force coefficients to small changes in soil strength. The experimental results show appreciable scatter because of this sensitivity. More important is that in this towed version of the tire-soil model three-dimensional effects are disregarded. This results in an underprediction of the towed force coefficient when that coefficient is higher than about 0.3. Soil failure in the third (lateral) dimension limits the normal stresses in the transverse direction beneath the tire, just as in the case of driven tires. The normal stresses in the front field are significantly reduced by this limitation and the contact area has to increase to balance the load. The entry angle also increases and a higher towed force coefficent results. This three-dimensional effect has not been considered in the two-dimensional model, therefore the underprediction of the towed force coefficient.

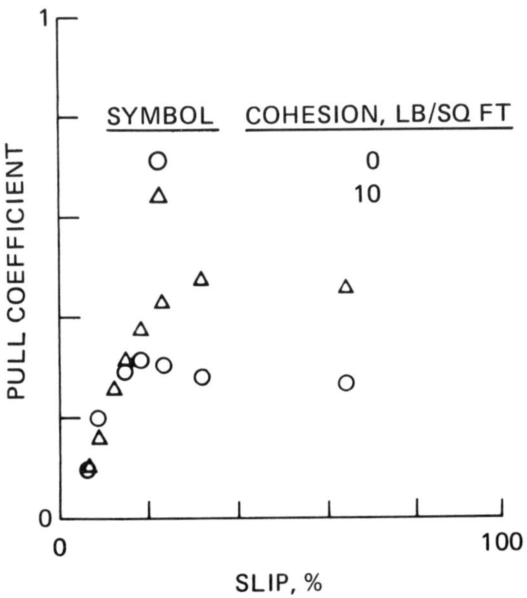

Fig. 3.79
Effect of a Small Cohesion on Pull Performance in Sand. Tire: 9.00–14. Inflation Pressure: 16.4 psi. Load: 830 lb.

Table 3.5
Comparison of Predicted and Measured Towed Force Coefficients
Tire size: 6.00 - 16
Soil: Yuma sand

Test No.	Cone Index Gradient lb/cu in	Load lb	Inflation pressure psi	Deflection % of sect. height	Towed Force Coefficient Measured	Towed Force Coefficient Predicted
1	5.8	213	8.5	15	0.155	0.088
2	12.1	215	8.5	15	0.070	0.081
3	15.6	222	8.5	15	0.059	0.075
4	12.4	293	11.4	15	0.065	0.085
5	10.4	458	17.2	15	0.131	0.121
6	13.5	240	4.5	25	0.042	0.078
7	15.0	223	4.5	25	0.063	0.083
8	15.6	455	10.3	25	0.040	0.092
9	2.3	429	10.3	25	0.424	0.238
10	13.8	865	21.0	25	0.088	0.127
11	9.5	863	21.0	25	0.200	0.155
12	5.8	225	2.5	35	0.116	0.111
13	16.4	239	2.5	35	0.046	0.078
14	17.3	446	7.0	35	0.018	0.092
15	3.5	674	10.3	35	0.365	0.217
16	15.0	870	13.0	35	0.055	0.125

As an example of the type of results generated by the towed version of the tire-soil model, the interface normal and shear stresses and the tire geometry computed by the model are shown in Figure 3.80 for the following conditions

	a)	b)
Tire size	9.00—14	4.00—20
Tire radius (nominal)	1.18 ft	1.17 ft
Tire width (nominal)	0.73 ft	0.37 ft
Infl. pressure	12.0 psi	40.0 psi
Defl. coefficient	0.905	0.945
Soil	Yuma sand	Buckshot clay
Cone Index	n. a.	18 psi
Cone Index Gradient	3.5 lb/cu in	n. a.

Case (a) is typical of a relatively flexible tire, while in case (b) the tire behaves like a rigid wheel due to the relatively high inflation pressure.

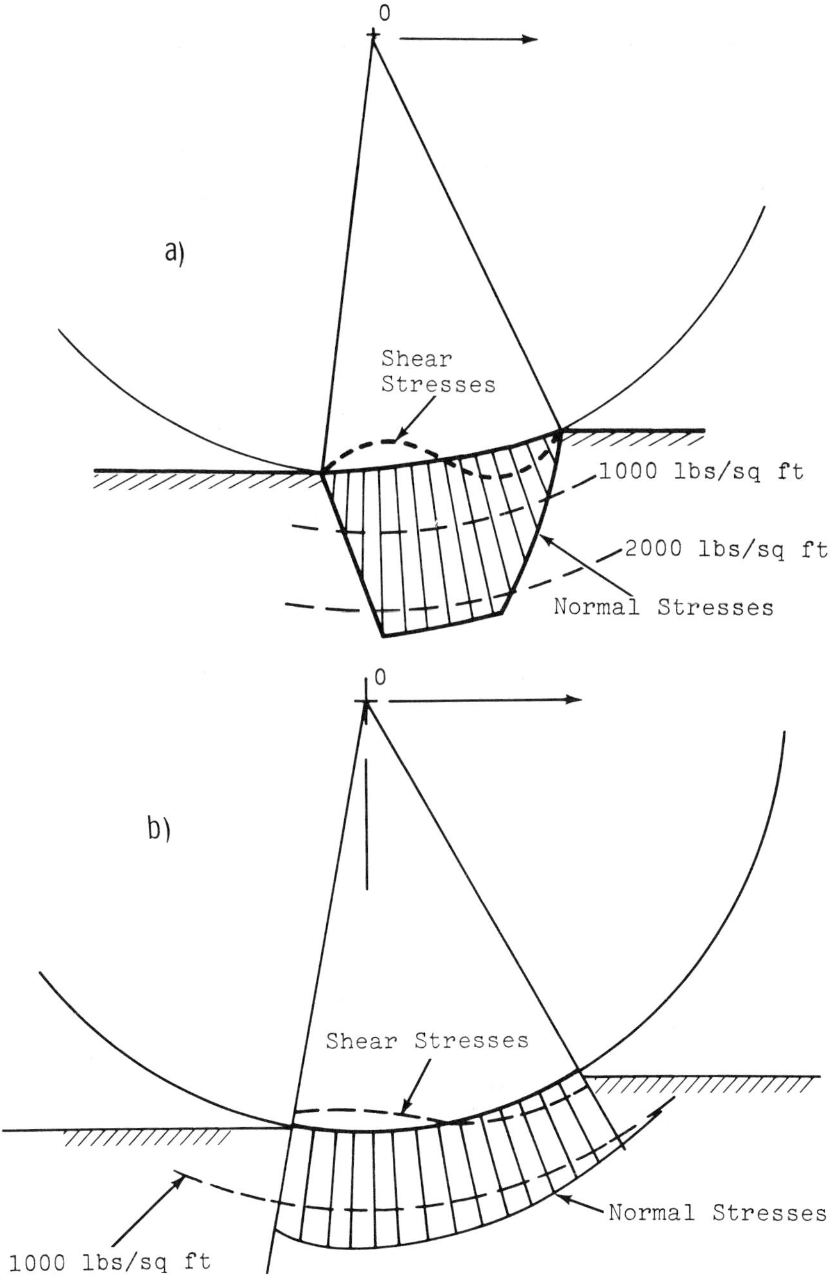

Fig. 3.80
Interface Normal and Shear Stresses and Tire Centerline Geometry
in the Case of Tire Towed a) in Sand b) in Clay

3.4.4 Tire Soil Interaction with Variable Soil Strength Profiles

A characteristic feature of soil deposits is that their strength and other properties inherently vary either continuously or discretely with depth. In soil mechanics, many theories and analytical methods have been put forward to allow proper consideration of this feature of soil deposits in the solution of the various soil engineering problems. In many of these solutions the theory of elasticity is applied to layered systems. In tire-soil interaction problems of interest the stress levels in soil far exceed those for which the theory of elasticity applies. Plasticity theory solutions for a continuous variation of soil strength with depth have been developed by the authors and applied to tire-soil interaction problems as discussed later in more detail in this section. Discrete layering poses certain boundary problems for plasticity theory solutions that are difficult to solve and, in some cases, depending on the relative strength of the adjoining layers, may not have solutions at all. Therefore, plasticity theory solutions do not lend themselves readily for application to tire-soil interaction problems in soils with discrete layers. An approximate method, based on a detailed analysis of bearing stresses in two-layer systems is proposed in the latter part of this section.

Computation Scheme for Continuous Variation of Soil Strength with Depth

The methods of numerical computations for the determination of the geometry of slip line fields and associated stresses have been discussed in

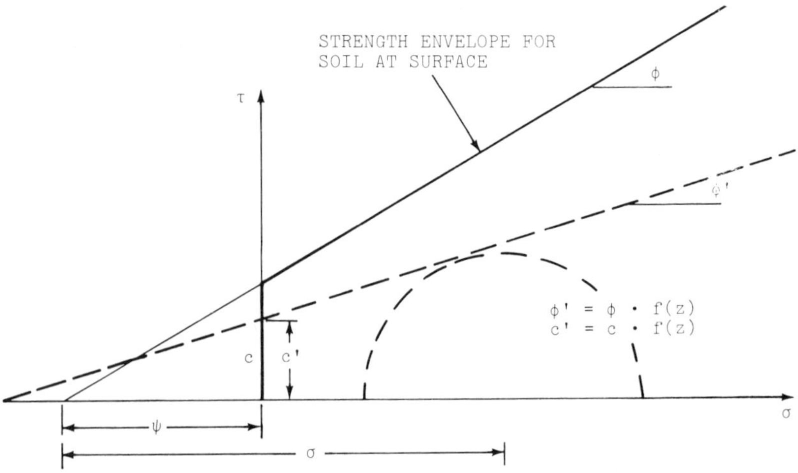

Fig. 3.81
Variation of Soil Strength with Depth

detail in Sections 3.3.3 and 3.4.2. For brevity, only the differences in the computation methods necessitated by the consideration of strength variation with depth are discussed in the following paragraphs.

The variation of strength properties with depth considered in the tire-soil model is shown in Figure 3.81. Generally, the ψ intercept varies with the assumed variation of soil strength. Because of this variation of the ψ intercept, it is necessary to modify the numerical methods developed for the solution of the differential equations of plasticity for constant strength. In these methods, the principal stress variable, σ, is defined as the distance between the center of the MOHR circle and the intersection of the MOHR-COULOMB envelope with the σ axis (Figure 3.81). If ψ varies with depth, then the σ values have to be adjusted to account for this variation. To this end another variable, $p_{i,j} = \sigma_{i,j} - \psi$ is introduced and computed for every nodal point. For the computation of the variables at an *i, j* point the σ values at the *i*-1, *j* and *i, j*-1 points are recomputed from the $p_{i-1,j}$ and $p_{i,j-1}$ values by adding the ψ value determined for the *i, j* point. Figure 3.82 shows the flow chart for the computation of the variables at an *i, j* nodal point with respect to the ψ variation. In practice, it was found that one iteration on the ψ values was satisfactory for the determination of the appropriate σ values.

Typical results obtained with the tire-soil model modified for a linear variation of the strength parameters with depth are shown in Figure 3.83 where pull performance relationships are shown for four cases, each depicting a different variation of soil strength with depth. Common input conditions for the computations were as follows.

Tire Characteristics:

Tire size	9.00—14
Nominal radius	1.18 ft
Nominal width	0.74 ft
Inflation pressure	18.7 psi
Deflection	25%
Defl. coefficient	0.88
Tire load	850 lbs

Soil: Yuma sand

Case 1, shown in the figure, represents uniform conditions corresponding to a cone index gradient *(CGR)* of 15 lbs/cu in, or $\varphi = 44.7°$. In Case 2 the soil strength decreases linearly from $\varphi = 44.7°$ at the surface to $\varphi = 39.7°$ at the deepest point of the slip line field. Case 3 again represents uniform soil conditions where the soil strength, φ, equals 39.7°, the minimum soil strength in Case 2. This friction angle corresponds to a *CGR* of 5.5. Finally, in Case 4 the soil strength increases linearly from

$\varphi = 39.7°$ to $\varphi = 44.7°$ at the deepest point of the slip line fields. As it is seen from Figure 3.83 the pull performance for variable strength is close to that in uniform soil having the same strength as the variable strength profile at the surface.

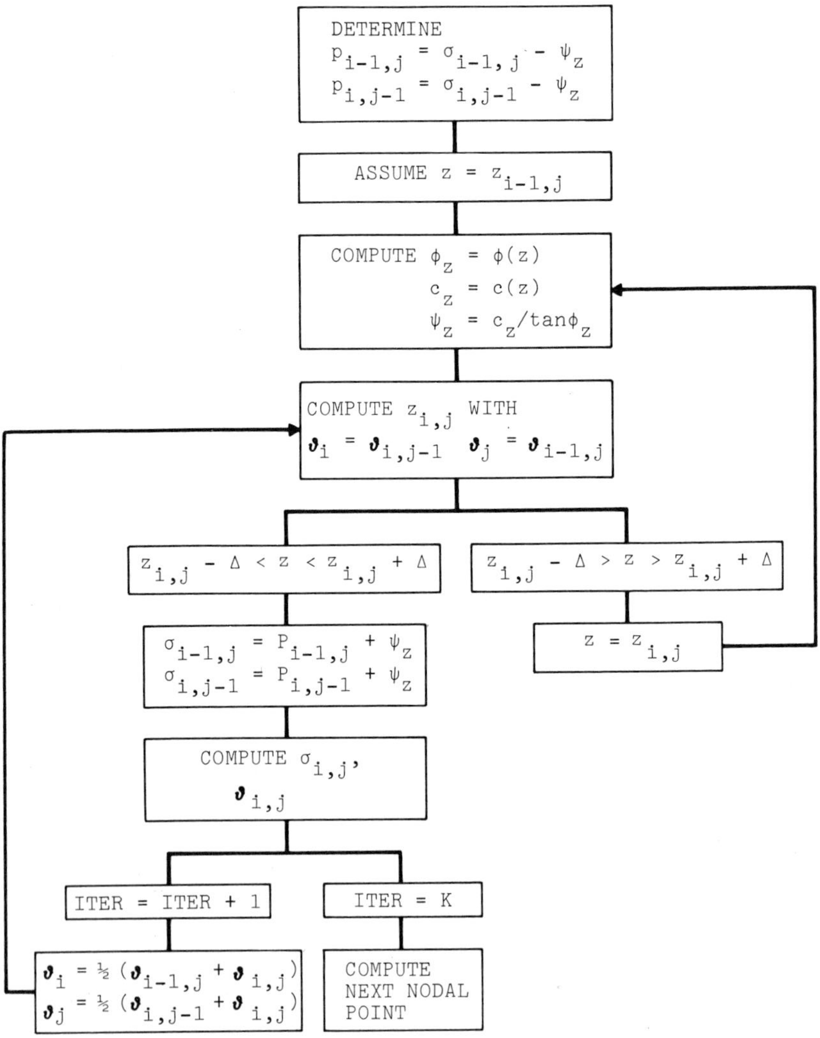

Fig. 3.82
Scheme for Computing the Variables σ and θ at Nodal Point i, j for Strength Varying with Depth z

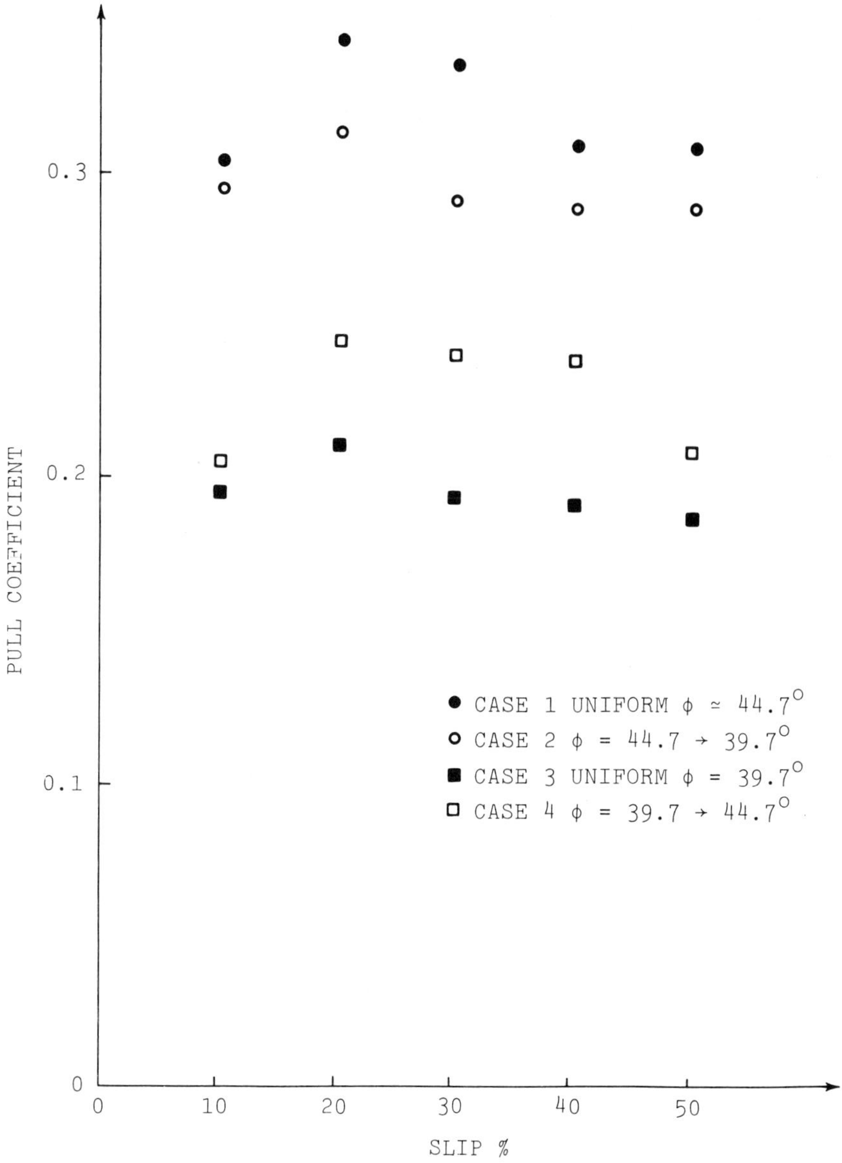

Fig. 3.83
Comparison of Pull Performances for Soil Strength Varying with Depth

Figure 3.84 shows the computed distribution of normal and shear stresses and the deflection of the tire for Case 1 at 20 % slip, as obtained in the computer graphics program. Figure 3.85 shows the same for Case 2. Note that in the radial plot a rigid wheel with the nominal tire diameter is shown for the convenience of plotting; the tire deformation is shown separately at the top. The difference in the interface stresses computed for the two cases is, indeed, minor and results in little difference in pull performance.

The effect of a decreasing shear strength on the slip line fields that develop underneath a tire is that the slip line fields encompass a greater depth than those for uniform strength. This growth of the slip line field in the z direction results from the stress encounter with soil horizons of less and less strength. At some rate of strength decrease, a progressive process takes place for which no slip line field solution may be found. This is interpreted as a condition where complete and deep reaching failure would take place in the soil under the tire load, indicating a "no go" condition.

In conclusion, in sand the surface strength is the dominating factor, but there is a limit to the rate of strength decrease at which a "no go" situation occurs. In cohesive soils the situation is very similar, as far as the limit of strength decrease is concerned at which a "no go" condition sets in. The effect of strength decrease on pull performance is less pronounced in clay than in sand. Paradoxically, sometimes a higher pull performance may be obtained with decreasing than with uniform strength, since the interface shear stress includes a relatively high adhesion, while the normal stresses are reduced by the decrease of strength with depth.

Computation Scheme for Discrete Variation of Soil Strength with Depth

The methods of constructing slip line fields for layered soil conditions, discussed in Section 2.3.4, are not well suited for direct application in tire-soil models. Instead, an approximate method proposed by Karafiath (1975b) may be applied for the estimation of interface stresses. The first step in this method is the computation of interface stresses with the strength parameters of the upper layer, as if the soil were uniform. Then the locations at the interface where the lower layer starts to interfere with the slip line field in the upper layer are determined. In the second step the interface stresses are computed with the strength parameters of the lower layer, assuming the same centerline geometry as in the first step. The interface stress distribution for the two-layer soil is then determined by shifting the normal stresses computed with the strength parameters of the

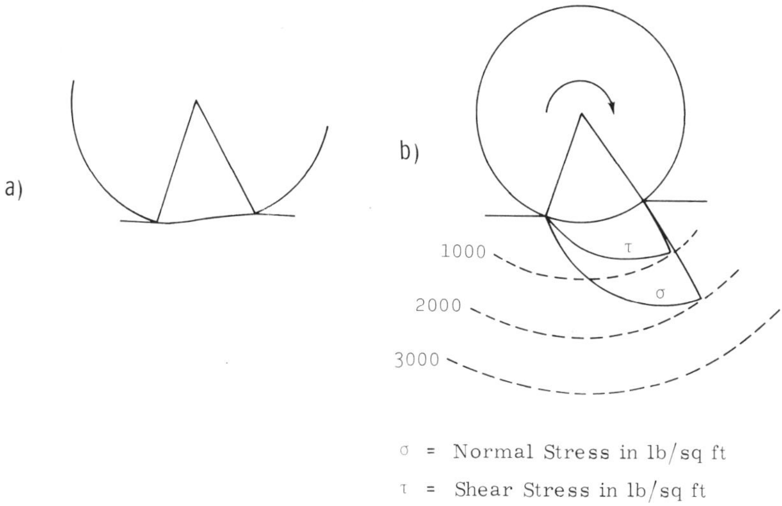

Fig. 3.84
Tire Deflection (a) and Interface Normal and Shear Stresses (b). Case 1, 20% Slip

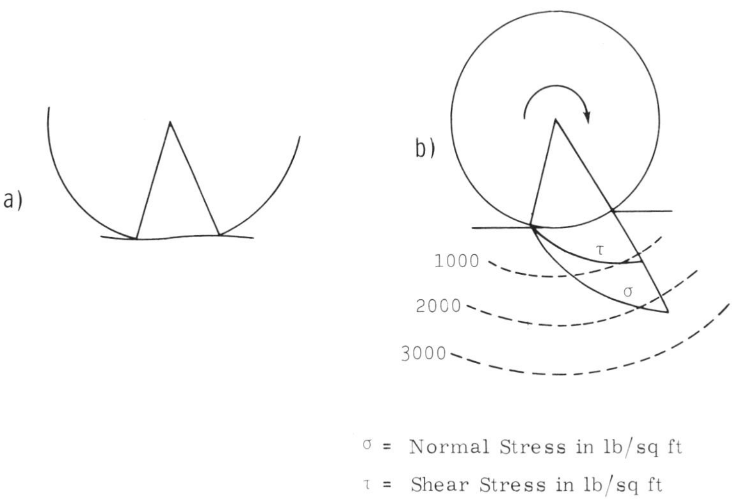

Fig. 3.85
Tire Deflection (a) and Interface Normal and Shear Stresses (b). Case 2, 20% Slip

lower layer by an amount, estimated on the basis of two-layer bearing stresses, within the locations of the lower layer interference determined earlier. The load, drawbar pull and torque for the two-layer soil are determined by integrating the interface stresses. The procedure is repeated,

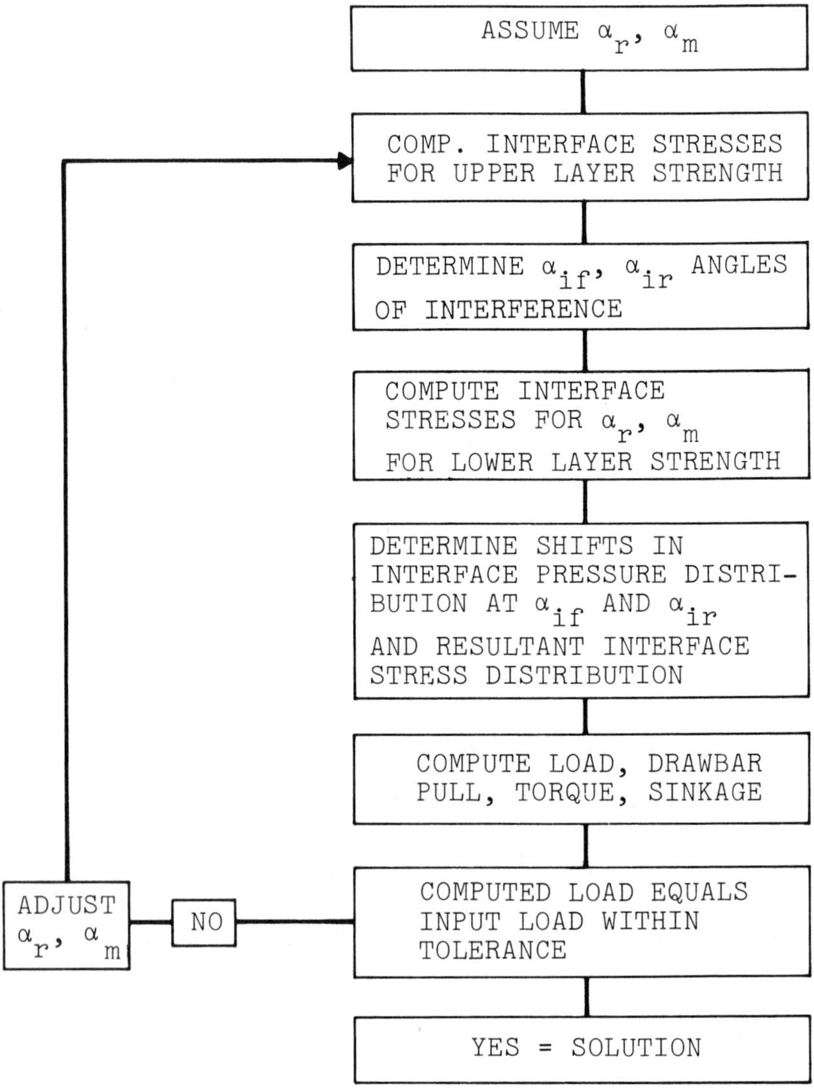

Fig. 3.86
Scheme of Computations for the Tire-Soil Model for Two-Layer Soils

if necessary, for a new centerline geometry (α_d and α_r angles) until the computed load is within the tolerance limits for the input load. The computation scheme is shown diagrammatically in Figure 3.86. A typical interface stress distribution computed by this method for two-layer soils is shown in Figure 3.87. There are limitations to the use of this approximate model: the deformed centerline of the tire must remain completely in the upper layer and the strength conditions must be such that the cohesion and the friction angle of the upper layer are both either higher or lower than those of the lower layer.

3.4.5 The Effect of Speed on Tire-Soil Interaction

The concepts of rigid wheel-soil and pneumatic tire-soil interaction discussed in Sections 3.3.1 and 3.4.1 are based on the assumptions that the velocity of travel is low, the effects of soil inertia are negligible and a quasi static, "steady state" condition exists in the soil. The speed of off-road vehicles in agriculture and heavy construction is, indeed, so low that no serious error results from this assumption as far as these vehicles are

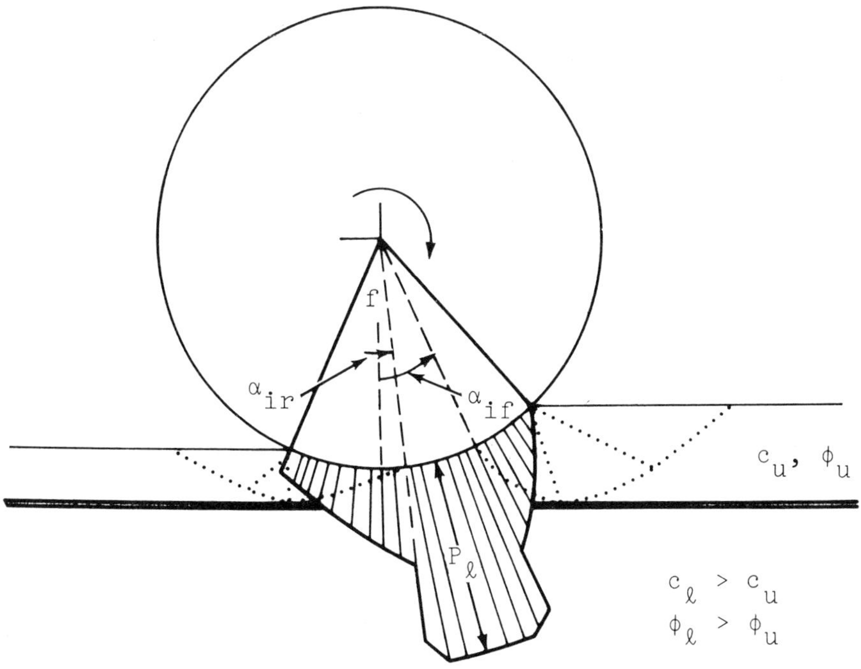

Fig. 3.87
Interface Normal Stress Distribution in the Case of Two-Layer Soils

concerned. However, many modern military vehicles are required to operate off-road at relatively high speeds, say above 20 mph. A special case is the landing of aircraft on unprepared airfields, where the velocity of landing is often in excess of 100 mph. At these velocities it would be incorrect to disregard the effects of soil inertia and changes in soil behavior due to this high speed, impact-like loading.

The effects of velocity on the pull performance of driven tires have been demonstrated in experiments performed at WES at velocities ranging from 1 to 18 ft/sec (TURNAGE, 1972). Although at these velocities no great change in the pull performance could be expected, the experiments conclusively proved that even a moderate increase in the velocity results in noticeable improvement in pull performance under the conditions tested. In another related experimental program the effect of penetration rate on the resistance of cones and plates of various sizes to penetration was investigated (TURNAGE 1970, 1973, 1974). These tests also showed that there was generally an increase in the resistance with the rate of penetration. The purpose of these investigations was partly to gain insight into the behavior of soils at high rates of loading and partly to establish some basis for the correlation of cone penetration resistances at various rates of loading and tire performances at various velocities. While these experiments provide very valuable information on the effect of velocity on tire-soil interaction and the variation of cone penetration resistance with the rate of loading, they contributed little to the understanding of the underlying phenomena.

The results of experiments performed for the determination of the variation of the drag force on the tires of aircraft landing gears with speed are reported by CRENSHAW et al (1971) and CRENSHAW (1975). Evaluation of these results indicated that the drag ratio (drag force/tire load) varied with the velocity in a rather unpredictable way for which rational explanation has not yet been found. Typical test results obtained with a 29 x 11.0—10.8 ply aircraft tire under 5300 lb load obtained in Buckshot clay ($CBR = 2.3$) with various inflation pressures are shown in Figure 3.88. Interestingly, similar results were obtained in sandy soil. This would suggest that the observed phenomena are caused by some factor that is independent of soil properties, such a soil inertia. However, a re-evaluation of the experimental results (SELIG and CHIEN-TZU-WANG, 1975) leaves some doubt about the validity of the drag ratio variation shown in Figure 3.88. This reevaluation contends that experimental scatter and data reduction techniques were responsible for the unpredictable drag force behavior reported by CRENSHAW. Reevaluated data points, shown in Figure 3.89 indicate a much smoother trend. Whether this explanation is correct or not, it is certain that at the velocity levels where this behavior

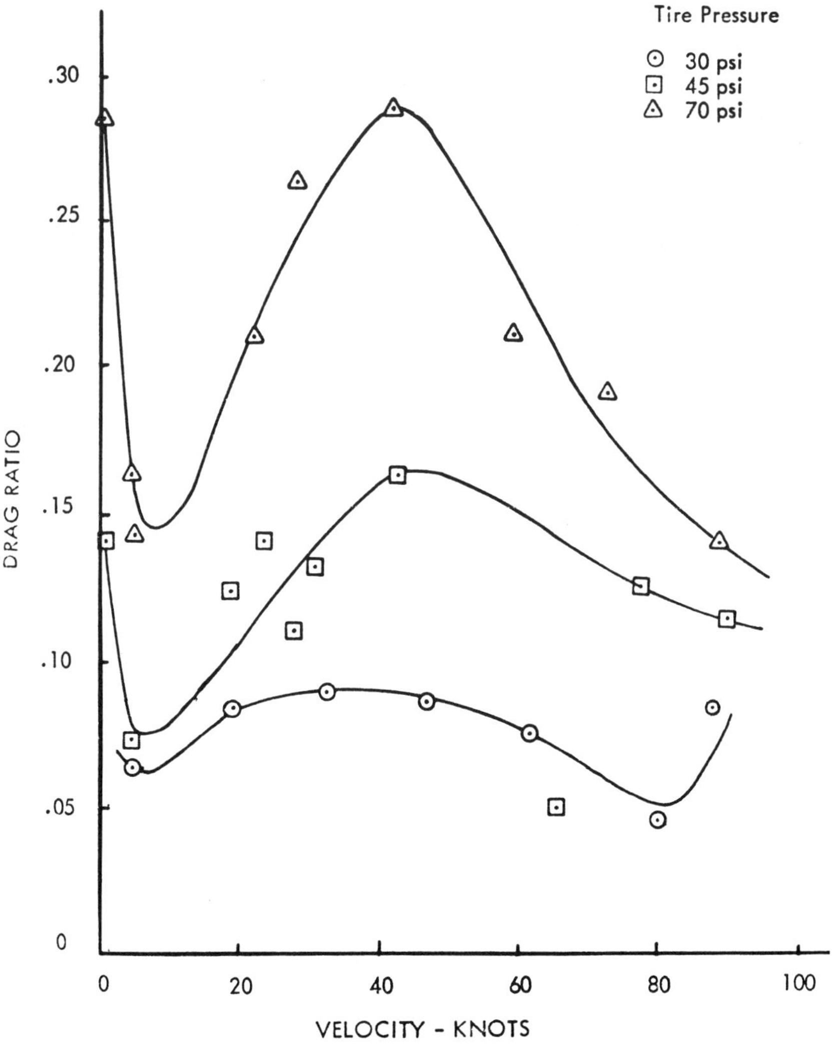

Fig. 3.88
Average Drag Ratio Versus Velocity for Free Rolling, Single Wheel Dynamometer Tests in Clay, $CBR = 2.3$.
(After CRENSHAW et al, 1971)

has been observed a valid tire-soil interaction concept must take into account all significant factors that influence the interaction at these velocity levels.

Travel velocity affects tire-soil interaction primarily in the following two ways:

a) Soil inertia forces are generated in the soil during the passage of the tire. The magnitude of these inertia forces depends on the velocity of the tire and is approximately proportionate with the square of the velocity of the tire.

b) The strength of the soil that controls the interface stresses is affected by the rate of loading that is directly proportionate to the velocity of travel.

The tire-soil model developed by the authors is suitable for taking into account the effect of changes in soil strength due to the velocity of travel

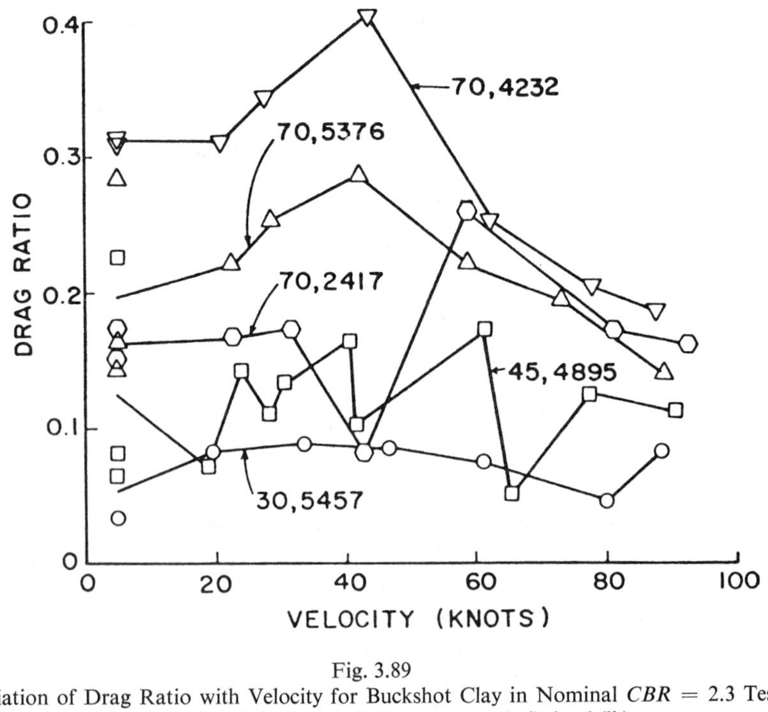

Fig. 3.89
Variation of Drag Ratio with Velocity for Buckshot Clay in Nominal *CBR* = 2.3 Test Sections. Labels indicate inflation pressure (psi), load (lb).
(After SELIG and CHIEN-TZU-WANG, 1975)

on tire performance. However, the soil inertia forces generated at high travel velocities make it necessary to account for them in the differential equations of plasticity that define the state of stresses in the soil when interacting with the tire load. For the calculation of slip line fields the differential equations of plasticity to be solved under these conditions are as follows.

$$dz = dx \tan(\theta \mp \mu)$$

$$d\sigma \mp 2\sigma \tan\varphi \, d\theta = \frac{\gamma}{g}\left[(a_x \mp (a_z + g)\tan\varphi)\, dx + (a_x + g \pm a_z \tan\varphi)\, dz\right]$$

Eq. 3.4.17

Note that in this application of the general Equation 2.2.25 the acceleration terms $\ddot{x}$ and $\ddot{z}$ have been substitued by a_x and a_z, respectively, to indicate that in the tire-soil interaction concept the slip line field refers to an instantaneous position of the tire (and a coordinate system that moves with the tire) while the soil inertia forces refer to a coordinate system that is fixed to the ground. For the determination of these accelerations, two methods, both approximate, have been proposed (KARAFIATH and SOBIERAJSKI, 1974). The first method is based on the theory of velocity fields, discussed in Chapter 2.4, that establishes the differential equations for the velocities along the "j" and "i" lines of a slip line field. The velocities that change along these lines with the changes in the direction of these lines are determined by numerical integration methods for a given geometry of the slip line field. The finite difference equations for this numerical integration procedure were given in Section 2.3.5. For a constant travel velocity, v, the accelerations at a point in the slip line field can be approximately calculated as follows.

$$a_x = \frac{\Delta v_x}{\Delta t} = \frac{\Delta v_x}{\Delta x} v$$

$$a_z = \frac{\Delta v_z}{\Delta t} = \frac{\Delta v_z}{\Delta x} v$$

Eqs. 3.4.18

The Δv_x and Δv_z velocities are obtained as differences in the velocities v_x and v_z, respectively, a distance Δx apart in the slip line field. For the determination of v_x and v_z velocities, however, the geometry of the slip line field has to be known. However, the geometry itself depends on these velocities when the acceleration terms are included in the differential Equation 3.4.17. An iterative procedure is needed whereby, starting from a slip line field for quasi static conditions, the velocities and the geometry of the slip line field are updated step by step.This method was found to work only at low velocities because the abrupt change in the direction of the slip lines at the zone boundaries (from a nearly straight line to a sharply curved one) results in an abrupt change in the velocities at these locations and hence unrealistic accelerations in the vicinity of these boundaries.

The other method developed for the calculation of soil inertia forces is semiempirical and is based on the geometry of the path that a soil particle follows from the time it is stirred by the approach of a tire until it comes to rest after the passage of the tire. Particle path geometries were determined by various researchers in laboratory experiments by the use of the flash X-ray technique (WILSON and KRZYWICKI, 1966; YONG and WEBB, 1969 and WINDISCH and YONG, 1970). These experiments show the same general pattern and the dependence of the particle path geometry on slip, as shown for example, in Figure 3.90. Theoretical considerations indicate that, for a constant velocity, the path geometry for particles initially located at the same depth must not change with the x coordinate, the direction of travel. Any varation in particle path geometry in the x direction that might

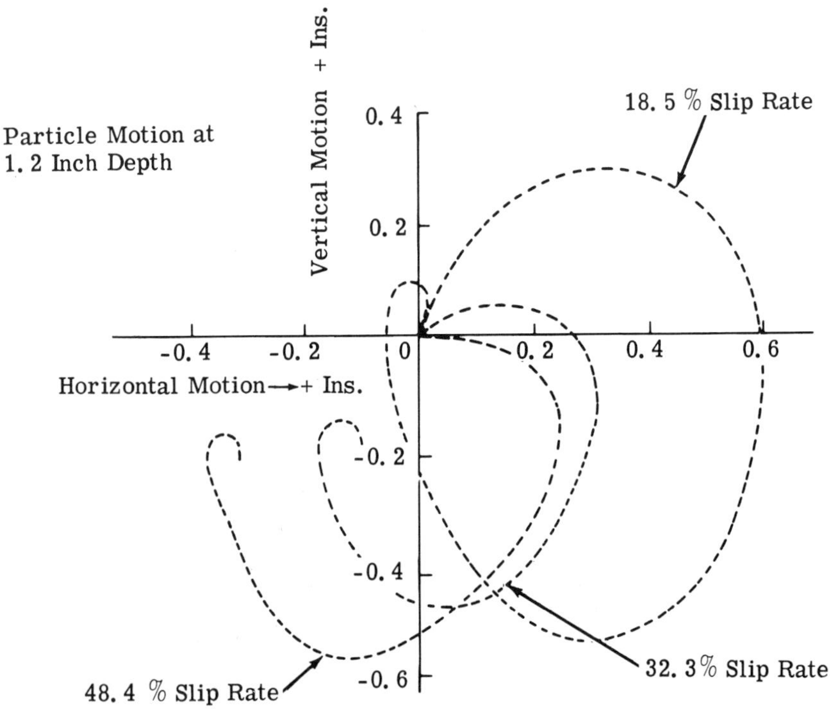

Fig. 3.90
Particle Motion as Influenced by the Slip Rate
(After YONG and WEBB, 1969)

have been observed in experiments must have been the result of experimental inaccuracy, in homogeneities in the soil bed, etc. The invariability of the particle path geometry with respect to the direction of travel also follows from the "steady state" concept of tire-soil interaction. The experiments also show that the shape of the paths of particles initially located at different depths is similar, but the size of the paths diminishes with the depth of the initial location of the particle and there is a certain limit depth below which particles are unaffected by the passage of a tire or wheel.

There are certain conditions that define the end points of the path of a particle that was originally at the surface. After the passage of a tire or a rigid wheel a soil particle from the surface winds up in the rut at some depth below the original surface. This depth evidently equals the vertical distance between the end points of the path of the particle. Experiments also show that the horizontal position of a particle originally at the surface is changed by the action of the tire or wheel as it passes over the particle. In the case of a slipping wheel, the particle at the surface is pushed backward from its original position, in the case of a skidding wheel, or negative slip, the particle at the surface is pushed in the forward direction. Figure 3.91 shows the displacement of dyed sand particles beneath a skidding and a slipping wheel, as determined by the authors in a small scale mobility bin. The horizontal displacement of a particle at the surface equals the horizontal distance between the origin and terminus of the path of a particle at the surface.

For the intended use of particle path geometries it is advantageous to describe these geometries by analytical functions. Experimentally determined particle paths have some resemblance to cardioids and in some publications they are referred to as such. The parametric equation of a cardioid (Figure 3.92) is:

$$\begin{aligned} x &= 2a \cos \omega - a \cos 2\omega \\ z &= 2a \sin \omega - a \sin 2\omega \end{aligned} \qquad \text{Eqs. 3.4.19}$$

Obviously, a cardioid is not a suitable curve to describe particle path geometries when constraints are set for the displacements of the end point in both the horizontal and vertical direction. Greater freedom to simulate particle path geometries is achieved by the following parametric expressions:

$$\begin{aligned} x &= a\,(\varrho_1 \sin \omega - \sin \varrho_1 \omega) \\ z &= a\,(\varrho_2 - 1 - \varrho_2 \cos \omega + \cos \varrho_2 \omega) \end{aligned} \qquad \text{Eqs. 3.4.20}$$

In these equations "a", ϱ_1 and ϱ_2 are constants that can be determined from the end constraints and other conditions. The constant "a" deter-

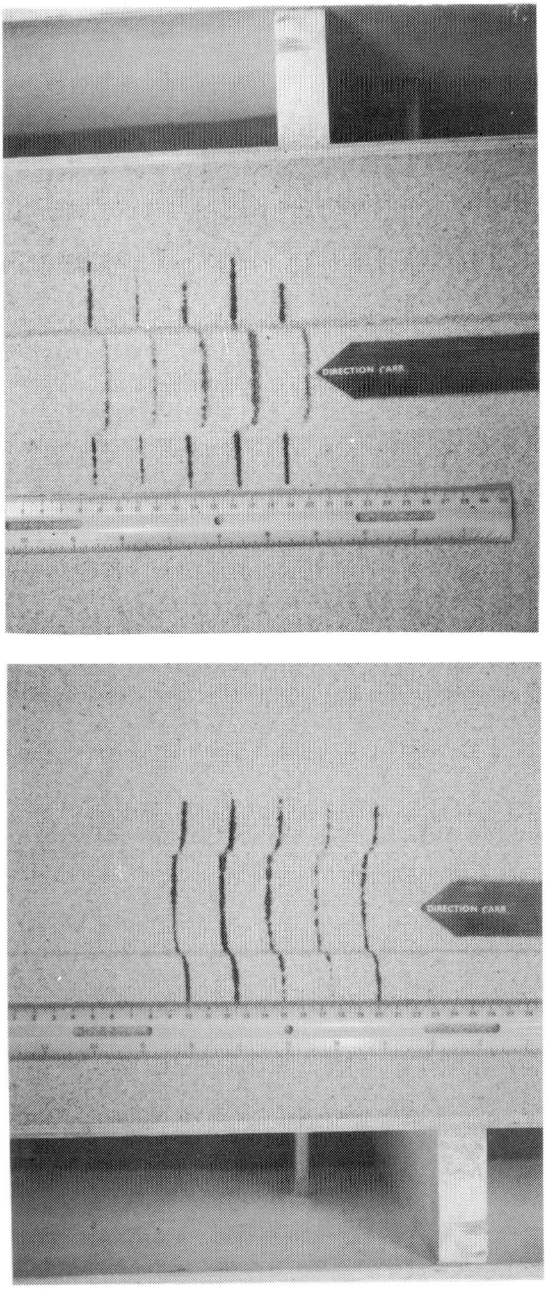

(a)

(b)

Fig. 3.91
Displacement of Sand Particles Under a Slipping Wheel (a) and a Skidding Wheel (b). Slip Rate: (a) 55%, (b) —40%

mines the scale of the particle path. It is chosen so that for a point at the surface the vertical distance between the end points of the particle path is equal with the rut depth. It may be assumed that the path of the particles at some depth below the surface is similar, but its size decreases linearly with depth. The value of "a" becomes zero at the depth where the soil is unaffected by the passage of the tire. The constants ϱ_1 and ϱ_2 determine the shape of the particle path. Figure 3.93 shows particle path geometries for selected combinations of these constants.

Time derivatives of the coordinates of the particle path yield the velocities and accelerations of the particle at the time the particle is at point x, z. To calculate these time derivatives, the parameter ω has to be related to time, t, preferably by a differentiable function. If

$$\omega = f(t) \qquad \text{Eq. 3.4.21}$$

then the time derivatives of the coordinates of the particle path are:

$$\dot{x} = a\varrho_1\dot{\omega}(\cos\omega - \cos\varrho_1\omega)$$
$$\dot{z} = a\varrho_2\dot{\omega}(\sin\omega - \sin\varrho_2\omega)$$
$$\ddot{x} = a\varrho_1\ddot{\omega}(\cos\omega - \cos\varrho_1\omega) + a\varrho_1(\dot{\omega})^2(-\sin\omega + \varrho_1\sin\varrho_1\omega)$$
$$\ddot{z} = a\varrho_2\ddot{\omega}(\sin\omega - \sin\varrho_2\omega) + a\varrho_2(\dot{\omega})^2(\cos\omega - \varrho_2\cos\varrho_2\omega)$$

Eqs. 3.4.22

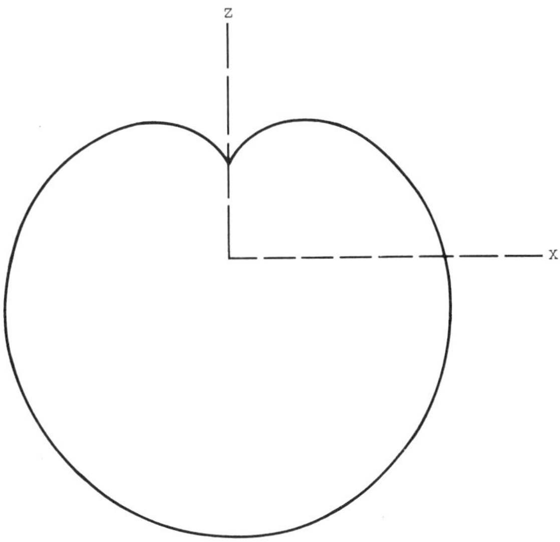

Fig. 3.92
Cardioid Geometry

To compute the accelerations from Equation 3.4.20 the relationship between the parameter ω and time t has to be defined. To this end it is useful to consider those changes in the direction of the particle movement that can be associated with some relative position of the tire. The direction of the particle at any point along the particle path is given by the tangent

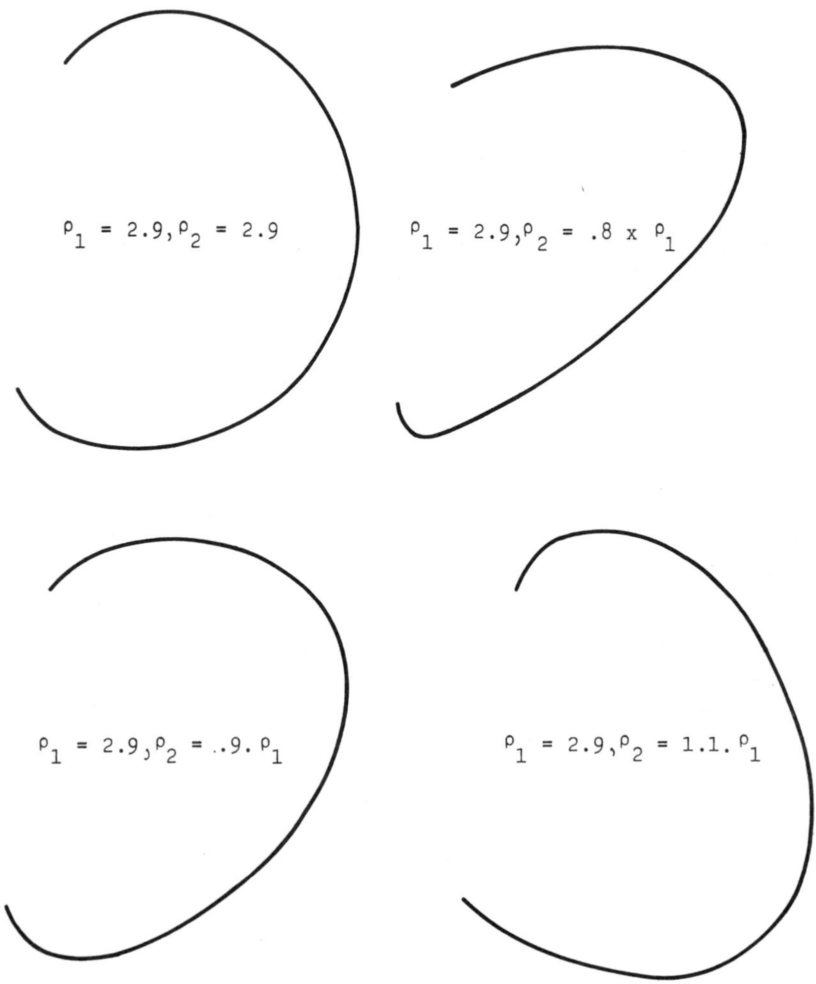

Fig. 3.93
Particle Path Simulation

of the path at that point. From Equation 3.4.20 the tangent of the particle path can be calculated as follows.

$$\frac{dz}{dx} = \frac{\frac{dz}{d\omega}}{\frac{dx}{d\omega}} = \frac{\varrho_2}{\varrho_1} \cdot \frac{\sin \omega - \sin \varrho_2 \omega}{\cos \omega - \cos \varrho_1 \omega} \qquad \text{Eq. 3.4.23}$$

The points along the particle path that may be associated with various positions of the tire are shown in Figure 3.94. The value of the parameter ω at these points may be determined from the condition that the tangent of the particle path is either horizontal or vertical. Table 3.6 shows the ω values at these points.

The position of the tire that may be associated with these points of the particle path is shown in the lower part of Figure 3.94 together with the time elapsed while the tire passes from one point to another. These considerations serve primarily as a guide for the mathematical formulation of the $\omega = f(t)$ relationship. A more detailed discussion of this method is given by Karafiath and Sobierajski (1974).

In the computerized tire-soil model the calculation of accelerations by the particle path method can be most conveniently performed in a subroutine that is called from the subroutine for the computation of the slip line field after the first approximation of the coordinates x, z is computed for a nodal point of the slip line field. The accelerations computed in the particle path subroutine for the nodal point are then used in the calculation of σ and θ and in updating the x and z coordinates of that nodal point. Results of sample calculations performed to evaluate the effect of soil inertia forces on tire performance by the particle path method are shown in Table 3.7. It is seen that up to 10 ft/sec travel velocity the effect of soil inertia forces is minor, even though the inertial accelerations, computed by the particle path method, often exceeded 10 g in these tire-soil interaction problems. At higher velocities the solution of the differential equations of plasticity often becomes problematical, because in the

TABLE 3.6
Values of the Parameter ω at Various Points of Particle Path.

Point	Tangent	ω
A	Vertical	0
B	Horizontal	$\pi/(1 + \varrho_2)$
C	Vertical	$2\pi/(1 + \varrho_1)$
D	Horizontal	$3\pi/(1 + \varrho_2)$
E	Vertical	$2\pi/(\varrho_2 - 1)$

solution the slip lines overlap each other. This means that the mathematical solution requires two different stress states to exist at the same location at the same time. Obviously, such a mathematical solution is physically inadmissible. Further experimental and theoretical research is needed to clarify what is governing the soil behavior under such conditions.

Travel velocity affects tire-soil interaction not only by the generation of soil inertia forces, but also by directly influencing the strain rates imposed on the soil in tire-soil interaction. As it has been discussed in Sections 1.3.4 and 1.3.5, the strength properties of soil depend to some extent on the time rate of straining. If the strength parameters of a soil are determined as functions of the strain rate, then it is possible to use these

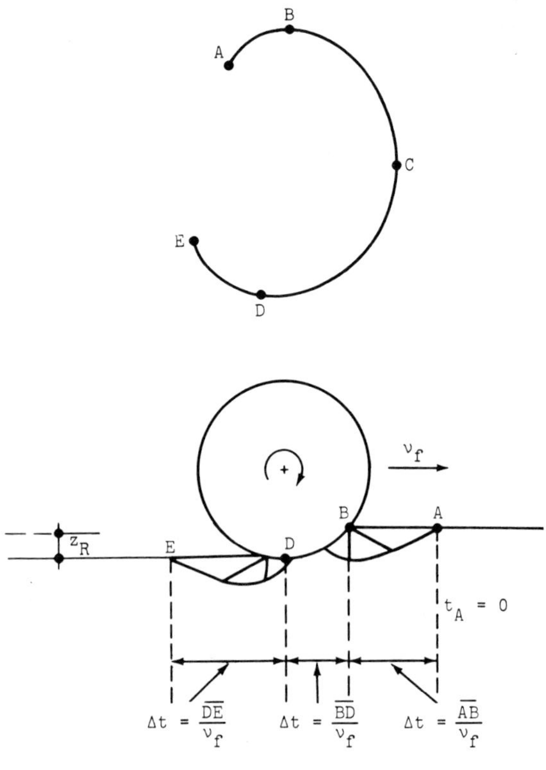

Fig. 3.94
Characteristic Points of Particle Path and Their Relation to the Position of Tire

strain rate dependent strength parameters in the tire-soil model. In the numerical calculation of slip line fields, variable strength properties may be considered in essentially the same way as non-linear strength properties (Refer to Section 2.2.3). The problem is to determine strain rates for the nodal points of slip line fields. Conceptually, it is possible to calculate strain rates from either the velocity fields or practicle paths. However, up to now only a very crude analysis of the effects of strain rate on tire performance has been made. In this analysis an average strain rate was estimated for the tire-soil interaction problem being analyzed and uniform strength properties, corresponding to this average strain rate, were used in the analysis (KARAFIATH and SOBIERAJSKI, 1974). The results of these analyses were inconclusive inasmuch as tire performances were generally overpredicted with the strength parameters corresponding to an average strain rate. It appears that the strain rates for each of the nodal points in the slip line field must be computed for a more meaningful analysis of their effect on tire performance.

As we have seen, the tire-soil model, as an analytical tool is better suited to analyze certain phenomena in tire-soil interaction than experiments. This is especially true when the physical factors that cause certain interaction behavior are inseparable in experiments, as in the case of the combined effect of soil inertia and strain rate on tire performance.

TABLE 3.7
Effect of Soil Inertia Forces on Tire Performance at Various Velocities

Tire and soil input data	Case 1		Case 2	
Tire size	9.00–14		4.00–7	
Tire radius (nominal)	1.18 ft		0.59 ft	
Tire width (nominal)	0.74 ft		0.40 ft	
Tire load	614 lb		225 lb	
Inflation pressure	10.9 psi		10.3 psi	
Limit pressure	11.0 psi		10.6 psi	
Deflection coefficient	0.9		0.85	
Slip	10%		30%	
Interface friction angle	22.8°		27.8°	
Cone index gradient	15 lb/cu in		19.6 lb/cu in	
Translational velocity (ft/sec)	Pull coefficient	Sinkage in	Pull coefficient	Sinkage in
0	0.3268	0.724	0.3217	1.11
5	0.3334	0.599	0.3270	1.08
8	0.3340	0.588	0.3291	1.07
10	0.3346	0.583	0.3508	0.93

CHAPTER 3.5

SOIL MECHANICS THEORIES APPLIED TO THE ANALYSIS OF THE PERFORMANCE OF TRACKED VEHICLES

3.5.1 Tracks as Traction Devices

Tracks were originally conceived as movable roadways that are laid down in the front of the vehicle, traveled over and then picked up again by the vehicle. The application of the concept of movable roadways to off-road vehicles led to the development of the various types of tracks used today with military, heavy construction and agricultural vehicles, whenever high traction or travel over soft terrain is required. The different uses of these tracked vehicles bring about various, and often conflicting requirements regarding mobility, steerability, speed, maintenance, etc. It is the task of the designer of the track to reach the best compromise. A common characteristic feature of the various types of tracks is the low ground pressure that enables tracked vehicles to travel over ground generally not negotiable by wheeled vehicles. The average ground pressure (the weight of the vehicle divided by the contact area of the track; also called nominal ground pressure) is an important characteristic that is sometimes identified as the measure of mobility. While there is a certain correlation between track performance and nominal ground pressure, the actual track-soil interaction that controls track performance is far more complex than to be representable by the magnitude of a hypothetical uniform ground pressure. The distribution of pressures beneath track laying vehicles is far from uniform as, for example, measurements by ROWLAND (1972), shown in Figure 3.95, indicate. It is apparent from the figure that the number and spacing of road wheels, their diameter and presumably their suspension system influence the variation of pressures and, thereby, the track-soil interaction. In applying soil mechanics theories to the formulation of track-soil interaction concepts it is essential to recognize and characterize the role of the track and suspension system in transferring vehicle load to the soil. Because of the interdependency of soil and track behavior it is expedient to classify the various types of tracks and use appropriate models of these types in the formulation of track-soil inter-

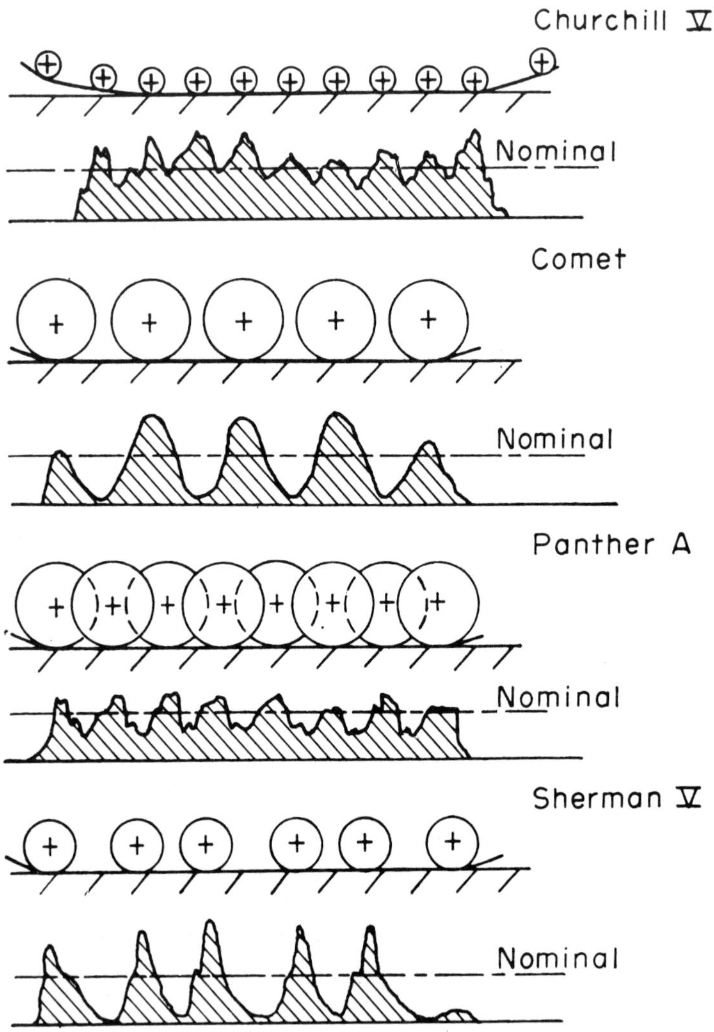

Fig. 3.95
Examples of Pressure Distributions Underneath Various Tanks
Measured at 0.23 m Depth
(After ROWLAND, 1972)

action concepts. For this purpose the following two general classes of tracks may be distinguished:

a) rigid tracks

b) flexible tracks

Rigid tracks are those where the interlocking of the links permits the track to form a convex but not a concave curve with respect to the soil, as in the so-called rigid girder tracks. A rigid girder track is designed to prevent upward flexing of the track and insure thereby a fairly uniform ground pressure. This type of track cannot be used with a sprung suspension system that would permit the road wheels to displace vertically. Therefore, the use of rigid girder tracks has been restricted to slowly moving vehicles, such as most of the tracked machinery used in heavy construction.

There are variations of the rigid girder track that use rubber blocks in the joints and allow a slightly convex curvature. From the viewpoint of track-soil interaction these will be treated as rigid tracks.

The flexible type tracks embrace a variety of track designs. From the viewpoint of track-soil interaction, it is convenient to group flexible tracks as follows:

a) continuous tracks

b) spaced link tracks

The group of continuous flexible tracks includes both *endless band type* and *block and pin type* tracks. The deflected geometry of these tracks is similar, although the geometry of a block and pin type track is a polygon rather than a continuous curve. However, from the viewpoint of track-soil interaction it is convenient to treat the block and pin type tracks as continuously flexible tracks, since the location of pins is continously changing with the track advancement. The interaction of spaced link tracks with soil differs from the continuously flexible tracks in that there are no external stresses on the soil in between the links.

These differences in track design have a profound influence on track-soil interaction. Nevertheless, little attention has been paid to them in the various methods proposed for the determination of track performance. In the following discussions of the applications of soil mechanics theories to the problem of track-soil interaction, the significance of variations in track design will be put in proper perspective. Mathematical models of track-soil interaction for these various types of tracks have not been developed yet by the authors. Nevertheless, conceptual formulations are discussed in sufficient detail to serve as a basis for mathematical modeling.

3.5.2 Similarities and Differences in the Interaction of Wheels and Tracks with Soil

As it was discussed in Chapter 3.2, the geometry of the contact area and the magnitude of interface stresses play a major role in running gear-soil interaction. The overall ground contact area of tracks changes but little with the sinkage of the vehicle and, for all practical purposes, the ground contact area of tracks may be considered constant. Because of this insensitivity of the contact area of tracks to changes in load or interface shear stresses, the interaction between track and soil is generally weaker than that between wheel or tire and soil. This feature of tracks affects the formulation of track-soil interaction concepts in two ways. First, the soil response is not necessarily governed by failure conditions in the soil that obey the laws of plasticity theory. Second, the sinkage of tracks cannot be determined from equilibrium conditions only, even if the soil underneath the track is in failure condition. This is in contrast to the rigid wheels where the equilibrium of the wheel requires a certain contact area which, in turn, determines the sinkage.

The problem of the determination of track sinkage has important implications regarding the characterization of soils for mobility purposes. In the wheel-soil and tire-soil interaction model the soil is characterized by its Coulombic strength parameters and its unit weight. These soil properties are sufficient to determine both the soil response to the wheel loads and the sinkage that is directly related to the size of the contact area. In the case of tracks, the total sinkage is not related to the minor changes in the contact area during the sinkage process, but is dependent upon the volume changes that occur under the particular loading conditions in the soil. Thus, in principle, there is a need for a descriptor of volume changes if the sinkage of tracks is to be determined correctly. In existing track models this problem is resolved by the use of pressure-sinkage relationships presumed to be obtainable from a plate-sinkage test. The inadequacy of this method will be discussed in connection with the role of interface shear stresses in track-soil interaction. The problem of the characterization of volume change properties of soils for mobility purposes is difficult indeed. In soil mechanics research, volume change properties of soils are determined either by consolidation tests for uniaxial stress conditions, or by triaxial tests for three-dimensional, axially symmetric test conditions. The deformation of soil under the track load is far from uniaxial and, therefore, uniaxial volume change properties, even if they were available, would be of little use for the determination of track sinkage. The determination of volume change properties of soil by triaxial tests, although laborious, is, in the authors' opinion, indispensable for the meaningful application of rigorous soil mechanics theories to track sinkage problems. Unfortunately, the volume changes that various types of soils exhibit under a triaxial stress system do not lend themselves readily to the formulation of a general constitutive law that allows the development of general relationships between sinkage and constants in the constitutive law. Thus, although the computation of sinkage using volume change properties determined by triaxial tests and soil mechanics theories is possible in specific cases and is probably the most reliable method for research purposes, it is not practical for use in track-soil interaction models.

The problem of the determination of the sinkage of tracked vehicles is also related to the interactive effect of the shear stresses applied at the track-soil interface. The nearly constant ground contact area of tracks accounts for a fundamental difference between wheel-soil and track-soil interaction. In the case of tracks a very effective instrument of interaction, the compliance of the area of contact with the loading conditions, is absent. In contrast, the role of the interface shear stresses in track-soil interaction is basically similar to that in wheel-soil interaction. Shear stresses acting in the direction of potential failure reduce the bearing stresses that can be developed in the soil. If the ground pressure underneath the track is less than the bearing stresses corresponding to the applied shear stresses, then the soil is not in failure condition beneath the track. Nevertheless, track-soil interaction is affected by the applied interface shear stresses: the sinkage of the track under the applied stress system depends on how close the stress state in the soil is to the plastic state. Therefore, a decrease of bearing capacity due to the applied shear stresses is always accompanied by an increase of the sinkage, even though the applied normal stresses remain the same. This fact is sometimes referred to as slip-sinkage, a misleading term inasmuch as slip is an accompanying phenomenon and not the cause of the sinkage. The increase in sinkage is caused by the interface shear stresses that reduce the ultimate normal stresses that the soil is able to carry. This reduction also means that the stress states in the soil approach the plastic state, hence the increased sinkage.

The interaction between applied shear stresses and sinkage must be an integral part of any track-soil interaction concept that undertakes to simulate and predict track performance under all conceivable soil conditions with credibility. Present methods of computing track performance generally disregard this interaction primarily for reasons of convenience but also because the importance of this interaction is often not fully understood. Perhaps the most widely known method of computing track performance is the one originated by BEKKER (1956) and condensed in the following formula:

$$DB = H - R \qquad \text{Eq. 3.5.1}$$

where

$H = A \cdot c + W \cos \varepsilon \tan \varphi$
A = Nominal ground contact area
ε = Slope angle
$R = R_\varepsilon + R_r + R_c + R_\lambda$
R_ε = Resistance due to slope
R_r = Mechanical rolling resistance
R_c = Resistance due to soil compaction
R_λ = Resistance due to trim angle (λ) of track

In this method the R_c resistance due to soil compaction is computed by assuming that the pressure-sinkage curve is anologous to that obtained in plate sinkage tests. The resistance R_λ is caused by the track tilting by the trim angle λ from its original position. This tilting has been observed to occur as traction is increased. Although various methods have been proposed to compute the trim angle, none of them has proven to be practical or gained acceptance. Obviously, both R_c and R_λ depend on the applied traction, and treating them as resistances that are independent of traction, as implied by the formula, is conceptually incorrect. The errors introduced by disregarding the dependence of these resistances on the traction become greater as the traction increases and greatest in the critical situation when "no go" conditions occur. To compensate for underestimates of R_c in these situations another nebulous resistance term, the "bulldozing resistance", is commonly introduced. The term, if added to R_c at will, may be helpful to explain discrepancies between observed and predicted motion resistances. Nevertheless, in many everyday situations where soil conditions are not extremely bad and only a moderate amount of traction is needed, the interactive effect of the applied shear stresses is minor and the traction computation by Equation 3.5.1 is acceptable.

An approximate method to take into account the effect of interactive shear stresses on the sinkage is proposed in Section 3.5.4.

The driven version of the tire-soil interaction model, as discussed in Chapter 3.4, was found to be insensitive to three-dimensional effects. In track-soil interaction, potential failure in the transverse direction always exists and it is necessary to consider its effect on the bearing stresses. Actually, lateral failure conditions govern the interaction of rigid tracks and soil over a wide range of loading conditions. The aspect ratio (width : length) of the ground contact area of rigid tracks is usually 1:8 or less.

The bearing stress under a particular point of a rectangular loaded area is controlled by that two-dimensional failure condition which yields the lower bearing stress. The bearing stress generally increases with the distance from the edge of the loaded area. With an aspect ratio of 1:8 or less, transverse failure predominantly controls the bearing stresses when traction is low and the effect of shear stresses on the longitudinal bearing stresses is minor.

3.5.3 The Sinkage of Vehicular Footings and the Governing Soil Proceses

In civil soils engineering the structural members that transmit the load of the structure to the soil are called footings. In off-road vehicle engineering that part of the running gear that is momentarily in contact with the ground plays the same role. In this book this part is called a *vehicular footing* to indicate the similarity in its behavior with structural footings when in the consideration of its instantaneous interaction with soil the motion of the running gear is disregarded.

In the terminology of off-road vehicle engineering the vertical displacement of vehicular footings is called *sinkage* to distinguish it from *settlement,* the soil mechanics term for the usually time dependent vertical displacement of foundations. This distinction is necessary not only because sinkage is instantaneous, but also because in the case of vehicular footings the ratio of the vertical displacement to footing width is of a different order of magnitude than in the case of foundations and, consequently, the behavior of the soil is fundamentally different in the two cases. In the case of foundations the soil, by design, is far from the plastic state and elastic theory can be used satisfactorily for the determination of the stresses in the soil mass. In contrast, the soil underneath vehicular footings, in critical situations even under low ground pressure tracks, is either in the elastic-plastic or in the completely plastic state. In either case, the elastic theory is no longer applicable for the computation of stresses and displacements under these conditions. Vehicular footing sinkage is thus an extremely complex process that may be simulated with some success by finite element methods but that is difficult to predict by theoretical formulation. This difficulty is compounded by the fact that for the purposes of off-road vehicle engineering it is impractical to use elaborate concepts or laboratory procedures for the determination of soil properties, and soil characterization based on the results of simple field tests are preferred.

Figure 3.96 shows a typical pressure-sinkage relationship obtained in plate sinkage tests. The state of stresses in the soil at various stages of the sinkage is also indicated. The terminology in the figure is used in a very loose sense, since the terms are intended to show but a broad picture of the nature of the different processes involved while a vehicular footing sinks into the ground. An elastic state of stresses might have been more exactly defined to mean either linear or recoverable behavior, but these distinctions are immaterial for the present discussions, since the elastic state encompasses a negligible sinkage range by either definition. The important point is that over a relatively narrow range of the sinkage elastic-plastic response of the soil balances the load, while over a larger range the soil is completely in the plastic state. In the elastic-plastic state sinkage is controlled by the volume change properties of the soil, while in the plastic state sinkage is controlled by the geometry changes influencing the plastic equilibrium in the soil. Were it not for these geometry changes, the footing would sink indefinitely without any further increase of the load.

In determining the sinkage of tracks under given loading conditions, it should be first ascertained whether the soil is in the elastic-plastic or in the completely plastic state under the given load. This can be best accomplished by determining the bearing stresses corresponding to the plastic

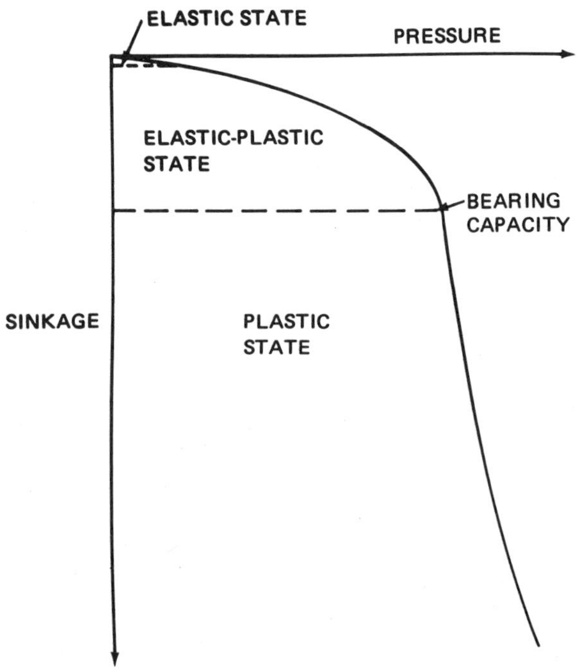

Fig. 3.96
Typical Pressure-Sinkage Relationship Obtained in Plate Sinkage Test

state of stresses in the soil by plasticity theory methods. The procedure is essentially the same as discussed in detail in Section 3.3.3 in connection with the determination of interface stresses acting on rigid wheels. Integration of the bearing stresses over the loaded area yields the ultimate load that the soil is able to carry in the completely plastic state. If this ultimate load is higher than the given load, then the soil is in the elastic-plastic state. If the ultimate load is equal to or lower than the given load, then the soil is in the completely plastic state and sinkage is controlled by potential increase of the ultimate load due to additional sinkage. In this case, the additional vertical displacement required to bring the ultimate load up to the level of the given load determines the sinkage independently of whatever sinkage may be computed on the basis of volume changes.

3.5.4 Pressure-Sinkage Relationships for Tracks

In off-road vehicle engineering a pressure-sinkage relationship is generally associated with plate-sinkage tests. These tests are usually carried out to depths several times the plate diameter, therefore, the sinkage range encompasses depths where the soil is in the elastic-plastic state and where the soil is completely in the plastic state and sinkage is controlled by the effect of geometry changes. The mathematical modeling of this relationship by the well-known BERNSTEIN (1913) equation

$$p = k \cdot z^{n} \qquad \text{Eq. 3.5.2}$$

or similar equations does not recognize that the sinkage in a plate sinkage test is produced by two entirely different physical processes. This type of equation forces the results of plate sinkage tests to conform with the single functional relationship represented by Equation 3.5.2 in both stages of the sinkage. Usually, the sinkages obtained in the completely plastic state dominate the pressure-sinkage curve and the sinkages in the elastic-plastic state lose their significance when the constants in Equation 3.5.2 are evaluated by a curve fitting procedure. For this reason and because the effect of shear stresses on the sinkage is disregarded, this equation and all BERNSTEIN-type equations are conceptually inadequate for the determination of track sinkage. Any agreement with test results is either purely coincidental or the result of manipulation with the evaluation of the constants in Equation 3.5.2.

Obviously, there is a need for a pressure-sinkage relationship in a track-soil interaction concept, but the obstacles to a theoretically sound formulation are formidable. The framework of an approximate procedure that is thought to yield sufficiently accurate results for the purpose of estimating sinkages in track-soil interaction is described in the following paragraphs.

The complete development of plastic failure zones in the soil is associated with volume changes that cause a loaded plate to sink a certain distance. PERLOFF and RAHIM (1966) have shown that the pressure-sinkage relationship obtained with plates of different size and shape are similar if expressed in the dimensionless form $z/\sqrt{A}$, where A = area of footing. The sinkage associated with the complete development of failure zones, or the *sinkage at bearing capacity* may be expressed as

$$z_B = K_B\sqrt{A} \qquad \text{Eq. 3.5.3}$$

where K_B = coefficient of sinkage

This coefficient can be determined by plate sinkage tests discussed in Section 3.6.2. The tangent of the pressure-sinkage curve at $z = z_B$ expresses the effect of geometry changes and may be approximated on the basis of bearing capacity equations by the following expression (see also Section 3.6.2 and Figure 3.113)

$$\frac{dp}{dz} = \gamma s_q N_q \qquad \text{Eq. 3.5.4}$$

If results of plate sinkage tests are not available, a crude estimate of K_B may be made on the basis of the friction angle of the soil. Stress-strain curves of soils obtained by triaxial tests indicate that the strain at which triaxial samples fail is related to the friction angle; the higher the friction angle, the lower the strain at which the sample fails. Tentatively the following relationship is proposed

$$K_B = 0.5 - 0.01\,\varphi \text{ (degrees)} \qquad \text{Eq. 3.5.5}$$

PERLOFF and RAHIM also showed that a dimensionless hyperbolic relationship fitted well all pressure-sinkage curves that they obtained with different size and shape plates in cohesive soils. To arrive at a dimensionless expression, PERLOFF related the pressure to the unconfined compressive strength of soil. To make this expression more general and better suited for the estimation of track sinkage under all conditions, it is expedient to relate the pressure to the ultimate bearing capacity of soil that can be determined from the strength properties of soil by plasticity theory methods. The following expression is, therefore, proposed for the mathematical modeling of the pressure-sinkage curve in the range of pressures up to the ultimate bearing capacity.

$$p = p_{ult}\,\frac{z/\sqrt{A}}{M + Qz/\sqrt{A}} \qquad \text{Eq. 3.5.6}$$

The tangent of the pressure-sinkage curve represented by Eq. 3.5.6 is obtained by differentiation as follows

$$\frac{dp}{dz} = p_{ult} \frac{M/\sqrt{A}}{(M/\sqrt{A} + Qz)^2} \qquad \text{Eq. 3.5.7}$$

At $z = z_B$, $p = p_{ult}$ and from Equation 3.5.6

$$M = K_B (1 - Q) \qquad \text{Eq. 3.5.8}$$

Also, at $z = z_B$, the tangent $\frac{dp}{dz}$ equals $\gamma s_q N_q$ and the combination of Equations 3.5.7 and 3.5.8 yields the following relationship for Q:

$$Q = 1 - \frac{\gamma s_q N_q z_B}{p_{ult}} \qquad \text{Eq. 3.5.9}$$

The question arises how z_B would be influenced by shear stresses. Unfortunately, there is very little information available on sinkages under inclined loads. As HARRISON (1972) pointed out, the direction of the displacement of a plate under an inclined load is generally not coincident with the direction of the load. It may be assumed that the direction of the plate displacement is that of the major principal stress in the soil. Another consideration is that the work expended by an inclined load to fail the soil cannot be more than that expended by a vertical load. The horizontal component of the inclined load performs work as the plate is displaced horizontally. On the basis of these considerations the sinkage under an inclined load may be expressed as follows

$$z_B^{(\delta)} = \frac{p_{ult}\, z_B}{p_{ult}^{(\delta)} (1 + \tan \delta / \cot \theta)} \qquad \text{Eq. 3.5.10}$$

where the superscript in parantheses is to indicate that the value pertains to a load that is inclined at an angle δ from the vertical. The angle θ (the direction of the major principal stress at the interface) can be computed from Equation 2.2.21.

Pressure-sinkage curves for variously inclined loads computed by this method are shown in Figure 3.97 for a 1 ft wide strip load and the following soil strength parameters

$$c = 10 \text{ lbs/sq ft}$$
$$\varphi = 20^\circ$$
$$\gamma = 100 \text{ lbs/cu ft}$$

The bearing capacities for various δ angles of inclination were computed by plasticity theory methods and are indicated in the upper part of Figure 3.97. In the lower part of the figure the pressure-sinkage curves are shown for various δ values. It is seen that the static sinkage ($\delta = 0$) is always less than that for traction ($\delta > 0$). The pressure-sinkage curves computed by this method are responsive to the shear stresses that are generated when traction is applied. Qualitatively, they meet the criteria for an interactive pressure-sinkage relationship. The only information additional to the strength parameters that is needed for the computation of these relationships is the value of K_B. In this respect more experimental information is desirable to improve the accuracy of sinkage predictions.

Note that the pressure-sinkage relationship in Figure 3.97 refers to the average bearing pressure and the sinkage to an average uniform sinkage. The figure is not to be construed as the relationship between the pressure underneath a differential element of a loaded surface and its sinkage. The application of the BERNSTEIN-type equation, with constants derived from plate sinkage test, to the determination of pressure distribution beneath wheels and tracks, as proposed by BEKKER, is a flagrant violation of elementary mechanics, since average pressures are equated in that concept with pressures over an infinitesimal area. Plasticity theory yields pressure distributions conforming to the plastic state of stresses in the soil and the boundary conditions imposed by the problem; these pressure distributions have been validated by experiments and should be used in lieu of the BERNSTEIN-type equations.

3.5.5 Experimental Research on Track-Soil Interaction

Our knowledge of rigid wheel and pneumatic tire-soil interaction has been derived largely from experiments performed under controlled laboratory conditions. Especially useful in the development of tire-soil interaction concepts were those experiments where the deformations of tires were measured and the interface stresses determined under various conditions. The large number of tire performance tests performed in various laboratories permitted the analysis of tire-soil interaction and the validation of interaction concepts.

It is interesting, but unfortunate, that the experimental information on track-soil interaction is very limited and generally insufficient for the clarification of some very fundamental problems in track-soil interaction. Probably one reason for this state of affairs is that it is very difficult to conduct a track performance test in the laboratory so that it can be representative of the performance of the track of a vehicle without an elaborate duplication of the interacting load transfer mechanism and suspension system of the vehicle. Field tests conducted with full scale vehicles are more illuminating as far as track-soil interaction is concerned but at the same time, by their very nature, they lack the necessary control over the soil conditions that influence the results. Therefore, field tests are not ideal for concept verification and systematic research.

Experiments performed by Wills (1963) in the laboratory with full size rigid tracks using a forced slip type testing machine constructed for this purpose are noteworthy because in these experiments both the vertical and horizontal forces acting on a track link were measured by a dynamometer. The results of experiments obtained in loose sand with a 10 in. wide track with two configurations, one having a 50 in., the other a 37.5 in. long contact area, are shown in Figure 3.98. Wills noted that the periodic peaks and low points in the measured forces may be, at least to some extent,

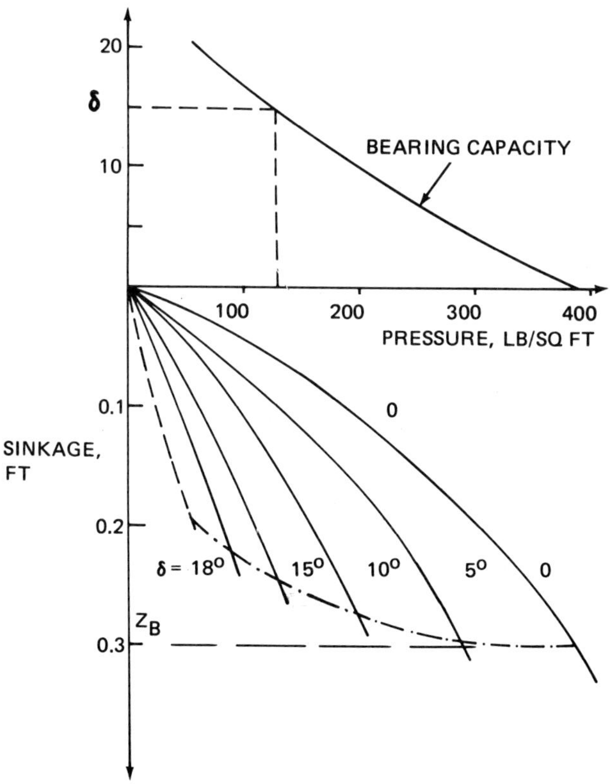

Fig. 3.97
Pressure-Sinkage Curves for Various Inclinations of Load

attributable to the so-called "polygon effect" that results from the drive sprocket lifting the back end of the track whenever a new link is grabbed by the sprocket. The same effect causes peaks in the horizontal forces but one pitch (length of a track link) out of phase with the vertical peaks. Nevertheless, the measurements give a good overall picture of the distribution of the normal and shear stresses at the track-soil interface. Note that the stress distribution shown in Figure 3.98 pertains to a fairly high tractive effort. Although the tracks in WILLS' experiments were loaded uniformly, the pressure distribution shifted to an approximately triangular one when traction was applied. This redistribution of the normal stresses is the

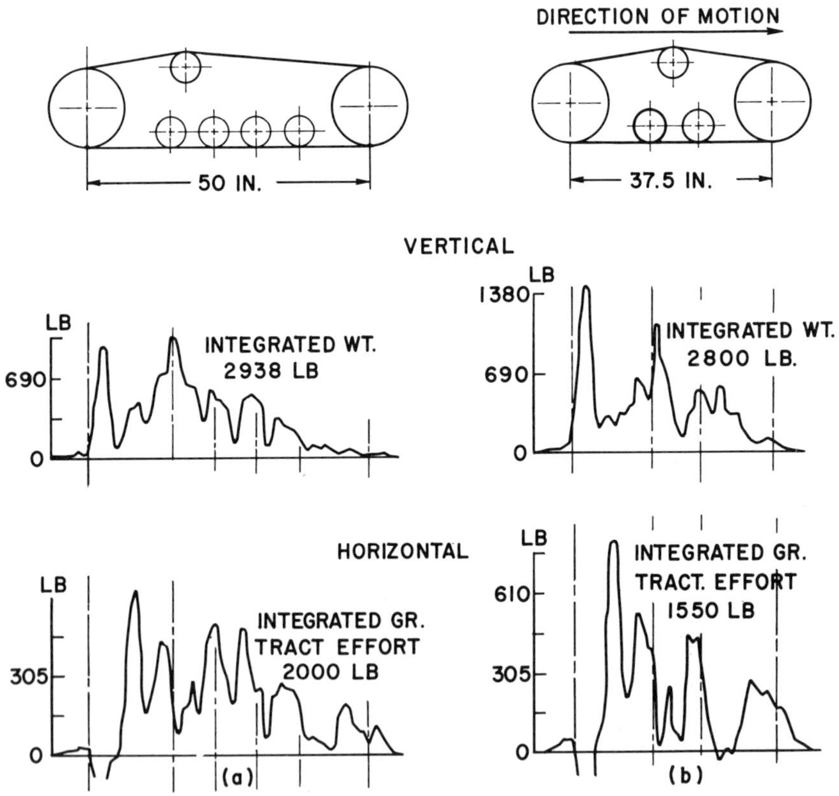

Fig. 3.98
Vertical and Horizontal Pressure Distribution Beneath Tracks.
Actual Weight on Track: a) 2950 lb b) 2950 lb
Gross Tractive Effort: a) 1720 lb b) 1754 lb
Slip: a) 15.4% b) 20%
(After WILLS, 1963)

direct result of the torque applied to the sprocket that must be belanced by the moment of the interface stresses about the center of gravity. This track-soil interaction phenomenon will be discussed in greater detail in Section 3.5.7.

Other experiments aimed at the determination of the pressure distribution beneath tracks were confined to the measurement of normal stresses. The pressure distribution beneath static tracks, measured 23 cm beneath the surface, is shown in Figure 3.95. The results reflect the effects of the suspension system and track flexibility. Ground pressure measurements beneath a 3 ton tractor were made by MITROPAN et al (1966) at various moisture contents, drawbar pulls and speeds. Unfortunately, the soil has not been identified in MITROPAN's experiments. The ground pressures measured show similar features to those in WILLS' experiments.

Figure 3.99 shows the distribution of normal stresses at the track-soil

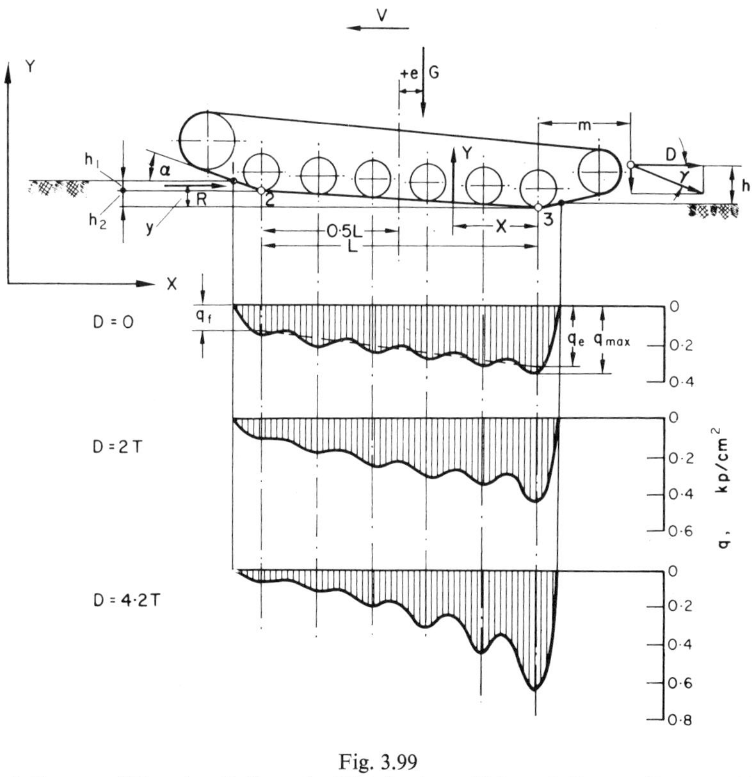

Fig. 3.99
The Influence of Drawbar Pull on the Distribution of Normal Contact Pressure Along the Length of Track
(After GUSKOV, 1968)

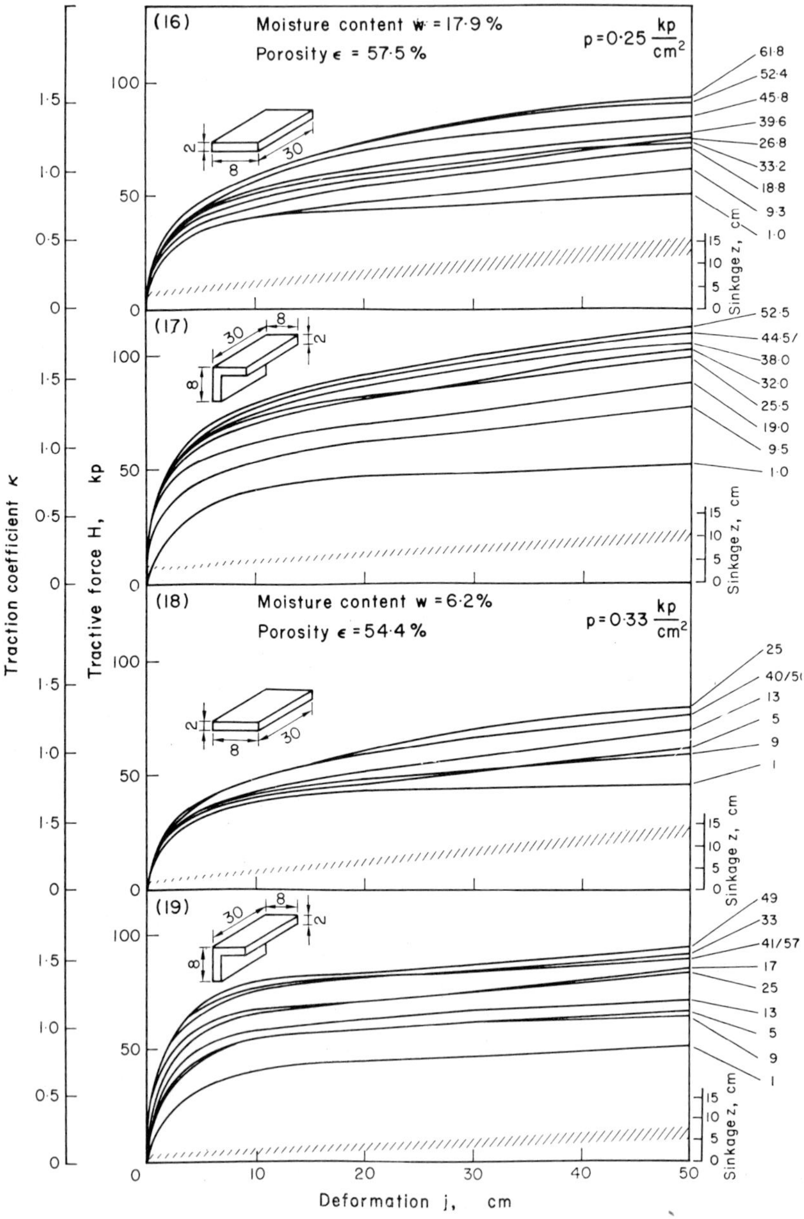

Fig. 3.100
Measured Curves of Thrust and Sinkage as a Function of Shear Deformation for a Slipping Single Plate Grouser
(After CHO et al, 1969)

interface at various drawbar pulls determined by GUSKOV (1968). The trapezoidal distribution at zero drawbar pull gradually changes to an approximately triangular one with the acute angle at the driving sprocket, as the drawbar pull increases. The redistribution of stresses clearly shows a fundamental interactive relationship between applied tractive effort and soil response.

While experimental information on the interaction of the whole track with soil is scarce and, from the viewpoint of soil mechanics, poorly documented, the interaction of one or more single elements of track, such as track shoes and grouser plates, has been investigated quite extensively by various researchers. For example, CHO, SCHWANGHARD and SYBEL (1969) investigated the effect of the spacing of track shoes on the development of traction and determined tractive force-deformation relationships for variously spaced track shoes and grouser plates. Figure 3.100 shows results of their experiments. The upper pair of plots show the tractive forces obtained in a wet soil; the lower pair show those obtained in a dry soil. Unfortunately, the soil is not identified beyond its moisture content and porosity and, therefore, from the soil mechanics point of view, these experiments contribute but little to the understanding of the phenomena involved. It appears that shear failure must have taken place in these experiments because the measured deformations were quite large. The tractive force reached a high level with a moderate amount of deformation and increased slowly afterwards. This slow increase can probably be attributed to the favorable effect of geometry changes in the failure pattern due to the sinkage accompanying the horizontal deformation. Note that the vertical load was constant in the tests and failure was brought about by increasing the horizontal force.

HARRISON (1972) pointed out that the direction of the displacement of a plate under an inclined load is generally not coincident with the direction of the load. From observations of failure patterns developing under plates loaded at an angle, HARRISON concluded that rigid, wedge shaped zones form adjacent to a grouser plate if the direction of motion at the lower edge of the interface is at a smaller angle to the horizontal (θ) than the slip line (θ_c) at that point, Figure 3.101 (a). In the case of wedge formation, slip lines form as shown in Figure 3.101 (b).

Apart from this wedge formation, the soil failure occurs along slip lines governed by the differential equations of plasticity. In the theoretical evaluation of the grouser problem, HARRISON assumed that the slip lines are either straight lines or logarithmic spirals, as in the PRANDTL case of weightless soils and arrived at closed form solutions for the computation of the vertical and horizontal components of the ultimate load that the grouser plate can carry. Figure 3.102 shows the slip lines and the rigid wedge assumed by Harrison. Note that the line *ac* is a slip line in his solution. The wedge *abc* corresponds to the active zone in plasticity theory solutions. The angle *abc* is defined by the direction of the displacement of the grouser plate from which an interface friction angle along the hypothetical face *ab* is computed. The conclusion derived from the experiments and theoretical evaluation is that a grouser plate acts exactly as if it were an inclined rough interface across the grouser tips. Figure 3.103 shows typical experimental results together with results of theoretical computations. It is especially important to note that both the horizontal and vertical components of the load that a grouser plate can carry depend on the direction of the grouser plate movement. Angular displacements of track links are often in the 15—20° range in which, according to Figure 3.103, the load carrying capacity of the grouser plate is affected in a degree that cannot be disregarded.

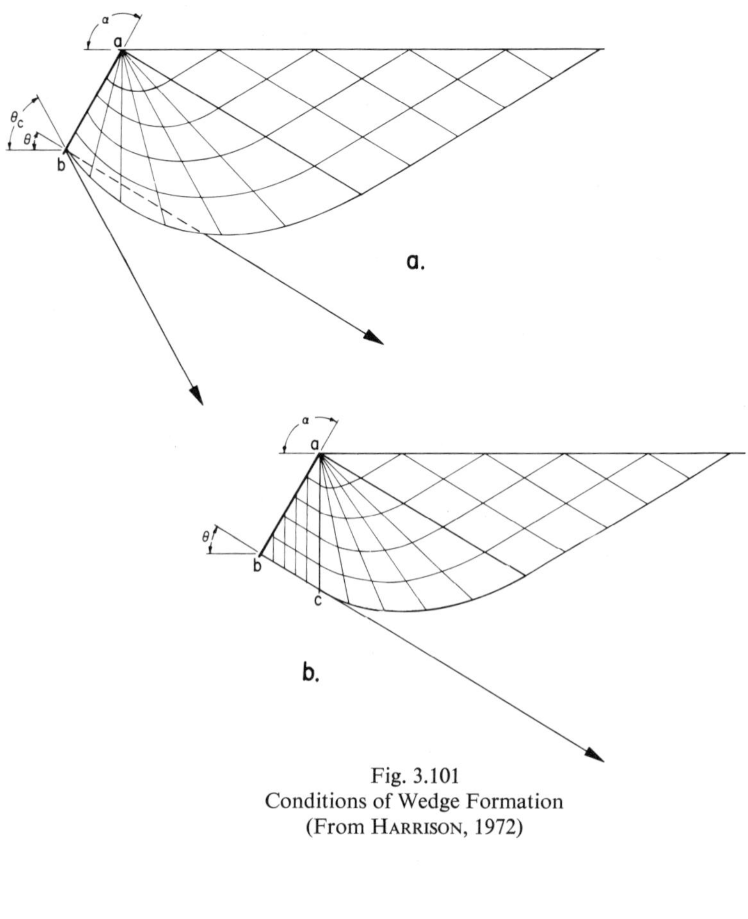

Fig. 3.101
Conditions of Wedge Formation
(From Harrison, 1972)

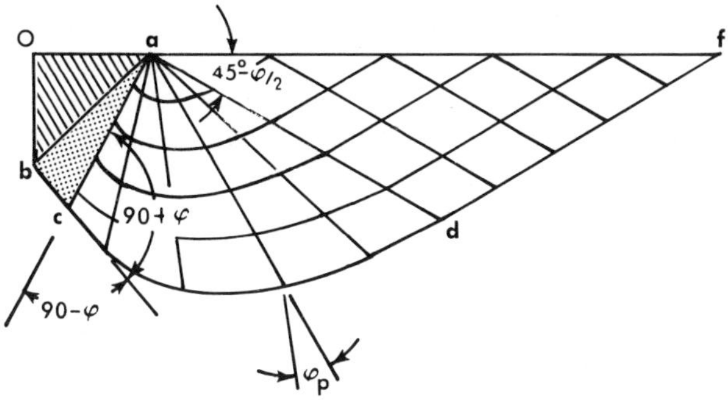

Fig. 3.102
Slip Lines and Rigid Wedge Forming Under the Action of Grouser Plate
(After HARRISON, 1972)

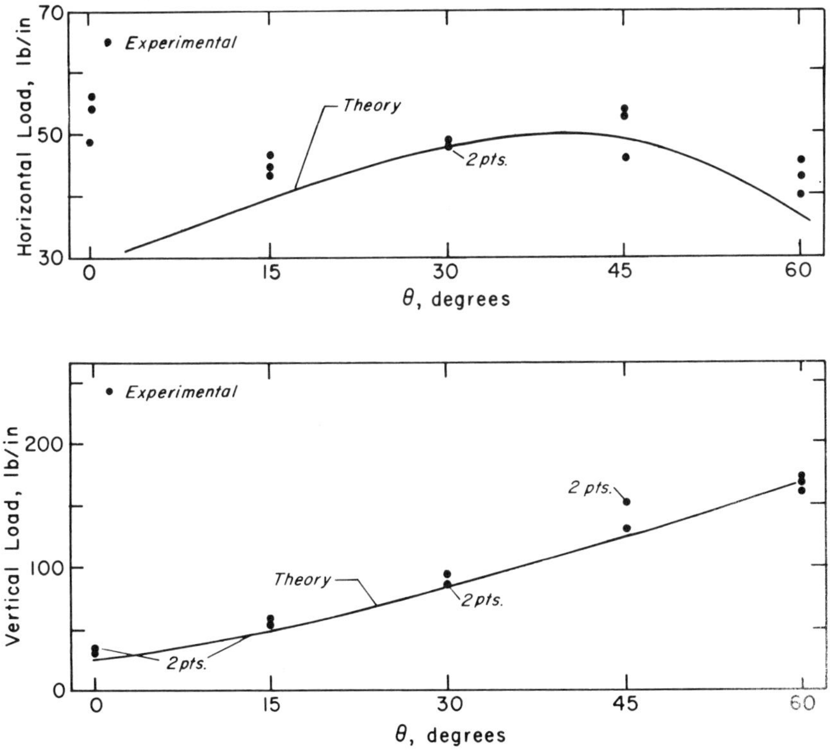

Fig. 3.103
Load Carrying Capacity of Grouser Plate as a Function of the Direction of Grouser Plate Movement (θ). Comparison of Experimental Results with Theory. *Oa* (Fig. 3.102) = 4 in, Angle *Oab* = 30°.
(From HARRISON, 1972)

The closed formulas developed by HARRISON for the computation of the vertical and horizontal components of the load are so lengthy that it is desirable to perform the computations on a computer. The same results can be achieved by computing the geometry and the appropriate slip line field by numerical integration techniques discussed in Section 3.3.3. Typical slip line fields are shown in Figure 3.104 for various values of the interface friction angle, δ, developed on the pseudo-interface, *ac*. In these numerical integration methods the weight of soil is correctly taken into account, therefore, they are expected to yield more accurate results than the approximate closed formula solutions, especially in purely frictional soils where the role of soil weight is the predominant factor in providing resistance.

3.5.6 Rigid Track Models

The formulas developed by various researchers for the computation of rolling resistance and tractive force may be considered as noninteractive models of rigid track performance. Tractive performances computed by these formulas approximate the true performance acceptably at low levels of traction when track-soil interaction effects are minimal. They fail to predict critical situations when, due to a high level of tractive effort, interactions between track and soil play a predominant role in the vehicle performance. The significance of track-soil interaction has been recognized by many investigators who attempted to incorporate interactive relationships in essentially non-interactive models. Proposed concepts of slip-sinkage (BEKKER, 1969) are intended to take the observed increase in sinkage with slip into account. Undoubtedly, correlation exists between slip and sinkage, but it is a fallacy to attribute the increase in sinkage to slip. Sinkage increases as the direct consequence of a rise in shear stresses transmitted to the soil by the track as more traction is developed. These shear stresses also cause horizontal deformations in the soil and, thereby, give rise to slip. This point is made forcefully here because it is essential to understand and recognize cause and effect in their proper relation in track-soil interaction.

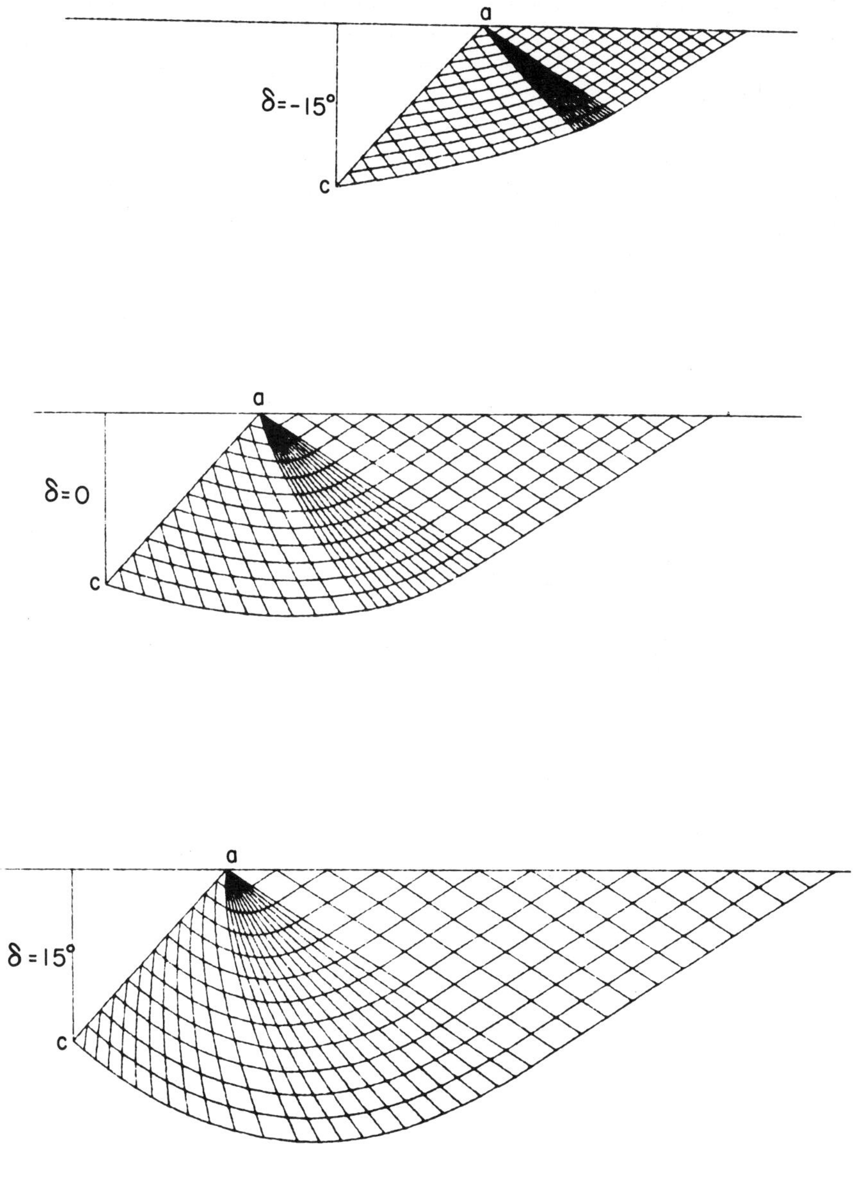

Fig. 3.104
Slip Line Fields for the Grouser Plate Problem for Various Interface Friction Angles (δ) Developed at the Pseudo-Interface *ac*.

It is interesting that many researchers have addressed themselves to the task of improving details of their own non-interactive rigid track performance models, but none of them have suggested a comprehensive, fully interactive model. The modifications proposed to improve these rigid track performance models often introduce some interactive features and, therefore, a brief review of these is included here.

JANOSI and HANAMOTO (1961) introduced the consideration of a trimmed position in rigid track performance computations. The sinkage "z" in the trimmed position varies linearly with the "x" distance (Figure 3.105). The ground pressure beneath the track is computed by using pressure-sinkage relationships obtained from plate sinkage tests. The resulting ground pressure distribution resembles a trapezoid with higher pressures at the rear end of the track, a distribution close to those observed in experiments. The trim angle is an interactive feature that allows for a better simulation of track performance. It is regrettable that no method for the estimation of the trim angle has been proposed by these authors.

VODYANIK (1966) proposed the rigid track model shown in Figure 3.106 where the moment of the drive sprocket, M, and its effect on the location of the point of attack of the resultant of soil reaction is correctly taken into account. The sinkages h and h_1 are computed on the basis of a deformation modulus and linear pressure distribution that yields the location of the resultant force as required by moment equilibrium. Thus, this model is interactive as far as the applied forces and stress distribution are concerned, but the presumed linear elastic behavior of soil, represented by

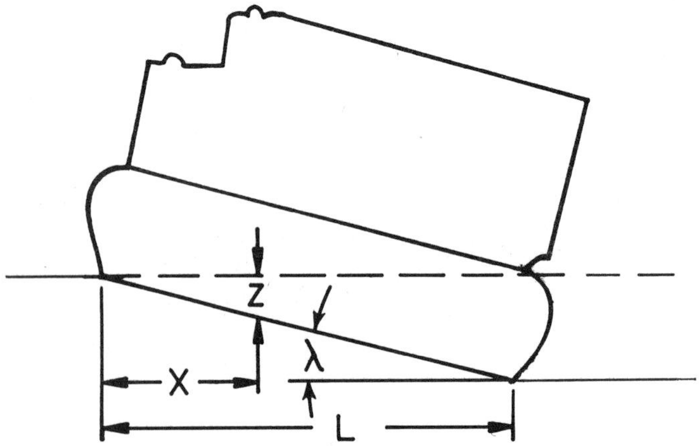

Fig. 3.105
Tracked Vehicle in Trimmed Position
(After JANOSI and HANAMOTO, 1961)

a deformation modulus, is neither realistic, nor has it any relation to the currently used field and laboratory tests for the determination of soil properties in off-road vehicle engineering.

Perloff (1966) developed a mathematical model to predict tank performance in soft soil. The soil parameters used in the model are the Coulomb strength parameters, a shear stress-displacement relationship measured in a standard direct shear test and a pressure-sinkage relation.

The main features of his two-dimensional model are shown in Figure 3.107. The model assumes the track to be a flat, rigid plate and a front ramp inclined at an angle Δ to the flat portion. Note that in the figure the flat portion is not parallel to the surface; it is inclined at an angle α to the horizontal, while the slope angle is θ. The difference $(\alpha—\theta)$ is the trim angle. Passive earth pressure acts on the front ramp, while shear stresses along the flat portion provide traction.

In the calculation of tractive performance the forces normal and tangential to the main track area are considered separately. First the vehicle sinkage in the front (z_f) and the angle α are varied until the force equilibrium conditions in the direction normal to the main track area are satisfied. A pressure-sinkage relationship is applied for the determination of ground pressures and their resultant (V). The normal component of the weight

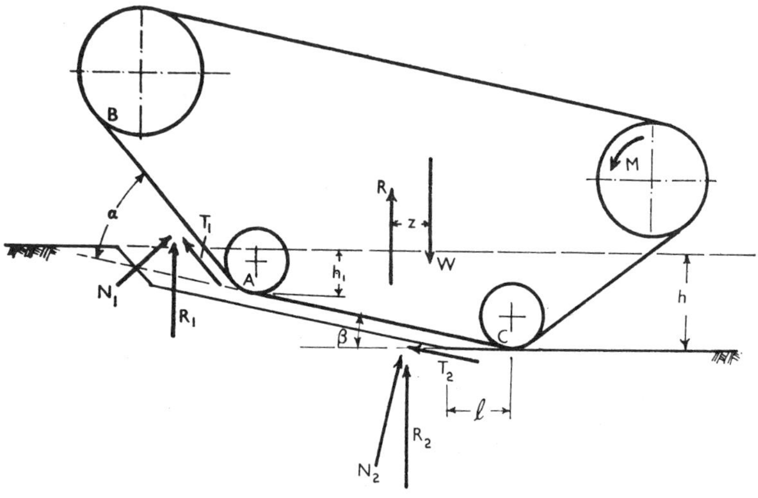

Fig. 3.106
Rigid Track-Soil Interaction Model Proposed by Vodyanik (1966)

force W is balanced by V and the normal component of the passive earth pressure, P_e, acting on the front ramp. Once z_f and α are determined on the condition that the components of these forces normal to the main track area are in equilibrium, the minimum tractive force required to maintain steady motion in this position is obtained from the tangential component of all these forces. The available tractive effort is determined from the summation of the shear stresses (τ) acting on the main track area. These are assumed to be distributed in depth so as to vanish at a depth equal to twice the track width. The shear strains in the soil and the tangential ground displacement resulting from these shear strains are computed using direct shear test data. Power train characteristics are used to determine slip-velocity-tractive force relations and the maximum velocity of the vehicle under the given soil conditions. A computer is needed to perform the iterative calculations required to solve the problem.

The Perloff model is valuable in that it incorporates an iterative scheme for the determination of trim angle. No attempt has been made to validate the model, therefore, its value for prediction purposes is open to question.

3.5.7 Concept of Rigid Track-Soil Interaction

In the preceding discussions examples of interaction between track and soil were given and the importance of these interactive features in the simulation of track performance was emphasized. In a fully interactive

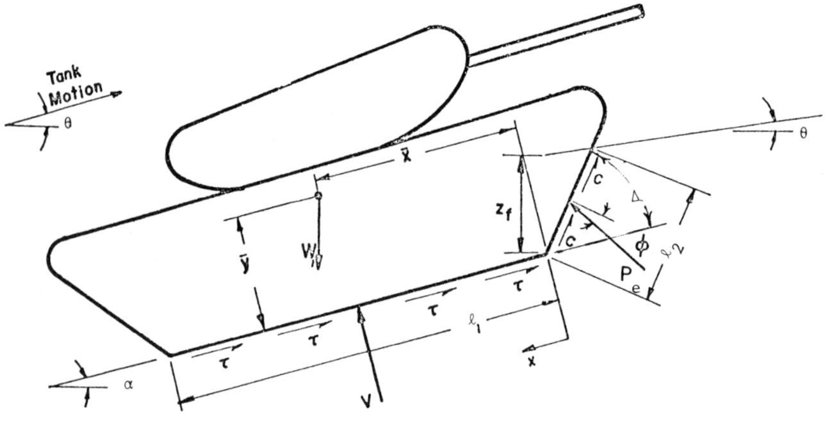

Fig. 3.107
Rigid Track-Soil Interaction Model Proposed by Perloff (1966)

track-soil model all interactions between track and soil have to be represented. In an interactive rigid track-soil model, interactions between the suspension system and, implicitly, between track deflections and soil are suppressed, but interactions between the forces applied to the track and the effects of rigid body motions on these forces are accounted for. The merit of a rigid track-soil interaction model is that the overall requirements of free body equilibrium may be maintained without attempting to solve the exceedingly complex interaction between track flexibility and soil.

A theoretically sound rigid track-soil interaction concept must account for all mutual effects that the applied forces and soil reaction have on each other. These effects are as follows:

a) The applied traction generates shear stresses at the track-soil interface. These shear stresses change the boundary conditions for the slip line fields that determine the ultimate normal stresses (bearing stresses) that the soil can carry. Thus the limitation to the normal stresses at the interface imposed by failure conditions in the soil changes with the magnitude of the applied shear stresses.

b) The soil reaction and the associated soil deformation affects the traction required to maintain steady motion. Sinkage increases the passive resistance acting on the inclined front portion of the track. The trim angle resulting from differential sinkage between the front and rear end of the track changes the force equilibrium conditions. The traction and the shear stresses act along a track face that is inclined at an angle to the surface. The tangential component of the weight force that must be overcome by the applied traction changes with the trim angle.

Generally, the interrelationships governing these interactions cannot be expressed by closed form formulas and iterative schemes are needed to incorporate these interrelationships in track performance models. A concept of an interactive track performance model suitable for computer programming is discussed below.

The basic problem of the off-road mobility of tracked vehicles may be formulated as follows. Find the sprocket torque required to develop a given drawbar pull at steady motion of the vehicle under given soil and terrain conditions and determine from this sprocket torque the maximum speed at which the vehicle can travel under these conditions given the engine and transmission characteristics. For the calculation of vehicle speed the track slip is calculated from developed interface shear-slip relationships (Equation 3.2.5). An incidental result of the solution of this fundamental problem is the sinkage of the vehicle and its trim angle.

The best approach to the solution of track-soil interaction problems as stated above is to determine the interface stresses acting on the track. Once the interface stresses are known, the track can be considered as a free body and the unkrown forces can be determined for the equilibrium conditions of the free body. In this process it is necessary to assume the position of the rigid track with respect to the ground surface as defined by the sinkage and trim angle. The resolution of the forces acting on the free body yields the track forces pertaining to the assumed position of the track. Obviously, this approach to the solution of the rigid track-soil interaction problem does not generally give the answer *directly* to the problem of the off-road mobility of the tracked vehicle as formulated previously unless the drawbar pull resolved from the force equilibrium coincidentally equals that given by the problem. An iteration procedure is necessary to solve the problem as posed.

Conceptually, the rigid track-soil interaction problem may be solved in the following steps.

a) Assume the interface friction angle, δ, and the sinkage and trim angle parameters that define the position of the track. Unless the position can be guessed with reasonable confidence for the particular problem, it is best to assume that both the sinkage and trim angle are zero initially.

b) Determine the bearing capacity of the main track area for the assumed δ angle by plasticity theory methods. Compute the interface normal stresses first by assuming soil failure in the longitudinal plane (along the long axis of the track in the plane of travel). Then compute the interface normal stresses by assuming soil failure in the plane perpendicular to that of travel (along the short axis of the track). The bearing stress beneath any point of the track is the lower of the interface normal stresses computed for that point for either of the assumed directions of failure (upper part, Figure 3.107). The bearing capacity equals the average of the bearing stresses. If the average ground pressure is greater than the computed bearing capacity, repeat the calculations for a new assumed value of sinkage.

c) Determine the constants M and Q in the pressure-sinkage equation

$$p = p_{\text{ult}} \frac{z / \sqrt{A}}{M + Qz / \sqrt{A}} \qquad \text{Eq. 3.5.6}$$

from Equations 3.5.8 and 3.5.9 as discussed in Section 3.5.4. Determine the average sinkage of the track that corresponds to the average (nominal) ground pressure from Equation 3.5.6.

d) Establish a relationship between trim angle and eccentricity of the load. Although the trim angle is unquestionably related to the eccentricity of the load, as of now there has not been any satisfactory relationship proposed for the estimation of the trim angle. Perhaps PERLOFF's model is the only one where the trim angle is treated interactively. Unfortunately, his approach requires the determination of soil parameters that are generally not available and difficult to determine. In lieu of anything better, the following crude approximation is suggested, as a stopgap measure, until a more accurate method becomes available, for the determination of the trim angle. Assume

$$\lambda = K_t \cdot e \qquad \text{Eq. 3.5.20}$$

where

λ = trim angle
K_t = constant
e = eccentricity

The constant K_t may be determined on the assumption that in the case of a triangular stress distribution beneath the track area (corresponding to a load eccentricity of $e = L/6$) the sinkage is zero at that end of the track where the stress is zero and the sinkage at the other end is twice the average sinkage. For small trim angles the values of tangent and arctangent may be interchanged allowing the derivation of the following simple expression for the computation of K_t.

$$K_t = \frac{12\, z_{av}}{L^2} \qquad \text{Eq. 3.5.21}$$

e) Determine the resistance force acting on the inclined front portion of the track by computing the bearing stresses from the surface to a depth of z_{av}. The trim angle may be assumed initially as zero. The bearing stresses are computed on the basis of the same considerations as were applied to the determination of the bearing capacity of the main track area. Failure in two planes, perpendicular to each other may be considered and the corresponding normal stresses computed by plasticity theory methods (Figure 3.108, lower part). The bearing stress is the lesser of the normal stresses computed for these two conditions. The resistance force is the resultant of the bearing stresses.

f) Compute the sprocket torque required to maintain the track tension balancing the interface shear stresses. The track tension force can be computed as the sum of the tensions in the front inclined portion and in the main portion of the track, assuming that the road wheels and idlers are perfectly smooth. Thus

$$T = T_1 + T_2 \qquad \text{Eq. 3.5.23}$$

where

$T \;\; =$ total track tension

$T_1 =$ track tension generated in the inclined front part

$T_2 =$ track tension genrated in the main part of the track

Also,

$T_1 \;\; = N_1 \cdot \tan \delta_1$

$T_2 \;\; = N_2 \cdot \tan \delta_2$

where

$N_1 =$ normal component of resistance R_1

$N_2 = (W - V_1) \sin (\varepsilon + \lambda)$

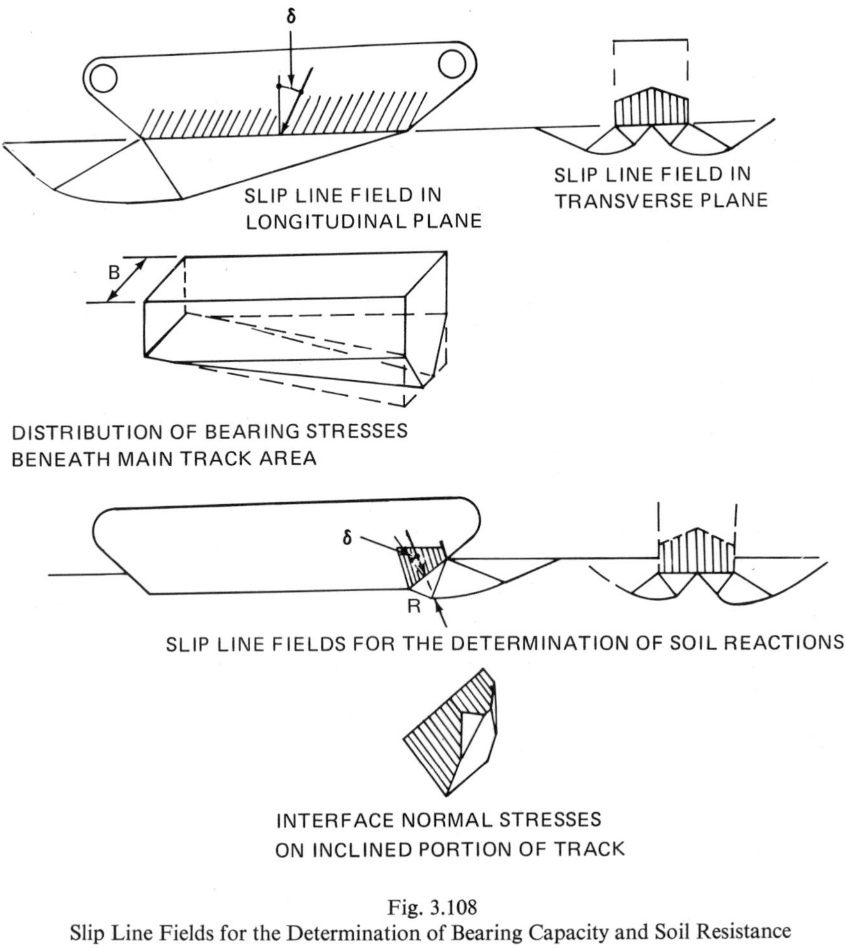

Fig. 3.108
Slip Line Fields for the Determination of Bearing Capacity and Soil Resistance

W = weight of vehicle on track
V_1 = vertical component of resistance R_1
δ_1 = interface friction angle in the inclined front part
δ_2 = interface friction angle in the main part of track

The sprocket torque required to maintain tension equals

$$M = T \cdot r \qquad \text{Eq. 3.5.24}$$

where r = effective radius of the sprocket.

In this calculation the internal resistances and the driving torque used up by these resistances are disregarded, since these internal forces do not affect the external interaction of track and soil. The losses by the internal resistances, however, must be taken into account when the velocity of the vehicle is determined from the sprocket torque and engine and drive train characteristics.

g) Determine the eccentricity of the resultant soil reaction on the main portion of the track from the moment equilibrium conditions (Figure 3.109).

The resultant of the soil reaction on the main portion of the track provides the counterbalancing moment. Thus

$$R_2 \cdot c_2 = M - R_1 \cdot c_1 + DB \cdot h_d \qquad \text{Eq. 3.5.25}$$

where

c_1, c_2 = moment arm of the forces R_1, R_2, respectively about the center of gravity of vehicle
h_d = moment arm of drawbar pull about the $C.G.$

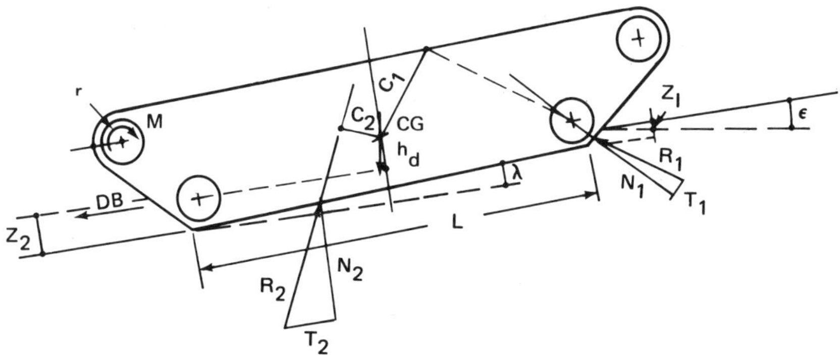

Fig. 3.109
Forces acting on a tracked vehicle

In this equation DB is the given drawbar pull in the problem. At this point the force components in the direction of the drawbar pull (assumed to be parallel to the surface) are not necessarily in equilibrium. If the difference between the given drawbar pull and the tractive components of the soil reaction is substantial, then it may be expedient to modify the δ angle and repeat steps a) through g) with the modified δ angle.

The eccentricity is computed by expressing the moment $R_2 \cdot c_2$ by the moment of the normal and tangential components of R_2.

$$R_2 \cdot c_2 = N_2 \cdot e + T_2 \cdot h_2$$

where h_2 = moment arm of T_2 about the $C.\,G.$ of vehicle and

$$e = \frac{R_2 \cdot c_2 - T_2 \cdot h_2}{N_2} \qquad \text{Eq. 3.5.26}$$

h) Compute the trim angle and the front and rear sinkages from eccentricity and the average sinkage.

The trim angle is computed from the equation $\lambda = K_t \cdot e$

The trim angle also equals approximately

$$\lambda = \frac{z_1 - z_2}{L}$$

The average sinkage equals

$$z_{av} = \frac{z_1 + z_2}{2}$$

From these equations

$$z_1 = \frac{\lambda L - 2\, z_{av}}{2}$$

$$z_2 = \frac{2\, z_{av} - \lambda L}{2} \qquad \text{Eqs. 3.5.27}$$

i) Repeat the procedure for the position of the track defined by the first approximations of the trim angle and sinkages z_1 and z_2 determined in the preceding steps. Check the equilibrium of force components parallel to the surface for the new position of the track and iterate on δ until the given drawbar pull and the tractive forces are in equilibrium within the allowed tolerances.

3.5.8 Concept of Flexible Track-Soil Interaction

In the previous discussions fundamental interrelationships were discussed that govern track-soil interaction if the track is assumed to act as a rigid body. Flexibility of the track affects these interrelationships primarily in that the upward displacement of the track allows the development of passive failure zones in the soil that is not possible underneath a rigid track. Thus, the state of stresses in the soil is significantly influenced by the flexibility of the track, and completely plastic state of stresses may be produced in the soil by loads that are less than the bearing capacity of the track area as a whole.

Clearly, a flexible track-soil interaction concept cannot be formulated without a theory that predicts the interface stresses underneath a flexible track. At the present time, there is no readily applicable soil mechanics theory that would solve the problem, nor is there any experiment available that would shed light on the soil behavior under such intricate load and displacement conditions. The following considerations may serve as a basis for the development of a theory for the determination of the interface stresses generated by loads on a flexible track.

As a starting point it may be assumed that the soil is completely in the plastic state beneath a flexible track. While this may not be always the case, the assumption is reasonable for critical situations. As it was pointed out before, the upward flexing of the track allows the development of passive zones, whereas portions of the track beneath the road wheels obviously exert a downward pressure, resulting in the development of active zones. Thus, active and passive zones will alternate beneath the track and the question arises how they will be joined. In the bearing capacity problem the active and passive zones are joined by a radial zone that provides the transition between the stress states in the active and passive zones. At the surface the radial zone shrinks to a point that is a common point for all three — the active, radial and passive zones. Mathematically, the point is a singular point where there is a stress discontinuity and the direction of the major principal stress is multivalued. Theoretical considerations as well as available experimental data indicate that the interface stresses are continuous beneath a continuously flexible track. Thus, the active and passive zones must join in such a way that the interface stresses remain continuous.

There are two ways how the requirement for stress continuity can be met. If the stress at the singular point is theoretically zero (very small in practical numerical computations), as in the case of purely frictional soils, then there is no stress discontinuity. Thus, in purely frictional soils the active and passive zones may be joined by a radial zone, as in the bearing capacity problem, if the stress at the common point at the surface is negligibly small. A tentative model of flexible track-soil interaction under such conditions is shown in Figure 3.110. In soils with cohesion

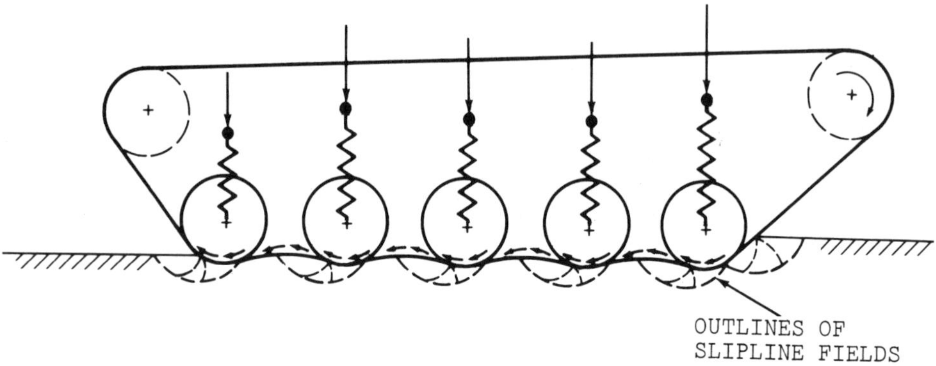

Fig. 3.110
Tentative Model for the Simulation of the Ultimate Performance of Tracks with Consideration of the Interaction Between Vehicle and Soil

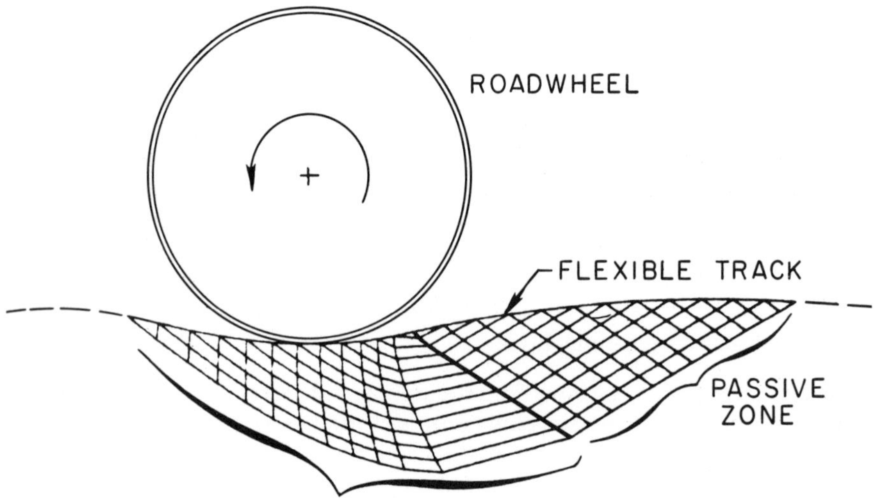

Fig. 3.111
Slip Line Field with Adjoining Active and Passive Zones Beneath Portion of Flexible Track

there is a stress discontinuity at the singular point even if the surface loading is zero. In such a case the stress discontinuity can be eliminated only by not allowing any change to take place in the direction of the major principal stress at this point. The multivaluedness of the direction of the major principal stress is replaced by a single value, that corresponding to the case that $\delta = \varphi$, the interface friction angle equals the friction angle of the soil. Under such condition an active and a passive zone may join without causing discontinuity in the interface stress. The θ angle, the direction of the major principal stress, can be computed from Equation 2.2.21 for this condition and its value is the same for both the active and passive state of stresses. Thus, for a state of stresses to exist in the soil that is not causing discontinuity in the interface stresses, it is necessary that an interface angle equal to the friction angle develop at the point of changeover from the active to the passive state. At other points along the interface the interface friction angle can be presumed to decrease to some value that is less than the friction angle of the soil. A slip line field computed for boundary conditions corresponding to the requirements described is shown in Figure 3.111. The shape of the flexible track for this computation was arbitrarily assumed.

The geometry of the flexible track and the soil reactions to loading are interdependent. The sum of the interface shear stresses determines the track tension, while the track deflections depend on both the track tension and the interface normal stresses. In addition, the road wheels providing support to the flexible track also displace by an amount proportional to the total load on the road wheel. In order that the flexible track and soil remain in contact, track deflections and soil displacements must be compatible. Soil displacement vectors may be computed from the velocity fields associated with the slip line fields. It is, indeed, a very difficult task to find a solution that satisfies all constraints of the problem.

As far as the whole track is concerned, the problem of moment equilibrium is basically the same as with the rigid track. The sprocket torque must be balanced by soil reactions that provide the balancing moment about the center of gravity of the vehicle. Thus the resultant of the soil reaction acts at some distance from the center. The load on the road wheels is generally increasing toward the rear as the driving torque increases.

The considerations give a general picture of the problems involved in the development of a flexible track-soil interaction model. Much work remains to be done until such an ideal model can be perfected. The problems outlined are by no means unsolvable and a great deal can be gained by developing a flexible track-soil interaction model that truly simulates the complex interaction phenomena.

It is of interest to note that, in contrast to tire-soil interaction where flexibility of tires improves tire performance, track performance deteriorates with increasing flexibility of the track. This apparent contradiction arises because in the case of tires flexibility is associated with an increase of the contact area under a given load, whereas in the case of tracks the overall contact area is not affected by the flexibility of the track. The useful contact area, as the track area adjoining active zones in the soil may be called, actually drecreases with track flexibility. This different relationship between flexibility and contact area explains the opposite role of flexibility in track and tire performance.

CHAPTER 3.6

FIELD DETERMINATION OF SOIL PROPERTIES FOR OFF-ROAD MOBILITY PREDICTION

The determination of soil strength and other properties can be best performed in the laboratory where tests are conducted under controlled conditions and evaluation procedures are well established. Laboratory tests results are particularly meaningful for tire and wheel experiments performed in soil bins where the preparation of the soil bed and its homogeneity are well controlled. Laboratory tests can, and in many cases should be used to determine soil properties for the evaluation of vehicle performance in the field. However, for the determination of the in situ properties of soil, undisturbed samples are needed. For use in off-road vehicle engineering these can be best obtained from open sampling pits. The sampling operation, sample transportation, and the preparation of specimens for laboratory testing requires skilled personnel and is time consuming. Since most of the important soil properties are of transient nature, all samples are to be taken within a short time span so that the effect of changes in the field environment may be minimal. In addition to these difficulties, an undesirable feature of the laboratory determination of soil properties is that the results of the tests are not immediately available. For these reasons, in off-road vehicle engineering, field testing methods are preferred for the determination of in situ soil properties.

A variety of field testing methods has been developed for the determination of soil properties and a few of them are in use in off-road vehicle engineering. Year after year, new methods or modifications of old techniques are proposed. This indicates that the existing methods, for some reason or other, are not entirely satisfactory. Most of the field techniques used for soil property determination are closely connected with theories of off-road locomotion and dissatisfaction with a technique has more often reflected dissatisfaction with the associated theory of off-road locomotion rather than with the technique itself. In the following detailed discussion of the better known field testing techniques, an evaluation of their suitability for soil property determination will be of primary concern. However, comments will also be made on the use of the various parameters and indices associated with these field techniques.

3.6.1 Determination of the In Situ Moisture Content and Unit Weight of Soil

Although simple field techniques are available for the determination of the in situ moisture content and unit weight of soil, these techniques are rarely employed in off-road vehicle engineering practice. The importance of obtaining information on the moisture content and unit weight for any project where vehicle performance is evaluated and correlated with soil conditions cannot be overemphasized. The transient nature of these properties makes it imperative to record them at the time of vehicle operation. Without this information the evaluation of vehicle performance becomes meaningless.

For the determination of the in situ moisture content, a sample representative of the soil for a certain area is obtained and placed in a container that is resistant to corrosion. The size of the sample depends on the maximum size of particles and may vary from about one ounce (28 grams) for silt and clay to about one pound (450 grams) for gravel. The container should be as small as practicable in keeping with the size of the sample and should be sealed immediately after sampling with tape or wax to preserve the moisture content of the soil sample. Appropriate records should be kept of sample locations and container designations. The moisture content of each sample is determined in the laboratory by weighing the sample in its condition as sampled and again after 5 hours of drying at 110 C°. As indicated in Section 1.2.3, the moisture content of the sample on a dry weight basis (expressed as a percentage) is given by the ratio of the weight difference before and after drying to the weight after drying (times 100).

Several techniques are in use to determine the in situ unit weight of soil. The most common methods are the sand cone, rubber balloon and drive cylinder methods. The first two methods are intended to determine the volume of the hole in the ground from which a sample has been taken by filling the hole with uniformly graded sand or by a rubber diaphragm filled with water. These methods are described in detail in ASTM Standards D-1556 and D-2167, respectively. These techniques require skilled personnel and yield valid results only if the hole retains its volume for some time after sampling.

The drive cylinder method of determining the in place unit weight of soils can be used satisfactorily in moist, cohesive fine-grained materials and in sands that possess some cohesion. An undisturbed sample is obtained by driving a small, thin-walled cylinder into the soil with a special driving head (Figure 3.112). The cylinder is driven in until its top is approximately an inch below the original surface. The driving head is then removed and the cylinder is dug from the ground. If the tare weight of the cylinder is known, the wet weight of the sample, with any excess soil trimmed off, can be obtained immediately. The sample is then removed from the cylinder and the moisture content determined. The volume of the sample is equal to the volume of the cylinder. The total and dry unit weight may be easily computed from these data. Weighing and drying of the sample may be conveniently performed in a field laboratory.

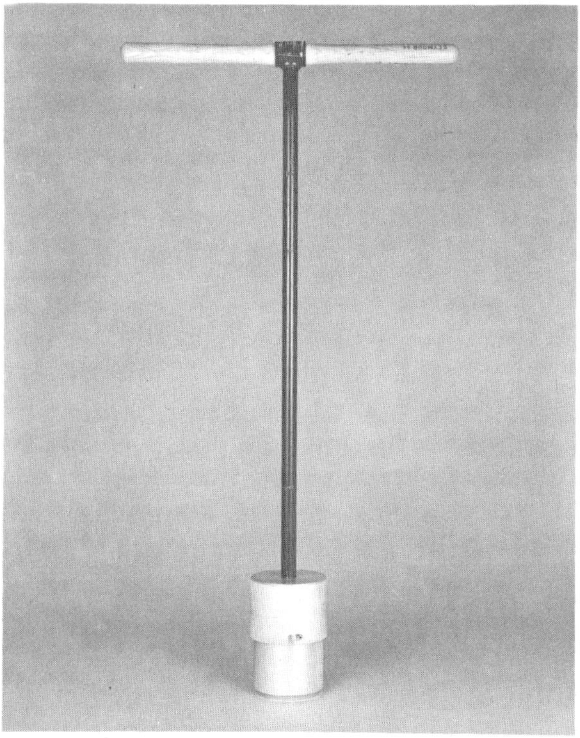

Fig. 3.112
Drive Cylinder for the Determination of In Situ Unit Weight of Soil
(Courtesy of Soiltest, Inc.)

3.6.2 Plate Sinkage Tests and the Parameters k_φ, k_c and n

Plate sinkage tests used for the characterization of soil for mobility purposes differ in many aspects from conventional plate bearing tests performed in civil soils engineering. Plate sinkage tests are performed at a constant rate of loading, usually between 1 and 2 in/sec, well beyond the depth at which bearing capacity failure occurs. The plate diameter varies between 2 and 6 inches. In the range of sinkages up to the depth where bearing capacity failure occurs, the sinkage is governed by stress-strain relationships in the elastic-plastic range. Beyond this depth the soil is in plastic equilibrium and the pressure-sinkage relationship is governed by the effect of the changes in the geometry of the failure zones brought about by the sinkage. Were it not for this effect, the plate would sink indefinitely into the ground under the pressure causing bearing capacity failure.

Pressure-sinkage curves obtained in plate sinkage tests can be used to evaluate the strength properties of soil. In a homogeneous soil a sharp break in the curvature of the pressure-sinkage curve, sometimes accompanied by a drop in pressure, marks the point at which continuous plastic zones develop in the soil. The pressure at this point is commonly called the "bearing capacity" of the soil. The bearing capacity, as it has been discussed in Section 1.4.3, depends on three soil parameters, γ, c and φ. Theoretically, it is possible to evaluate these parameters if results of three plate sinkage tests with different size plates are available. Although this procedure appears to be straight-forward and requires only the solution of three linear equations, it is not recommended for the following reasons. Three field tests cannot be performed under exactly identical conditions and, therefore, the results are to some extent inaccurate. For practical reasons, the variation in the size of the plate is limited. Therefore, the coefficients of the linear bearing capacity equations vary only slightly and the three equations are "ill-conditioned", i.e. slight inaccuracies in the coefficients or in the left side of the equations may cause gross inaccuracies in the evaluation of c, φ, and γ.

The problem is less severe if the unit weight of the soil is available from field tests. The number of unknown parameters is then reduced to two. In the evaluation of the strength parameters the bearing capacity equation and the bearing capacity factors given in Section 1.4.3 may be used to obtain approximate values for c and φ. However, it should be kept in mind that these bearing capacity factors are approximations themselves. More refined values can be obtained by using plasticity theory methods for the evaluation of the bearing capacity values. The numerical solution methods for the axially symmetric case, discussed in Section 2.4.1, can be used for this purpose. The following iterative procedure brings forth the desired result.

Compute the bearing capacity for the smaller plate with the estimated values of c and φ and a surcharge corresponding to the sinkage of the plate at bearing capacity.

Adjust the c value until the observed and computed bearing capacities match.

Compute the bearing capacity for the larger plate with the φ and adjusted c value. Adjust φ to match the observed bearing capacity.

Repeat procedure with the adjusted c and φ values until bearing capacities match the observed ones for both tests.

The following alternative procedure may be used if the results of only one plate sinkage test are available. If, as usual in a plate sinkage test, the pressure-sinkage relationship has been established for pressures higher than the bearing capacity, the friction angle of the soil may be evaluated from the tangent of the pressure-sinkage curve at bearing capacity. Although at bearing capacity the strength of the soil is fully mobilized and plastic flow takes place, at a further sinkage of the plate the "surcharge effect", that is, the effect of the weight of the surrounding soil that is above the base level of the plate, requires additional pressure to maintain the plastic flow. The magnitude of this surcharge is γz and its effect on the pressure can be evaluated from the classical bearing capacity equation for vertical loading ($i_\gamma = i_q = i_s = 1$)

$$q = \frac{1}{2}\gamma B s_\gamma N_\gamma + \gamma z s_q N_q + c s_c N_c \qquad \text{Eq. 1.4.26}$$

The tangent of the pressure sinkage curve at bearing capacity ($p = q$) may be obtained by differentiation as follows

$$\frac{dp}{dz} = \gamma s_q N_q \qquad \text{Eq. 3.6.1}$$

In some instances, in relatively dense soils, the pressure temporarily drops after bearing capacity has been reached (Figure 3.113). However, as sinkage is continued, the pressure rises again and reaches approximately the value that it would have without the temporary pressure relief. In such a case the tangent should be established as if the pressure drop had not occurred.

In the evaluation of the friction angle from the tangent of the pressure-sinkage curve, the N_q values, as established for the classical bearing capacity equation in Section 1.4.3, may be used with a shape factor $s_q = 1.4$. The value of the cohesion can be determined by trial and error using the numerical computation methods for the axially symmetric case. It is a good practice to recheck the value of the tangent at bearing capacity after the c and φ values have been evaluated. This can be done by computing the bearing capacity for a $(z + \Delta z)$ sinkage and determining the tangent as follows.

$$\frac{q_{(z+\Delta z)} - q_z}{\Delta z} \qquad \text{Eq. 3.6.2}$$

If the computed tangent is significantly different from that of the pressure-sinkage curve, a recomputation with appropriately adjusted φ values is in order.

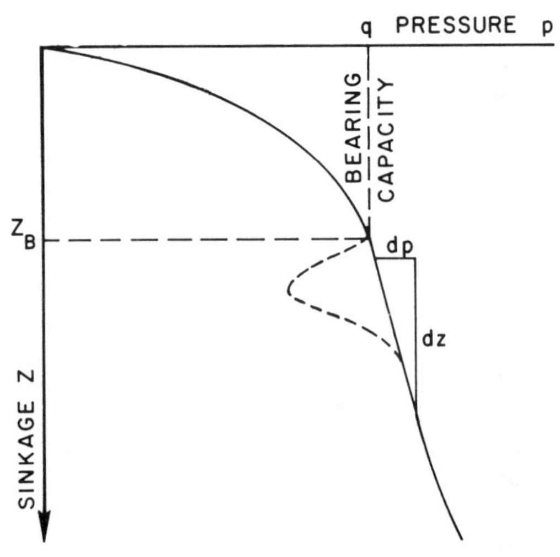

Fig. 3.113
Evaluation of Bearing Capacity From Pressure Sinkage Curve

The sinkage z_B at which the pressure equals the bearing capacity, is a measure of the deformation properties of soil. As discussed in Section 3.5.4 a sinkage coefficient K_B may be computed from z_B as follows.

$$K_B = \frac{z_B}{\sqrt{A}} \qquad \text{Eq. 3.6.3}$$

It is an important attribute of the plate sinkage tests that a measure of soil deformation can be established from the results. Other field tests employed today in off-road vehicle engineering, as it will be shown in the subsequent discussions, either shear the soil in a too narrow zone or strain the soil too little to be suitable for the evaluation of the deformation properties of soil as they are needed for the purposes of off-road vehicle engineering. In summary, the plate sinkage tests, if properly evaluated, furnish valuable information on both the strength and deformation properties of soil for use in off-road vehicle engineering. However, if the plate sinkage tests are intended as field analogies of running gear behavior and the so-called pressure-sinkage parameters are used for the characterization of soil behavior under vehicle load, then the performance of plate sinkage tests is nothing but an exercise in futility. The reader will quickly recognize this upon considering the following comments on the validity of the concepts underlying these uses of the plate sinkage tests.

The pressure-sinkage curves obtained in a plate sinkage test are modeled in this application of the tests by a hypothetical pressure-sinkage relationship. Initially, the following equation, attributed to BERNSTEIN (1913) was used to express this relationship:

$$p = k \cdot z^n \qquad \text{Eq. 3.6.4}$$

where

p = pressure

z = sinkage

k, n = pressure-sinkage parameters.

Later, when it became evident that the dimensions of the plate affect the results of plate sinkage tests, BEKKER (1956, 1969) proposed the following modification of Equation 3.6.4

$$p = \left(\frac{k_c}{b} + k_\varphi\right) \cdot z^n \qquad \text{Eq. 3.6.5}$$

where

b = diameter (width) of the plate

k_c, k_φ, n = sinkage parameters

When the parameters in these equations are used to characterize soil behavior and analogous soil behavior beneath running gears is assumed, an average pressure beneath the plate is equated with the pressure beneath an infinitesimal element of the running gear. Theory and experimental evidence indicate that the pressure beneath the plate in a plate sinkage test is far from uniform and varies considerably with the distance from the center of the plate. Thus, the plate sinkage test by itself proves a fundamental fallacy of the BEKKER concept: at a constant sinkage the pressures beneath infinitesimal elements of the plate are not constant but vary significantly!

Of far greater importance than the misinterpretation of average and infinitesimal pressures in this concept is the complete disregard of the effect of shear stresses on the pressure-sinkage relationship. The soil behavior beneath a running gear is not analogous to that beneath a plate because the function of the running gear is to transmit shear stresses to the soil and generate traction, whereas in a plate sinkage test the vertical loading does not generate shear stresses, or if it does, then they are self-cancelling. Thus, the primary function of running gears, the generation of shear stresses, is not duplicated in a plate sinkage test and, therefore, it cannot be expected that a pressure-sinkage relationship obtained from a plate sinkage test be valid for a running gear interaction with the soil independently of the applied shear stresses. Any agreement with running gear performance predicted on the basis of pressure-sinkage relationships is purely coincidental or is the result of after-the-fact manipulation of the pressure-sinkage parameters. The inherent uncertainties in the evaluation of these parameters are discussed in the following paragraphs.

As it was pointed out before, the pressure-sinkage relation in a plate sinkage test is governed by two different processes that cannot be represented by one smooth exponential relationship expressed by either Equation 3.6.4 or 3.6.5. For the evaluation of the parameters in a plate sinkage test, the results are plotted on log-log coordinates where the exponential equations plot as a straight line, the tangent of which yields the value of the exponent n. Hundreds of experimental data plotted in this manner indicate that the data cannot be well fitted to a straight line and data points in one part of the pressure-sinkage curve, usually in the first part, have to be suppressed to fit the rest of data points with a straight line.

In Equation 3.6.5 the diameter of the plate occurs in the denominator of the coefficient k_c. The vertical displacement of a plate in an elastic medium conforms with this relation. In the plastic range, however, the relation between plate width and sinkage is directly, and not inversely proportional with the plate width, as a glance at the bearing capacity equation indicates. Because of the two different processes involved in the sinkage of the plates, the pressure-sinkage curves of different size plates frequently cross over and result in a negative value for k_c, a physically impossible condition. Also, the n value for two different sized plates is different, proving that Equation 3.6.5 does not represent soil behavior properly. In summary, the idealization of pressure-sinkage curves by the exponential equations and their use for the determination of pressures beneath running gears are conceptually inadequate for the modeling of running gear-soil interaction.

3.6.3 Field Ring Shear Tests

Field ring shear tests were conceived and recommended by Bekker (1969) for the determination of both the strength properties of soil and its slip-shear parameters. Various field ring shear testing instruments, some of them hand-portable, others mounted on an off-road vehicle, have been built. Most of them have automatic recording instruments. These instruments consist essentially of a loading apparatus that transmits selected loads to a ring shear plate and a torsion device that rotates the ring shear plate with a given angular velocity and measures the torque required for this rotation. Vertical load, sinkage, torque and angular displacement of the ring shear plate are measured and recorded. The ring shear plate may be provided with cleats for the measurement of the shearing resistance of soil or it may have a solid surface to measure the frictional resistance between soil and various solid materials, such as rubber, steel, etc.

The attractive feature of the ring shear apparatus is that the sheared area remains constant during shearing and, therefore, in contrast to the direct shear and triaxial apparatus, there is no need for area correction due to the deformation of the sample. Also, the angular displacement that may be applied to the ring shear plate is not limited by the equipment.

There are, however, drawbacks that make the evaluation and interpretation of the results of field ring shear tests uncertain. In the original concept of the laboratory ring shear apparatus, the sample is confined everywhere but at the annular shear surface. Thus, failure is forced to occur along this surface and the maximum shear stress on this surface equals the shear strength of soil. If the tests are performed at various normal pressures, then the Coulomb shear strength parameters may be evaluated.

In contrast, the soil beneath the field ring shear apparatus is not confined laterally and, therefore, the failure surface is not necessarily the bottom plane of the ring shear plate. The principal stresses in the vertical peripheral plane increase and the originally vertical σ_1 becomes oblique as the applied torque generates shear stresses at the annular surface of shearing (refer to Figure 3.114). As soon as the lesser principal stress in this vertical plane becomes larger than the lateral stress, σ_3 will be the lateral stress and the σ_1—σ_3 plane becomes an oblique one. The failure surface is perpendicular to the σ_1—σ_3 plane and is inclined to σ_1 at an angle $45° - {}^1/_2\, \varphi$. In this case the annular surface is not a failure surface, therefore, the normal and shear stresses acting on this plane and measured in the experiments do not represent the shear strength of soil. The development of such an oblique failure plane manifests itself by an excessive sinkage or "digging in" of the ring shear plate, since plastic flow along the inclined failure plane moves soil out from underneath the annulus. A detailed discussion of this problem is given by LISTON (1973 a, b). He proposes an evaluation procedure that takes failure along the oblique plane into account.

Another way to avoid erroneous interpretation of the results of ring shear tests is to prevent the development of oblique failure planes. This could be accomplished by placing a surcharge (annular metal plates) around the shear ring and possibly in the open area in the center. Preliminary calculations indicate that a surcharge equal to the vertical stresses applied to the shear ring would be sufficient for this purpose. The schematic arrangement of a ring shear test with surcharge is shown in Figure 3.115. The application of surcharge would prevent any appreciable sinking of the ring shear device during a test. To test at depths below the surface, a cylindrical bottom split scooper would have to be attached to the device to remove the soil to the desired depth. The ring shear test would then be carried out at this depth to determine the strength properties of soil at this horizon.

Ring shear tests also furnish information on the shear stress-displacement relationship for soil, used in the various traction theories for the estimate of shear strength development with slip. Although the action of the ring shear plate is in many respects analogous to the traction mechanism of various running gears, similitude in the true sense of modeling laws has not yet been shown to exist. It appears that some scaling would be necessary if the shear-displacement curves are to be used directly in tractive force computations.

3.6.4 Cone Penetration Tests

Field measurements of the resistance of soils to static or dynamic penetration of cones of various sizes and shapes are widely employed in civil soils engineering for a variety of purposes. For off-road mobility

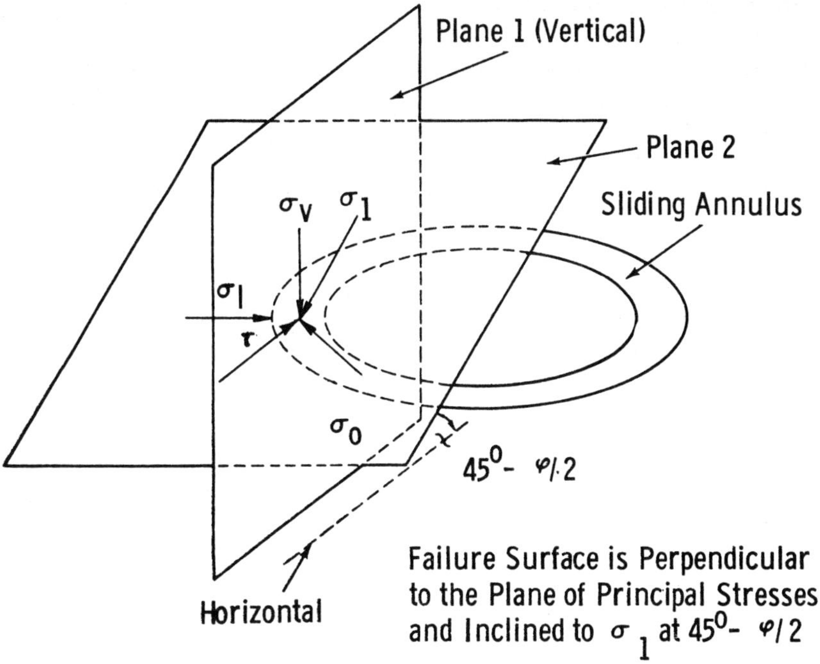

σ_V = Vertical Normal Stress

σ_l = Lateral Stress

τ = Shear Stress

σ_1, σ_3 = Principal Stresses

$\sigma_V, \tau, \sigma_l, \sigma_0$ in Plane 1

σ_l, σ_1 in Plane 2

Planes of Principal Stresses:

Plane 1 $\sigma_0 < \sigma_l$; $\sigma_0 = \sigma_3$

Plane 2 $\sigma_e < \sigma_0$; $\sigma_3 = \sigma_l$

Fig. 3.114
Principal Stresses in Soil in Ring Shear Tests

evaluation of soil conditions the cone penetrometer developed by WES is used almost exclusively, while for the evaluation of the suitability of soil runways for airplane landing and take-off the airfield penetrometer, also developed by WES, has been used.

The WES mobility cone penetrometer is a 30° apex angle circular cone with a $^1/_2$ sq. in. base area, mounted on a 36 in. long, $^3/_8$ in. diameter graduated shaft (Figure 3.116). A proving ring with a dial gage and handle is mounted on the top of the shaft. The calibration of the dial gage is such that the reading equals the unit pressure (in psi) calculated as the resisting force divided by the base area of the cone. This unit

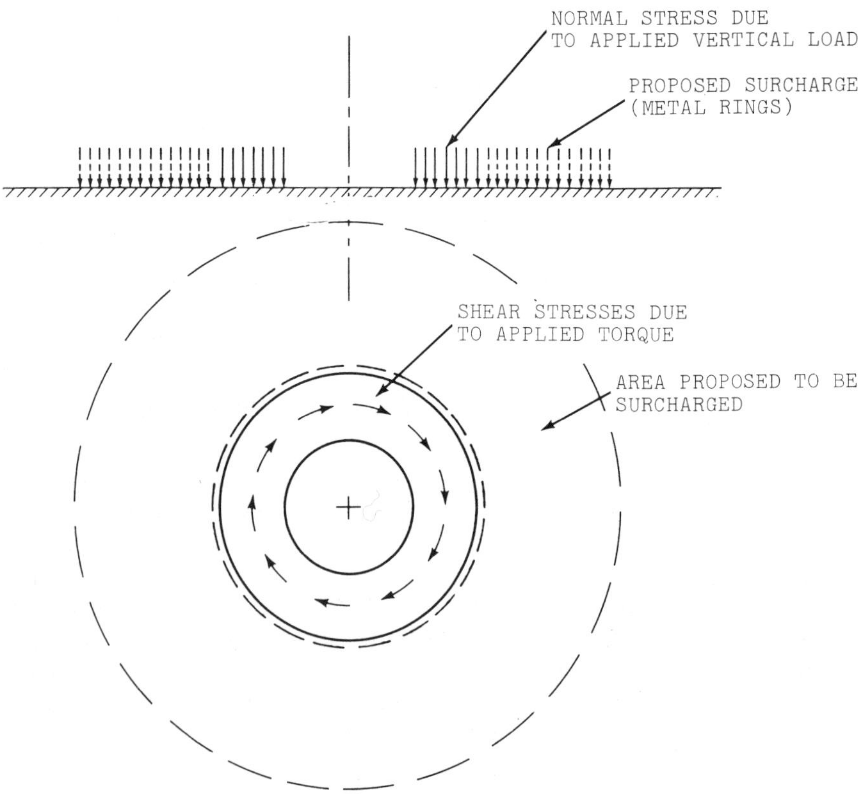

Fig. 3.115
Schematic Arrangement of Ring Shear Test with Surcharge

pressure is also called "cone index" *(CI)*. Since the penetration resistance changes somewhat with the rate of penetration, in WES practice a standard penetration rate of 72 in./min is employed.

Before starting a penetration test the dial indicator should be set at zero while the penetrometer is suspended by its handle. Then the operator forces the cone into the ground and reads the dial gage at every inch of penetration. For steady penetration and reliable record keeping two operators are needed. To simplify the operations, self-recording penetrometers have also been developed. The final result of a cone penetration test is a CI versus depth plot.

Sometimes cone penetration testing in the field includes tests on remolded soil. A 2-inch diameter sample tube is filled with soil and the resistance of the soil in the tube to the penetration of the cone is measured. This test gives some indication of the effect of remolding on soil strength but is of little scientific value. Removal of the soil from the ground and filling the sample tube with the removed soil is presumed to simulate the effect of multiple passage of vehicles.

The airfield cone penetrometer is a device similar to the WES cone penetrometer. It has a smaller base area (0.2 sq. in.) and a spring scale to measure the resistance of soil to penetration (Figure 3.117). The reading gives the force required to push the penetrometer into the ground in tens of pounds. This force is called the "airfield index" and is abbreviated as *AI*. The need for the airfield cone penetrometer arose because the mobility penetrometer cannot be easily used in stronger soils considered for potential aircraft landing. The operator's weight limits the maximum force that can be applied to any penetrometer. With the airfield penetrometer much stronger soils can be tested than with the mobility penetrometer because of the smaller base area of its cone.

The value of cone penetration tests for the determination of the strength properties of soils, as the analyses of cone penetration presented in Section 2.5.4 showed, is limited. The cone penetration test, however, is an excellent tool for the characterization of the variation of strength properties of a particular soil with its moisture content or density. For example, it was possible to establish correlations between cone penetration and the strength of Buckshot clay and Yuma sand. These are the soils used extensively in the tire tests performed at the Waterweys Experiment Station (KARAFIATH, 1974). The correlation for the Buckshot clay is

$$\begin{aligned} c\ (\text{psi}) &= 0.08\, CI \\ \varphi\ (\text{degrees}) &= 0.25\, CI \end{aligned} \qquad \text{Eq. 3.6.6}$$

In frictional soils the rate of the increase of cone penetration resistance with depth, the "cone index gradient" *(CGR),* is a measure of its density. The following correlation has been established between the relative density of Yuma sand and the *CGR* value (Turnage, 1972).

$$D_r = 71.1 \log_{10} CGR + 11.33 (\pm 6.8) \qquad \text{Eq. 3.6.7}$$

The strength of the Yuma sand was found to correlate with the relative density according to the following relationship:

$$\cot \varphi = 1.64 - 0.68 D_r \qquad \text{Eq. 3.6.8}$$

The correlations established for the Buckshot clay and Yuma sand are also approximately valid for other types of soils that are either purely cohesive or frictional.

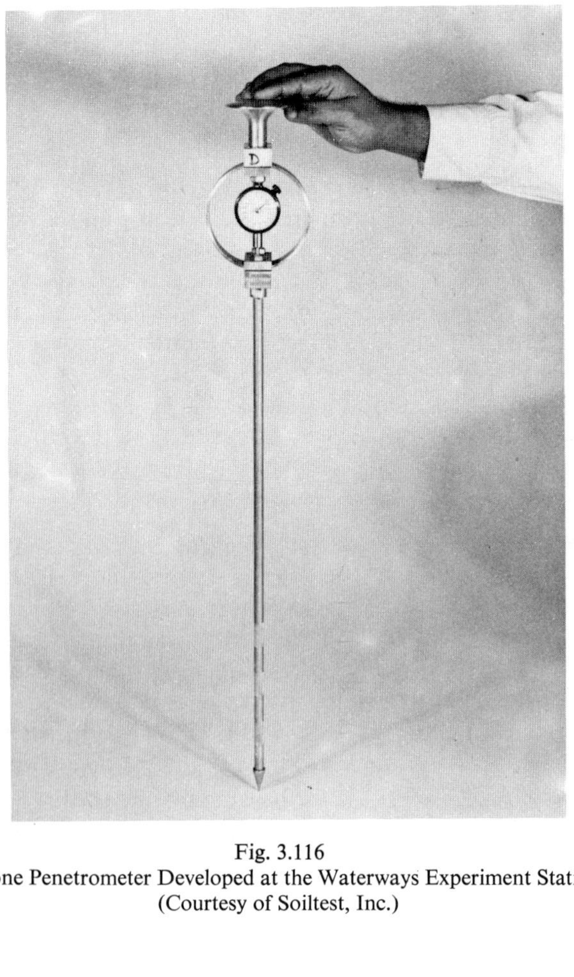

Fig. 3.116
Mobility Cone Penetrometer Developed at the Waterways Experiment Station (WES)
(Courtesy of Soiltest, Inc.)

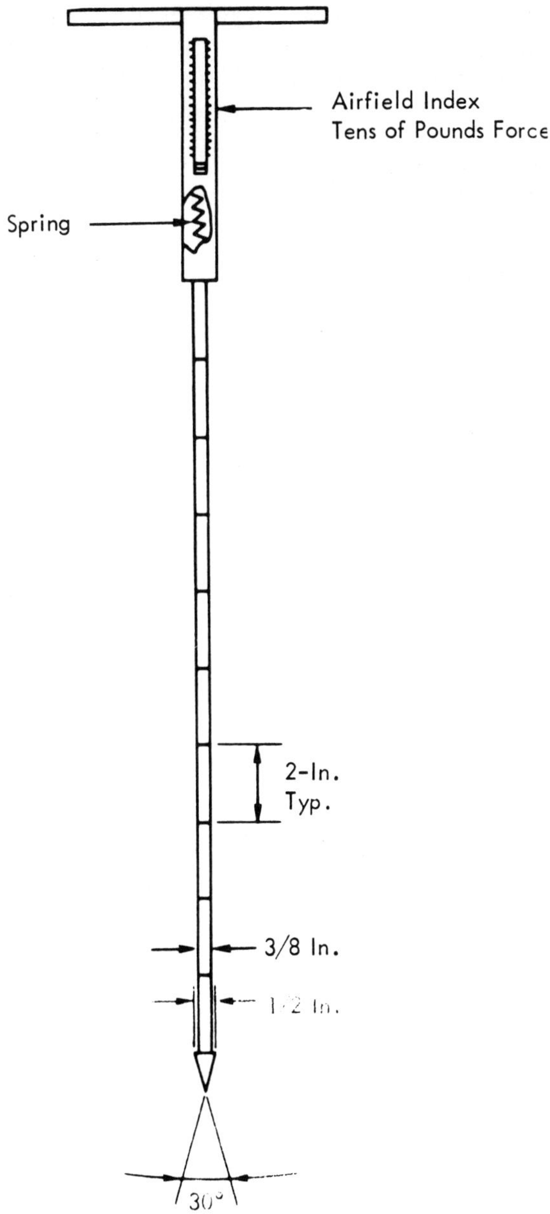

Fig. 3.117
Schematic of Airfield Penetrometer

Cone penetration tests, originally introduced as a practical means of obtaining information on soil strength properties, gained in significance when dimensional analyses showed that for either purely cohesive or purely frictional soils the cone index or the cone index gradient, respectively, can be used for soil characterization in dimensionless parameters directly related to tire performance (FREITAG, 1965). In the dimensional analyses it was possible to define the significant independent variables that govern tire performance and derive simple dimensionless parameters for the specific cases when the soil is either purely frictional or purely cohesive. These are as follows.

In frictional soil the "sand number", N_s, was found to correlate well with tire performance.

$$N_s = \frac{CGR\,(B \cdot D)^{\frac{3}{2}}}{W} \, \frac{\delta^{\frac{1}{2}}}{h} \qquad \text{Eq. 3.6.9}$$

In cohesive soils the "clay number", N_c, is used.

$$N_c = \frac{CI\,(B \cdot D)}{W} \, \frac{\delta}{h} \qquad \text{Eq. 3.6.10}$$

Experiments performed at the Waterways Experiment Station indicated that good correlation exists between the dimensionless tire performance parameter (pull and torque coefficients) and the "sand" and "clay" numbers, respectively, and that this correlation could be improved by using less simple diameter-width relations in the dimensionless "sand" and "clay" numbers (TURNAGE, 1972).

The experimentally established relationships between the dimensionless parameters are very simple to use and are self-validating. However, these are available only for tires in either purely frictional or purely cohesive soils and only for one slip rate (20 %). TURNAGE (1971) used dimensional analysis methods and statistical techniques to establish dimensionless prediction terms that could be correlated with the performance of tracks. Because of the interactions between track and vehicle discussed in Chapter 3.5, it is difficult to treat track performance independently of the vehicle. The relationships between track performance and the dimensionless prediction terms proposed by TURNAGE were determined by experiments in which the track was forced to ride at a constant trim angle, leaving the effect of the trim angle unresolved.

3.6.5 California Bearing Ratio (CBR) Test

The *CBR* method was originally developed for use in the design of asphaltic pavements. Occasionally it is used for the identification of soils in off-road mobility evaluation. Therefore, a brief description of the test together with an appraisal of its usefulness for mobility prediction is given here.

The *CBR* is a comparative measure of the resistance of soil to the penetration of a plunger of standard size at a specified rate to a standard depth expressed as a percentage of a reference load, that is, the load required to force the plunger into a standard crushed stone to the same depth under the same conditions. The area of the standard plunger is 3 square inches (1.95 in. diameter). The standard penetration rate is 0.05 in./min. The depth of penetration is usually 0.1 or 0.2 in., but depths of 0.3, 0.4 or 0.5 in. are sometimes used. For the performance of the test, particles over $^3/_4$ in. are removed from the soil; then the soil is placed in a 6 in. diameter mold and compacted by prescribed procedures. A 5 lb. annular disc surcharge weight is placed at the soil surface. This weight is intended to simulate the load of the pavement on the soil.

The test may also be conducted on undisturbed soil samples taken in the field by the *CBR* mold, or on soaked or swelling samples. An alternative method is to conduct in place *CBR* tests in the field by jacking the plunger against the rear of a truck and measuring its penetration by appropriately placed gages. Note that annular surcharge weights are always placed on the surface of the soil around the plunger, thereby making the in-place *CBR* test different from a plate sinkage test.

Design charts have been developed that relate pavement, base and subbase thicknesses to vehicle loading conditions and *CBR* values. The *CBR* testing procedure intends to simulate soil action underneath a loaded pavement, an entirely different situation from the running gear-soil interaction that takes place in off-road travel. At the small penetration at which the soil resistance is compared to that of crushed stone the ultimate shearing resistance is rarely mobilized. Thus, the *CBR* value is not a representative measure of soil strength. Therefore, it is not the best soil property descriptor for running gear-soil interaction controlled by the strength properties of soil. Its best use would be in the evaluation of the sinkage of tracked vehicles under loads that do not cause soil failure. However, it has been rarely, if ever, used for this purpose.

For a specific soil the *CBR* value is a measure of its compactness. Therefore, correlations between moisture content, density, or cone penetration resistance and CBR value may be established. For example, the following correlation was established between the cone index and CBR value for Buckshot clay compacted to 90 % saturation:

$$CI\,(\text{psi}) = 33\quad(CBR+1)$$

3.6.6 The COHRON Sheargraph

The COHRON sheargraph is a handy device (Figure 3.118) designed to obtain information on the in situ strength properties of the soil as well as on the shearing resistance between soil and metal and soil and rubber.

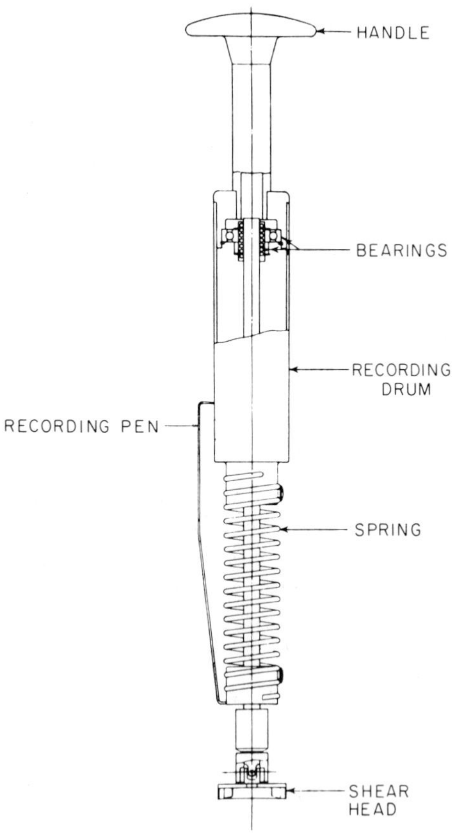

Fig. 3.118
COHRON Sheargraph

In operation, the shearhead is completely inserted into the soil, normal stress is applied to the shear surface through axial deflection of a spring, and shearing stress is applied by twisting the recording drum until the soil fails. After soil shear failure occurs, normal load is gradually reduced. Since the soil will sustain only a given amount of shearing stress for a particular normal load, the recording pen will trace the curve of shear stress versus normal stress as the latter is reduced to zero.

Soil-to-metal or soil-to-rubber shearing resistance may be determined by inserting a smooth metal or rubber faced shearhead into the device.

The Cohron sheargraph works according to the same principle as the ring shear device. The recorded shear and normal stresses are representative of the strength properties of the soil only if the base plane of the shear head is a failure plane. Should oblique failure planes develop for reasons explained in Section 3.6.3, the strength properties evaluated from the normal shear stresses measured in the test will be lower than the true shear strength of the soil.

3.6.7 The Field Vane Shear Test

A number of field vane shear testing devices exist which allow for the determination of the *in situ* undrained shear strength of cohesive soils. These include devices such as the U.S. Bureau of Reclamation vane testing apparatus which is attached to standard drill rods for testing soils at depth. Hand held devices such as the Torvane Shear Device and the Direct Reading Pocket Shear Vane manufactured by Soiltest, Inc. have more application for vehicle mobility evaluation. In principle all of these devices interact with the soil in the same way as described in Section 1.3.4 for the laboratory shear vane. The differences are mainly in the size of the vane and the manner in which soil resistance is indicated; some instruments are direct reading, others require conversion charts. In any case it must be remembered that only the undrained shear strength (refer to Section 1.3.4) can be obtained from tests performed with a vane shear apparatus.

CHAPTER 3.7

SPECIAL PROBLEMS

In the preceding chapters we discussed fundamental running gear-soil interaction problems where the application of soil mechanics principles to the problems and the use of computer techniques resulted in superior simulation of the interaction phenomena and thereby in a breakthrough in prediction methods. In these problems it was sufficient to characterize the soil by properties that can be readily determined by the field and laboratory techniques employed today in off-road vehicle engineering.

Beyond the fundamental problems there are many other special problems that originate from the various users of off-road vehicles. Even though these problems are often exceedingly complicated, they are real problems and generally the users immediate need calls for an "instant" solution. Since sufficient time, or money is usually not available to attack the problem in a scientific manner, often a compromise is adapted that temporarily satisfies the user's need but which can hardly be called a solution to the problem. In some other problems present state of the art soil mechanics methods would allow a theoretically sound treatment of the problem, but the acquisition of the necessary information on the soil properties that form the premises of the theoretical treatment poses difficulties. In other cases the formulation of the user's problem is so lax that a major part of the solution consists of qualifying the answers and possibly reformulating the problem. It is because of the interdisciplinary nature of off-road vehicle engineering that these problems arise. In the following discussions we attempt to present the soil mechanics aspects of some of these problems with the aim of examining the feasibility of solutions by present state of the art methods.

A general problem that surfaces in various ways in the diverse branches of engineering disciplines engaged in off-road vehicle engineering is the determination of the changes in the properties of soil upon passage of a wheel or track. In the simulation of off-road vehicle performance this problem occurs with multi-axle wheeled vehicles as the problem of determining the effect of the passage of the leading wheel on the soil properties controlling the performance of trailing wheels. In straight line travel the geometry of this problem is straightforward and the time elapsed between the subsequent action of the wheels is negligible. In military engineering a similar problem arises in connection with mobility problems when military vehicles travel in convoy or airplanes take off from or land on unprepared airfields. How many times can a vehicle use the same off-road route, or how many vehicles can use the same off-road route in succession without the route becoming unpassable? Or how many airplanes can use the same unprepared airfield in short time intervals? In these cases one may assume that the wheels travel in the same rut. Even then, the geommetry of rut formation and the lack of readily applicable theories, however, make the theoretical treatment of the problem unattractive. Interestingly, in civil engineering construction a very frequently employed means of improving the properties of earthfills has been the passes of self-propelling compactors or towed rubber tired rollers. A wealth of information is available on the effect of compaction on the mechanical properties of various earthfill materials, on "proof-rolling" and related matters that are relevant to the problem as posed in off-road vehicle engineering. In agriculture, compaction of the soil by farm machinery presents the opposite problem: how to prevent excessive compaction of the soil by the repetitive passage of farming vehicles? In recent years the demand for productivity resulted in more and more powerful and, therefore, heavier and heavier farm machinery and the development of machines for every phase of farmwork. The acreage of land that these machines can handle is so great that the machines are also required to travel on road at relatively high speed to reach the land to be cultivated. This requirement makes prohibitive the use of tracks that would reduce ground pressure and compaction. The problem of compaction by the heavy wheeled vehicles is getting more and more serious since it reaches the point where roots cannot penetrate the heavily compacted soil.

The running gear-soil interaction concepts and the performance computation techniques discussed in Chapters 3.3 through 3.5 provide an excellent tool for the investigation of most of the problems connected with the effect of vehicle passage on soil properties. These techniques make it possible to determine the stresses in the soil beneath the running gear and the loading path on a soil element during the passage of the running gear. Once the loading path is known, it becomes a matter of choice whether the effect of loading path on the strength properties of soil should be determined precisely in the laboratory by triaxial tests or should be estimated on the basis of general information on these effects available in the soil mechanics literature. In either way, a reasonable answer can be found provided sufficient information is available on the properties of the virgin soil.

The principle of effective stresses and knowledge of the effect of remolding or disturbing the structures of clay soils are also helpful for a proper approach to the problem solution. In this respect the following considerations may serve as a guide.

In dry granular soils the stress system imposed on the soil is an effective stress system that produces immediate volume changes in the soil. In dry granular soils the stress states at some point reach the failure state underneath the running gear. Depending on the properties of the particular soil the void ratio at failure may be higher or lower than the initial one. Thus, in dry granular soils the passage of the running gear may either densify or loosen the soil, but once it has produced a density that corresponds approximately to the void ratio at failure, further passage of the running gear is not likely to change the density of the soil and its strength appreciably.

In partially saturated soils (up to about 85% saturation) the passage of the running gear generally improves the soil properties and multi-passage of vehicles is unlikely to cause any mobility problem. The moisture-density relationships discussed in Section 1.2.3 clearly indicate that below approximately 85% saturation compaction takes place upon the application of stresses and, therefore, the strength properties of soil are improved by the passage of vehicles. At and below this degree of saturation the air voids are likely to form interconnecting air channels that allow the air to escape to the surface upon compression of the soil without any significant air or pore water pressure buildup. Therefore, the applied stresses produce effective stress changes in the soil that, in turn, result in an increase of the density.

It is the most difficult to assess the effect of the passage of running gears on the properties of highly saturated soils. The air voids in highly saturated soils are not interconnected but are in the form of air bubbles. Upon load application effective stresses develop in the mineral skeleton and excess stresses develop in the pore water and air as the soil is compressed. Upon load relief the air bubbles tend to expand and loosen the grain structure. The sinkage of wheels, determined by contact area requirements, forces a rut depth and a volume change upon passage of the wheel that often cannot be absorbed by the compression of the soil. In this case plastic flow takes place from underneath the wheels and the rut formation is accompanied by lip formation at the sides of the rut above the original ground level. This plastic flow is similar in some respects to the yielding of ductile metals which occurs as the result of crystalline dislocations due to shear stresses disrupting bonds between the metal atoms. In particulate media, such as soils, there is generally no disruption of crystalline structure (i.e. the particles do not fracture) upon application of shear stress. Plastic flow in the case of soils is due primarily to physico-chemical phenomena accompanying a reorientation of the soil structure.

In coarse-grained soils such as sands and some silts, the initial depositional structure and the final structure due to mechanical disturbance are influenced by externally applied forces and gravity only. There is essentially no influence from Coulombic forces or other physico-chemical factors. Therefore these materials do not ordinarily flow plastically in the sense used here. Fine-grained soils such as clays, on the other hand, possess a structure or fabric whose formation and reorientation are both profoundly influenced by the physico-chemical factors discussed in Section 1.2.2. For a given set of environmental conditions at the time of formation, the initial fabric of a fine-grained soil is controlled largely by the mineral composition of its particles. For depositional structures, the electro-chemical interaction between the particles and the depositing medium results in a "dispersed" fabric or a "flocculated" fabric. The former is generally the more stable and consists of particles in an essentially "face-to-face" orientation. The latter consists of particles or groups of particles in an "edge-to-face" attitude. In either case, this initial structure is usually modified by one or more of the structure-changing agents such as pressure, mechanical disturbance, chemical weathering and/or environmental changes (moisture content, electrolyte content, cation or anion exchange, pH change, temperature).

From an engineering viewpoint the fundamental differences between a dispersed and a flocculated structure are as follows:

a) Under a given pressure, a flocculated structure is less dense than a dispersed structure.

b) At the same void ratio, a flocculated structure is more rigid than a dispersed structure.

c) An increment of pressure causes greater particle reorientation in a flocculated structure than in a dispersed structure.

d) The effective pore diameter is greater in a flocculated structure than in a dispersed structure.

e) The effect of shearing strains (remolding) is to disperse a structure.

f) In general, the remolded strength of natural soils is less than their *in situ* strength. The ratio of the natural to remolded strength is called "sensitivity".

In light of the above considerations, the relationship between plastic flow in soils subjected to external loads such as those imposed by the passage of a wheel and soil fabric can now be explained more readily. If the interparticle bond is broken in a fine-grained soil the shear stress goes to adjacent bonds, the normal stress may go to adjacent bonds or into the pore water. If the normal stress is transferred to adjacent bonds, these bonds will become stronger. If the transfer rate of the normal stress to adjacent bonds is greater than the transfer rate of shear stress to adjacent bonds, the soil will get stronger and be able to resist the transferred shears. If the converse occurs, the adjacent bonds will be broken and the transfer process repeated. If enough interparticle bonds are broken, the mass of soil will begin to displace slowly since there is generally an irregular distribution of bond strengths in soils. The net effect is a plastic flow of the soil away from the stress center to a point where the shear stresses are reduced to a level at which interparticle bonds can be reestablished. If, on the other hand, the normal stress is transferred to the pore water first and then to the adjacent interparticle bonds, the shear failure described above will be accelerated and plastic flow will occur more rapidly than before. In general, a favorable rate of transfer is more apt to occur in flocculated soils than in dispersed soils because of the edge-to-face orientation. However, flocculated fabrics are also less stable than dispersed fabrics so that when an unfavorable rate of transfer has occurred it is more evident on a macroscale with them than with soils with dispersed fabrics.

Another group of problems concerns the changes in the *in situ* soil properties that environmental effects bring about. In connection with the characterization of soils discussed in Chapter 1.2, a point was made of the transient nature of the in situ soil properties that govern mobility. Environmental effects, primarily precipitation, evaporation and temperature changes cause diurnal and seasonal variations in the moisture profile of surface soils. The theory of these moisture profile variations has been extensively treated in the agricultural soil science, for example by Childs (1969). In military engineering the prediction of these moisture profile variations is of considerable interest since these variations greatly affect off-road mobility. The moisture profile variation at a particular location depends on the initial conditions and the subsequent changes in the surface boundary conditions (air humidity, temperature, free water, etc.) that the environment imposes. Theories for the calculation of these time dependent processes are available, but the physical constants (permeability, suction, etc.) are generally not available in off-road vehicle or military engineering.

Variations in the moisture profile due to environmental effects may affect the field testing of off-road vehicles and the field engineer should be keenly aware of this contingency. Even minor variations of the moisture profile may have a significant effect on vehicle performance. Therefore, the moisture content of the soil should be recorded at representative locations at frequent depth intervals at the time of the field testing of individual vehicles.

Perhaps the most widely encountered problem in off-road mobility caused by environmental effects is that of slipperiness. In certain soils a slight precipitation may wet the surface so that off-road velicles lose traction and get immobilized even though the motion resistance due to sinkage is minimal. The slippery condition is the result of moisture profile changes in relatively impervious soils. Surface water infiltrates the soil very slowly so that only the upper few tenths of an inch of the soil become saturated while the moisture profile for the deeper horizons remains practically unchanged for a long period of time. The traction that can be developed at the running gear-soil interface is limited by the strength properties of the soil that is in immediate contact with the interface. What is known as the cohesive strength of clay soil is in large part due to moisture tension in the pores. This moisture tension is relieved when the surface soil becomes saturated and a loss of strength occurs. In addition, the physico-chemical characteristics of some soils are such that when these soils are wetted the added water is attracted by the particle surfaces and the distance between these particles is increased. The bonding forces between clay particles decrease with the separation of clay particles with a concomitant loss of strength.

The soil profile that results from the saturation of the upper horizons may be modeled by a two-layer system in which the strength of the upper layer is very low. In such a system plastic flow occurs under the wheel load in the upper layer while the stress level in the lower layer is far from the plastic state and for all practical purposes may be considered as rigid. The application of plasticity theory to the flow in this upper layer shows that if the soil in this upper layer possesses some strength, however low, then the soil cannot be squeezed out completely from underneath the interface by pressure (Karafiath, 1975b). The implications of this theoretical result regarding the development of traction are discussed in connection with the tread design of tires.

In bad soil conditions the predominant cause of the immobilization of off-road vehicles is insufficient traction and only exceptionally is the cause insufficient power. Various traction devices (lugs, grousers, chains, etc.) that are employed with off-road vehicles are generally useful to improve off-road traction but disadvantageous on-road. Tire tread designs are aimed at improving traction off-road without limitations on the on-road use of the tire. The capability of various tread designs to improve traction may be analyzed by soil mechanics methods. A discussion of some espects of traction improvement by tread design follows.

The immediate effect of the treads on the development of traction is that the potential sliding surface is transferred from the actual running gear-soil interface to a surface enveloping the treads. The shearing resistance along this surface consists of that between solid and soil along the tread-soil interface and that developed in the soil between the treads.

The ultimate shearing resistance between solid and soil may be expressed as

$$s = a + \sigma_n \tan \varphi_s \qquad \text{Eq. 3.7.1}$$

while in the soil

$$s = c + \sigma_n \tan \varphi \qquad \text{Eq. 3.7.2}$$

Generally, this ultimate shearing resistance cannot be mobilized because the soil is not able to support the running gear when the shearing stresses decrease its bearing capacity. The shear stresses at the sliding surface that envelops the tread constitute the boundary conditions for potential slip line fields that control running gear-soil interaction. In the modeling of the running gear-soil interaction the interface friction angle δ is used to define the relation of these shear stresses to the normal stresses. Assuming that the angle δ also signifies the mobilized friction on the sliding surface that passes through the soil between the treads, the mobilized shear stress along the sliding surface may be expressed as follows.

At the tread-soil interface

$$\tau_{mob} = (a \cdot \cot \varphi_s + \sigma_n) \tan \delta \qquad \delta < \varphi_s \qquad \text{Eq. 3.7.3}$$

In the soil

$$\tau_{mob} = (c \cdot \cot \varphi + \sigma_n) \tan \delta \qquad \delta < \varphi \qquad \text{Eq. 3.7.4}$$

The total traction is the integral of the shear stresses over the hypothetical contact area at the sliding surface. The magnitude of total traction, as can be seen from Equations 3.7.3 and 3.7.4, also depends on the interface normal stresses that are multipliers of tan δ. The distribution of the interface normal stresses that is smooth for an untreaded tire, is affected by the treads because the stiff bars invite stress concentrations. Such concentrations are especially pronounced if a relatively firm layer exists at a shallow depth, since the tread bar reduces the thickness of the compressible layer underneath the tire and higher stresses are needed to produce sufficient compaction of the soil that can accomodate the tread bar. Figure 3.119 shows a probable distribution of the interface normal stresses under such conditions. If the angle of shearing resistance, φ_s, between the tread material and soil is low, then the limitation on the interface friction angle δ imposed by φ_s may seriously reduce the total traction that may be developed. Thus, from this point of view, narrow tread bars appear to be more advantageous than wide one.

On the other hand, in slippery conditions there is not likely to be a significant difference between the shearing resistance mobilized at the face of the tread and in the soil. For traction development the tread bars must "bite" into the firm layer, since the slippery layer cannot be displaced from underneath the treads by pressure alone. In technical terms, the tread bar must exert a high enough pressure to produce plastic failure conditions in the lower firm layer. These conditions can be analyzed by plasticity theory methods. An increase in the inflation pressure also increases the pressure underneath the tread bars and enhances the capability of them to cut into the underlying firm layer.

In the development of running gear-soil interaction models straight line travel has been assumed. However, for the mobility of off-road vehicles,

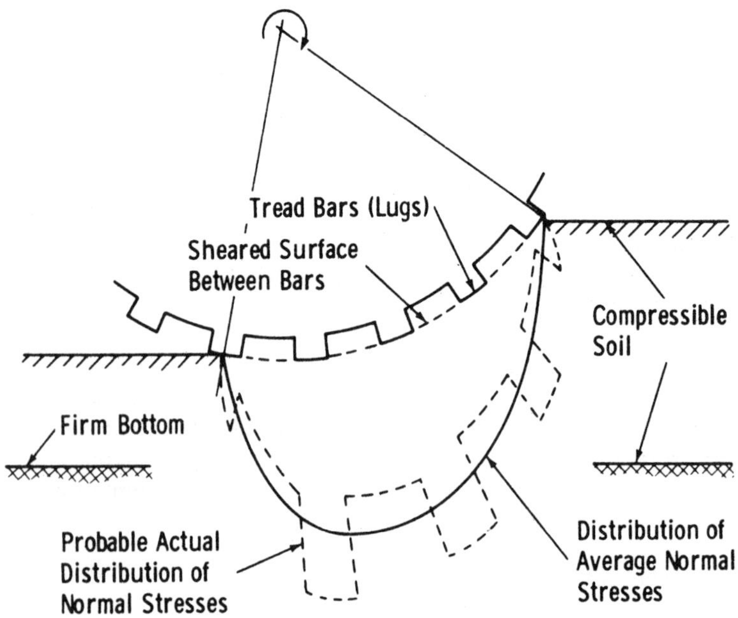

Fig. 3.119
Treaded Wheel — Distribution of Normal Stresses

conditions in turns are often more critical than those in straight line travel. In turns the tire is forced to move in a direction that is at an angle to its longitudinal axis. In the case of a free rolling tire it is conceptually possible to separate the motion resistance (or drag load) into two components: one in the direction of the longitudinal axis of the tire and the other one in the direction perpendicular to that axis. If it is assumed that the sinkage of the tire is controlled by the tire-soil interaction in the longitudinal axis of the tire, an assumption that is certainly realistic for small angles of turn, then the motion resistance in that direction can be determined by the methods presented in Chapter 3.4 for straight line travel. The motion resistance in the perpendicular direction would then have to be determined as a passive earth resistance for the given cross-sectional geometry. Note that in this concept the contact area is the same as in straight line travel and the effect of side loads on tire deformation is neglected. One of the problems that arises with a more rigorous treatment of the motion resistance of tires to turning is that the tire deformation under these complex loading conditions cannot be determined by present state of the art methods. Thus, at this time the semi-empirical treatment of the problem (Kraft and Phillips, 1975; Krick, 1973) appears to be more appropriate.

The turning of tracked vehicles poses a problem different from that of tires. Tracks, except for special designs, stay in their longitudinal axes when the vehicle executes a turn. A concept proposed by Bekker (1956) for the determination of steering resistance of tracked vehicles hypothesizes that the track-soil interface is originally in a level plane and remains in the same plane during turning. The steering resistances are assumed to consist of frictional forces that develop at the track-soil interface, always in the direction opposing the turning motion. The frictional stresses are assumed to be equal to the interface normal stresses times a coefficient of friction that may not be the same as for forward motion. Unfortunately, there are no experiments available that would indicate how well this concept conforms with reality. It is likely that besides the friction coefficient there is also an adhesional component that contributes to the resistance to turning. To apply this concept for the determination of steering resistances, the distribution of interface normal stresses has to be known. The methods discussed in Chapter 3.5 are suitable for this purpose.

A more complicated situation arises when the turn is executed in a trimmed position of the vehicle. Since the turning is around a vertical axis and the track-soil interface is in an inclined plane, the interface cannot remain in its original plane during turning. More experimental information is needed to formulate the soil mechanics of this problem realistically.

One of the objectives that has long motivated military mobility research is the development of a capability to determine the trafficability of terrain by military vehicles and the suitability of sites for aircraft landing by remote sensing techniques. The space program, by necessity, contributed significantly to the advancement of research in this area. Today (1977), remote sensing of terrain is a separate branch of science and even a short description and evaluation of the available techniques would exceed the immediate objectives of this book. Suffice it to say that there now exist various forms of remote sensing imagery by which such geologic factors as topography, the presence of shallow rock and water, the location of weak soils and the existence of potential hazards such as landslides, collapsing ground, flood prone areas and seismically active zones may be determined. These forms include Earth Resource Technology Satellite (ERTS) imagery, Skylab photography, side looking airborne radar (SLAR), and conventional black and white, color, color infrared and multiband photography. The actual imagery utilized depends upon the user requirements, the size of the area under study, and the availability of the imagery. When any one or a combination of these remote sensing techniques is applied to the evaluation of terrain for mobility purposes, then the crucial question is how well the strength properties of the terrain that control mobility can be estimated by these techniques. From this point of view remote sensing, although advanced in the last decades, is somewhat deficient inasmuch as no direct correlation yet exists among the responses in any wavelength of the electromagnetic spectrum regardless of frequency and the strength properties of terrain. Among the various techniques, the aerial photographs in the visible or near infrared are by far the most important remote sensing tools that can be used to estimate the trafficability of soils (WES, 1963). Expert interpretation of aerial photographs together with the results of some active type of remote sensing, such as radar, can be extremely useful for mobility predictions. However, at the current state of the art, desk top interpretations should be confirmed by ground reconnaissance and supplemented by field or lab testing. In this respect their usefulness is limited.

PART 3
BIBLIOGRAPHY

AGEIKIN, Y. S. (1959), "Determination of the Deformation and the Ground Pressure Parameters in Soft Ground," (in Russian), *Automobilnaya Promyshlennost* No. 5.

AGEIKIN, Y. S. (1973), "Evaluation of Ground Deformability with Respect to Vehicle Mobility," *Journal of Terramechanics,* Vol. 10, No. 1.

BEKKER, M. G. (1956), *"Theory of Land Locomotion,"* The University of Michigan Press.

BEKKER, M. G. and Z. JANOSI (1960), "Analysis of Towed Pneumatic Tires Moving in Soft Ground," U. S. Army OTAC, *Land Locomotion Laboratory Report* RR–6.

BEKKER, M. G. (1969), *"Introduction to Terrain-Vehicle Systems,"* The University of Michigan Press.

BERNSTEIN, R. (1913), "Probleme zur experimentellen Motorpflugmechanik," *Der Motorwagen,* Vol. 13.

BODE, G. (1962), "Kräfte und Bewegungen unter rollenden Lastwagenreifen," *A.T.Z.,* Vol. 64, No. 10.

BOGNER, F. K. (1972), "Multiwheel Landing Gear/Soil Interaction – Phase III Braked Wheel Sinkage Prediction Technique and Computer Programs," U.S.A.F. Flight Dynamics Laboratory, *Technical Report* 72–111.

BURT, E. C. and A. C. BAILEY (1974), "Thrust-Dynamic Relationship of Rigid Wheels," *ASAE* Paper No. 74–1554.

CHILDS, E. C. (1969), *"An Introduction to the Physical Basis of Soil-Water Phenomena,"* J. Wiley, London–New York.

CHO, S. W., SCHWANGHARD, H. and H. VON SYBEL (1969), "The Spacing Effect of Track Shoes on Loose Soils," *Journal of Terramechanics,* Vol. 6, No. 3.

CLARK, S. K. (1965), "The Rolling Tire Under Load," *SAE* Paper No. 650493.

CLARK, S. K. (1971), *Mechanics of Pneumatic Tires,* U. S. National Bureau of Standards, Monograph 122.

CLARK, W. J. and J. B. LILJEDAHL (1969), "Model Studies of Single, Dual and Tandem Wheels," *Transactions, ASAE,* Vol. 12, No. 2.

COHRON, G. T. (1963), "Soil Sheargraph," *Agricultural Engineering,* Oct. issue.

COSTES, N. C., FARMER, J. E. and E. B. GEORGE (1972), "Mobility Performance of the Lunar Roving Vehicle: Terrestrial Studies – Apollo 15 Results", NASA *Technical Report* TR R–401.

COSTES, N. C. and W. TRAUTWEIN (1973), "Elastic Loop Mobility System – A New Concept for Planetary Exploration," *Journal of Terramechanics,* Vol. 10, No. 1.

CRENSHAW, B. M., BUTTERWORTH, A. K. and W. B. TRUESDALE (1971), "Aircraft Landing Gear Dynamic Loads from Operation in Clay and Sandy Soil," U.S.A.F. Flight Dynamics Laboratory, *Technical Report* TR–69–51.

CRENSHAW, B. M. (1972), "Aircraft Landing Gear Dynamic Loads Induced by Soil Landing Fields," U.S.A.F. Flight Dynamics Laboratory, *Technical Report* TR-70–169, Vol. 1.

CRENSHAW, B. M. (1975), "Development of an Analytical Technique to Predict Aircraft Landing Gear/Soil Interaction," U.S.A.F. Flight Dynamics Laboratory, *Technical Report* TR–74–115, Vol. 1.

CZAKO, T. (1968), "Methods of Vehicle Soft Soil Mobility Evaluation Based on the Soil Vehicle Interaction," *Proceedings,* 1st Int. Conf. on Vehicle Mechanics, Wayne State University.

CZAKO, T. F. (1974), "The Influence of the Inflation Pressure on Cross Country Performance," *Journal of Terramechanics,* Vol. 11, Nos. 3 & 4.

DODGE, R. (1965), "The Dynamic Stiffness of a Pneumatic Tire Model," *SAE* Paper No. 650491.

EBERAN-EBERHORST, R. (1965), "Zur Theorie des Luftreifens," *A.T.Z.* Vol. 67, No. 8.

FREITAG, D. (1965), "A Dimensional Analysis of the Performance of Pneumatic Tires on Soft Soil," U. S. Army Corps of Engineers, Waterways Experiment Station *Technical Report* No. 3–688.

FREITAG, D., GREEN, A., and N. MURPHY (1965), "Normal Stresses at the Tire-Soil Interface in Yielding Soils," *Highway Research Record,* No. 74.

FREITAG, D. and M. SMITH (1966), "Center-line Deflection of Pneumatic Tires Moving in Dry Sand," *Journal of Terramechanics,* Vol. 3, No. 1.

FREITAG, D. R., GREEN, A. J. and K. J. MELZER (1970), "Performance Evaluation of Wheels for Lunar Vehicles," U. S. Army Corps of Engineers, Waterways Experiment Station *Technical Report* M–70–2.

FREITAG, D. R., GREEN, A. J., MELZER, K. J. and N. C. COSTES (1972), "Wheels for Lunar Vehicles," *Journal of Terramechanics,* Vol. 8, No. 3.

GREEN, A. J. and M. R. MURPHY, Jr. (1965), "Stresses Under Moving Vehicles," U.S. Army Corps of Engineeres, Waterways Experiment Station *Technical Report* No. 3–545, Report 5.

GUSKOV, V. (1968), "The Effect of Drawbar Pull on the Rolling Resistance of Track Laying Vehicles," *Journal of Terramechanics,* Vol. 5, No. 4.

HARRISON, W. L. and T. CZAKO (1961), "Over Snow Vehicle Performance Studies – Appendix: Drawbar Pull of Tracked Vehicles," U.S. Army OTAC Research Division, *Research Report* RR–46.

HARRISON, W. L. (1972), "Soil Failure Under Inclined Loads," U.S. Army Cold Regions Research and Engineering Laboratory, *Research Report* No. 303.

HEGEDUS, E. (1965), "Pressure Distribution Under Rigid Wheels," Transactions, *ASAE.*

HOLM, I. C. (1969), "Multi-pass Behaviour of Pneumatic Tires," *Journal of Terramechanics,* Vol. 6, No. 3.

Hovland, H. and J. Mitchell (1971), "Mechanics of Rolling Sphere-Soil Slope Interaction," *Final Report,* Space Sciences Laboratory, University of California.

Hovland, H. J. (1973), "Soil Inertia in Wheel-Soil Interaction," *Journal of Terramechanics,* Vol. 10, No. 3.

Janosi, Z. (1959), "Prediction of WES Cone Index by Means of a Stress-Strain Function of Soils," U.S. ATAC *Land Locomotion Laboratory Report* No. 46.

Janosi, Z. (1961), "An Analysis of Pneumatic Tire Performance on Deformable Soils," *Proceedings,* 1st Int. Conf. on the Mechanics of Soil-Vehicle Systems, Torino, Italy.

Janosi, Z. and B. Hanamoto (1961), "The Analytical Determination of Drawbar Pull as a Function of Slip for Tracked Vehicles in Deformable Soils," *Proceedings,* 1st Int. Conf. on the Mechanics of Soil-Vehicle Systems, Torino, Italy.

Janosi, Z. J. (1963), "Theoretical Analysis of the Performance of Tracks and Wheels Operating on Deformable Soils," Transactions, *ASAE.*

Janosi, Z. J. (1963), "Tracks Versus Wheels," *Proceedings* of the Fourth Conference of the Quadripartite Working Group on Ground Mobility, London, England.

Janosi, Z. J. (1965), "Analysis and Presentation of Soil Vehicle Mechanics Data," *Journal of Terramechanics,* Vol. 2, No. 3.

Janosi, Z.J. (1966), "Obstacle Performance of Tracklayer Vehicles," *Proceedings,* 2nd Int. Conf. for Terrain-Vehicle Systems, Quebec City, Canada.

Janosi, Z. J. (1967), "Development in Modern Terrain Vehicles," *The Indian and Eastern Engineer,* 108th Anniversary Number.

Janosi, Z. J. (1970), "Commercial Off-Road Vehicles," *SAE* Paper No. 700012.

Janosi, Z. J. and J. A. Eilers (1972), "Application of Dynamic Programming to Off-road Mobility Problems," *Proceedings,* 4th Int. Conf. for Terrain-Vehicle Systems, Stockholm, Sweden.

Jurkat, M. P., Nuttal, C. J. and P. W. Haley (1975), "The AMC'74 Mobility Model" U.S. Army TACOM Mobility Systems Laboratory, *Technical Report* No. 11921 (LL–149).

Karafiath, L. (1953), "Erddruck auf Wände mit kreisförmigen Querschnitt," *Bauplanung und Bautechnik,* Vol. 7, No. 7.

Karafiath, L. (1954), "Einfluß der Verfestigung und der Zeitdauer der Lastaufbringung auf die Grenzbelastung des Baugrundes," *Gedenkbuch für Prof. Dr. Jaky,* Budapest, Hungary.

Karafiath, L. (1955), "Rationelle und schnelle Berechnung des zeitlichen Setzungsverlaufs," *Bauplanung und Bautechnik,* Vol. 9, No. 6.

Karafiath, L. (1957), "An Analysis of New Techniques for the Estimation of Footing Sinkage in Soils," U.S. ATAC, *Land Locomotion Laboratory Report* 11–19.

Karafiath, L. L. (1970), "Analysis of Stress Distribution Beneath Wheels by the Theory of Plasticity with Respect to Lunar Locomotion," *Proceedings,* ISTVS-TRW Off-Road Mobility Symposium, Los Angeles, U.S.A.

Karafiath, L. L. (1970), "Shape Factors in Bearing Capacity Equation," *Journal* SMFD, ASCE, Vol. 96., No. SM 4.

KARAFIATH, L. L. (1971), "Plasticity Theory and the Stress Distribution Beneath Wheels," *Journal of Terramechanics,* Vol. 8., No. 2.

KARAFIATH, L. L. (1972a), "Soil-Tire Model for the Analysis of Off-Road Tire Performance," *Paper* presented at the Eigth National Off-Road Mobility Symposium, Purdue University.

KARAFIATH, L. L. (1972b), "On the Effect of Pore Pressures on Soil-Wheel Interaction", *Proceedings,* 4th. Int. Conf. for Terrain Vehicle-Systems, Stockholm, Sweden.

KARAFIATH, L. L. and E. A. NOWATZKI, (1972), "Tractive Performance of Wheels in Soft Soils," *ASAE* Paper No. 72–632.

KARAFIATH, L. L., NOWATZKI, E. A., EHRLICH, I. R. and J. CHAPIN (1973), "An Application of Plasticity Theory to the Solution of the Rigid Wheel-Soil Interaction Problem," U.S. Army TACOM *Technical Report* No. 11758 (LL–141).

KARAFIATH, L. L. (1974), "Development of Mathematical Model for Pneumatic Tire-Soil Interaction," U.S. Army TACOM Mobility System Laboratory, *Technical Report* No. 11900 (LL 147).

KARAFIATH, L. L. and F. S. SOBIERAJSKI (1974), "Effect of Speed on Tire-Soil Interaction and Development of Towed Pneumatic Tire-Soil Model" U.S. Army Mobility Systems Laboratory *Technical Report* No. 11997 (LL 151).

KARAFIATH, L. L. (1975a), "Running Gear-Soil Modeling for Off-Road Vehicles," *Proceedings,* 5th Int. Conf. for Terrain-Vehicle Systems, Detroit.

KARAFIATH, L. L. (1975b), "Development of Mathematical Model for Pneumatic Tire-Soil Interaction in Layered Soils," U.S. Army TACOM, Mobility Systems Laboratory *Technical Report* No. 12509, (LL 152).

KARAFIATH, L. L. (1977) "Development of a Mathematical Model for the Prediction of the Off-road Performance of 4×4 Vehicles" U. S. Army Tank-Automotive Research and Development Laboratory, *Technical Report* No 12227 (LL-153)

KRAFT, D. C. and J. R. HOPPENJANS (1970), "Aircraft Surface Operation-Soil Surface Correlation Study," U.S.A.F. Flight Dynamics Laboratory *Technical Report* TR–70–30.

KRAFT, D. C. and H. LUMING (1971), "Multiple Rolling Tire Sinkage and Drag Interaction Effects," *SAE* Paper No. 710180.

KRAFT, D. C. and N. S. PHILLIPS (1975), "Turning Forces Developed by a Pneumatic Tire Operating in Soils with Application to Vehicle Design Criteria," *Proceedings,* 5th. Int. Conf. for Terrain-Vehicle Systems, Detroit.

KRICK, G. (1969), "Radial and Shear Stress Distribution Under Rigid Wheels and Pneumatic Tires Operating in Yielding Soils with Consideration of Tire Deformation," *Journal of Terramechanics,* Vol. 6., No. 3.

KRICK, G. (1971), "Schräglaufverhalten angetriebener Reifen in nachgiebigen Böden," *A.T.Z.* Vol. 73, No. 7.

KRICK, G. (1973), "Behaviour of Tyres Driven in Soft Ground with Side Slip," *Journal of Terramechanics,* Vol. 9, No. 4.

LISTON, R. A. (1973a), "A Strip Load Approximation for a Track," *ASAE* Paper No. 73–1507.

LISTON, R. A. (1973b), "The Combined Normal and Tangential Loading of Soil," *Ph. D. Thesis,* Michigan Technological University.

MELZER, K. J. (1971), "Performance of Dual-Wheel Configuration in Coarse Grained Soil," U.S. Army Corps of Engineers, Waterways Experiment Station *Technical Report* M–71–8.

MITROPAN, D. M., SHEPELENKO, G. I., LEVITANUS, A. D. and L. T. TCHERVONYI (1966), "Ground Pressure Study of Wheeled and Tracked Tractors of 3 Ton Class," (In Russian) *Traktory i Selkhozmashiny,* No. 9.

MURPHY, N. R., Jr. and A. J. GREEN, Jr. (1965), "Stresses Under Moving Vehicles – Distribution of Stresses Beneath a Towed Pneumatic Tire in Air-Dry Sand," U.S. Army Corps of Engineers Waterways Experiment Station, *Technical Report* No. 3–545, Report No. 5.

NOWATZKI, E. A. and L. L. KARAFIATH (1972), "Effect of Cone Angle on Penetration Resistance," *Highway Research Record,* No. 405.

NOWATZKI, E. A. and L. L. KARAFIATH (1974), "General Yield Conditions in a Plasticity Analysis of Soil-Wheel Interaction," *Journal of Terramechanics,* Vol. 11, No. 1.

NUTTALL, C. J., Jr. (1965), "A Dimensionless Consolidation of WES Data on the Performance of Sand Under Tire Loads," U.S. Army Corps of Engineers Waterways Experiment Station, *Contract Report* No. 3–130.

NUTTALL, C. J., Jr. (1971), "Traction Limits for Tracked Vehicles Crawling the Sea Bottom," *Journal of Engineering for Industry.*

ONAFEKO. O. and A. R. REECE (1967), "Soil Stress and Deformation Beneath Rigid Wheels," *Journal of Terramechanics,* Vol. 4, No. 1.

PERLOFF, W. H. (1966), "Mobility of Tracked Vehicles on Soft Soils," *Research Report,* Purdue University, School of Civil Engineering, Lafayette, Indiana.

PERLOFF, W. H. and K. S. A. RAHIM (1966), "Study of the Pressure-Penetration Relationsship for Model Footing on Cohesive Soil," *Highway Research Record*, No. 145.

RASPER, L. (1972), "Zur Problematik des Bodendrucks unter Raupenfahrgestellen von Großgeräten," *Braunkohle,* Vol. 24, No. 4.

RASPER, L. (1975), *The Bucket Wheel Excavator,* Trans Tech Publications, Clausthal, Germany.

REECE, A. R. (1964), "Problems of Soil Vehicle Mechanics," U.S. ATAC Land Locomotion Laboratory, *Report* LL–97.

ROWLAND, G. (1972), "Tracked Vehicle Ground Pressure and its Effect on Soft Ground Performance," *Proceedings,* 4th Int. Conf. for Terrain-Vehicle Systems, Stockholm, Sweden.

SCHLÖR, K. (1959), "Einfluß der Bodenbelastbarkeit auf Laufwerk und Gleiskette eines Raupenfahrzeugs," *A.T.Z.* Vol. 61, No. 5.

SCHURING, D. (1966), "The Energy Loss of a Wheel," *Proceedings,* 2nd. Int. Conf. for Terrain-Vehicle Systems, Quebec City, Canada.

SEITZ, N. (1969), "Experimentelle und Theoretische Untersuchungen der in der Aufstandsfläche frei rollender Reifen wirkenden Kräfte und Bewegungen," *Dissertation,* Technische Hochschule München, Clearinghouse Reproduction N 69–33739.

SELA, A. (1964), "The Shear to Normal Stress Relationship Between a Rigid Wheel and Dry Sand," U.S. ATAC *Land Locomotion Laboratory Report* LL–99.

SELIG, E. T. and C. T. WANG (1975), "Effect of Velocity on Drag and Sinkage of Free Rolling Tires on Soil," *Proceedings,* 5th Int. Conf. for Terrain-Vehicle Systems, Detroit, Michigan.

SIMON, M.(1964),"Les Compacteurs a Pneus en Construction Routiers," *Annales de l'Institut Technique du Batiment et des Travaux Public,* No. 193.

SMITH, J. L. (1965), "A Study of the Effects of Wet Surface Soil Conditions on the Performance of Single Pneumatic Tired Wheels," U.S. Army Corps of Engineers Waterways Experiment Station *Technical Report* No. 3–703.

SMITH, M. E. and D. R. FREITAG (1963), "Deflection of Moving Tires – Centerline Deflection Studies through 1963," U.S. Army Corps of Engineers Waterways Experiment Station, *Technical Report* No. 3–516, Report No. 3.

SWANSON, G. D. and T. R. PATIN (1975), "Small Scale Mobility Test in Fine Grained Layered Soils," U.S. Army Corps of Engineers Waterways Experiment Station, *Technical Report* M–71–1.

SWANSON, G. D. (1971), "Dual-Rigid-Wheel Performance in Sand," *ASAE* Paper No. 71–602.

TAYLOR, J. H. and G. E. VANDEN BERG (1966), "The Role of Displacement in a Simple Traction System," *Journal of Terramechanics,* Vol. 3, No. 1.

TAYLOR, J. H., VANDEN BERG, G. E., and I. F. REED (1967), "Effect of Diameter on Performance of Powered Tractor Wheels", *Transactions, ASAE,* Vol. 10.

TAYLOR, J. H. (1973), "Lug Angle Effect on Traction Performance of Pneumatic Tractor Tires," *Transactions, ASAE,* Vol. 16, No. 1.

TAYLOR, J. H. and E. C. BURT (1973), "Track and Tire Performance in Agricultural Soils," *ASAE* Paper No. 73–1509.

TAYLOR, J. H. (1974), "Traction, Compaction and Flotation in Soft Soils." *Proceedings* XV Congress of Int. Soc. of Sugar Cane Technologists, Durban, South Africa.

TRABBIC, G., LASK, K. and W. BUCHELE (1959), "Measurement of Soil-Tire Interface Pressures," *Agricultural Engineering,* Nov. issue.

TRUESDALE, W. B. and R. D. NELSON (1972), "Aircraft Landing Gear Dynamic Loads Induced by Soil Landing Fields," U.S.A.F. Flight Dynamics Laboratory, *Technical Report* TR-70–169.

TURNAGE, G. W. (1970), "Effects of Velocity, Size and Shape of Probes on Penetration Resistance of Fine-Grained Soils," U.S. Army Corps of Engineers Waterways Experiment Station *Technical Report* No 3–652 Report 3.

TURNAGE, G. W. (1971), "Performance of Soils Under Track Loads," U.S. Army Corps of Engineers Waterways Experiment Station, *Technical Report* M–71–5.

TURNAGE, G. W. (1972), "Performance of Soils Under Tire Loads," U.S. Army Corps of Engineers Waterways Experiment Station, *Technical Report* No. 3–666, Report 8.

TURNAGE, G. W. (1973), "Resistance of Fine Grained Soils to High Speed Penetration," U.S. Army Corps of Engineers Waterways Experiment Station, *Technical Report* No. 3–652, Report 5.

TURNAGE, G. W. (1974), "Resistance of Coarse Grained Soils to High Speed Penetration," U.S. Army Corps of Engineers Waterways Experiment Station, *Technical Report* No. 3–652, Report 6.

TURNAGE, G. W. and D. N. BROWN (1974), "Prediction of Aircraft Ground Performance by Evaluation of Ground Vehicle Rut Depths," U.S.A.F. Weapons Laboratory, Kirtland AFB, New Mexico, *Technical Report* TR–73–213.

TURNAGE, G. W. (1975), "Behavior of Fine Grained Soils Under High-Speed Tire Loads," U.S. Army Corps of Engineers Waterways Experiment Station, *Technical Report* No. 3–652, Report 7.

UFFELMANN, F. L. (1961), "The Performance of Rigid Cylindrical Wheels in Clay," *Proceedings,* 1st Int. Conf. on the Mechanics of Soil-Vehicle Systems, Torino, Italy.

VANDEN BERG, G. and W. GILL (1962), "Pressure Distribution Between a Smooth Tire and Soil," *ASAE, Transactions,* Paper No. 59–108.

VODYANIK, I. I. (1966), "The Motion of a Tracked Vehicle on Deformable Ground," *Journal of Terramechanics,* Vol. 3, No. 1.

WES (1963), "Forecasting Trafficability of Soil – Airphoto Approach," U.S. Army Corps of Engineers Waterways Experiment Station, *Technical Memorandum* 3–331.

WES (1964), "Stresses Under Moving Vehicles," U.S. Army Corps of Engineers Waterways Experiment Station *Technical Report* No. 3–545.

WES (1969), "Strength-Moisture-Density Relations of Fine Grained Soils in Vehicle Mobility Research," U.S. Army Corps of Engineers Waterways Experiment Station, *Technical Report* No. 3–639.

WES (1973), Unpublished report.

WILLS, B. M. D. (1963), "The Measurement of Soil Shear Strength and Deformation Moduli and a Comparison of the Actual and Theoretical Performance of a Family of Rigid Tracks," *Journal of Agricultural Engineering Research,* Vol. 8, No. 2.

WILSON, N.E. and H.R. KRZYWICKI (1966), "Soil Mechanics as it Affects Vehicle Performance", *Canadian Geotechnical Journal,* Vol. 3, No. 4.

WINDISCH, E. J. and R. N. YONG (1970), "The Determination of Soil Strain-Rate Behaviour Beneath a Moving Wheel," *Journal of Terramechanics,* Vol. 7, No. 1.

WISMER, R. D. (1962), "Performance of Soils Under Tire Loads – Tests in Clay through November 1962," U.S. Army Corps of Engineers Waterways Experiment Station, *Technical Report* No. 3–666, Peport 3.

WISMER, R. D. and H. J. LUTH (1972), "Off-road Traction Prediction for Wheeled Vehicles," *ASAE* Paper No. 72–619.

WONG, J. Y. and A. R. REECE (1966), "Soil Failure Beneath Rigid Wheels," *Proceedings,* 2nd Int. Conf. for Terrain-Vehicle Systems, Quebec City, Canada.

YONG, R. and G. WEBB (1969), "Energy Dissipation and Drawbar Pull Prediction in Soil-Wheel Interaction," *Proceedings,* 3rd Int. Conf. for Terrain-Vehicle Systems, Essen, Germany.

CONVERSION FACTORS
U. S. CUSTOMARY TO METRIC S. I.
UNITS OF MEASUREMENT

Multiply	**By**	**To Obtain**
atmoshperes	10332	kilograms/square metre
cubic feet	0.0283	cubic metres
cubic inches	1.639×10^{-5}	cubic metres
cubic yards	0.7646	cubic metres
feet	0.3048	metres
feet/minute	0.3048	metres/minute
feet/second	1.097	kilometres/hour
feet/second	18.29	metres/minute
feet/second/second	0.3048	metres/second/second
gallons	3.785×10^{-3}	cubic metres
horse power	0.7457	kilowatts
inches	2.54	centimetres
kips (force)	4.448×10^{-3}	newtons
kips (force)/ square foot	4.788×10^{-3}	newtons/square metre*
miles (statute)	1.609	kilometers
miles/hour	1.609	kilometers/hour
ounces	28.35	grams
pounds (mass)	0.4536	kilograms
pounds (mass)/ cubic foot	16.02	kilograms/cubic metre
pounds (mass)/ cubic foot	16.02×10^{-2}	grams/cubic centimetre
pounds (force)	4.448	newtons
pounds (force)/ square inch	6.895×10^{3}	newtons/square metre*
pounds (force)/ square foot	4.788	newtons/square metre*
square feet	0.9029	square metres
square inches	0.0645	square metres
square miles	2.59	square kilometres
tons (mass)	907.2	kilograms
tons (force)	2.224×10^{-3}	newtons
tons (force)/ square foot	2.394×10^{-3}	newtons/square metre
yards	0.9144	metres

* A newton/square metre is now called a "Pascal".

COMMON ABBREVIATIONS FOR UNITS

atmosphere	atm
cubic feet	cu ft; ft^3
cubic inches	cu in.; $in.^3$
feet	ft
feet/min	fpm
feet/sec	fps
foot pounds	ft, lbs
gallons	gals
gallons/minute	gpm
horsepower	hp
inches	in.
kips (force)	k
miles/hour	mph
ounces	oz
pounds	lbs
pounds/square inch	psi; lbs/in. sq
pounds/square foot	psf; lbs/ft sq
square feet	ft sq; ft^2
square inches	in. sq; $in.^2$
tons	t
tons/square foot	tsf

LIST OF SYMBOLS (ENGLISH)

(The following symbols have not been defined by functional expressions in the text)

A	area, ground contact area, pore pressure parameter, adhesive resistance, activity index.
A_f	pore pressure parameter at failure.
A_t	total cross-sectional area.
a	adhesion, parameter in cardioid equation, percentage of total area in soil cross-section occupied by solids.
a_x, a_y, a_z	acceleration in the x, y, z direction, respectively.
a_v	ratio of void volume change to stress change in soil.
B	pore pressure parameter.
B_f	pore pressure parameter at failure.
b	percentage of total area in soil cross-section occupied by water voids.
CBR	California Bearing Ratio.
CD	consolidated drained triaxial test.
CGR	cone index gradient.
CI	cone index.
CU	consolidated undrained triaxial test.
$\overline{CU}$	consolidated undrained triaxial test with pore pressures measured.
C_s	soil void shape factor.
C_u	uniformity coefficient.
c	cohesion.
c_l	cohesion in lower layer.
c_u	cohesion in upper layer, undrained cohesion.
c_v	coefficient of consolidation.
D	diameter (particle size, wheel, tire), pore pressure parameter.
D_{10}	diameter at which 10% of the soil is finer.
DB	drawbar pull.
D_r	relative density.
D_s	diameter of hypothetical sphere.
D_f	depth of embedment of footing.
d	displacement, diameter, derivative, constant defining curvature of MOHR failure envelope.
d_c, d_γ, d_q	depth factors in bearing capacity equation.

E	YOUNG's modulus
e	base of natural logarithm, void ratio, eccentricity, critical void ratio.
e_{cr}	critical void ratio.
e_i	initial void ratio.
e_f	void ratio at failure.
e_{max}	void ratio of soil in loosest state.
e_{min}	void ratio of soil in densest state.
e_o	initial void ratio.
F	force.
f	function.
G	shear modulus.
G_d	downward slope stress gradient.
G_s	specific gravity of solids.
G_u	upward slope stress gradient.
G_w	specific gravity of water.
GWL	ground water level.
g	gravitational acceleration.
H	soil thrust, grid size designation.
h	height, water head, section height of tire, distance of instantaneous center of rotation from wheel bottom, distance of center of gravity from track.
h_o	initial sample height.
h'	deformed sample height.
i	hydraulic gradient, slip line and nodal point numeral designation.
i_c, i_γ, i_q	inclination factors in bearing capacity equation.
j	slip, slip line and nodal point numeral designation.
j_o	slip parameter.
j'	contact slip.
K	slip parameter, grid size designation, lateral pressure ratio.
K_B	coefficient of sinkage.
K_a, K_c, K_γ, K_q	soil resistance coefficients in HETTIARATCHI and REECE equation.
K_γ, K_s, K_{ca}	modified soil resistance coefficients.
K_o	coefficient of lateral earth pressure at rest.

K_p	passive earth pressure coefficient.
K_{pc}, K_{pq}, $K_{p\gamma}$	passive earth pressure coefficients in TERZAGHI bearing capacity theory.
K_t	constant in trim angle—eccentricity relation.
k	sign constant in formula for orientation of major principal stress, coefficient of permeability, parameter in pressure-sinkage equation, constant defining curvature of MOHR envelope.
k'	a constant in the extended TRESCA yield criterion.
k''	a constant in the extended VON MISES yield criterion.
k_c, k_φ	parameters in BEKKER pressure-sinkage equation.
k_z	coefficient of permeability in the z direction.
L	length, length of contact area, length of passive zone at surface, load.
LI	liquidity index.
LL	liquid limit.
l	length.
M	moment, constant in differential equations of plasticity for effective stresses, constant in PERLOFF pressure-sinkage relationship.
m	constant defining curvature of MOHR failure envelope.
m_{tv}	compressibility coefficient of total voids in soil.
m_{vl}	compressibility coefficient of mineral skeleton (triaxial loading).
m_{vl1}	compressibility coefficient of mineral skeleton (uniaxial loading).
m_{vlo}	expansivity coefficient of mineral skeleton (uniaxial loading).
N	normal force, coordination number.
N_γ, N_c, N_q	bearing capacity factors (general shear).
N'_γ, N'_c, N'_q	bearing capacity factors (local shear).
$\overline{N}_\gamma$, $\overline{N}_c$, $\overline{N}_q$	bearing capacity factors including load inclination effect.
N_c	dimensionless tire performance parameter for cohesive soils.
N_s	dimensionless tire performance parameter for sand.
n	exponent in pressure-sinkage equation, porosity, dummy variable, an integer.

n_{max}	porosity in loosest state.
n_{min}	porosity in densest state.
P	force, externally applied load, cone penetration resistance.
PI	plasticity index.
p	pressure.
$\bar{p}$	a constant in the extended von Mises yield criterion.
p_a	active earth pressure.
p_i	inflation pressure.
p_l	limit pressure.
p_p	passive earth pressure.
Q	load, constant in Perloff pressure-sinkage relation, total flow.
Q_{ult}	ultimate load.
q	surcharge, normal stress.
q_d, q_m	normal stress at angle α_d and α_m respectively.
q_{max}	maximum bearing stress on slope.
q_{mf}	normal stress at angle α_m from the forward field.
q_{mr}	normal stress at angle α_m from the rear field.
q_{uv}	ultimate unit stress perpendicular to a surface.
R	resistance, resultant force, radius.
R_o	outside radius of cylindrical soil sampler.
r	radius, radial coordinate.
r_o	initial radius in log spiral.
S	percentage saturation, soil scale index.
S_a	adhesion number.
S_c	cohesion number.
S_q	surcharge number.
s	shear strength.
s_c, s_q, s_γ	shape factors in bearing capacity equation.
s_u	undrained shear strength.
T	tangential force, torque.
t	time.
UU	unconsolidated undrained triaxial test.
$\overline{UU}$	unconsolidated undrained triaxial test with pore pressures measured.
u	pore water pressure, velocity in the x-direction.

u_a	pore air pressure.
u_h	excess pore water pressure due to hydrostatic stress.
u_i	initial excess pore water pressure.
u_r	residual pore water pressure.
u_w	pore water pressure.
V	volume, vertical component of force.
V_g	volume of gas.
V_o	initial volume.
V_s	volume of solids.
V_t	total volume.
V_{tv}	volume of total voids.
V_v	volume of voids.
V_w	volume of water.
v	velocity in z-direction, valence.
$\bar{v}$	velocity vector.
$\bar{v}_f$	velocity vector in direction of travel.
$\bar{v}_p$	peripheral velocity vector.
$\bar{v}_t$	tangential velocity vector.
v_x, v_y, v_z	velocity components in x, y, z direction respectively.
v^{α}, v^{β}	velocity vectors along α, β characteristics.
W	weight.
W_g	weight of gas.
W_s	weight of solids.
W_t	total weight of soil including solids, liquids and gases.
W_w	weight of water.
W_x, W_y, W_z	weight of soil in x, y, z directions respectively.
w	water (moisture) content, uniformly distributed surface load, equivalent surcharge, velocity in y-direction.
w_l	liquid limit.
w_p	plastic limit.
w_s	shrinkage limit.
w_t	sticky limit.
w_{st}	saturation limit.
y	coordinate
X	body force in x-direction.
x	coordinate.
$\ddot{x}$	component of acceleration in x-direction.

Y	body force in y-direction.
$\ddot{y}$	component of acceleration in y-direction.
Z	body force in z-direction.
z	vertical coordinate, depth, sinkage.
$\ddot{z}$	component of acceleration in z-direction.
z_B	sinkage at bearing capacity.

LIST OF SYMBOLS (GREEK)

α	central angle, rake angle, angle of orientation of failure plane, apex angle of cone penetrometer.
α'	angle of tangent of deflected interface, angle defining start and end of tire deflection.
α_d	central angle at the inner end of the forward slip line field.
α'_d	central angle at the inner end of the rear slip line field.
α_e	entry angle.
α_f	angle of orientation of failure plane.
α_m	angle of separation.
α_o	initial central angle.
α_r	rear angle.
α_{sp}	angle between tangent of logarithmic spiral and circle of same radius.
α_u	angle of orientation of failure plane based on undrained strength.
α_ε	central angle at which ε is defined.
α_τ	angle at which shear stress becomes zero.
β	constant in logarithmic spiral equation, complement to soil sampler cutting tip angle, complement to half the apex angle of a cone, direction of motion of soil-blade interface with respect to horizontal.
γ	unit weight, shear strain.
γ_b	buoyant unit weight of soil in general.
$\gamma_{b\,sat}$	buoyant unit weight of saturated soil.

γ_d	dry unit weight of soil.
$\gamma_{d\,min}$	dry unit weight of soil in loosest state.
$\gamma_{d\,max}$	dry unit weight of soil in densest state.
γ_s	unit weight of solids.
γ_{sat}	saturated unit weight of soil.
γ_t	total unit weight of soil.
γ_w	unit weight of water.
δ	interface friction angle, tire deflection, obliquity angle.
δ_i	interface friction angle at layer interfaces.
Δ	difference operator.
ε	slope angle, deflection coefficient, strain.
ε_x, ε_y, ε_z	strain in x, y, z directions respectively.
$\dot{\varepsilon}_x$, $\dot{\varepsilon}_y$, $\dot{\varepsilon}_z$	strain rate in x, y, z directions respectively.
$\dot{\varepsilon}_1$, $\dot{\varepsilon}_2$, $\dot{\varepsilon}_3$	strain rate in major, intermediate, and minor principal stress directions.
η	dummy variable (method of characteristics).
θ	angle of major principal stress with x-axis.
θ'	angle of velocity vector with z-axis.
θ_o	angle of major principal stress with x-axis at free surface side of singular point, initial value of θ.
θ_e	angle of major principal stress with x-axis at loaded surface side of singular point.
θ^α	angle of velocity vector v^α from vertical axis.
θ^β	angle of velocity vector v^β from vertical axis.
$\varkappa$	deflection parameter.
λ	trim angle, elastic constant.
μ	viscosity, angle enclosed between major principal stress and slip plane, Poisson's Ratio.
ξ	tolerance limit.
ϱ_1, ϱ_2	parameters in particle path equation.
φ	angle of internal friction of soil.
$\bar{\varphi}$	effective friction angle.
φ_e	"true" friction angle (Hvorslev strength parameter).

φ_l	friction angle in lower layer.
φ_s	friction angle between soil and another solid.
φ_u	undrained friction angle, friction angle in upper layer.
χ	dummy variable (method of characteristics)
ψ	negative intercept on σ-axis of MOHR construction.
σ	normal stress, distance between strength envelope intercept and center of MOHR circle.
$\bar{\sigma}$	effective normal stress.
σ'	normal stress in dimensionless form.
σ_c	triaxial chamber pressure.
σ_i	initial stress at a point.
σ_l	normal stress in lateral direction.
σ_o	initial value of σ.
σ_n	normal stress.
σ_{nf}	normal stress on failure plane.
σ_r, σ_θ	normal stress in r, θ direction — polar coordinates.
σ_r, σ_z, σ_λ	normal stress in r, z, λ direction — polar coordinates.
σ_x, σ_y, σ_z	normal stress in x, y, z direction — cartesian coordinates.
σ_s	σ variable in differential equation for purely cohesive soil.
σ_t	total stress at a point.
σ_u	ultimate bearing pressure.
τ	shear stress.
τ_l	shear stress at layer interface.
τ_{max}	maximum shear stress.
τ_{mob}	mobilized shear stress.
$\tau_{r\lambda}$, $\tau_{z\lambda}$, τ_{zr}	shear stress on face of element — polar coordinates.
τ_{xy}, τ_{xz}, τ_{yz}	shear stress on face of element — cartesian coordinates.
ω	angular velocity, pull coefficient.